7th International Conference on Environmental Science and Development (ESMA 2021)

E3S Web of Conferences Volume 338 (2022)

Xi’an City, China
19-20 December 2021

Editors:

L. Li
S. Zhu

ISBN: 978-1-7138-4280-4

Printed from e-media with permission by:

Curran Associates, Inc.
57 Morehouse Lane
Red Hook, NY 12571

Some format issues inherent in the e-media version may also appear in this print version.

For additional information, please contact EDP Sciences – Web of Conferences
at the address below.

EDP Sciences – Web of Conferences
17, Avenue du Hoggar
Parc d'Activité de Courtabœuf
BP 112
F-91944 Les Ulis Cedex A
France

Phone: +33 (0) 1 69 18 75 75
Fax: +33 (0) 1 69 28 84 91

contact-edps@webofconferences.org

Additional copies of this publication are available from:

Curran Associates, Inc.
57 Morehouse Lane
Red Hook, NY 12571 USA
Phone: 845-758-0400
Fax: 845-758-2633
Email: curran@proceedings.com
Web: www.proceedings.com

TABLE OF CONTENTS

Experimental Study on Mechanism of Water-Alternating-Gas Injection in Thick Sandstone Reservoir 1
Xiaofei Li, Aifen Li, Wanjiang Guo, Shiqi Liu, Shiti Cui

Electric Supplementary Heating Technology of Municipal Heating for City Heat Exchange Station 7
Sirui Zhang, Hao Li, Qing Zhang, Haidong Zhang, Limin Jiang, Bingqing Guo

Application of Geophysical Technology in Engineering Investigation 13
Chuanting Zhao, Jiantao Ran, Lijun Xue, Kaifei Wang, Yangang Cui

Study on Sedimentary Characteristics of Chang 9 Member of Triassic in Ordos Basin 17
Jingbiao Bai

Synthesis and Characterization of Hydroxyl-Pinacolone Retinoate 22
Hexing Zhang, Baicheng Feng, Yan Jin

Capacity Estimation Based on Incremental Capacity and Gaussian Process Regression for Retired Lithium-Ion Batteries 26
Wei Sun, Peng Jin, Xiawei Liao, Xiaoming Ma, Bo Yang

Effect of Long-Term Fertilization on Bacterial Community in a Sandy Loam Soil and Its Relation to Organic Carbon Accumulation 31
Huanjun Zhang, Xixi Wang, Yi Li, Weixin Ding

Research on Gas Drainage Laws of SRV-Fractured Horizontal Wells in Different Types of Tight Gas Reservoirs 38
Xucheng Li, Jian Cao, Yajie Gao, Huiyan Zhao, Zhai Shuo

Performance Evaluation of Temperature-Resistant Nano-surfactants 43
Qunyi Wang, Yongbin Bi, Tongfeng Cao, Yang Zhang, Dong Liu, Haiyan He, Xuena Zhang

Feasibility Study for Well Pattern Encryption in Complex Fractured Block Reservoirs--Taking the Liu 90 South Fault Block in the Jidong Oilfield as an Example 47
Qunyi Wang, Yongbin Bi, Tongfeng Cao, Yang Zhang, Dong Liu, Haiyan He, Xuena Zhang

Research on Application and Benefits of Energy Storage Systems 52
Nana Li, Jing Wu, Qionghui Li, Jing Hu, Hao Fan, Bibin Huang

Fast Prediction Method of Tight Gas Production Based on Segmented Decline 58
Zhiqiang Fan, Kaifeng Wen, Tao Zhang, Tingting Jiang, Xiaoke Gong, Min Jing

Simulation and Analysis of Force on Connection of Casing Thread Under Alternating Load of Gas Storage 62
Hanhua Song, Wei Tian, Chen Li, Zaishun Li, Lianlian Fan, Jian Lu, Yufeng Gong

Research on Stimulation of Injection and Production Capacity for Single Well in Underground Gas Storage 66
Chen Li, Xiaoyong Wen, Zhihao Shen, Li Li, Peng Liu, Hu Peng

Synthesis of Organic Boron Crosslinker for Polyvinyl Alcohol Gel 70
Zhenhuo Zhang, Haijun Liang, Xiaolong Wei

Evaluation of Temperature Resistance of Gelatinized Modified Starch Drilling Fluid 75
Wei Liu, Mingming Zhu, Fan Fan

Study on CO_2 Emission Characteristics of China VI Heavy Duty Diesel Engine 80
Mingzhi Zhang, Mingshi Chen, Fengbin Wang, Mingqiu Gao, Tieqiang Fu

Full Life-Cycle Economic Evaluation of Integrated Energy System with Hydrogen Storage Equipment 86
Yuqiong Zhang, Qiang Zhao, Jindi Ao, Zhaozhen Wang, Yuqing Wang

Optimization of Hot-Press Process and Structural Characterization of PF Camellia Oleifera Cake Adhesive 92
Xiao Hu, Rui Zeng, Yuyuan Li, Jinghua Zhou, Xi Li, Yong Wang, Xiang Li, Dong Wang

Preparation of Cellulose-Based Cationic Adsorbents and Their Removal of Pb (II) from Water 97
Xiao Hu, Rui Zeng, Weidong Xie, Zhixin Hu, Yuyuan Li, Dong Wang, Xiang Li

Parameter Optimization of Acid Fracturing in Ultra-Deep Fault Zone Carbonate Reservoir 101
Yudi Geng, Jun Zhou

Study on the Difference of Pore Structure Characteristics Between the Main Oil Reservoir and the Second Oil Reservoir in Daqing Oilfield 105
Hongda Teng

Effect of Pyrolysis Temperature on Adsorption and Degradation of THI and IMI by Biochar 109
Siyao Wang, Hongbo Peng

The Key Application Technology of Desulfurized Gypsum in Dry-Mixed Mortar 115
Guangxu Fang, Jin Pan, Rui Ma, Huan Wang, Jipeng Wang

Seismic Imaging and Recognition Technology of Medium and Shallow Channel Sand Body 119
Dongna Wang

Controlling Factors of Matrix Acidizing Potential of Low Permeability Clastic Reservoir in Faulted Lacustrine Basin 122
Ningning Xu, Yongshi Wang, Shoupeng Zhang, Bo Li, Zhengwei Fang

Main Controlling Factors and Models of Tight Oil Accumulation in Zhaoyuan Area 126
Yanhua Fu

A Brief Discussion on Environmental Impact Assessment Reporting System and Suggestions 130
Zhou Hang, Wang Jian

A Review of Hyperspectral Remote Sensing of Crops 134
Liheng Xia, Xueying Wu

A Review of Research Methods for Evaluation and Analysis of Suitability of Well-Facilitated Farmland Construction 140
Yutong Zhao, Shiqian Gao, Bo Zhao

Research of Rotor Unmanned Aerial Vehicle (UAV) Production and GIS Integration Based on 3D Panorama 144
Jingsi Li, Jian Wang, Chenxi Yang

Effect of Organic Ecological Soilless Culture Substrate on Tomato Fruit 148
Yan Xu, Jian Wang, Hang Zhou

Effects of Different Land Consolidation Methods on Soil Properties of Cultivated Land 152
Jianglong Shen, Yilun Dai

Investigation and Research on the Current Situation of Erosion Gully in Northeast Semi-Arid Region 156
Shiqian Gao, Yutong Zhao

Literature Review on Farmland Landscape Pattern Change Analysis 160
Zhezhe Mu

Population Characteristics and Influencing Factors of Terrestrial Earthworms in Qinling Mountains 165
Jian Wang, Chenxi Yang, Jingsi Li

Research on Monitoring Information Management of Deep Foundation Pit Engineering Based on BIM Technology 169
Peng Wang, Yan Li, Na Wang

Research Status of Different Improvement Measures for Saline-Alkali Land 173
Jian Li

Review and Analysis on Trajectory Big Data 177
Xueying Wu, Liheng Xia

Study on the Single Toxicity of Five Azole Fungicides for Green Algae 181
Yilun Dai, Jianglong Shen, Yutong Sun, Yanan Li

Research Progress of the Salt Barrier in Saline Alkali Land 186
Xiaomei Sun, Jian Wang, Dongwen Hua

The Significance of Soil Micromorphology Research in Land Reclamation 190
Tingting Cao, Jian Wang, Haiou Zhang

Treatment of Waterborne Coating Wastewater by Coagulation Sedimentation Fenton Oxidation Process 194
Chenxi Yang, Jian Wang

Preparation of Supercapacitors Based on Sludge Utilization 198
Qingying Ye

Study on Advanced Treatment of Wastewater by Advanced Oxidation Based on Sulfate Radical 202
Qingying Ye

Application of Adjacent Heating Technology in Thermal Power Unit 206
Yongqiang Che, Yanfei Zhang, Haizhen Lv

Technical Study on the Treatment of PCB Production Waste Liquid and Copper Extraction 211
Chen Ru

An Economic-Technical Method of Calculating Power Grid Reliability Improvement Scheme 215
Jiefu Lia, Peng Xin, Zhongfeng Kan, Zhenxin Li, Donglin Li, Bo Jiang, Xuerui Zheng

Construction of a New Levelled Cost Model for Energy Storage Based on LCOE and Learning Curve 219
Zhe Chai, Xing Chen, Shuo Yin, Man Jin, Xin Wang, Xingwu Guo, Yao Lu

Research on Thermal Power New Energy Integration Transaction Model Based on Power Reform System 224
Xingwu Guo, Shuo Yin, Xing Chen, Shiqian Wang, Man Jin, Jiabin Feng

Research on the Regeneration Technology of Etching Waste Solution 228
Chen Ru

Analysis of Well and Layer Selection Method for Fracturing Displacement in Thin-And-poor Layers in the Transition Zone of a Oilfield 232
Yanhong Pan

Author Index

Statement of Peer review

In submitting conference proceedings to *Web of Conferences*, the editors of the proceedings certify to the Publisher that

1. They adhere to its **Policy on Publishing Integrity** in order to safeguard good scientific practice in publishing.
2. All articles have been subjected to peer review administered by the proceedings editors.
3. Reviews have been conducted by expert referees, who have been requested to provide unbiased and constructive comments aimed, whenever possible, at improving the work.
4. Proceedings editors have taken all reasonable steps to ensure the quality of the materials they publish and their decision to accept or reject a paper for publication has been based only on the merits of the work and the relevance to the journal.

Title, date and place of the conference

ESMA 2021
December 19-20, 2021
Xi'an City, China

Proceedings editor(s):

Lintao Li, Shanhong Zhu

Date and editor's signature **Jan. 12, 2022**

https://doi.org/10.1051/e3sconf/202233800001

Preface

The organizing committee of ESMA 2021 is proud to present the proceedings of the 2021 7th International Conference on Environmental Science and Material Application (ESMA 2021: http://www.icesma.org/), held in Xi'an, China from 19 to 20 December, 2021. We warmly welcome prospected authors submit new research papers to ESMA 2021, and share the valuable experiences with the scientist and scholars around the world.

The conference is an international forum for the presentation of technological advances and research results in the fields of natural resources, environmental science, environmentally friendly materials, green energy and power engineering. The conference will bring together leading researchers, engineers and scientists in the domain of interest from around the world.

ESMA 2021 received more than 126 manuscripts, and 52 submissions have been accepted by our reviewers. By submitting a paper to ESMA 2021, the authors agreed to the review process and understood that papers would undergo a peer-review process. Manuscripts were reviewed by appropriately qualified experts in the field selected by the conference committee, who took detailed comments and the authors would submit a revised version that took into account this feedback. All papers were reviewed using a double-blind review process: authors declared their names and affiliations in the manuscript for the reviewers to see, but reviewers did not know each other's identities, nor did the authors receive information about who had reviewed their manuscript.

The committees of ESMA 2021 invested great efforts in reviewing the papers submitted to the conference and organizing the sessions to enable the participants to gain maximum benefit. We do believe your great participation will make our conference success and we would appreciate your participation.

With our warmest regards,

Conference Organizing Chair

Xi'an, China

Experimental Study on Mechanism of Water-Alternating-Gas Injection in thick Sandstone Reservoir.

Xiaofei Li [1,*], Aifen Li [2], Wanjiang Guo [2], Shiqi Liu [2] and Shiti Cui [2]

[1] School of Petroleum Engineering, China University of Petroleum (East China), Qingdao, China
[2] Exploration and Development Research Institute, Petro China Tarim Oilfield Company, Xinjiang, China

Abstract. For the thick sandstone reservoir, due to gravity differentiation, water drive mainly uses the bottom oil of the reservoir, while gas drive mainly drives the oil along the top of the reservoir. Water-alternating gas (WAG) injection can effectively combine the advantages of water flooding and gas injection, so that gas and water can work in synergy, thus further expanding swept volume and enhancing oil recovery. Over the past half century, the technology has been successfully applied to more than 60 oilfields worldwide, but its mechanism remains to be further studied. In this paper, a total of three tests were conducted through conventional water-flooding (WF), water flooding followed by gas flooding and WAG in sand-packed 2d-model. These experimental processes are recorded by video with time so that the saturation distribution of each phase in porous media can be observed, migration law of gas and water is studied, and the mechanism of WAG displacement is analyzed. The results show that gravity and capillary force have great influence on the process of gas water alternation, thus increasing the overall swept volume of water and gas; The water/gas alternating injection has the highest oil recovery factor (RF) of 75.45% in test 3, in comparison with water flooding followed by gas flooding (70.85% in test 2) and water-flooding (66.7%in test 1); Increase in cycles of WAG tends to reduce residual oil saturation.

1. Introduction

Alternate gas-water injection, consisting of two traditional water flooding and gas flooding enhanced oil recovery (EOR) techniques, is a promising method for secondary and tertiary recovery.1-5 Water flooding, the volumetric sweep efficiency is relatively high but the microscopic displacement efficiency is low; gas flooding, the microscopic displacement efficiency is relatively high but the volumetric sweep efficiency is low. When gas and water are alternately injected into the reservoir, the gas seepage ability is stronger than that of water. Under the action of pressure, the gas can enter into some small pore oil-bearing channels which are difficult for water to enter. The remaining part of gas and water not only occupy the pore space originally occupied by oil, making oil flow into the low seepage resistance layer, but also redistributes oil, gas and water in the reservoir. At the same time, due to the interference of gas and water phases, the relative permeability of gas and water phases is reduced, and the oil recovery is improved.6-13 In this way, the advantages of water flooding and gas flooding can be combined by sweeping oil-bearing channels with different pore sizes by gas and water flooding, which can not only increase the macro sweep volume, but also improve the micro displacement efficiency.14-17 In addition, it can well control the fluidity of the leading edge, inhibit viscous fingering, and make the leading edge displacement stable, so as to improve sweep efficiency. 18-21

This technology was first used in North Pembina oil field in Alberta, Canada in 1957.22 In 1962, Seelington was the first to apply gas water simultaneous injection in the field practice. 23-24 By the 21st century, gas water alternate injection has become a mature technology in foreign countries and has been successfully applied in many oil fields. The application of gas water alternate injection technology is mainly concentrated in the United States (63%), Canada (15%) and the former Soviet Union. According to statistics, the incremental oil recovery of WAG is from 5% to 25% approximately. 25

However, due to many factors, it is a very complex process to simulate the three-phase flow in the process of alternating gas and water. So far, scholars have done a lot of experimental and theoretical research on the mechanism of gas water alternate injection to enhance oil recovery, but the understanding is not deep enough.

In this paper, the mechanism of enhancing oil recovery by gas-water alternation is obtained by the experiment of 2-D plate sand filling model. It is of great significance for the development of thick sandstone reservoirs.

2. Experiments and methods

2.1 Model fabrication

The sand-packed 2d-model for experiment was composed of perspex sheet and cemented quartz sand. The perspex sheet was bonded into a frame by an acrylic adhesive. The

* Corresponding author: 1239037300@qq.com

 https://doi.org/10.1051/e3sconf/202233801001

quartz sand and binder were mixed and filled inside the perspex frame in the proportion of 5:1, and then compacted and encapsulated. The filling medium is oil-wet with a permeability of 1058mD.The model size is 50×10×0.5cm, see Fig. 1.

Figure 1. Sand-packed 2d-model

2.2 Experiment condition

All the flooding experiments were performed at atmospheric pressure of 1.01×105Pa and temperature of 25°C. The oil in the experiment is aviation kerosene with viscosity of 2.2mPa•s and density of 0.794g/cm3. Sudan red was added to the oil to make it appear red. The injected water in the test is distilled water, which is stained with methyl blue, the viscosity 0.894 m Pa•s and the density 0.997 g/cm3. The injection gas is nitrogen supplied by the cylinder. It is colorless. The viscosity is 0.011mPa•s and the density is 0.0069 g/cm3.

2.3 The experimental steps

(1) Established the experimental process according to Figure 3, and checked the leakage of the process. If there was a loss, it should be made up in time according to the cause of the loss before the start of the experiment. (2) In the experiment, the effective pore volume of the model would be determined first.

Weighed the dry weight of the model; The model would be vacuumed for 4 hours; Saturated with simulated oil: The oil displacement rate was kept at 0.2 ml/min, when the oil production rate at the exit was consistent with the oil injection rate, slowly increasing the injection rate to 1 ml/min to fully saturate model with oil; And the wet weight of the model was weighed, calculated the volume of saturated oil. (3) Water flooding, water flooding followed by gas flooding and water / gas alternate flooding were carried out respectively, and the distribution of oil, gas and water was recorded in real time by camera. The oil and water separator was used to record the amount of oil produced, and the gas produced was recorded by gas flowmeter. Water cut was calculated according to water production divided by the liquid production. (4) Stopped pumping and completed the experiment until the producing well was no longer producing oil.

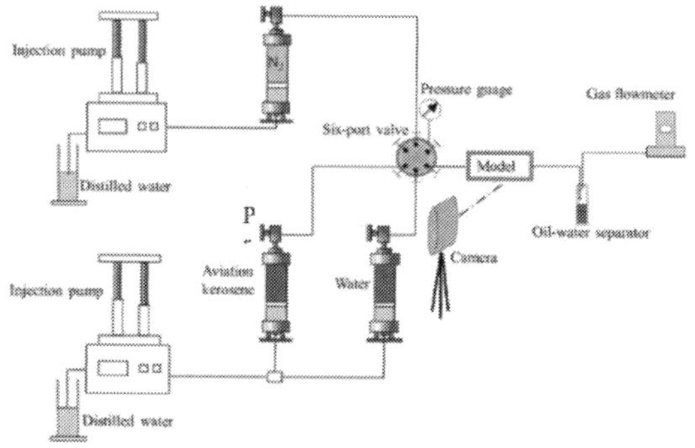

Figure 2. Flow chart of Water-Alternating-Gas Injection.

In this work, three different flooding schemes were applied to study the mechanism of WAG displacement in the sandstone formation, i.e., water flooding, Water flooding followed by gas flooding, and water/gas alternating displacement.

The detailed experimental data are listed in Table1.

Table 1. Parameter and Conditions of Experiments.

The serial number	Tests	Injection rate	Slug Size
1	Water flooding	1.5mL/min	-
2	Water flooding followed by gas flooding	1.5mL/min	-
3	Water/gas alternating experiment	1.5mL/min	0.1PV

3. Results and discussion

3.1 Water flooding experiment

In water displacing oil (test 1), the oil recovery of continuous water injection was mainly determined by the layer located in the lower part. With the increase of the injected water, the swept area was expanding, it flowed towards the outlet of the model. When the water broke through, a water channel was formed in the model along which the re-injected water preferentially went across the model. Ultimately, a large amount of residual oil was still left behind after WF is applied. (see Figure 3).

Fluid saturation distribution when water injection volume is 0.34PV.

Fluid saturation distribution at the end of Water flooding
①pure oil region ②oil-water region

Figure 3. Fluid saturation distribution during the Water flooding.

https://doi.org/10.1051/e3sconf/202233801001

3.2 Water flooding followed by gas flooding

Water flooding followed by gas flooding (test 2), as depicted in Figure 5, was observed to have higher areal sweep efficiency than water flooding. After water injection, the displacement process mainly occurred in the middle and lower layers of the model. In the ensuing N2 injection processes, gas and water worked together to use oil. In addition, because the gas density was much less than that of water, oil and water were separated under the action of gravity, and the gas used the oil at the top of the upper layer. At that point, there were four flow zones: pure oil region, oil-water region, gas-water region, oil - gas and water three-phase region. More oil was displaced as the gas migrates. Gradually, an air channel appeared at the top of the model. After the gas broke through, the oil production decreased obviously.

In gas displacing oil, gas not only drove the upper oil which was not contacted by water, but enlarged the area of water flooding, making the oil-water front moved slightly forward, so that the remaining oil could be produced. (see Figure 4).

①pure oil region ②oil-water region ③gas-water region ④oil-gas-water three-phase region.

Figure 4. Fluid saturation distribution at the end of Water flooding followed by gas flooding.

Figure 5 reveals the relationship between recovery, water cut, and the PV of injected fluids in the Water flooding followed by gas flooding experiment. It is can be seen that, at the initial stage of water injection, the crude oil RF is almost linear with the injected water PV, up to 0.68pv. In this rapid oil recovery period, the injected water replaced the crude oil in the two-dimensional flat plate model (almost equal volume replacement). After water broke through, water and oil were produced together, the oil production rate began to decline, and the water cut increased rapidly. However, there were still a small amount of recovery (5%) at the water-cut rising stage. With the increase of amount of water, the injection water has a stronger drag and wash effect on the oil film on the inner wall of the model, and the oil volume decreases. Therefore, there was still a small amount of recovery during the water cut rise stage. At 0.78 PV, the model produced water completely, and water drive no longer yielded oil. The ultimate recovery of water injection was 66.7%. The subsequent nitrogen flooding can be roughly divided into two liquid production stages. At the beginning, water and oil were produced at the same time, the oil production rate was lower than that of water drive, and the water cut decreased significantly. In the second stage, after the gas broke through (0.97PV), oil, gas and water were produced at the same time, the oil production rate was greatly reduced, and the water cut increased. Till 1.21PV, and the gas drive no longer produce oil. The final recovery rate was 70.85%, which was 4.15% higher than that of water flooding.

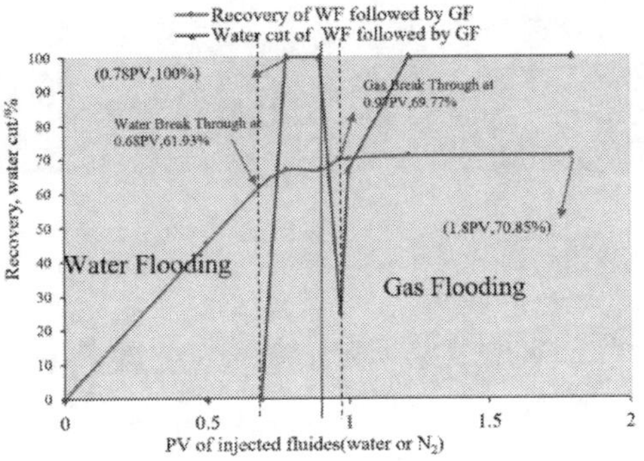

Figure 5 reveals the relationship between recovery

Water/gas alternating experiment

In the WF of the first WAG cycle, the residual oil in the middle and lower part of the model was obviously reduced, as shown in Figure 6. In the GF of the first WAG cycle, the gas drove the water forward and flowed along the upper layer of the model, forming the new oil displacement channels. This is because in the oil wet model, the seepage resistance of the gas in the oil channel is greater than that in the water channel, the injected gas preferentially enters the water channel and pushes the water forward. Then, the gas was separated upward, the injected gas flowed along the upper part of the model to displace the remaining oil under capillary force and buoyancy, as shown in Figure 7.

In the WF of the second WAG cycle, with the injection of water, the oil-water interface moved forward, and the water and oil invaded the gas channel upward under the capillary force. The gas channel was gradually occupied by oil and water, and the longitudinal and transverse swept volume of water expanded at the same time, so as to reduce the remaining oil, as shown in Figure 8. In the GF of the second WAG cycle, the gas entered the model, to establish gas channel and to use more residual oil, as shown in Figure 9.

The following gas water alternation process repeated the above displacement mode. The oil-water interface moved forward continuously, the gas went forward along the upper part, and the gas water transverse sweep area enlarged continuously. The fluctuation of water gas interface and oil gas interface made the volume of water gas longitudinal wave increase. In addition, the three-phase region was larger and larger. Finally, the displacement channels of gas and water reached the expansion limit and continued to alternate without oil production, as shown in Figure 10.

Figure 6. Fluid saturation distribution at first water flooding of WAG

 https://doi.org/10.1051/e3sconf/202233801001

Figure 7. Fluid saturation distribution at first water and gas flooding of WAG

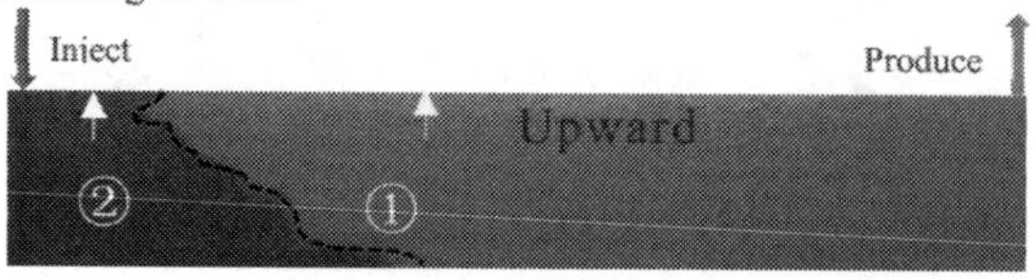

Figure 8. Fluid saturation distribution at second water flooding of WAG

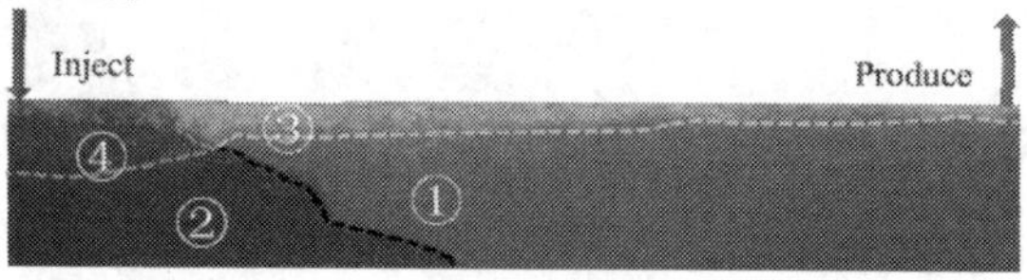

Figure 9. Fluid saturation distribution at second water and gas flooding of WAG

Figure 10. Fluid saturation distribution at the end of WAG displacement

Therefore, through the above experiment, we can clearly understand the gas-water alternation process in the thick sandstone reservoir. As shown in Figure 1, in the process of water gas alternation, the injected water pushes the crude oil forward and downward under the effect of displacement pressure and gravity, mainly contacts the middle and lower parts of the formation, and enters the reservoir macro pores to displace the crude oil, forming a water-oil two-phase zone; Under the displacement pressure, the injected gas migrates forward and downward, invades the oil-water two-phase zone, and works with water to contribute to the oil-gas-water three-phase zone, which greatly improves the displacement efficiency; In addition, due to the large difference of gas and water density, the gas is separated upward, and intrudes into the oil phase area under the action of capillary force and buoyancy, forming the gas-oil two-phase zone. In the end, the pure oil area not affected by gas and water is left.

With the injection of gas and water, the three-phase region of oil-gas-water expands, the oil-water interface advances forward, and the oil invades the oil-gas two-phase region under the action of capillary force, which makes the circulating injected gas displace the crude oil in the same position repeatedly.

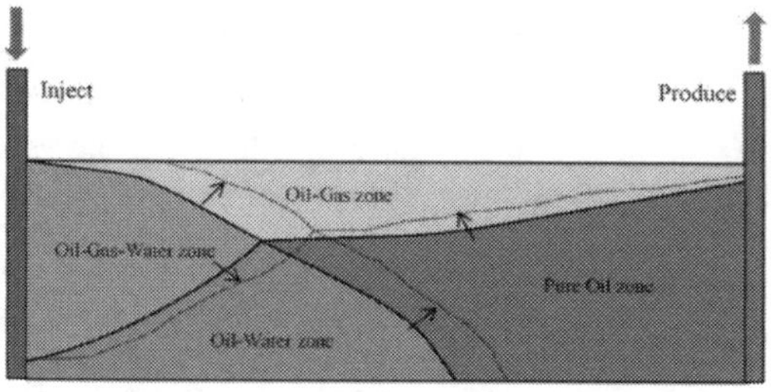

Figure 11. Schematic representation of WAG injection.

The relationship between recovery efficiency, water cut and the PV of injected fluids in WAG mode is plotted in Figure 12. The WAG injection can be roughly divided into three production stages. At first, only oil was produced before gas breakthrough, an increased PV of the displacing phase (i.e., the water and N2) led to an increased oil recovery. Specifically, from 0 to 0.2PV, the recovery increased almost linearly; Nevertheless, from 0.2 to 0.23PV (at the beginning of the second WAG cycle), the oil production rate decreased significantly. It was speculated that the water entering the model mainly drove the crude oil to gas channel, discharging gas to the outlet of model. In the second stage, after gas breakthrough and before water breakthrough, the products were oil and gas. It is worth noting that, generally, after the gas breakthrough, the oil production rate should be greatly reduced, but in this experiment, the oil production rate increased. This was because the gas breakthrough occurred in the early stage of water drive of the second WAG cycle. After the gas was discharged by WF, water continued to drive the crude oil, therefore, a amount of the residual oil was further recovered after N2 breakthrough. Finally, after water breakthrough, oil, gas and water were produced simultaneously. Compared with the previous production, the overall oil production rate declined significantly. The oil production rate was reduced gradually and the final oil RF reached a maximum value at 2PV. It is found that the water cut does not increase monotonically, dropping at 1.4 PV and 1.8 PV. This was because gas re-entered the pores and effectively displaced crude oil, resulting in higher oil recovery than during the water-injection phase of the same cycle.

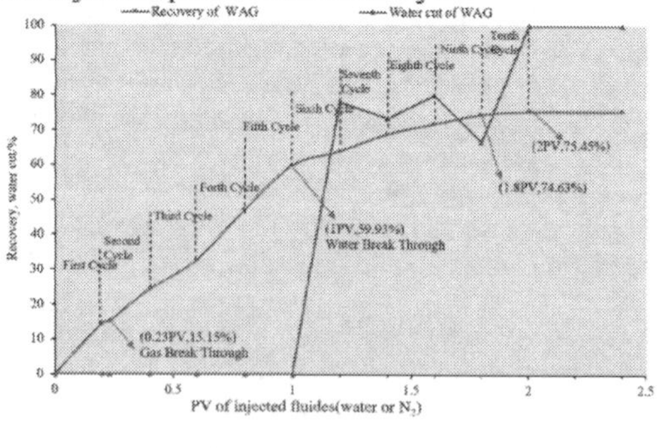

Figure 12. Oil recovery and water cut versus PV of injected fluid in the water/gas alternating experiment.

Obviously, compared with figure 13 and figure 6, when the injected fluid PV is 1.8, the recovery of WAG is higher than that of Water flooding followed by gas flooding. Hence, the number of WAG cycles has a strong effect on the oil Recovery, if the injected fluid volume is fixed, the more WAG cycles (that is, the smaller the size of gas water alternation slug), the higher the oil recovery. Compared with pure water flooding, water flooding followed by gas flooding and WAG, it is seen that WAG has the highest oil RF. The increase in recovery becomes smaller and smaller as the number of WAG cycles increase (see Fig13)

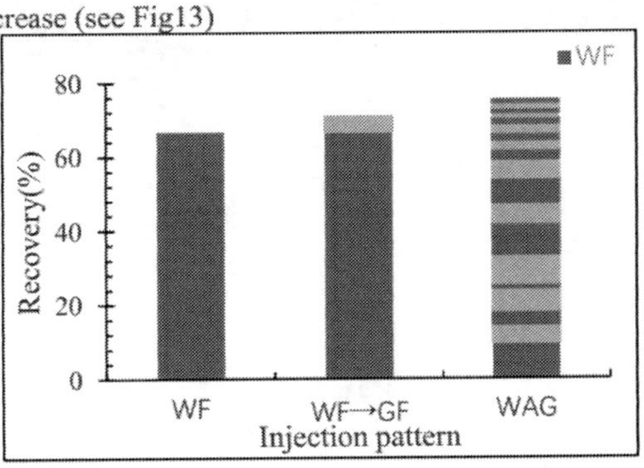

Figure 13. Oil recovery under different injection patterns.

4. Conclusion

(1) The WAG injection process overcame the disadvantages of small sweep volume and large residual oil volume by only water displacement, and gave the better sweep control, mobility control of water, and the recovery factor was obviously better than that of water flooding. Therefore, now the application of WAG injection methods is more and more widely.

(2) Gravity and capillary force played an important role in the alternating process. Due to the gravity differentiation, water and gas acted on the bottom and upper layer of the model respectively to displace together; Due to the existence of capillary force, water and oil intruded into the gas drive area, and gas displaced crude oil at the same location for many times to improve the displacement efficiency.

(3) The effect of multiple WAG was better than that of single WAG. The more the alternation cycles were, the higher the efficiency was.

Acknowledgments

This work was financially supported by Key Science and Technology Program of Petro China. (ZD2019-183-008).

References

1. Sohrabi, M.; Tehrani, D. H.; Danesh, A.; Henderson, G. D., Visualization of Oil Recovery by Water-Alternating-Gas Injection Using High-Pressure Micromodels. SPE Journal2004, 9, (03), 290-301.
2. Kulkarni, M. M.; Rao, D. N., Experimental investigation of miscible and immiscible Water-Alternating-Gas (WAG) process performance. Journal of Petroleum Science and Engineering2005, 48, (1-2), 1-20.
3. Christensen, J. R.; Stenby, E. H.; Skauge, A., Review of WAG field experience. Presented at the International Petroleum Conference and Exhibition of Mexico, Villahermose, Mexico, March 3-5, 1998; Paper SPE 39883.
4. Li, Z.; Yin, Y.; Wang, Q.， Research progress on mechanism of enhanced oil recovery by water alternating gas injection. Journal of Southwest Petroleum University2007, 2, 2226, 180．
5. Guo, P.; Du, Z.; Zhang, M.， Study on the development of water alternating gas injection hydrocarbon miscible flooding in Pubei oilfield. Journal of Southwestern Petroleum In- stitute2004, 4, (25- 27)，37-90.
6. Christensen, J. R.; Stenby, E. H.; Skauge, A. Review of WAG Field Experience. SPE Res. Eval. Eng. 2001, 4 (2), 97–106. Paper SPE 71203.
7. Surguchev, L. M.; Korbol, R.; Krakstad, O.S.,Optimum Water Alternate Gas Injection Schemes for Stratified Reservoir. Presented at the Annual Technical Conference and Exhibition, Washington, DC, October 4-7, 1992. Paper SPE 24646.
8. Tiffin, D. L.; Yelling, W. F., Effects of Mobile Water on Multiple-Contact Gas Displacements. SPEJ1983, June, 447.
9. John, D. R., A Literature Analysis of the WAG Injectivity Abnormalities in the CO2 Process. SPE Reservoir Evaluation & Engineering: 2001.
10. Guzman, R. E., Three-Phase Flow in Field-Scale Simulation of Gas and WAG Injections. Presented at the SPE European Petroleum Conference, London, October 25–27, 1994; Paper SPE 28897.
11. Han, L.; Gu, Y. Optimization of Miscible CO 2-WAG Injection in the Bakken Formation. Energy Fuels 2014, 28 (11), 6811–6819.
12. Fatemi, S. M.; Sohrabi, M. Recovery Mechanisms and Relative Permeability for Gas/Oil Systems at Near-Miscible Conditions: Effects of Immobile Water Saturation, Wettability, Hysteresis, and Permeability. Energy Fuels 2013, 27 (5), 2376–2389.
13. Godec, M. L.; Kuuskraa, V. A.; Dipietro, P. Opportunities for Using Anthropogenic CO2 for Enhanced Oil Recovery and CO 2 Storage. Energy Fuels 2013, 27 (8), 4183–4189.
14. Christensen, J. R.; Larse, M.; Nicolaisen, H., Compositional simulation of water-alternating-gas processes. Presented at the Annual Technical Conference and Exhibition, Dallas, Texas, USA, October 1–4, 2000; Paper SPE 62999.
15. Aleidan, A. A.; Mamora, D. D. SWACO2 and WACO2 Efficiency Improvement in Carbonate Cores by Lowering Water Salinity. Presented at the SPE Canadian Unconventional Resources and International Petroleum Conference, Calgary, Alberta, October 19–21, 2010; Paper SPE 137548.

https://doi.org/10.1051/e3sconf/202233801001

16. Shetty, S.; Hughes, R. G.; Afonja, G. Experimental Evaluation of Simultaneous Water and Gas Injection using Carbon Dioxide. Presented at the SPE EOR Conference at Oil and Gas West Asia, Muscat, Oman, March 31–April 2, 2014 ; Paper SPE 169690.
17. 17. Kulkarni, M. M.; Rao, D. N. Experimental Investigation of Miscible and Immiscible Water-Alternating-Gas (WAG) Process Performance. J. Pet. Sci. Eng. 2005, 48 (1), 1–20.
18. Nezhad, S. A. T., Mojarad, M. R. R., Moghadas, J. S., Experimental study on applicability of water-alternating-CO2 injection in the secondary and tertiary recovery. SPE 103988: 2006.
19. 19. Chen, S; Li, H.; Yang, D., Optimal parametric design for water alternating-gas (WAG) process in a CO2-miscible flooding reservoir. Journal of Canadian Petroleum Technology2010, 49,(10),75-82.
20. Ramachandran, K. P.; Gyani, O. N.; Sur, S., Immiscible hydrocarbon WAG: Laboratory to field. SPE 128848: 2010.
21. 21. Taheri, A.; Sajjadian, V. A., WAG performance in a low porosity and low permeability reservoir. SPE 100212: 2006.
22. Du, J.; Liu, W.; Guo, P., Study on variation rule of water-alternating-gas injection capacity in low permeability reservoirs. Journal of Southwest Petroleum University (Natural Science Edition)2011, 33, (5), 114-117, 198 .
23. 23. Zhang, Z., Alternate injection of water and gas to improve recovery efficiency. Journal of Daxian Teachers College2002, (2),33-35.
24. 24. Walker, J. W.; Turner, J. L., Performance of Seeligson Zone 20B-07enriched- gas- drive project. Journal of Petroleum Technology1968, 20, (4), 369-373.
25. 25. Koottungal, Leena, SPECIAL REPORT: EOR/Heavy Oil Survey: 2010 worldwide EOR survey, Oil and Gas Journal, April 19, 2010.

Electric supplementary heating technology of municipal heating for city heat exchange station

Sirui Zhang [1,*], Hao Li [1], Qing Zhang [2], Haidong Zhang [2], Limin Jiang [1], Bingqing Guo [1]

[1] State Grid Corporation of Joint Laboratory of Electric Energy Substitution Technology (China Electric Power Research Institute Co., Ltd.), Beijing, China
[2] State Grid Beijing Electric Power Company, Beijing, China

Abstract. Municipal heating in northern areas generally suffers from heat sources, heat grid gaps, and high dependence on fossil fuels. It is difficult to guarantee the heating effect of incremental buildings at the end of the building, and relying on traditional capacity expansion methods has caused a waste of social resources to a certain extent. A "no capacity increase" municipal heating electric supplementary heating technology for urban heat exchange stations is proposed. First, the design concept of the electric supplementary heating system is explained. Then, the investment calculation model of the electric supplementary heating system is established. Finally, an office building in Shijingshan, Beijing is used as a research example to perform simulation calculations.

1 Introduction

At present, vigorously developing clean energy and reducing carbon emissions have become the consensus of the society [1]. In recent years, the northern region has vigorously promoted clean heating[2], further reduced carbon emissions caused by fossil fuels, improved the ecological environment[3], and promoted green development. Electric heating has the advantages of green environmental protection, reliable supply, and wide application. It has been widely promoted in urban and rural areas [4]. It is currently the main technical means for heating renovation in winter. The first paragraph after a heading is not indented.

In recent years, there have been many researches on electric heating at home and abroad. Zhang et al. established a model of heating equipment, heat storage equipment and related auxiliary equipment, and carried out an economic analysis of heat storage electric heating based on the annual cost of the whole life cycle [5]. Miao et al. proposed an evaluation method for electric heating projects with a critical low price, and carried out an economic analysis of different electric heating schemes [6]. Cheng et al. proposed a heat pump instead of coal-fired boilers and gas-fired boilers for heating programs [7]. Taking the Beijing-Tianjin-Hebei region as a research sample, the results show that this program can greatly reduce pollutant emissions and improve heating efficiency. Zhang et al. proposed a day-ahead optimal scheduling method for thermal storage electric heating considering the minimum heat demand of users during power outages, established a calculation model for minimum heating load during power outages, and studied heat pumps and hot water storage tanks in the event of power outages [8]. The state of power output reduces heating costs while ensuring the heating needs of users. Yu et al. and Senemar et al. considered a variety of equipment such as combined heat and power, photovoltaic, electric energy storage, thermal energy storage and so on for the regional integrated energy system and residential area energy hub respectively, and used mixed integer linear programming to optimize the type and capacity of the equipment [9-10].

At present, relevant scholars at home and abroad have carried out relevant research in the aspects of thermoelectric coupling modeling, heat source planning and configuration, and operation optimization of municipal heating. Gu et al. established a general model of energy transmission in a district heating network and a heat loss model of a heating network, and then proposed a heating network energy flow model and a temperature-flow equation, and analyzed the energy exchange of the heating network of a multi-region integrated energy system [11]. Xu et al. considered the heat storage characteristics of the heating network and heat users in the heat source capacity planning, and proposed an optimized configuration of the heat source capacity that takes into account the thermal characteristics of the thermal system, which can effectively improve the wind power absorption capacity of the system [12]. Bai et al. established a regional thermoelectric coordinated planning model considering coal power, gas power and thermal energy, and proposed an improved normal distribution quantum particle swarm algorithm to solve the model [13]. Current research focuses on the planning and configuration of heat source side capacity, operation optimization, and research on new energy consumption, and the research on electric heating focuses on the transformation of traditional new

* Corresponding author: zhangsirui02@163.com

https://doi.org/10.1051/e3sconf/202233801002

power distribution network capacity. However, in practice, due to the long transmission distance of the heat pipe network and the aging of the pipes, the heat from the heat source to the user has experienced a large loss, the user's heating demand has not been fully met, and the heating effect is poor. The power distribution network capacity plan is not feasible in most cases. Because the heating is a seasonal load, it causes a waste of social resources to a certain extent. At present, under the condition of the open capacity of the distribution network, the electric heating configuration for end users has not been studied.

The planning and configuration of electric heating system is essentially a mixed integer linear programming model solution problem (MILP). Currently, there have been many studies on distributed energy and regional integrated energy system [14-16]. In addition, the planning and configuration of electric heating system needs to consider the investment cost and operating cost of equipment. Li et al. and Zhe et al. studied the planning and configuration of integrated energy system under the condition of large-scale distributed energy access through a two-stage optimization method. The capacity of equipment is optimized in the first stage, and the operating output of equipment is optimized in the second stage [17-18]. A two-layer optimization model based on particle swarm optimization-interval linear programming was constructed considering the uncertainty of load during the planning operation of integrated energy system, prediction error of renewable energy and energy purchase price fluctuation [19]. Lei et al. proposed a two-stage planning-operation joint optimization method for integrated energy system considering the uncertainty of renewable energy and multi-energy load, and compared and analyzed the advantages and disadvantages of two-stage random optimization and two-stage robust optimization [20].

Based on the above-mentioned problems, this paper proposes a method of electric supplementary heating planning for urban heat exchange stations with "no capacity increase" in the distribution network, which fully considers the influence factors of the open capacity of the distribution network and the thermal inertia of the building. Through the two-stage planning-operation joint optimization method, the optimal configuration model of the electric heating supplementary heating system with the smallest total annual cost is established. Through the comparison and analysis of typical cases, the configuration schemes of various electric heating and heating systems are analyzed. The analysis results show that the proposed method can effectively reduce the peak-valley difference of the distribution network while meeting the open capacity of the distribution network, and meet the heating demand of end users. It has good economic efficiency and provides a reference for the project.

2 The basic structure of electric heating and supplementing system for urban heat exchange station

As shown in Figure 1, the composition of municipal heating includes heat source side, primary pipe network, urban heat exchange station, secondary pipe network and user side. The heat source side is thermal power plant, which usually includes gas turbine, cogeneration and other heating units. Urban heat exchange station is located in the middle place of heat exchange between heat source and user, and it is the connection and interchange of primary pipe network and secondary pipe network. The urban heat exchange station consists of plate heat exchanger, primary water outlet and return pipe, secondary water outlet and return pipe, water pump and other devices. Plate heat exchanger is a device for heat exchange between primary pipe network and secondary pipe network. Through the plate heat exchanger, the primary pipe network transfers the heat from the heat source side to the secondary pipe network. The primary pipe network is a circulating pipe connected from the heat source to the urban heat exchange station, where heat is transferred to the secondary pipe network through the heat exchanger. The secondary pipe network is a circulating pipe connected from the urban heat exchange station to the end of the user. The heat of the primary pipe network is obtained through the plate heat exchanger, and the heat from the heat source side is transferred to the user. On the user side, users 1 and 2...... User N and other users, for urban heat exchange stations, the end users of heating are often the same type, which can be divided into residential communities, commercial bodies, hospitals, etc.

Thermal power plant in the production of hot water in the process of delivery, because the distance is longer, pipeline aging because of its heat a bigger loss, cannot satisfy users at the end of the heating demand, urban incremental building heating effect also sell at a discount greatly, this paper puts forward a kind of city heat exchanger station oriented electric heating system, heat exchanger station of the system is deployed in city, Is composed of heating equipment and heat storage equipment, make full use of the electrical load and thermal load of winter complementary characteristics, use of the existing urban heat exchanger station nearby valley of spare capacity and lower cost of the distribution of electricity, the calories in secondary pipe network water place, can safeguard residents, business, and hospitals, various scene heating needs of different users, at the same time reduce the peak valley load difference, has the high efficiency.

 https://doi.org/10.1051/e3sconf/202233801002

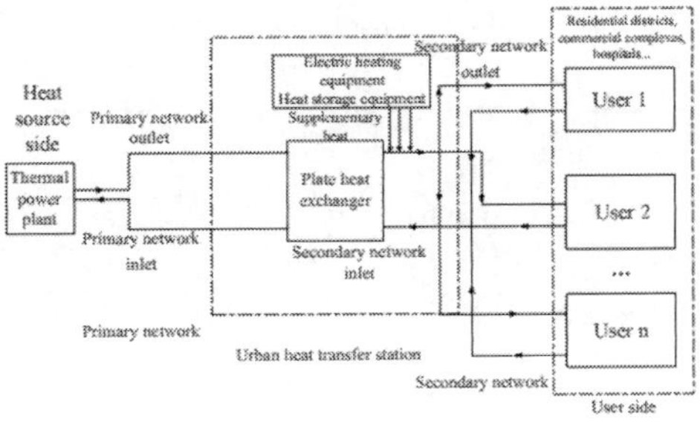

Figure 1. Basic structure of a conventional electric supplementary heating system.

3 Modeling of electric supplementary heating system

3.1 Model of heating equipment

The heating equipment considered in this paper are electric boilers, heat pumps, and ultra-low-temperature high-efficiency units, which convert electrical energy into heat. The heating power is shown in the following formula (1):

$$Q_{i,t}=P_i^{H,t}\eta_i \tag{1}$$

In the formula: $P_i^{H,t}$ is the electric power of the i-th heating equipment at time t, in kW. η_i is the heating efficiency of the heating equipment. $Q_{i,t}$ is the heating power of the heating equipment at time t, in kW.

3.2 Model of heat storage equipment

According to the heat storage medium used and considering the practical applicability of the project, we divided heat storage equipment into three categories, in this paper: water heat storage, phase change heat storage, and solid heat storage. The basic principle can be expressed by the following formula (2):

$$E_{j,t+1}=E_{j,t}(1-\eta_{j,loss})+(\eta_{j,in}P_{j,in}^{S,t}-P_{j,out}^{S,t}/\eta_{j,out})\Delta t \tag{2}$$

In the formula: $E_{j,t}$ is the heat storage capacity of the heat storage equipment at the time t, kWh. $\eta_{j,loss}$ is the self-loss rate of the heat storage equipment. $\eta_{j,in}$ is the input efficiency of the heat storage equipment. $P_{j,in}^{S,t}$ is the input power of the heat storage equipment at time t, in kW. $P_{j,out}^{S,t}$ is the heat release power of the heat storage equipment at time t, in kW. $\eta_{j,out}$ is the heat release efficiency of the heat storage equipment. Δt is the simulation step length, in h. $E_{j,t+1}$ is the heat storage capacity of the heat storage equipment at the time t+1, in kWh.

3.3 Two-stage optimization configuration model

3.3.1. Optimization model of the first stage

In the planning stage, the objective function of the first stage is the total annual cost, which is equal to the sum of the annual investment cost of the equipment and the annual operation and maintenance cost of the equipment, as shown in equation (3):

$$C_{tot}=C_{inv}+C_{ope} \tag{3}$$

In the formula: C_{tot} is the total annual cost, C_{inv} is the annual investment cost of the equipment, and C_{ope} is the annual operation and maintenance cost of the equipment. Considering the time cost of capital, the capital recovery coefficient is calculated as shown in Equation (4):

$$\alpha=\frac{r(1+r)^N}{(1+r)^N-1} \tag{4}$$

In the formula: N is the life of the equipment and r is the annual interest rate.

Therefore, the annual equipment investment cost can be calculated using equation (5):

$$C_{inv}=\sum_{i=1}^{n}\alpha_i u_i^H P_i^H+\alpha_j u_j^S P_j^S \tag{5}$$

In the formula: n is the type of heating equipment. u_i^H is the investment cost per unit capacity of the i-th heating equipment, in RMB/kW. P_i^H is the capacity of the i-th heating equipment, in kW. There are three types of heat storage equipment (water heat storage, phase change heat storage, solid heat storage). u_j^S is the investment cost per unit capacity of the j-th heat storage equipment, in RMB/kWh. P_j^S is the capacity of the j-th heat storage equipment, in kW.

3.3.2. Second stage optimization model

At the operational level, the objective function of the second stage is the annual operation and maintenance cost of the equipment, which is equal to the sum of the fixed maintenance cost of the equipment and the fuel cost. It can be expressed by the following formula (6):

$$C_{ope}=C_{mai}+C_{ele} \tag{6}$$

In the formula: C_{mai} is the fixed maintenance cost of the equipment, C_{ele} is the fuel cost, namely electricity price cost.

The fixed maintenance cost of the equipment can be expressed by the following formula (7):

$$C_{mai}=\sum_{i=1}^{n}m_i^H P_i^H+m_j^S P_j^S \tag{7}$$

In the formula: m_i^H is the annual fixed maintenance cost coefficient per unit capacity of the i-th heating equipment, while m_j^S is the annual fixed maintenance cost coefficient per unit capacity of the j-th heat storage equipment.

Fuel cost can be expressed by the following formula (8):

https://doi.org/10.1051/e3sconf/202233801002

$$C_{ele}=120\sum_{t=1}^{T}\sum_{i=1}^{n}e_t P_i^{H,t} \tag{8}$$

In the formula: T is the total daily operating hours of the equipment. e_t is the electricity price at the t-th hour. $P_i^{H,t}$ is the electric power of the i-th heating equipment at the t-th time.

3.4 Economic calculation of electric heating and supplementary heating

It is necessary to consider the economics of electricity-to-heat conversion for electric heating and supplementary heating and to calculate its income relative to traditional municipal heating. Traditional municipal heating is usually billed according to heat or area, and billing according to area is usually charged to end consumers. In this paper, the heating season is 120 days, and the break-even point electricity price is calculated. The operating income of the heating season is calculated, as shown in the following formulas (9) ~ (10).

$$e_{be}=e_{heat}\times\eta_i\times 0.0036 \tag{9}$$

$$I=120\sum_{t=1}^{T}\sum_{i=1}^{n}P_i^{H,t}(e_{be}-e_t) \tag{10}$$

In formulas (9) ~ (10): e_{heat} is the heating price charged by calories, in RMB/GJ. e_{be} is the break-even point electricity price, in RMB/kWh. I is the annual revenue of the heating season.

4 Case study

Taking an office building in Shijingshan, Beijing as an example, the heating area is 27,000 square meters. According to the energy consumption characteristics of the office building, calculate the 24-hour heat load gap on a typical winter day, taking into account the site size, environment and other influencing factors. Parameters such as heating equipment, heat storage equipment, Beijing electricity price, heating price, and buildings are shown in Table 1-Table 3. Heating equipment considers electric boilers, air source heat pumps, and ultra-low-temperature high-efficiency units. Heat storage equipment considers water heat storage, phase change heat storage and solid heat storage. Four operating conditions of heating, heating + heat storage are designed for analysis.

Table 1. Economic and technical parameters of heating equipment.

Equipment	COP	Unit investment cost /(RMB/kW)	Coefficient of fixed maintenance costs	Lifespan/ (years)	Maximum capacity/ (kW)	Interest rate
Electric boiler	0.95	700	0.04	15	500	6%
Air source heat pump	2.5	2500	0.03	15	100	6%
ultra-low Temperature high-efficiency unit	3.6	5556	0.03	15	200	6%

Table 2. Economic and technical parameters of heat storage equipment.

Equipment	Input and output efficiency	Unit investment cost /(RMB/kW)	Coefficient of fixed maintenance costs	Lifespan/ (years)	Maximum capacity/ (kW)	Self-loss rate
Water heat storage	0.95	40	0.01	15	500	2%
Phase change heat storage	0.95	240	0.03	10	1500	2%
Solid heat storage	0.95	90	0.03	10	2000	2%

Table 3. Economic and technical parameters of heating equipment.

Items	Time period	Price/(RMB/kWh)
Peak section	10:00-15:00 18:00-21:00	1.2710
Flat section	07:00-10:00 15:00-18:00 21:00-23:00	0.7523
Valley section	23:00-07:00	0.2849

Due to the heat supply gap in the heating network and heat source, the electric supplementary heating system partially replaces the original municipal heating, and supplements the required heat to the municipal heating in a specific period of time. The thermal load gap curve is shown in Figure 2, and the open capacity curve of the distribution network is shown in Figure 3.

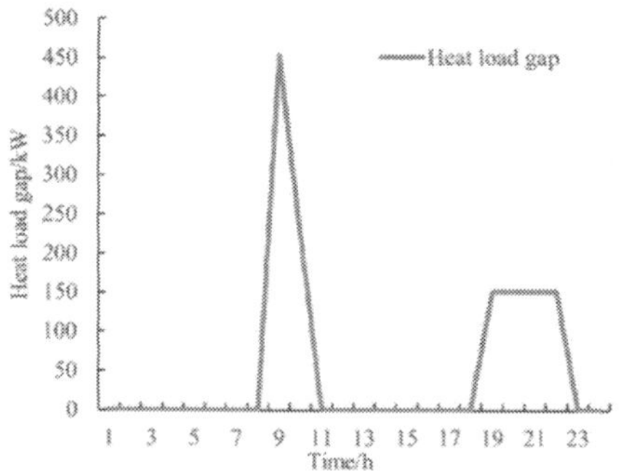

Figure 2. 24-hour heat load gap on a typical day.

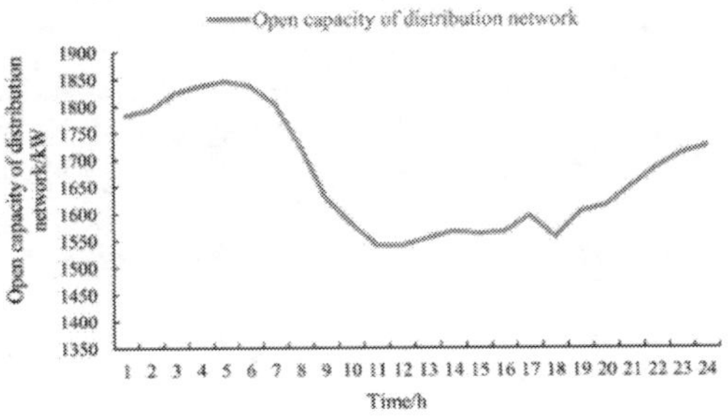

Figure 3. Openable capacity of distribution network.

Table 4 and Table 5 are the solution results of the calculation examples. It can be seen that because the heat load gap of office buildings is relatively large at some moments, if heat storage equipment is not added, larger capacity heating equipment is required, and its investment and operating costs are relatively high. After considering the heat storage equipment, the low electricity price at night is used for heat storage, and the heat is released during peak hours during the day, which greatly saves investment and operating costs. In terms of comprehensive operating income, electricity heating + water heat storage is the most economical.

Table 4. Comparison of equipment capacity under different conditions.

Combination type	Air source heat pump/kw	Ultra-low temperature high efficiency unit/kw	Capacity of heat storage equipment/kwh
Electric heating	121	42	/
Electric heating + water heat storage	0	30	674
Electric heating + phase change heat storage	0	26	532
Electric heating + solid heat storage	0	25	568

Table 5. Economic comparison under different conditions.

Combination type	Annual investment cost/RMB 10,000	Annual operating cost/RMB 10,000	Total annual cost/RMB 10,000	Annual operating income/RMB 10,000
Electric heating	5.52	4.16	9.68	1.33
Electric heating + water heat storage	1.99	2.64	4.63	3.86
Electric heating + phase change heat storage	1.49	3.03	4.52	3.15
Electric heating + solid heat storage	1.44	2.99	4.43	3.25

Figure 4 is the optimized result of heating conditions. It can be seen that during the time when the heat load gap is the largest throughout the day from 8:00-10:00 in the morning, the air source heat pump and the ultra-low temperature and high-efficiency unit operate at the same time to supplement heat, and in other periods, only the ultra-low-temperature and high-efficiency unit is used to supplement heat. Figure 5 is the optimization result of heating + solid heat storage conditions. It can be seen that at night 0:00- 7:00 in the valley electricity period and at 16:00-17:00, the input power of the heat storage device is used for heat storage, and the heat load gap is the largest. The output power is released from 8:00-10:00 and 18:00-21:00 when the heat load is higher and the electricity price is higher.

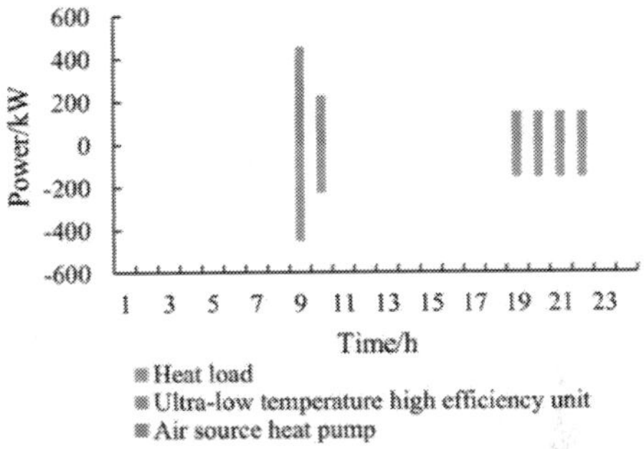

Figure 4. Optimization results of heating conditions

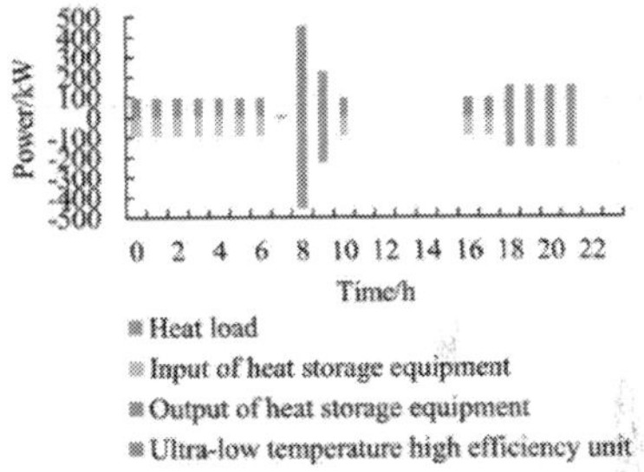

Figure 5. Optimization results of heating and solid heat storage conditions

5 Conclusion

This paper proposes a double-layer optimized configuration method for electric supplementary heating considering the open capacity of the distribution network. The following conclusions are obtained through the simulation and analysis of four different working conditions through calculation examples.

The electric heating supplementary heating planning configuration method can make full use of the surplus capacity of the urban heat exchange station adjacent to the distribution network to supplement heat to the secondary pipe network of the urban heat exchange station to ensure the heat supply effect at the end, which has high economic efficiency. By deploying heat storage equipment, the total annual cost can be further reduced and the annual operating profit can be increased.

Acknowledgments

This work was financially supported by science and technology project of State Grid Corporation of China (Research and application of municipal heating electricity supplementary heating for grid-heating network coupling, No. 5400-202111161A-0-0-00)

References

1. Wang X. China strives to achieve carbon neutrality by 2060, J. Ecological Economy, 2020,36(12):13-16.
2. Information on http://www.gov.cn/xinwen/2017-12/20/content_5248855.htm
3. Information on http://www.gov.cn/zhengce/content/2018-07/03/content_5303158.htm
4. Chen C, Chen X, Zhang J, et al. Stochastic operational optimal strategy for ground source heat pump system under TOU price, J. Power System Protection and Control,2019,47(12):57-64.
5. Zhang J, Huo X, Li S, et al. Economic evaluation of regenerative electric heating based on equivalent annual cost in life cycle, J. Power Demand Side Management, 2020, 22(03):31-37.
6. Miao C, Bai Z, Wang W, et al. Economic comparison and analysis of typical regenerative electric heating projects, J. Power Demand Side Management, 2018, 20(06):42-45.
7. Cheng X, Wang C, Gang X, et al. Thermodynamic and environmental evaluation of an improved heating system using electric-driven heat pumps: a case study for Jing-Jin-Ji region in China, J. Journal of Cleaner Production, 2017, 165:36-47.
8. Zhang J, Mu Y, Jia H, et al. Day-ahead optimal scheduling method for regenerative electric heating considering thermal demand of users during power outage, J. Automation of Electric Power Systems, 2020, 44(21):15-22.
9. Yu, L, Lei, J, Guo, X, et al. Planning of central energy station in community integrated energy system with electrical and heat storage devices, C. 2019 IEEE Innovative Smart Grid Technologies - Asia (ISGT Asia),Chengdu, China, 21-24 May 2019;. IEEE: 2019, 1-6.
10. Senemar S, Rastegar M, Dabbaghjamanesh M, et al. Dynamic structural sizing of residential energy hubs, J. IEEE Transactions on Sustainable Energy, 2020, 11(3): 1236-1246.
11. Gu W, Lu S, Wang J, et al. Optimal configuration of multi-energy storage in regional integrated energy system considering multi-energy complementation, J. Proceedings of The Chinese Society for Electrical Engineering, 2017, 37(05):1305-1315.
12. Xu Y, Huang Y, Sun Y, et al. Optimal capacity allocation of heat power supply and its economic analysis considering thermal characteristics of heat energy system, J. Electric Power, 2020, 53(11):101-109.
13. Bai X, Zeng M, Li Y, et al. The model and algorithm of thermoelectric collaborative planning of regional energy supply network, J. Power System Protection and Control, 2017, 45(005):65-72.
14. Ren H, Gao W. A MILP model for integrated plan and evaluation of distributed energy systems, J. Applied Energy, 2010, 87(3):1001-1014.
15. Yang Y, Zhang S, Xiao Y, et al. An MILP (mixed integer linear programming) model for optimal design of district-scale distributed energy resource systems, J. Energy, 2015, 90:1901-1915.
16. Li X, Li W, Zhang R, et al. Collaborative scheduling and flexibility assessment of integrated electricity and district heating systems utilizing thermal inertia of district heating network and aggregated buildings, J. Applied Energy, 2020, 258(Jan.15):114021.1-114021.20.
17. Zhe Z, Zhang J, Pei L, et al. A two-stage stochastic programming model for the optimal design of distributed energy systems, J. Applied Energy, 2013, 103(MAR.):135-144.
18. Yang Y, Zhang S, Xiao Y, et al. Optimal design of distributed energy resource systems based on two-stage stochastic programming, J. Applied Thermal Engineering, 2017, 110:1358-1370.
19. Chou Z, Wang B, Ben S, et al. Two-level collaborative optimal allocation method of integrated energy system considering wind and solar uncertainty, J. Power System Technology, 2019, 39(08):176-185.
20. Lei J, Guo Z, Chen C, et al. Two-stage planning-operation co-optimization of IES considering uncertainty and electrical/thermal energy storage, J. Electric Power Automation Equipment, 2019, 39(08):169-175.

Application of Geophysical Technology in Engineering Investigation

Chuanting Zhao[1,*], Jiantao Ran[2], Lijun Xue[1], Kaifei Wang[1], and Yangang Cui[1]

[1] The Third Geological Exploration Institute of China Metallurgical Geology Bureau, Taiyuan, China
[2] Shanxi Huaye Survey Engineering Technology Co., Ltd, Taiyuan, China

Abstract. With the development of science and technology and the progress of society, various high and new technologies have increasingly shown their respective advantages. Among them, geophysical prospecting technology is a typical representative. Because it can greatly improve the speed and efficiency of engineering, and at the same time, it also plays an important role in engineering safety and prevention. Therefore, it is widely promoted and applied, especially in engineering survey work. This article studies the importance of geophysical prospecting in engineering exploration, the methods of geophysical prospecting technology, the application of geophysical prospecting technology, and the development trend of geophysical prospecting technology. How to better understand the application of geophysical prospecting technology and rationally choose working methods and methods, so as to serve the geological exploration work to the utmost extent, is an important topic that needs to be solved and studied urgently.

1. Introduction

At this stage, relying on the development of science and technology and economic and social progress, my country's geological prospecting work has achieved unprecedented rapid development, and various high and new technologies represented by geophysical technology have been promoted and applied in this field. As we all know, as a basic project for work construction, geological survey work plays an irreplaceable role in the quality, safety and overall benefits of the entire project. Compared with traditional drilling and exploratory well technologies, geophysical prospecting technology has more advantages in the role and function of engineering construction, its application field and scope are wider, the restrictions are less, and the effect is more obvious. But it is undeniable that there are also problems and defects of this kind and that need to be further studied and solved in order to be able to play the greatest role and utility in the engineering geological survey and improve the overall quality and level of engineering construction.

2. Significance of geophysical methods in engineering investigation

At this stage, with the development and progress of basic technology and the continuous purchase of goods in society, geophysical prospecting technology is becoming more and more mature, and it has been widely promoted and applied in many fields and industries, and has received good economic and social Effect. Especially in the field of geological exploration, it has played an irreplaceable role. For example, in hydrogeological exploration and material disaster investigation and design, its role is unattainable by other technologies. In the work and construction, geophysical prospecting technology can not only greatly improve the construction progress and speed of project construction, but also provide an important guarantee for the quality and safety of the project. At the same time, it has also played a great guiding and key role in the prediction, prevention, and prevention of geological disasters. It can be seen that the role of geophysical prospecting technology for geological exploration is very obvious and important, and it has an important position and irreplaceable significance for establishing a public safety guarantee system and maintaining social security and stability. It should be noted that if we want to give full play to the role of geophysical technology, we must further strengthen research, earnestly delve into it, and play a better role.

3. Geophysical methods

Geophysical exploration technology is abbreviated as geophysical exploration technology. It is an exploration technology that uses the principles and methods of geophysics to observe the distribution and changes of various physical fields through the density difference, radioactivity, and magnetism of rocks, strata and surrounding rocks.

Geophysical prospecting technology can not only provide technologies and methods for detecting the internal structure of the earth, searching for energy, and monitoring the environment, but also for disaster forecasting.

* Corresponding author: web@cmgb.cn

Geological engineering prospecting is the investigation work carried out to find the geological factors that affect the construction of the project. The prospecting factors mainly include geological structure, hydrology, geomorphology, rock and soil and other physical properties and natural geological phenomena.

At present, geophysical prospecting technology is not only applied in geological engineering exploration of groundwater resources and mineral resources, but also used in geological disasters and archaeological surveys. The main exploration methods include gravity prospecting, electrical prospecting, seismic prospecting, magnetic prospecting, radiological prospecting, etc. See Figure 1. Brief description of the technical route of geophysical prospecting technology.

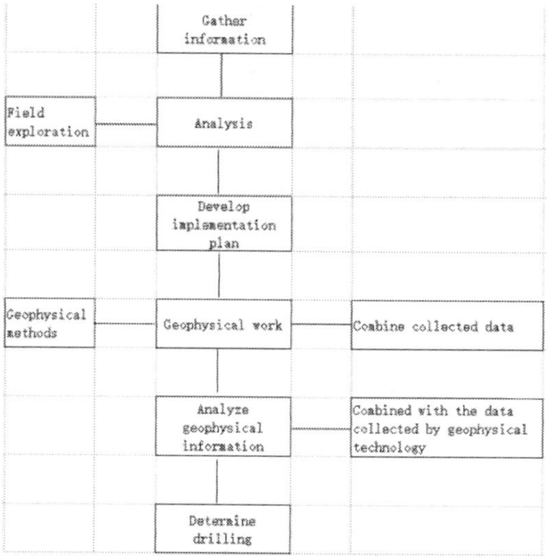

Figure 1. Brief description of the technical route of geophysical prospecting technology

3.1 Ground penetrating radar

The working principle of ground penetrating radar is similar to that of optics, mainly by launching high-frequency electromagnetic waves to the target medium, screening and analyzing the reflected electromagnetic wave frequency to conduct detailed survey and analysis of relevant geological conditions. Especially for metal minerals, it can carry out more in-depth detection and screening, so as to draw analysis conclusions and provide a basis for further work. It should be noted that in order to more accurately understand and grasp the characteristics of geology, it is necessary to strictly follow the principle of electromagnetic wave work, comprehensively analyze the topography and geology of the target site for comprehensive analysis and research, and in similar or identical geological conditions Below, the frequency obtained is also similar, which requires that the ground penetrating radar must have a higher resolution and recognition rate.

3.2 Magnetic method

The natural magnetic field method is mainly based on the full utilization of the natural underground electric field resources. The distribution and storage of groundwater and minerals can be judged by measuring the changes in the geoelectric field on the ground. It can exert a good effect on certain occasions. However, the limitation of this method is also obvious. At present, it only plays a good role in the target ground with obvious hydraulic slope and not deeply buried.

3.3 Transient electromagnetic method

This method is mainly based on the change of electromagnetic waves at different times to detect and survey the target surface. It is mainly based on the different conductivity of different minerals, which induces different signals, and analyzes the law of electromagnetic field and time changes, so as to Detect and analyze the storage location and depth of minerals.

3.4 Seismic exploration method

The working principle of this method is to analyze the rock structure and structure of the crust by analyzing the propagation law of artificially excited elastic waves in different crusts. And this elastic wave is what we call seismic wave. In this process, if explosives are used as the seismic source, the surface is excited by the action at the bottom layer, which will affect the changes in the surrounding environment and topography.

In this way, the rock at a certain distance from the earthquake source will produce a certain elastic change, which will trigger the resistance of the rock itself, and this resistance will form a structural deformation. However, once this elastic change disappears, the rock will return to its original condition. In this process, the seismic point changes of the seismic source are constantly changing with different deformations, so that by analyzing the position of each deformation, the necessary basis and original materials can be provided for subsequent analysis and detection.

4. Application of geophysical prospecting technology

4.1 Application in Geological Engineering Investigation of Groundwater Resources

In order to ensure the accuracy of geological engineering survey of groundwater resources, before conducting geophysical exploration, technicians need to collect the topographic and geomorphic features, climatic features, human environment, traffic conditions and other data of the exploration area, and make appropriate surveys based on the above data. Plan, select the appropriate geophysical exploration technology, method and survey instrument. Among them, the induced polarization method has a small impact on the hydrological environment and landform characteristics, and can measure multiple parameters at the same time. It is the most commonly used geophysical prospecting technology in the exploration of groundwater resources.

The operation of the induced polarization method in the geological engineering survey of groundwater resources is as follows:

(1) Choose to place an average of 3 detectors at 3 locations in the exploration area for IP detection, and collect the measured parameters such as polarizability, deviation, and resistivity.

(2) The parameter information collected by the three detectors is analyzed and processed through the terminal computer to obtain the geophysical prospecting results; in order to lose the parameter information during the data processing, the original data needs to be backed up.

(3) Combine the geophysical prospecting results with the exploration experience of the technicians, and finally get the location of the groundwater boreholes in the exploration area.

4.2 Application in geological engineering prospecting of mineral resources

Similarly, in order to ensure the accuracy of the geological engineering exploration of mineral resources, it is necessary to collect data before proceeding with geophysical exploration technology, and determine the exploration plan based on the collected data, and select the appropriate geophysical exploration technology, method and exploration instrument.

The operations of using geophysical prospecting technology to explore mineral resources are as follows:

(1) Choose measuring instrument: The audio geoelectric field instrument has become the most commonly used geological exploration instrument for mineral resources due to its compact equipment, little influence by topographic features, simple operation, and large amount of mineral resources exploration information obtained.

(2) Scan and probe the stratum in the exploration area: select a location with a relatively stable potential difference to place the detector; at the same time, at least 3 scan measurements are required to ensure accuracy.

(3) Draw a report on the results of geophysical prospecting: scan and detect through the terminal computer, the obtained stratum images, charts and data information are analyzed and integrated, and finally a report of the geophysical prospecting results is obtained.

(4) Determine the location of the borehole: Combine the geophysical prospecting results with the exploration experience of the technicians, and finally get the location of the mineral resources in the exploration area.

With the application of geophysical prospecting technology in geological engineering exploration, not only has it greatly reduced the difficulty of geological engineering exploration, improved work efficiency, but also effectively increased the accuracy and scientificity of the exploration results, providing a basis for the development and utilization of geological resources And security.

5. Development trend of geophysical technology

5.1 Innovation in detection technology

With the development of science and technology and the progress of society, people are becoming more and more important and necessary for geological exploration. Under such circumstances, the research and exploration of geophysical prospecting technology also appears more urgent and imperative. In this situation, the introduction of high-tech and advanced equipment has even more advantages and markets. For example, it is possible to make full use of wavelet analysis theory, give full play to the advantages and characteristics of this theory, carry out data collection and screening, analysis and induction, so as to maximize the depth, precision and accuracy of exploration to adapt to modern society and engineering quality requirements for geophysical prospecting technology.

5.2 Treatment of geophysical engineering technology

In the specific construction process, collecting and translating engineering geophysical data is an indispensable link and procedure. On the one hand, keen observation and data capture capabilities are required. This is the basis and prerequisite for geological survey work. If there is no accurate and timely original data, geological survey and analysis work is like a source of no root. And if there are loopholes and mistakes in this link, it will inevitably affect the entire investigation work. This is called data collection. On the other hand, since the collected data are all primitive, some of them may even have a strong professional and theoretical nature. For the subsequent survey work, detailed analysis and translation must be carried out by engineers. This is very necessary and important to ensure the accuracy and applicability of the data. Only through translation and conversion can the next step of the survey and translation Analyze and test work to provide compliance and provide a basis for the next decision. Through the above analysis, we can see that the practitioners of geophysical prospecting technology must have deep professional technical knowledge and comprehensive ability and quality to meet the needs of this task, and to deal with the various problems encountered in geological exploration, and complete them well. work tasks.

6. Conclusion

All in all, with the development of modern science and technology and the progress of society, geophysical prospecting technology has also shown a good momentum of development, and has played an increasingly important role in geological exploration. In this large category, various professional technical means, such as gravity, electromagnetic, seismic wave and other specialized technologies, have also shown their own characteristics and functions. However, it cannot be ignored that our mastery of geophysical prospecting technology is far from adapting to the application of current geological exploration work, and it is far from meeting actual needs. Therefore, we must attach great importance to further strengthen research, improve the professional level and comprehensive ability of practitioners, and provide an inexhaustible source of power for the development of geophysical prospecting technology and even basic geological technology.

References

1. Application of Engineering Geophysical Prospecting in High Slope Investigation [J]. Zhang Jianfeng,Li Chenghao. World Nonferrous Metals. 2017(04)
2. Application and prospect of engineering geophysical technology in geotechnical engineering [J]. Wang Chenglong. Housing and Real Estate. 2017(18)
3. Vigorous development of engineering geophysical prospecting [J]. Zhang Zhixun. Marine Geology Developments. 1985(12)
4. Probing into the application and prospect of engineering geophysical detection methods [J]. Tian Zengbiao. China Metal Bulletin. 2019(03)
5. Technical application of engineering geophysical detection methods [J]. Wang Zeng. Resource Information and Engineering. 2018(02)
6. Application of engineering geophysical technology in general contracting project geotechnical engineering [J]. Shang Zhiyu, Wu Jin, Wu Weijie, Wang Xiaojun, Zheng Changwei. Cement Engineering. 2016(06)
7. Application of Engineering Geophysical Prospecting in Geological Hazard Investigation [J]. Bai Jun. Heilongjiang Science and Technology Information. 2017(11)
8. Application of high-density electrical method in engineering geophysical prospecting [J]. Cai Jin. World Nonferrous Metals. 2017(07)
9. Application analysis of engineering geophysical technology in geological survey [J]. Deng Andi. World Nonferrous Metals. 2017(08)
10. Discussion on the application of engineering geophysical prospecting technology in geological survey [J]. Wei Xiangqian. Innovation and Application of Science and Technology. 2017(28)

Study on Sedimentary Characteristics of Chang 9 Member of Triassic in Ordos Basin

Jingbiao Bai*

No.5 Oil Production Plant of Changqing Oilfield Branch of Petrochina, Xi'an, China

Abstract. The Triassic Yanchang Formation in the Ordos Basin is one of the main exploration targets. Based on the detailed exploration of the outcrop at the southern margin of the Ordos Basin, combined with previous results, a systematic analysis of lithology, rock assemblage, sedimentary facies characteristics and temporal evolution is carried out. The results show that the Changchang 9 oil-bearing group on the southern margin of the Ordos Basin can be divided into 9 lithofacies types, and three types of sedimentary facies, meandering river, meandering river delta, and braided river delta are developed. The meandering river facies develops riverbed retention deposits, beaches, and There are four types of microfacies in natural dikes and rupture fans. There are five types of microfacies in meandering river deltas: underwater distributary channels, underwater natural dikes, divert bays, estuary dams, and remote sand dams. Braided river deltas develop underwater distributary channels, There are two kinds of microfacies between distributary channels; the Chang 9 oil-bearing group has a coarse-fine-coarse compound rhythm in the vertical direction; meandering river sand bodies and delta front sand bodies are the main places for oil and gas migration and accumulation.

1. Introduction

The Upper Triassic Yanchang Formation in the southern margin of the Ordos Basin is a key horizon for the exploration and development of the Changqing Oilfield. Its sedimentology research began in the 1970s. Due to the large scale of the sandbody's horizontal distribution, the vertical stacking of complex and diverse sedimentary facies belts Changes are rapid and there are few studies on geological outcrop profiles in the field. Many scholars have inconsistent understanding of the sedimentary system in the study area. They believe that lakes and delta deposits mainly develop, which can be further divided into four types of deposits: delta plains, delta fronts, shallow lakes, and deep lakes. Subfacies; Jiang Qi et al. believed that sandy clastic flow deposits developed in the southern Ordos Basin, not traction flow deposits. The scale of single-stage clastic flows is generally small, and the thickness of multi-layer clastic flows increases. Based on the outcrop profiles of Luhe Village in Luochuan County and Yijun Road Crossing in Jinsuoguan on the southern margin of the Ordos Basin, the Upper Triassic in the southern margin of the basin is discussed on the basis of lithofacies characteristics, sedimentary facies signs and sedimentary sequence analysis, combined with the regional geological background. Sedimentary facies distribution characteristics and distribution evolution law of the Chang 9 member of Yanchang Formation.

2. Geological background

The Ordos Basin is located in the west of the North China Platform. It is a multi-cycle sedimentary basin with stable subsidence and depression migration. The basin area is about 25×105 km2. In the Late Triassic, the basin was affected by the Qinling Mountains to the southwest
—The influence of compression strike-slip and edge thrust nappe caused by the Qilian Mountain orogen is steep in the southwest and gentle in the northeast. The study area is located on the southern margin of the Ordos Basin, with the north part of the northern Shaanxi slope in the southeast, the east part adjacent to the flexure belt in western Shanxi, and the south part of the northeastern part of the Weibei uplift.

From bottom to top, the Yanchang component consists of 10 oil-bearing groups, of which the Chang 10-Chang 9 oil-bearing group is the target horizon. The Chang 10 sedimentary period is the formation stage of the lake basin, which is mainly composed of flesh-red and gray-green medium-coarse feldspar sandstone with silty mudstone, with a deposition thickness of 210-350 m; the Chang 9 sedimentary period is the expansion period of the lake basin, and The underlying Chang 10 oil layer group is in integrated contact, with gray-green medium-fine sandstone intercalated with dark mudstone and silt fine sandstone deposits, with a deposition thickness of 80 to 110 m. On the whole, the Upper Triassic Yanchang Formation in the Ordos Basin was formed in a complete cycle of the inland depression lake basin. The lake basin

* Corresponding author: bjb1_cq@petrochina.com.cn

experienced four stages of initial subsidence, strong depression, rebound uplift, and shrinkage.

3. Sedimentary characteristics

Through detailed survey and comprehensive analysis of the outcrop profile in the field, the Chang 10-Chang 9 oil-bearing group of the Yanchang Formation mainly developed sedimentary facies types such as meandering river, meandering river delta and braided river delta. Among them, the outcrop profile of Luhe Village in Luochuan County is located in the northeast of the study area, with meandering rivers and meandering river delta fronts mainly developed. The outcrop section of Jinsuoguan-Yijun intersection is located in the southwest of the study area, and mainly develops braided river delta front subfacies.

3.1 Lithofacies

Lithofacies reflects the strength and weakness of hydrodynamic conditions, transportation methods, and depositional mechanisms during sediment deposition, and is an important theoretical basis for dividing sedimentary facies. By summarizing the characteristics of the lithology, grain size and sedimentary structure of the outcrop profile in the study area, the following nine lithofacies types have been identified

3.1.1 Positive-grained sequence bedding and gravel-bearing coarse sandstone facies (S-Gg)

It often develops on the scouring surface of the river channel and is composed of sorted, rounded and medium coarse sandstone. A small amount of fine gravel can be seen at the bottom of the river channel. The hydrodynamic force gradually weakened.

3.1.2 Trough-like cross-bedding medium-coarse sandstone facies (Sct)

It often develops inside the river channel and is composed of well-sorted and well-rounded middle-coarse sandstone. The trough-like cross bedding has a large scale, and the laminae are parallel to the interface of the strata. The depression direction of the two is the same. Migrate and fill the deposited product.

3.1.3 Sandstone facies in parallel bedding (Smh)

It is composed of well-sorted and well-rounded middle sandstone with parallel bedding. It is a product under strong hydrodynamic conditions and is commonly found in shallow water sedimentary environments in river beaches and underwater distributary channels at the delta front.

3.1.4 Massive bedding medium-fine sandstone facies (Sm)

It is composed of gray medium-fine sandstone, which is uniform and massive as a whole. The sediments are rapidly accumulated, and it is too late to differentiate and form.

3.1.5 Wedge-shaped cross-bedding sandstone facies (Sw)

It is composed of well-sorted, well-rounded medium-fine sandstone, with wedge-shaped cross-bedding and obvious wedge-shaped changes in the thickness of the strata. It is common in the depositional environment of the estuary dam in the front edge of the meandering river delta.

3.1.6 Inverse-granular sequence bedding sandstone facies (Sgi)

It is composed of well-sorted and well-rounded dark gray medium-fine sandstone. The bottom is dominated by sedimentary fine sandstone, and it gradually transitions upward to medium sandstone. From bottom to top, the sediment grain size changes from fine to coarse, and the hydrodynamic conditions gradually increase , Is a typical symbol of estuary dams and remote sand dams.

3.1.7 Massive bedding silt fine sandstone facies (Fm)

It is composed of silt-fine sandstone that is sorted and well-rounded. It is uniform and massive as a whole without any laminar structure. It often appears in stable and low-energy hydrodynamic environments such as natural dikes and remote sand dams.

3.1.8 Climbing sand grain bedding silt fine sandstone facies (Fr)

The silt fine sandstone with climbing sand-line bedding is the product of wave-breaking migration. The hydrodynamic strength is relatively weak, and it often develops in the natural embankment environment on both sides of the river.

3.1.9 Mudstone Facies (M)

Mainly gray-green, gray-black massive mudstone and silty mudstone, with a thickness of 10 to 100 cm, fine-grained sediments suspended below the lake base level slowly accumulate vertically under low-energy static water conditions.

3.2 Sedimentary facies

3.2.1 Meandering river facies

The typical sand body is selected from the 10 oil layer group in the Luhe Village section of Luochuan County, about 65 m long and 12 m thick, with a large channel

width-to-depth ratio and east-west trending. This set of sand bodies is a meandering river deposit. The channel sand bodies are composed of two-stage channel units. The thickness of the single-stage channel sand bodies is 2-6 m, and the appearance is similar to the top flat bottom concave shape. Macroscopically, meandering river sediments have an obvious "dual structure", and the grain size of sediments gradually becomes finer from bottom to top, which is a positive-grained sequence bedding. Among them, channel unit I is relatively complete, from bottom riverbed sedimentation→side beach→natural embankment → burst fan and other vertical superimposition. The typical lithofacies sequence is S-Gg →Sct→Smh→Fm→Sm; channel unit Ⅱ Remaining sediments from the bottom riverbed
→Boundary beach→Natural dike vertical stacking or directly from the beach→Natural dike group
The typical lithofacies sequence is S-Gg→Sct→Smh→ Fm or Smh→Fm. The river channel unit I was formed with a large curvature. Later, due to the event of flooding, a new river bed was scoured along the direction of the convex bank by the gully, which straightened the river channel, causing the "string gully straightening" effect, and then the channel unit II was formed. On the basis of previous studies on meandering rivers, perfect and establish a model.

3.2.2 The meandering river delta facies

The typical sand body is selected from the Chang 9 oil layer group in the Luhe Village section of Luhe Village, Luochuan County, north-east of the study area, with a length of about 60 m, a thickness of about 17 m, and an east-west strike. Through a comprehensive analysis of the rock types, sedimentary structures, and lithofacies combination of the outcrop section, it is believed that this set of sand bodies belongs to the sub-facies deposition of the meandering river delta front, which is probably formed by the vertical superimposition of 13 stages of underwater channel units. The thickness of the single-stage channel unit is 0.3 to 3 m, and the lateral migration range is relatively large. The sand body deposits are thicker near the main channel, and the sand body deposits are significantly thinner away from the main channel, and the appearance is approximately Lens-like form. At the bottom of the outcrop profile, the grain size of the sediment gradually thickens upwards, that is, the typical inverse granular bedding, which belongs to the estuary bar sediment. The typical lithofacies sequence is Sgi→Sw. River course
→Underwater natural dike or underwater distributary channel→Underwater natural dike→Vertical stacking of diversion bays, gradually narrowing grain size from bottom to top, the typical lithofacies sequence is Sct→Fr or Sct→Fm→M; in the outcrop section On the upper part, it gradually transitions from far sand dam → estuary dam → underwater distributary channel → underwater natural embankment or directly superimposes from far sand dam → estuary dam. The sediment grain size of the former is fine → coarse → fine composite from bottom to top Rhythm, the latter is directly composed of fine-grained anti-granular bedding. The typical lithofacies sequence is Sm→Sgi→Sw→Sct→Fm or Sm→Sgi→Sw. Compared with braided river deltas, meandering river delta fronts have the characteristics of complete facies belt development, diverse rhythm types, and rich lithofacies assemblage sequences.

3.2.3 Braided river delta facies

The typical sand body is selected from the Chang 9-Chang 8 oil layer group at the outcrop section of the south west Jinsuoguan Yijun road. The interface between Chang 9 and Chang 8 can be clearly seen on the outcrop section, and the distribution types of the two sand bodies are significantly different. The channel of Chang 9 oil-bearing group is east-west, about 75 m long and 15 m thick. The channel has a large width-to-depth ratio, coarser sediment grain size, and lower sandstone component maturity and structural maturity than meandering river deltas. Due to the relatively steep paleo-topography, along with the rise of the lake level, sedimentation was formed under the background of lake transgression. The exposed sand bodies belonged to the front subfacies of braided river delta, and the positive rhythm channel sand bodies superimposed vertically in multiple stages developed. It can be seen that the scouring surface, the channel undercutting and eroding the channel sand body of the previous stage, and the development of trough-shaped cross bedding and parallel bedding, reflecting the multiple underwater distributary channels in the front of braided river delta under strong hydrodynamic force The deposition process of migration, scouring and stacking. In addition, in the eastern part of the outcrop section, a thin layer of dark oil shale with a thickness of about 0.3 to 0.5 m was deposited in the late Chang 9 oil layer group, commonly known as "Lijiapan Shale". The 12-stage underwater channel unit is superimposed in the vertical direction. The thickness of the single-stage channel unit is 0.3 to 25 m. The lateral migration range is smaller than that of the meandering river delta, and the sediment grain size is larger than that of the meandering river delta. Since the southwest outcrop profile is relatively close to the provenance area and is often modified by waves and bank currents, the braided river delta has the characteristics of incomplete facies belt development. The outcrop profile does not develop estuary dams and remote sand dam deposits. The microfacies between underwater distributary channels and distributary channels are developed.

4. Sedimentary evolution characteristics

During the period of the Upper Triassic Yanchang Formation, the Ordos Basin was affected by the Indosinian movement, forming a large asymmetrical skip-shaped foreland basin with a steep southwest and a gentle northeast. It has the characteristics of multiple water systems, multiple provenances, and sufficient supply of provenance. . The two major provenance systems of southwest and northeast directions bring a large amount of clastic sediments, which are the deposits of the braided river delta at the Jinsuoguan-Yijun intersection in the southwest direction of the study area and the meandering river and meandering river delta of Luhe Village in Luochuan County from the northeast direction. The system provides the material basis. In this context, the Chang 10-Chang 9 oil layer group of the Yanchang Formation in the southern margin of the Ordos Basin mainly developed sedimentary facies types such as meandering river, meandering river delta, and braided river delta.

In the early depositional period of the Yanchang Formation (the period of the Chang 10 oil layer formation), the orogenic belt in the southwestern margin of the basin was not uplifted high, and no large-scale thrusting occurred. A set of meandering river deposits was deposited in the background. During the middle depositional period of the Yanchang Formation (the depositional period of the Chang 9 oil-bearing group), due to the influence of the Indosinian movement, the orogenic belt on the southwestern margin of the basin quickly uplifted and began to undergo large-scale thrusting. The topography has steep slopes and abundant sediment supply. The subsidence rate of the southwestern margin has accelerated. The frontal outcrop profile of the braided river delta at the south-west direction of Jinsuoguan-Yijun intersection in the study area was formed during this thrust load settlement process. In the study area from the northeast to the outcrop profile of Luhe Village in Luochuan County, the basin as a whole was compressed and depressed, and the climate changed from arid and rainless (Chang 10 layer deposition period) to humid and rainy (Chang 9 layer deposition period) , Leading to a significant increase in the base level. The base level was in the low-stand system tract period in the early stage (the Chang 10 layer group deposition period), and meandering river deposits developed. Later (the Chang 9-layer group deposition period) the base level rose, reforming the low-stand stage sedimentation and causing diversion. Channel sand bodies regressed towards the land, forming meandering river delta deposits.

Looking at the sedimentary microfacies and lithofacies types of the Chang 10-Chang 9 oil-bearing group in the southern margin of the Ordos Basin, it can be seen that the vertical sedimentary sequence has obvious compound rhythm characteristics. From the perspective of sedimentary microfacies, from bottom to top, the riverbed sediments, beaches, natural dikes, and rupture fans of meandering rivers are transformed into remote sand dams, estuary dams, and underwater distributary channels on the delta front. From the perspective of lithofacies, the pebbly coarse sandstone facies of the trough-shaped cross-bedding and the positive-grained sequence bedding, which indicate strong hydrodynamics, transition upwards to the massive bedding medium-fine sandstone facies, and then upwards become the interaction between rivers and lakes. Wedge-shaped cross-bedding and anti-granular bedding medium-coarse sandstone facies formed by the action. On the whole, it is a set of coarse-fine-coarse composite rhythm sand bodies, reflecting the result of the base level rising and sand body degrading.

5. Conclusion

(1) A total of 9 lithofacies types have been identified in the outcrop profile in the wild, and three sedimentary facies types: meandering river, meandering river delta and braided river delta are developed.

(2) During the deposition period of Chang 9 oil layer group, the northeastern area of the study area transitioned from meandering river facies to meandering river delta facies, which was inherited sedimentation; during the deposition period of Chang 9 oil layer group, the sedimentary facies changed from the southwest to northeast of the study area. The river delta turns into a meandering river delta, with obvious differences in sedimentary facies; the Chang 9 oil-bearing group has a coarse-fine-coarse compound rhythm in the vertical direction.

(3) Meandering river sands and delta front sands are important places for oil and gas migration and accumulation. The muddy sediments on the delta front can be used as a cover layer for oil and gas accumulation and form a favorable reservoir-caprock combination in the vertical direction, which is an important place for oil and gas exploration, it's the favorable zone.

References

1. The Influence of Reservoir Heterogeneity on Oilfield Development Effect[J]. Xu Jianhong,Qian Lidan,Kurban. Fault Block Oil and Gas Field. 2017(05).
2. The influence of reservoir heterogeneity on the degree of oil and gas enrichment[J]. Li Jinpeng. Inner Mongolia Petrochemical Industry. 2017(06).
3. Delta deposition and evolution of the Upper Triassic Yanchang Formation in the Ordos Basin[J]. Wu Fuli, Li Wenhou, Li Yuhong, Xi Shengli. Journal of Palaeogeography. 2014(03).
4. Analysis of control factors of ultra-low porosity and permeability sandstone reservoirs of Yanchang Formation in Fuxian County, Northern Shaanxi[J]. Li Chunyu, Xie Yuan, Liu Shaoguang, Huang Hongwei, Li Minghui. Journal of Chengdu University of Technology. 2012(03).
5. Accumulation conditions and characteristics of Nanniwan Oilfield[J]. Ji Yongtao, Liu Jianhong. Northwest Geology. 2012(02).
6. Sequence stratigraphic division and hydrocarbon-bearing properties of Yanchang Formation in northern Shaanxi[J]. Yang Lei, Mei Zhichao, Xiong Wei. Journal of Palaeogeography. 2021(03).
7. Discussion on sedimentary characteristics and provenance of Yanchang Formation in southern Ordos Basin[J]. Lin Hongbin, Yao Jingli. Journal of Xi'an Petroleum Institute (Natural Science Edition). 2020(05).
8. Reservoir characteristics and oil displacement efficiency analysis of Chang 6 reservoir in Pingqiao area and Wangyao area of Ansai Oilfield[J]. Zhu

 https://doi.org/10.1051/e3sconf/202233801004

Yushuang, Qu Zhihao, Kong Lingrong, Chen Rong, Li Jinfeng. Acta Sedimentologica Sinica. 2020(02).

9. A preliminary study on the law of oil and gas enrichment in Nanniwan Oilfield[J]. Dong Yilong, Wang Weixi, Liu Jianhong. Natural Gas Geoscience. 1998(02).
10. Sedimentary facies characteristics and storage conditions of Chang 6 reservoir group in Chuankou Oilfield[J]. Li Wenhou, Liu Yiqun, Feng Qiao. Journal of Northwest University (Natural Science Edition). 1996(02).

E3S Web of Conferences **338**, 01005 (2022)
ESMA 2021
https://doi.org/10.1051/e3sconf/202233801005

Synthesis and Characterization of Hydroxyl-Pinacolone Retinoate

Hexing Zhang, Baicheng Feng, Yan Jin*

Qingdao University of Science and Technology, Qingdao, China

Abstract. All-trans retinoic acid (10) was synthesized by β-ionone (5) through knoevenagel condensation, reduction and hydrolysis reaction. Then, hydroxyl- pinacolone retinoate (11) was prepared by the esterification with 1-hydroxy- 3, 3-dimethylbutan-2-ketone. This route not only reduces the synthesis steps but also helps to increase the yield. The structure of the product was characterized by ^{1}H NMR and ^{13}C NMR.

1. Introduction

Vitamin A also known as retinol, vitamin A in a broad sense also includes retinol derivatives(Figure 1) such as retinene (1) retinoic acid (2) retinyl acetate (3) and retinyl palmitate (4) [1-4]. The structures are interconvertible [5,6]They have a wide range of physiological functions [7], including in vision[8] ,immune function [9]and tumor suppression [10]. vitamin A or vitamin A derivatives have been explored extensively. The long electron-rich conjugated polyene chains of the vitamin A molecule are highly unstable, it can be easily destroyed [11,14]. To avoid inactivation, vitamin A is often converted into vitamin A derivatives. It has been found that vitamin A ester derivatives have all the physiological functions of vitamin A, with higher stability and a wider range of applications [15-18]. Hydroxyl-pinacolone retinoate(12), one of the important derivatives of retinoic acid, could regulate the metabolism of the stratum corneum, which has been widely used in cosmetics fields, so the searches for efficient synthetic routes to these compounds are becoming increasingly important. The main synthetic routes for retinoic acid are C14+C6 represented by Roche[19] and C15+C5 represented by BAST [20] . In addition, the synthesis of retinoic acid was made by transition metal-catalyzed cross-coupling [21]. However, the method has major drawbacks. For example, the residue of transition metals is difficult to be separated. We have attempted to design a route with simple steps and mild conditions by adopting the knoevenagel condensation method.

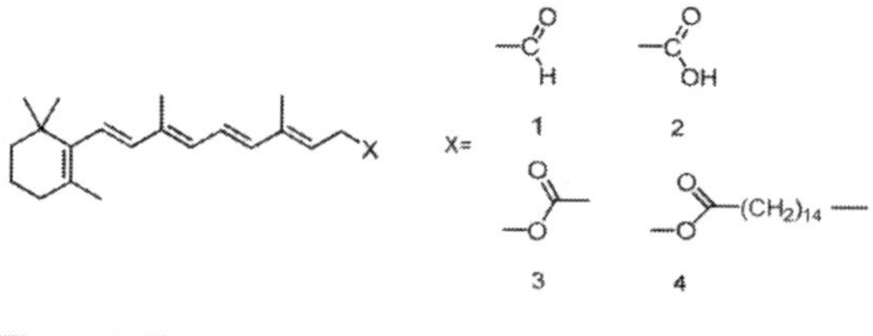

Figure 1. The molecular formula of vitamin A derivatives

2. Results and discussion

2.1 Chemical synthesis

The C15+C6-C1 route was applied to the syntheses of all-trans retinoic acid. Starting from commercial β-ionone(5), the synthesis of C15 nitrile was made by the condensation with cyanoacetic acid and further decarboxylation, and the reduction of C15 nitrile to C15 aldehyde with DIBAL-H in tolueneinto. A knoevenagel condensation of C15 aldehydes with 3-methyl-2-butenoate in methanol led to retinoic acid methyl ester (8). Hydrolysis under alkaline conditions gave retinoic acid (9). Subsequent chlorination with PCl_3 and finally esterification with 1-hydroxy-3, 3-dimethylbutan -2-ketone provided hydroxyl-pinacolone retinoate (12).

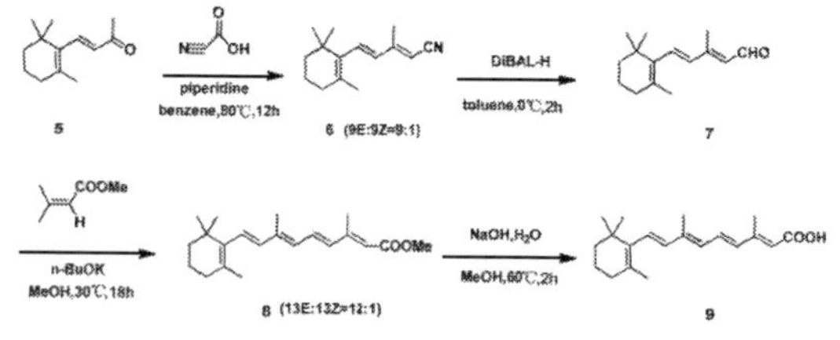

Figure 2. Synthesis route of all-trans retinoic acid

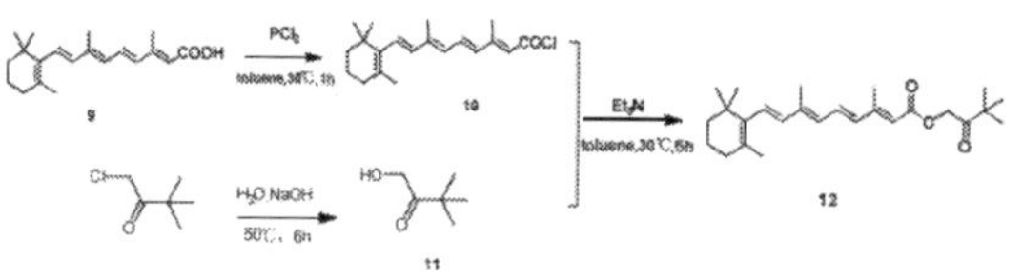

Figure 3: Synthesis route of hydroxyl-pinacolone retinoate

* Corresponding author: aurock@126.com

Table 1 Influence of the PCl_3 dosage on the synthesis of compound(10)

n(retinoic acid):n(PCl_3)	Quality /g	Yield/%
1:0.5	14.6	65.7
1:0.6	19.18	86.0
1:0.7	20.5	92.0
1:0.8	18.5	91.2

As can be seen from Table 1, the yield gradually increased as the dosage of PCl_3 increased, and when n(retinoic acid):n(PCl_3) = 1:0.7, the product quality was 20.5g, yield 92%, and the dosage continued to increase with a slight decrease in yield. Therefore, the optimum amount of PCl_3 is n(retinoic acid):n(PCl_3) = 1:0.7.

Table 2 Influence of the Triethylamine dosage on the synthesis of compound(12)

n(Compount10): n（Et_3N）	Quality /g	Yield/%
1:1.0	15.6	65.3
1:1.2	19.8	82.8
1:1.5	16.5	79.0

As can be seen from Table 2, the yield gradually increased with the increase of triethylamine dosage, when n(retinyl chloride): n(triethylamine) = 1:1.2, the product quality was 19.8g, yield 82.8%. Therefore, the optimum amount of triethylamine is n(retinyl chloride):n(Et_3N) = 1:1.2.

Table 3 Influence of the dropping time of compound(11)on the synthesis of compound(12)

Time/min	Quality/g	Yield/%
10	15.6	65.3
20	17.5	73.2
30	19.8	82.8
40	18.9	81.5

As can be seen from Table 3, the yield gradually increased with the extension of the titration time, and the product quality was 19.5g with a yield of 82.8% at a titration time of 30min, and the yield decreased slightly with further extension. Therefore, the optimum titration time is 30 min.

Table 4 Influence of the time on the synthesis of compound(12)

Time/h	Quality/g	Yield/%
2	14.6	61.1
4	19.8	82.8
5	19.5	81.8
6	19.1	81.3

As can be seen from Table 4, the reaction yield increases with the increase of reaction time, when the reaction time is 4h the yield is the largest, 82.8% continue to increase the reaction time yield increase is not obvious, because with the increase of time by-products increase, the yield decreases. Therefore, the optimum reaction time is 4h.

Table 5 Influence of the temperature on the synthesis of compound(12)

Temp/°C	Quality/g	Yield/%
10	15.6	65.3
20	17.5	73.2
30	19.8	82.8
40	18.6	77.8

As can be seen from Table 5, with the increase of temperature, the yield gradually increased, and the product quality was 19.8g with a yield of 82.85% at a temperature of 30°C. The yield decreased slightly when the reaction temperature continued to increase. Because the reaction temperature is too high to produce more by-products, so the yield is reduced, therefore, the best reaction temperature is 30 ℃.

3. Experimental section

3.1 General

All chemicals are purchased from commercial sources and do not require further purification. (^{1}H&^{13}C) spectram were recorded in $CDCl_3$/DMSO-d6 on a Bruker Avance 500 MHz. Samples are analyzed by high performance liquid chromatograph P230 (Dalian Elite Corporation) and gas chromatograph GC-6890 (Jinglu Weiye Corporation)

3.2 Synthesis of 3-methyl-5-(2, 6, 6-trimethyl-1-cyclohexen-1-yl)-2, 4-Pentadienenitrile (6)

β-ionone (5) (20g,10mmol) was suspended in benzene(100ml) and a solution of cyanoacetic acid(13.2g,15mmol) was added. Subsequent addition of piperidine (15ml), holding reaction at 80°C for 12 h. At the end of the reaction water was added . Mixture extracted with ethyl acetate. Organic phase is concentrated.Purification by silica column chromatography eluting with 1% ethyl acetate/petroleum ether to gave the compound 6 (17.5g, 78%, E/Z=9:1). ^{1}H NMR (500 MHz, $CDCl_3$) δ 6.50 (d, J=16.1 Hz, 1H), 6.11 (d, J=16.1Hz, 1H), 4.62 (s, 1H), 2.44(s,3H), 1.92 (t, 2H), 1.71(s,3H), 1.61(m,2H), 1.32(m,2H), 1.01(s,6H);^{13}C NMR (126 MHz, CDCl3) δ 208.16, 136.5, 126.3, 42.2, 31.0, 23.6, 22.5, 17.6, 16.8.

3.3 Synthesis of 3-Methyl-5-(2, 6, 6 -trimethylcyclohex-1-enyl) penta -2, 4-dienal (7)

Compound 6 (18g, 83.7mmol) was added to dry toluene(120ml), cooled to 0°C and DIBAL-H (1M in toluene, 83.7ml) is added to hold the reaction for 2 h. A refrigerated solution of 1M H_2SO_4 was added .Mixture extracted with ether, Organic phase is concentrated. Purification by silica column chromatography eluting with 10% Et2O/hexane to gave the compound 7 (14.5g, 74.4%).^{1}H NMR (500Hz, $CDCl_3$)δ 10.06 (d,J=8.1Hz,1H), 6.52 (d, J=16.2Hz, 1H), 6.18 (d,J=15.6Hz, 1H), 5.84

https://doi.org/10.1051/e3sconf/202233801005

(d,J=8.13Hz,1H),2.3 (s,3H), 2.01 (m, 2H),1.65(s, 3H), 1.60 (m, 2H),1.45 (m,2H),1.12 (s,6H); ^{13}C NMR (126 MHz, $CDCl_3$) δ 136.2, 132.5, 128.8, 46.5, 36.5, 30.6,23.2,18.6, 11.4.

3.4 Synthesis of all-trans retinoic acid methyl ester (8)

A slurry of n-BuOK(5.6g,49.6mmol) was in MeOH(80ml) at 0 °C.Methyl 3-methyl-2-butenoate (7.9g, 33mmol) was added.After stirring for 30 min. Compound 7 (7.4 g, 49.5 mmol) was added react for 18 h at 30 °C. The solvent methanol is removed in a vacuum and then water is added. Mixture extracted with methyl tert-butyl ether, Organic phase is concentrated. Purification by silica column chromatography eluting with 5% EtOAc/hexane to gave the compound 8 (6.4g, 62%, E/Z=12:1). ^{1}H NMR (500 MHz, DMSO) δ 7.07 (dd, J = 15.0, 11.6 Hz, 1H), 6.42 (d, J = 15.1 Hz, 1H), 6.23 (dt, J = 36.5, 16.1 Hz, 3H), 5.85 (s, 1H), 3.62 (s, 3H), 2.30 (s, 3H), 2.04-1.95 (m, 5H), 1.69 (s, 3H), 1.62-1.52 (m, 2H), 1.48-1.38 (m, 2H), 1.01 (s, 6H);^{13}C NMR (126 MHz, DMSO) δ 166.62, 152.74, 139.38, 137.21, 136.89, 135.02, 131.49, 129.75, 129.51, 128.01, 117.74, 50.73, 33.82, 32.57, 28.76, 21.47, 18.67, 13.49, 12.59.

3.5 Synthesis of all-trans retinoic acid (9)

Compound 8 (5g, 16mmol)was added to MeOH(60ml), followed by NaOH(2M 20ml) and the temperature was raised to 60 °C for 2 h, neutralized with 1M HCl and extracted with dichloroethane. Organic phase is concentrated. Recrystallisation with methanol to give compound 9 (4.0g,82.4%). ^{1}H NMR (500 MHz, DMSO) δ 12.03 (s, 1H), 7.02 (s, 1H), 6.40 (d, J = 15.1 Hz, 1H), 6.19 (t, J = 24.8 Hz, 3H), 5.77 (s, 1H), 2.28 (s, 3H), 2.01 (dd, J = 14.7, 8.8 Hz, 2H), 1.98 (s, 3H), 1.69 (s, 3H), 1.59 (s, 2H), 1.43 (s, 2H), 1.04 (d, J = 27.5 Hz,6H); ^{13}C NMR (126 MHz, DMSO) δ 167.76, 151.61, 138.89, 137.22, 136.92, 135.40, 130.80, 129.84, 129.42, 127.78, 119.41, 33.82, 32.57, 28.77, 21.48, 18.68, 13.37, 12.57.

3.6 Synthesis of 3, 7-dimethyl-9-(2, 6, 6-trimethyl-1-cyclohexen-1-yl) nona -2, 4, 6, 8- tetraenoyl chloride (10)

Compound 9 (4 g, 14 mmol) was added to toluene (20 mL) and PCl_3 (1.38 g, 10 mmol) was added dropwise at 0°C, then the temperature was raised to 30°C for 1 h. At the end of the reaction, the reaction was partitioned and the phosphite was separated to give compound 10 (3.92g, 92%). (Note: Compound 10 is used directly in the next step without treatment).

3.7 Synthesis of 1-hydroxy- 3,3-dimethylbutan-2-ketone (11)

To the flask was added a 1-chloro-3,3-dimethylbutan-2-one(2.7g 20 mmol), 72 g of water, stirred well and then warmed up to 50°C in a water bath. 45.2 g of aqueous sodium hydroxide solution with a mass fraction of 20% was added dropwise and the reaction was held for 6 hours after the dropwise addition, and the end point was detected by gas chromatography. The organic phase was extracted with ethyl acetate three times, the solvent was evaporated under reduced pressure, and the organic phase was combined and washed with 10% aqueous sodium chloride solution, dried over anhydrous sodium sulfate, filtered, and the filtrate was distilled under reduced pressure to obtain compound 11(1.95g,84%).^{1}H NMR (500 MHz, DMSO) δ 4.82(s 1H),4.56(d, J = 6.0 Hz, 2H),1.19(s, 9H); ^{13}C NMR (126 MHz, DMSO) δ 213.0,64.2,41.5,26.5.

3.8 Synthesis of hydroxyl-pinacolone retinoate (12)

Under Ar. To a solution of 1-hydroxy-3,3-dimethyl-2-butanone (3.5g,30mmol)in toluene(40ml) was added dry Et_3N (2.4g,23.3mol). Add compound 10 (6.7g,20mmol) dropwise at 0°C. Reacted at 30 °C for 6 h.The salts were filtered off and then concentrated. The residue was added to anhydrous ethanol and a yellow solid was precipitated to obtain compound 12 (6.5g,82%). ^{1}H NMR (500 MHz, DMSO) δ 7.12 (dd, J = 15.1, 11.5 Hz, 1H), 6.49 (d, J = 15.1 Hz, 1H), 6.30 (t, J = 16.0 Hz, 2H), 6.20 (d, J = 16.1 Hz, 1H), 5.95 (s, 1H), 5.05 (s, 2H), 2.40 – 2.23 (m, 3H), 2.10 – 1.94 (m, 5H), 1.73 (d, J = 17.9 Hz, 3H), 1.59 (d, J = 6.0 Hz, 2H), 1.47 (dd, J = 7.5, 3.9 Hz, 2H), 1.16 (s, 9H), 1.04 (s, 6H); ^{13}C NMR (126 MHz, DMSO) δ 208.16, 167.51, 156.58, 139.98, 137.64, 137.24, 135.16, 132.01, 130.21, 130.04, 128.54, 119.13, 64.62, 42.54, 34.15, 32.97, 29.18, 26.03, 21.87, 19.07, 13.97, 12.95. Infrared spectra are shown in Figure 4.

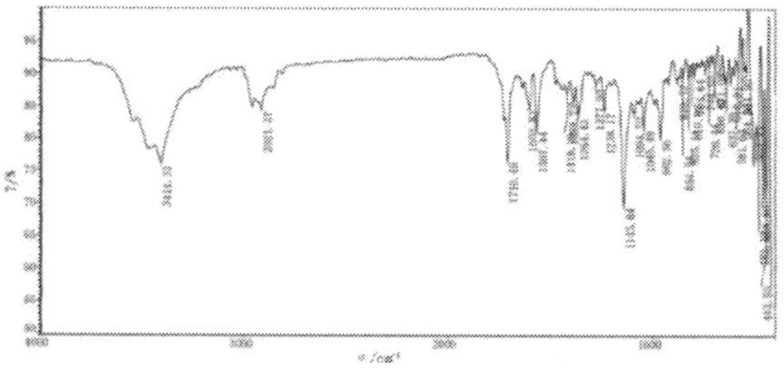

Figure 4. IR of the compound 12

4. Conclusion

The intermediate retinoic acid was synthesised through a series of reactions using β-ionone as the starting material and further synthesised as hydroxyl-pinacolone retinoate. In the process of synthesizing retinoic acid, methyl 3-methyl-2-butenoate was used as C6 module to reduce the synthesis steps and helps to increase the yield.

Acknowledgments

This work was financially supported by the Natural Science Foundation of Shandong Province of China (ZR2020MB132).

References

1. Zhiwei Zhu,The earliest discovered vitamin--vitamin A, University Chemistry.25(2010) 54-56.
2. Zhuancheng Li , Review of vitamin A synthesis process, Chemical Engineering and Equipment. 2009 95-100.
3. Amangui-Amati, The importance of vitamin A for the human body, Science and Technology Communication. 2010, 16-17.
4. Connie Guo,Xu Zhilan. Current status of research on vitamin A and its physiological functions, Micronutrients and Health Research. 35(2018) 62-64.
5. C.Patrick Reynolds,Katherine K. Matthay,Judith G. Villablanca,Barry J. Maurer, Retinoid therapy of high-risk neuroblastoma. Cancer Letters.2003,197,185-192.
6. Ross S A,McCaffery P J,Drager U C,De Luca L M. Retinoids in embryonal development, Physiological reviews.2000,80, 1021-54
7. Álvarez Rosana,Vaz Belén,Gronemeyer Hinrich,de Lera Ángel R. Functions, therapeutic applications, and synthesis of retinoids and carotenoids, Chemical reviews. 2014,114, 1-125.
8. Kahremany Shirin,Kubas Adam,Tochtrop Gregory P,Palczewski Krzysztof. Catalytic synthesis of 9-cis-retinoids: mechanistic insights, Dalton transactions . 48(2019) 10581-10595.
9. Stephensen Charles B.,Jiang Xiaowen.Vitamin A Deficiency Increases the In Vivo Development of IL-10–Positive Th2 Cells and Decreases Development of Th1 Cells in Mice, Narnia. 134(2004) 2660-2666.
10. Ricardo Carvalho,Muhammad Islam,Ana Mata,Reyca E Silva,Márcia Paz,Marcus Alencar,Hercília Rolim,Maria Medeiros,João E Sousa,Ana Amélia Melo-Cavalcante. Vitamin A in prevention and treatment of cancer, International Journal of Medicine. 5(2017) 199-205.
11. Mian N. Riaz,Muhammad Asif,Rashida Ali. Stability of Vitamins during Extrusion, Critical Reviews in Food Science and Nutrition. 49(2009) 361-368.
12. Julie Courraud, Jacques Berger, Jean-Paul Cristol, Sylvie Avallone. Stability and bioaccessibility of different forms of carotenoids and vitamin A during in vitro digestion, Food Chemistry. 136(2013) 871-877.
13. Mulry M C,Schmidt R H,Kirk J R. Isomerization of retinyl palmitate using conventional lipid extraction solvents, Journal Association of Official Analytical Chemists.1983,66, 746-750.
14. Cherng Shu-Hui,Xia Qingsu,Blankenship Lonnie R. Photodecomposition of retinyl palmitate in ethanol by UVA light-formation of photodecomposition products, reactive oxygen species, and lipid peroxides, Chemical research in toxicology.2005,18, 129-138.
15. Massimo Milani. Evaluation of a Combination of Retinol, Hydroxyl-Pinacolone Retinoate (Retinsphere), An Antibacterial Agent (BIOPEP.15), Salicylic Acid and Vitamin E in Subjects Suffering from Predominant Comedonal Acne-An Italian multicenter Prospective Open study, Journal of Dermatology and Clinical Research.2016,4.
16. Hiroshi Toshida, Akira Murakami, Chikako Suto,Koike, Tabuchi, Ohta, Odaka. Efficacy of retinol palmitate eye drops for dry eye in rabbits with lacrimal gland resection, Clinical Ophthalmology. 2012(2012)1585-1593.
17. Maryce M. Jacobs. Vitamins and Minerals in the Prevention and Treatment of Cancer. CRC Press. 2018-05-04.
18. Advanced Polymer Systems, Inc. Retinyl esters of a-hydroxy acids for topical improvement of skin function and apperance.WO9720812A1,1997.
19. Isler O, Treadwell P, Guex W. Processes for the manufacture of vitamin A-acetate. CA467542A, 1950.
20. Wittig G,Pommer H.Production of compounds of the vitamin-A series.CA526833A,1956.
21. Montenegro Javier, Bergueiro Julián, Saá Carlos, López Susana. Hiyama cross-coupling reaction in the stereospecific synthesis of retinoids, Organic letters. 11(2009) 141-4.

https://doi.org/10.1051/e3sconf/202233801006

Capacity estimation based on incremental capacity and Gaussian process regression for retired lithium-ion batteries

Wei Sun, Peng Jin *, Xiawei Liao, Xiaoming Ma and Bo Yang

School of Environment and Energy, Peking University Shenzhen Graduate School, Shenzhen, China

Abstract. Fast capacity estimation for retired batteries is necessary when batteries are recycled for echelon utilization. Here, a fast capacity estimation method is proposed for retired LiFePO4 battery. First, a full survey of battery pack and cells degradation after a long period of service is studied. Then the filtered ICA is used to study degradation variation phenomenon of retired batteries, the relationship between IC curve feature and remaining capacity was studied. Finally, a fast capacity estimation using incremental capacity and Gaussian process regression is proposed. Our results show high efficiency and accuracy of the proposed method.

1 Introduction

Recently, electric vehicles (EVs) have become a significant trend in many countries for the reason of concerns about energy security and environmentally friendly [1]. However, lithium-ion batteries, which is one of the core components in EVs, need to be transposed to guarantee safe operation and sufficient mileage when their capacity drops to 80% [2]. The retired batteries echelon utilization can prolong the useful battery life-span, thus reducing harmful environmental effects and resources conservation [3]. However, for their inconsistency, retired batteries cannot be firsthand recycled for echelon utilization [4], so the capacity estimation and screening methods of retired batteries are of great significance to the echelon utilization of retired batteries and the healthy development of electric vehicles.

In order to analyze degradation mechanism of large scale of cells and estimate their state of health (SOH), incremental capacity analysis (ICA) is employed [5-7]. IC curve cannot only indicate the subtle and slowing-changing electrochemical feature of the electrochemical reactions inside cells, it can also depict current acceptance capability in various potentials. In view of the merit of convenient properties for modeling without specific function, Gaussian process regression has been widely adopted in the field of machine learning and statistics [8].

In this thesis, a rapid capacity estimation is applied for retired LiFePO4 battery. First, a comprehensive survey of a battery pack aging and cells after a long period of employment is studied. Then the filtered ICA is used to study degradation variation phenomenon of retired batteries, the relationship between IC curve feature and remaining capacity was analyzed. Finally, a fast capacity estimation method based on incremental capacity and Gaussian process regression is proposed.

2 Experiment and test results

2.1 Test setup and experimental method

Our retired battery pack is received from an electric bus which is operated for more than three years. As is shown in Fig. 1, the experimental pack consists of 42 series-connected battery modules, 28 battery cells are parallel-connected in each module. Air cooling is adopted for battery heat dissipation in the whole battery pack.

Fig. 1 Experimental retired battery pack

The battery cell is manufactured by OptimumNano Energy CO., LTD of China, and their

* Corresponding author: jinpeng@pkusz.edu.cn

 https://doi.org/10.1051/e3sconf/202233801006

parameters are itemized in Table 1. The 32700-type cell is configured with LiFePO4/graphite as electrode, whose nominal capacity is 5.0 Ah, upper and lower limit voltages are 2.65–3.7V. All of our tests are carried out at room temperature. An 8-channel battery test system (Shenzhen Repower Technology Co.,Ltd ACTS 5V-10A) whose current range is −5A~5A and voltage range is 0~5V(±0.02% at full scale) is used for battery test.

Table 1 Parameters for the LiFePO4 cell.

Items	Parameters
Manufacturer	OptimumNano
Group pattern	28 parallel-42 series
Cathode material	LiFePO4
Anode material	Graphite
Nominal capacity	5.0Ah
Nominal voltage	3.2V
End-of-charge voltage	2.65V
End-of-discharge voltage	3.7V

In order to obtain the remaining capacity, we apply the charging current rate of 1/3 C, i.e., 1.66 A. and test the internal resistance by hybrid pulse power characterization (HPPC) method.

2.2 Test results

Capacity and resistance of all 1176 retired battery cell is surveyed by battery test system, Fig.2 shows the distribution histogram of these batteries. As shown in Fig.2, the capacity data of 1176 single cells in the entire battery pack shows that most of the cells have a capacity between 4.2Ah and 4.6Ah and obey a normal distribution. 90.2% of the cells still maintain the rated capacity. 80%, 98.7% batteries maintain 70% of the rated capacity. In the histograms, the distribution of battery capacity is left-skewed with s=−0.755 and the distribution of battery resistance is s=−1.18.

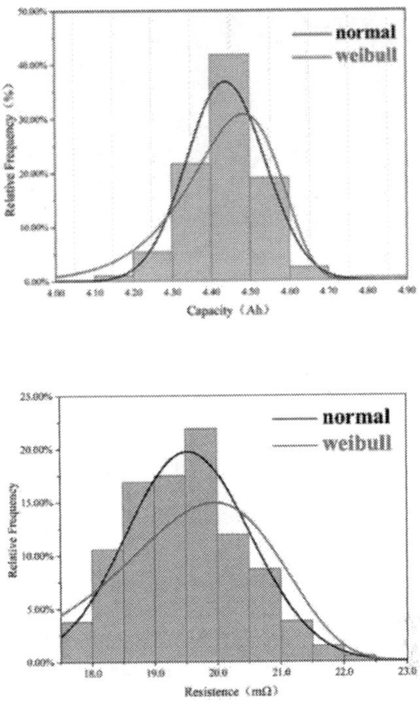

Fig. 2. Battery cell capacity and resistance bargraph and probability plots

For both battery capacity and resistance probability plots, some cells are outside the confidence intervals. However, normal probability has a better fitting quality than that of Weibull probability, for the reason that in the low resistance range of the probability map, there are some points far away from the lower confidence interval. Therefore, the normal distribution is more suitable than the Weibull distribution for the batteries that we study with parallel connections.

3 Methodology

3.1 Incremental capacity analysis

The incremental capacity is obtained from a full charging/discharging cycle, where we get the changing rate of capacity with the voltage as the vertical coordinate, and the changing voltage as the horizontal ordinate, which is shown as following:

$$\frac{dQ(t)}{dV(t)} \approx \frac{\Delta Q(k)}{\Delta V(k)} = \frac{Q(k)-Q(k-N)}{V(k)-V(k-N)} \quad (1)$$

In Eq. 1, $\Delta Q(k)$ and $\Delta V(k)$ are the rate of electric quantity and terminal voltage during charging/discharging, respectively. As a result,

https://doi.org/10.1051/e3sconf/202233801006

$\frac{\Delta Q(k)}{\Delta V(k)}$ can be described as $\frac{dQ(t)}{dV(t)}$ when the sample interval N is short enough.

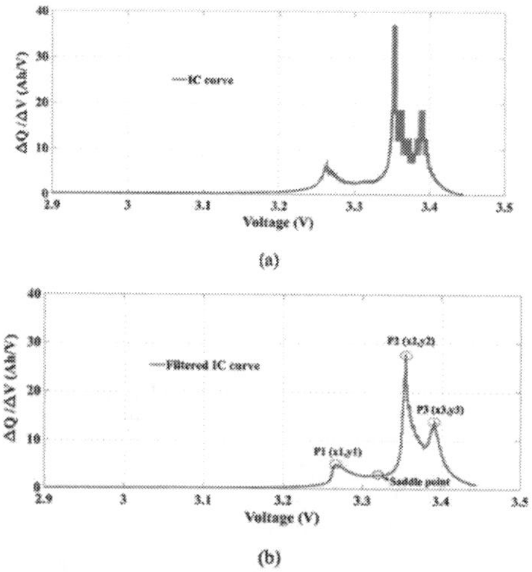

Fig. 3. (a) Initial IC curve; (b) Filtered IC curve

As a novel technique to analysis aging phenomenon and survey state of health (SOH) of lithium battery, ICA is applied in fast estimation in our essay. In order to extract capacitance features of incremental capacity, preprocessing needs to be conducted previously. Figure.3 illustrates the initial IC curve contaminated by noises and filtered IC curve using Kalman filter in the 1/3C current rate. Finally we need to record the coordinates of the characteristic peak(P1， P2 and P3) which are highly related to the attenuation of battery capacity.

3.2 Gaussian process regression

Gaussian process regression (GPR) is a neoteric regression approach in machine learning, so we explain how apply the algorithm to estimate attenuation of battery capacity.

First, in our training dataset D=(X, y) , the input variable and output variable are indicated as X and y accordingly. As the formula $X=\{x_1^D, x_2^D, x_3^D, \cdots x_N^D\}$ shows, there are D-dimensional N input vectors in variable X, which follows multivariable distribution with mean function and covariance function of m(x) and $k_f(x,x')$, respectively. We express the properties of f(x) as following:

$$\begin{cases} m(x) = E(f(x)) \\ k_f(x,x') = E[(m(x) - f(x))(m(x') - f(x'))] \end{cases} \quad (2)$$

For the GPR algorithm, in order to express the prior assumptions for the properties of latent funtion, calculating the the kernel function $k_f(x,x')$ is necessary. We use the squared exponential covariance (SE) to complete this step, as shown in Eq. (3):

$$k_f(x,x') = \sigma_f^2 \exp\left(\frac{-(x-x')^2}{2l^2}\right) \quad (3)$$

Considering there are D-dimensional N input vectors in variable X, we can converse Eq. (3) as follows:

$$k_f(x_i,x_j) = \sigma_f^2 \exp\left(-\frac{1}{2}\sum_{d=1}^{D}\frac{(x_i^d - x_j^d)^2}{l_d^2}\right) \quad (4)$$

Here, the noise covariance matrix $\sigma_n^2 I$ is appended into Eq. (4) as below:

$$k(x_i,x_j) = k_f(x_i,x_j) + \sigma_n^2 I \quad (5)$$

Considering the input variable X and the properties of the latent function f, the distribution of y is denoted as follows:

$$p(y|X) = \int p(y|f,X)p(f|X)df = N(0, K + \sigma_n^2 I) \quad (6)$$

Then, we denote the marginal log-likelihood of y as:

$$\log p(y|X,\Theta) = -\frac{1}{2}y^T\left(K+\sigma_n^2 I\right)^{-1}y - \frac{1}{2}\left|K+\sigma_n^2 I\right| - \frac{n}{2}\log 2\pi \quad (7)$$

Here, for the marginal log-likelihood function, we employ the gradient method to optimize the hyper-parameters, and the calculation process of the gradient descending is:

$$\begin{cases} \frac{\partial \log p(y|X,\Theta)}{\partial \theta_i} = -\frac{1}{2}\mathrm{tr}\left(\varphi^{-1}\frac{\partial \varphi}{\partial \theta_i}\right) + \frac{1}{2}y^T\varphi^{-1}\frac{\partial \varphi}{\partial \theta_i}\varphi^{-1}y \\ \varphi = K + \sigma_n^2 I \end{cases} \quad (8)$$

Here, in training dataset, we employ a small representative subset for the sparse approximation propose to handle GPR. The joint prior distribution of the training output y and the test output y^* is deduced and expressed as [8]:

$$p(y,y^*|X,x^*,\Theta) = N\left(\begin{bmatrix}0\\0\end{bmatrix}, \begin{bmatrix}\varphi & k^* \\ (k^*)^T & k^{**}+\sigma_n^2\end{bmatrix}\right) \quad (9)$$

Based on Eq. (10), the posterior distribution can be derived as:

$$p(y^*|x,y,x^*) = N(y^*|\bar{y}^*, \mathrm{cov}(y^*)) \quad (10)$$

Then, in the predictive distribution, we calculate the mean $\bar{y}^*$ and covariance $\mathrm{cov}(y^*)$:

$$\bar{y}^* = (k^*)^T\varphi^{-1}y \quad (11)$$

$$\mathrm{cov}(y^*) = \sigma_n^2 + k^{**} - (k^*)^T\varphi^{-1}k^* \quad (12)$$

Finally, a full GPR algorithm modeling is done.

4 Validation and discussion

In view of the proposed GPR battery screening model mentioned above, 5 LFP retired batteries data of 190 cycle are employed to verify the validity of battery estimation. In our experiment, we regard the first 80% data of charging/discharging period as the training datasets and the rest 20% data as testing part.

https://doi.org/10.1051/e3sconf/202233801006

The results for battery No. 61, 62, 63, 64 and 65 are shown in Table. 2.

Table 2 Capacity estimation results vs. real capacity of the screening method

Cell number	Estimation results (Ah)	Real capacity (Ah)	error (%)
C61	3.94	4.04	1.76
C62	3.69	3.64	1.41
C63	4.92	4.79	2.59
C64	4.15	4.01	1.53
C65	3.91	3.96	1.93

As illustrated in Table 2, error of the estimation of battery No. 61, 62, 63, 64 and 65 are 1.76%, 1.41%, 2.59%, 1.53%,1.93%, respectively. As a result, the battery SOH estimation of GPR shows strong performance. In addition, we also employ the mean absolute error (MAE) and the root mean square error (RMSE) to analyze the performance of the model quantitatively, whose definition is shown as:

$$\mathrm{MAE} = \frac{1}{N}\sum_{i=1}^{N}|y_i - \bar{y}_i^*| \tag{18}$$

$$\mathrm{RMSE} = \sqrt{\left(\frac{1}{N}\sum_{i=1}^{N}(y_i - \bar{y}_i^*)^2\right)} \tag{19}$$

Where $\bar{y}_i^*$ is the estimated value, the y is the real value, and it is worth noting that N represents how many times battery cycles, so MAE and RMSE could be used to assess the algorithm modelling of different cells in view of absolute sign.

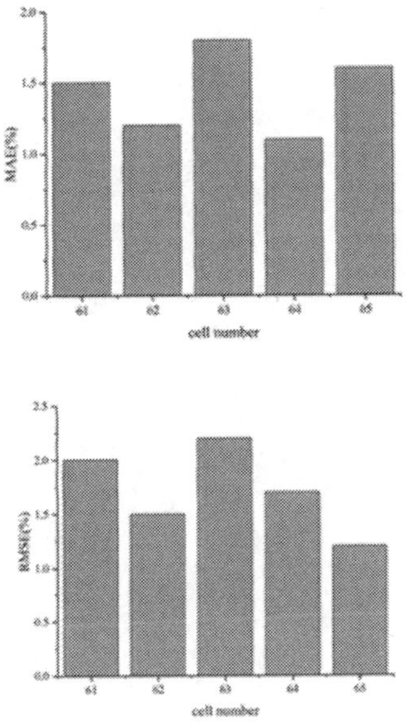

Fig.4. The error analysis of battery estimation based GPR

MAE reflects the mean absolute error between real value and estimated value in our cells SOH estimation, we calculate MAE and RMSE of battery No. 61, 62, 63, 64 and 65. As Fig.4 shows, battery No.63 has the maximum MAE with 1.8% which is not overrun 2%, while battery NO.64 has the minimum MAE with 1.1%. In term of RMSE, all 4 LFP cells are nearly 1.7%, battery NO.63 has the maximum RMSE with 2.2%, and battery NO.65 has the minimum RMSE with 1.4%. As a result, our proposed SOH fast estimation based on GPR indicates high accuracy and reliability.

5 Conclusion

This paper presents an efficient capacity estimation based on ICA and Gaussian process regression for retired lithium-ion batteries. The main contributions are summarized as follows: (1) a detailed survey of a retired battery pack and cells was conducted, normal distribution is more suitable than the Weibull distribution for the batteries that we study with parallel connections. (2) The GPR is employed to establish SOH estimation model and how the algorithm works is demonstrated. (3) Our novel method is verified by LFP retired cells charging and discharging datasets. Verification result with a maximum MAE and RMSE of 1.8%, 2.2% shows strong performance.

Acknowledgments

This work was financially supported by Shenzhen Science Research Project under Grant GJHZ20180928162210431.

References

1. Debnath, U.K., I. Ahmad and D. Habibi, Quantifying economic benefits of second life batteries of gridable vehicles in the smart grid. International Journal of Electrical Power & Energy Systems, 2014. 63: p. 577-587.
2. Cusenza, M.A., et al., Reuse of electric vehicle batteries in buildings: An integrated load match analysis and life cycle assessment approach. Energy and Buildings, 2019. 186: p. 339-354.
3. Canals Casals, L., M. Barbero and C. Corchero, Reused second life batteries for aggregated demand response services. Journal of Cleaner Production, 2019. 212: p. 99-108.
4. Zhou, L., et al., A study on parameter variation effects on battery packs for electric vehicles. Journal of Power Sources, 2017. 364: p. 242-252.

5. Tang, X., et al., A fast estimation algorithm for lithium-ion battery state of health. Journal of Power Sources, 2018. 396: p. 453-458.
6. Xiaoyu, L., et al., State of health estimation for Li-ion battery using incremental capacity analysis and Gaussian process regression. Energy, 2020. 190: p. 116-467
7. Weng, C., et al., State-of-health monitoring of lithium-ion battery modules and packs via incremental capacity peak tracking. Applied Energy, 2016. 180: p. 360-368.
8. Zhongkai, Z., et al., An efficient screening method for retired lithium ion batteries based on support vector machine. Journal of Clean Production, 2020. 267: p. 121-882

Effect of long-term fertilization on bacterial community in a sandy loam soil and its relation to organic carbon accumulation

Huanjun Zhang [1], Xixi Wang [1], Yi Li [1,*], Weixin Ding [2]

[1] Key Laboratory of Integrated Regulation and Resource Development on Shallow Lakes, Ministry of Education, College of Environment, Hohai University, Nanjing 210098, China
[2] State Key Laboratory of Soil and Sustainable Agriculture, Institute of Soil Science, Chinese Academy of Sciences, Nanjing 210008, China

Abstract. Fertilization can affect the transformation of soil organic carbon (SOC) and soil microbial community composition. However, thus far, how SOC accumulation in association with bacterial community is still unclear. We collected arable soils (aquic inceptisol) from a long-term fertilization experiment (20 years) including compost (CM), inorganic nitrogen + phosphorus + potassium (NPK), half compost N plus half inorganic fertilizer N (HCM), NP, NK, PK, and untreated (Control). We investigated the relationship between the SOC accumulation rate and bacterial community composition measured by high-throughput sequencing. The highest SOC accumulation rate was observed in the compost treatments. Furthermore, compost and balanced NPK treatments increased soil carbohydrate content significantly ($P < 0.05$), while no such enhancement was observed following NK and PK application. Compared with the Control, fertilization substantially reduced the effective diffusion coefficient of oxygen in soil. Meanwhile, fertilization lowered the relative abundance (RA) of Bacteroidetes but increased the RA of Proteobacteria. Compost application increased the RA of Firmicutes, while inorganic fertilizers reduced it. The RA of Proteobacteria and Firmicutes were significantly and positively correlated with the SOC and carbohydrate content and the SOC accumulation rate ($P < 0.05$). SOC accumulation was also accompanied with the reduction in the effective diffusion coefficient of oxygen in soil. Our results indicated that poor aeration may induce a shift in the microbial community composition and a transition from aerobic to anaerobic degradation of SOC, thereby favoring SOC accumulation.

Keywords: Long-term fertilization; High-throughput sequencing; Microbial community; Organic C accumulation.

1. Introduction

Bacteria play significant roles in biogeochemical cycles in agricultural ecosystems, such as decomposition and conversion of soil organic carbon (C) and accompanied release of nutrients for plant growth [1]. Soil microbial communities are greatly impacted by soil chemical and physical properties such as nutrient level, pH, quantity and quality of organic C, water content, and oxygen level. In agricultural ecosystems, fertilizer management practices can affect nearly all these edaphic factors, leading to shifts in the microbial community composition. Although, in recent years, the response of soil microbial community to organic and inorganic fertilization have been extensively investigated [2], the information about the relation between alterations in bacterial community composition and soil organic carbon (SOC) sequstration as affected by different soil fertilization treatments is still limited.

Organic fertilization may positively influence microbial diversity, biomass, activity, and help maintain or increase the SOC content, while inorganic fertilization is less effective relative to organic fertilization [3]. Several researches have revealed that soil bacterial community is highly sensitive to organic and inorganic fertilizations, but such responses differ among phyla [1]. Nonetheless, some studies also revealed that current application of inorganic fertilizers has a major deleterious impact on the inherent soil microbial community, such as decreases of microbial biomass [4] and microbial diversity [5]. For instance, Jangid et al. [1] revealed that inorganic fertilization in croplands and pastures significantly reduced the microbial diversity and altered the composition of bacterial phyla, involving *Acidobacteria*, *Bacteroidetes*, *Firmicutes*, *Betaproteobacteria* and *Gammaproteobacteria*. The overloading of nitrogen (N) fertilizer reduced microbial biodiversity and enhanced nitrification [6]. However, it was found that variations in the soil bacterial community structure resulting from

* Corresponding author: envly@hhu.edu.cn

https://doi.org/10.1051/e3sconf/202233801007

inorganic fertilization could be resumed by organic fertilization [2].

Fertilization-related alterations in microbial community structure can be related to variations in the soil environmental conditions. However, the response of diverse bacterial communities to the varying environment in arable soils has not been clearly stated. Here, we evaluated variations in the bacterial community composition in a sandy loam soil as influenced by various long-term organic and inorganic fertilizations. This study aimed to elucidate the key factors regulating the shifts in the bacterial community composition and to understand the relationships between SOC accumulation and bacterial community composition. The hypothesis was that the bacterial community composition corresponds to variations in soil properties, which will in turn change the SOC accumulation rate.

2. Materials and methods

2.1. Field experiments and soil property analysis

Fengqiu Agro-ecological Experimental Station was located in Henan province, China (35°00′N, 114°24′E). A long-term fertilization experiment was established in the Agro-ecological Experimental Station in September 1989. The soil was originated from alluvial sediments of the Yellow River with a sandy loam texture. The mean annual temperature was 13.9 °C and the mean annual precipitation was 615 mm, representing a semi-arid, sub-humid monsoon climate in this region. In 1989, the soil (0–20 cm) parameters were: organic carbon, 4.48 $g \cdot kg^{-1}$; total nitrogen, 0.43 $g \cdot kg^{-1}$; total phosphorus, 0.50 $g \cdot kg^{-1}$; and total potassium, 18.60 $g \cdot kg^{-1}$; pH, 8.65.

In the long-term experiemnt, seven fertilization treatments with four replicates were included: (1) only compost (CM), (2) half compost nitrogen plus half inorganic nitrogen fertilizer (HCM), (3) combined inorganic nitrogen + phosphorus + potassium fertilizers (NPK), (4) combined inorganic nitrogen + phosphorus fertilizers (NP), (5) combined inorganic nitrogen + potassium fertilizers (NK), (6) combined inorganic phosphorus + potassium fertilizers (PK), and (7) no fertilization (Control). A total of 28 plots were analyzed. Table 1 presents the details of N, P, and K application rates for each treatment. Each plot had a size of 9.5 m in length and 5 m in width. The experiment design was a randomized block for all the plots. The compost was made by fermenting cakes of soybean and cottonseed, and wheat straw for 2 months and had 422 g $C \cdot kg^{-1}$. The cropping system was a rotation of summer maize (*Zea mays* cv. Zhengdan 958) and winter wheat (*Triticum aestiv¹um* cv. Xinmai 19). Basal fertilizers were evenly applied in the respective plots before tillage which was conducted by hoes to a soil depth of 20 cm every season. Then the maize and wheat were sowed after tillage in early June and early October, respectively. Moreover, the soil surface was treated with supplemental N fertilizer in HCM, NPK, NP and NK treatments in late July and in late February for maize and wheat, respectively, followed by irrigation or rainfall. All the plots applied same field management practices other than fertilization during the experiment. Detailed information regarding the experiment management has been reported by Yu et al. [7].

An auger with 2.5-cm-diameter was used to collect soil samples in each plot to a depth of 20 cm on 7 June 2009. The soil cores were homogenized, stored at 4 °C, and taken to the lab as soon as possible for further analysis. Fresh soil samples were gently ruptured along natural fissures and sieved to < 8 mm, and then visible plant residues and organic debris were carefully eliminated by forceps. These fresh samples were utilized for molecular analyses. An air-dried subsample passing through a 2 mm sieve was prepared to measure soil properties.

A pH meter (DMP-2, Quark Ltd., Nanjing, China) was applied to determine soil pH. The wet oxidation-redox titration method were performed to measure SOC content and the micro-Kjeldahl method were performed to measure total N content in soil. The soil carbohydrate content was determined following Puget et al. [8].

2.2. Effective oxygen diffusion coefficient

In each plot eight undisturbed soil core samples with volume of 100 cm^3 were collected. The ceramic pressure plate method was employed at equilibrium matric potentials of −1, −2, −10, −35, −60, −100, −330, −500, −1000, −2000, −5000, and −15000 hPa to measure soil water retention curve.

The effective soil oxygen diffusion coefficient (D, $m^2 \cdot s^{-1}$) was computed as follows [9]:

$$D = \frac{1}{N^2} \times \left[\left(D_{a0} \times Q_a^{\,p} \right) + \left(KH \times D_{w0} \times Q_w^{\,p} \right) \right]$$

Table 1 Amount of nutrient inputs (N, P, and K) through organic or inorganic fertilization in each cropping season under different treatments

Treatment	Basal fertilizer						Supplementary fertilizer urea (kg $N \cdot ha^{-1}$)
	N (kg $N \cdot ha^{-1}$)		P (kg $P_2O_5 \cdot ha^{-1}$)		K (kg K_2O ha^{-1})		
	Compost	Urea	Compost	Calcium superphosphate	Compost	Potassium sulfate	
Maize							
Control	0	0	0	0	0	0	0
HCM	75	0	25.5	49.5	32.5	117.5	75
CM	150	0	51	24	65	85	0
NPK	0	60	0	75	0	150	90
NP	0	60	0	75	0	0	90
NK	0	60	0	0	0	150	90
PK	0	0	0	75	0	150	0
Wheat							
Control	0	0	0	0	0	0	0
HCM	75	15	22.5	52.5	31.5	118.5	60
CM	150	0	45	30	63	87	0
NPK	0	0	0	75	0	150	60
NP	0	0	0	75	0	0	60
NK	0	0	0	0	0	150	60
PK	0	0	0	75	0	150	0

where N is the soil porosity (%) calculated by soil bulk density (ρ) and particle density (2.65 $g \cdot cm^{-3}$); D_{a0} is the free diffusion coefficient of oxygen in the air at 20 °C

(1.8×10^{-5} $m^2 \cdot s^{-1}$); *KH* is Henry's equilibrium constant at 20 °C (0.03); D_{wo} is the free oxygen diffusion coefficient in the water at 20 °C (2.2×10^{-9} $m^2 \cdot s^{-1}$); Q_a is the ratio of soil porosity filled with air and Q_w is the ratio of soil porosity filled with water, i.e., $Q_a + Q_w = 1$; and p is a power constant (3.4). The Q_w was calculated by:

$$Q_w = \rho \times \theta_m / N$$

where θ_m is the water content of soil ($cm^3 \cdot g^{-1}$).

2.3. Measurement of the specific C mineralization rate

To measure the specific C mineralization rate (SCMR), 10 g soil seieved to < 2 mm was put in a glass jar with volume of 150-mL. The moisture content of soil was regulated to 60% of WHC (water-holding capacity) for all soil samples during the incubation. The jars covered by ventilated film were placed in an incubator at 25 °C and the deionized water was added once every two days to maintain soil moisture content the same as initial condtion during the incubation. The CO_2 emission rate was measured on the 0.5, 1, 2, 3, 5, 7, 9, 11, 13, 15, 18, 21, 24, 28, and 32 days of the incubation. For measuring CO_2 emissions, the jar was plugged with a rubber lid perforated by centered Perspex tubes. Then, an hermetic syringe was utilized to collect 1 mL headspace gas immediately and at 6 h after closure to dertermine the CO_2 concentration by a gas chromatograph (Agilent 7890, Santa Clara, CA, USA). The CO_2 emission rate representing organic C mineralization rate (CMR) was computed by assuming the CO_2 concentration was linearly changed during the 6-h incubation in the airtight jar at temperature of 20 °C. The SCMR was calculated using the following equation [7]:
SCMR = CMR/SOC content.

2.4. Soil DNA extraction

Fresh soil samples of 0.5 g (on the oven-dried basis) was used to extract total DNA by a Fast DNA Spin Kit for Soil (MP Biomedicals, CA, USA) based on the manufacturers' protocols. The gel electrophoresis and NanoDrop spectrophotometer (NanoDrop Technologies, Wilmington, USA) were employed to measure the quality and concentration of the extracted DNA, respectively, and then the extracted DNA was subsequently preserved at –20 °C.

2.5. Illumina sequencing and data analysis

The primers 802R (5′-TACNVGGGTATCTAATCC-3′) and 520F (5′-AYTGGGYDTAAAGNG-3′) were utilized for amplifying the V4 hypervariable regions of bacterial 16S rRNA gene, with a sample-specific 12 bp barcode added to 520F. The PCR reaction was conducted in the thermal cycler (Bio-Rad Laboratories, Hercules, CA, USA). Library quality was assessed by an Agilent Bioanalyzer 2100 and a Qubit 2.0 fluorometer. At last, high-throughput sequencing of 16S rRNA genes was performed by Illumina MiSeq (Personalbio Technology Co. Ltd., Shanghai, China) and 300-bp paired-end reads were obtained. The data were submitted to the NCBI (number: PRJNA763332).
Read pairs from raw data were initially merged in FLASH version 1.2.7, in which forward and reverse reads had more than 10-bp overlaps and no base mismatches. Illumina sequence reads were processed by the quantitative insights into microbial ecology (QIIME) pipeline. In briefly, low-quality sequence reads were removed, and the 12-bp barcode was inspected to allocate the multiplexed reads to samples. Chimeric sequences were identified with the Uchime algorithm in a chimera-free reference database using the Usearch tool. The high-quality sequences with a 97% similarity were allocated to OTUs (operational taxonomic units) with Uclust clustering method. A representative sequence from each OTU was aligned with PyNAST against the GreenGene Database (v13_5). The taxonomic classification of OTUs was conducted with the RDP Classifier against the GreenGene Database (v13_5) with a percent similarity threshold of 97%.

2.6. Statistical analysis

The soil organic C accumulation rate was computed as follows:
Accumulation rate = (organic C content in 2009 – organic C content in 1989)/20.
One-way analysis of variance was employed to assess the effects of long-term fertilization on soil properties. The least significant difference method was carried out using SPSS 18 for Windows (SPSS Inc., Chicago, IL, USA) to test statistically significant differences among treatments at the 5% level. The relations between the soil microorganisms and soil properties as well as the effects of long-term fertilization on microbial community composition were evaluated using canonical correspondence analysis (CCA).

3. Results

3.1. Soil properties

The SOC and total N contents increased to a greater extent after 20-year compost application than inorganic fertilization (Table 2). The CM treatment had the highest accumulation rate of SOC (0.39 g C $kg^{-1} \cdot yr^{-1}$), followed by HCM (0.24 g C $kg^{-1} \cdot yr^{-1}$), while the NK treatment presented the lowest accumulation rate of SOC (0.04 g C $kg^{-1} \cdot yr^{-1}$). The CM, HCM and NPK treatments also presented significantly greater soil carbohydrate content than the Control ($P < 0.05$), while the NK and PK application did not. The highest SCMR was 0.52 mg $C \cdot g^{-1}$ $SOC \cdot day^{-1}$ in the PK treated soil, while the lowest was in the CM treated soil (0.32 mg $C \cdot g^{-1}$ $SOC \cdot day^{-1}$). Compost and inorganic N treatments decreased the soil pH significantly ($P < 0.05$).

Table 2 Soil properties, organic C accumulation rate and SCMR in soil following 20 years of organic and inorganic fertilizer application.

Treatment	pH	SOC (g C·kg⁻¹)	Total N (g N·kg⁻¹)	C/N	Carbohydrates (g C·kg⁻¹ soil)	SOC accumulation rate (g C·kg⁻¹ soil·yr⁻¹)	SCMR (mg C·g⁻¹ SOC·d⁻¹)
Control	8.39 (0.02) a	4.45 (0.03)e	0.47 (0.02)f	9.47 (0.34) a	0.49 (0.04)e	0.00 (0.00)f	0.34 (0.01)c
CM	8.06 (0.06) c	12.20 (0.08)a	1.56 (0.03) a	7.82 (0.10) c	1.00 (0.04)a	0.39 (0.00)a	0.32 (0.02)c
HCM	7.90 (0.01) d	9.28 (0.08)b	1.10 (0.03) b	8.44 (0.19) b	0.78 (0.06)b	0.24 (0.01)b	0.41 (0.00)b
NPK	8.00 (0.05) c	7.00 (0.04)c	0.80 (0.03) c	8.75 (0.23) b	0.60 (0.02)c	0.13 (0.01)c	0.43 (0.02)b
NP	8.24 (0.00) b	6.64 (0.05)c	0.76 (0.02) d	8.74 (0.15) b	0.58 (0.04)d	0.11 (0.01)c	0.38 (0.00)bc
NK	8.03 (0.09) c	5.22 (0.06)d e	0.88 (0.02) c	5.93 (0.07) a	0.55 (0.03)e	0.04 (0.00)e	0.32 (0.02)c
PK	8.34 (0.01) a	5.80 (0.10)d	0.62 (0.01) e	9.35 (0.01) d	0.51 (0.04)e	0.07 (0.00)d	0.52 (0.05)a

The standard deviations (sd) are shown in parentheses (n = 4). Different letters represent significant differences between treatments at $P < 0.05$.

The Control treatment had significantly greater D (5.19×10^{-6} $m^2 \cdot s^{-1}$, Fig. 1) than the other treatments ($P < 0.05$), while the CM treatment had the lowest vaule (1.30×10^{-6} $m^2 \cdot s^{-1}$). The D significantly differed among treatments ($P < 0.05$) and were in the order of CM < HCM < PK, NP and NPK < NK < Control.

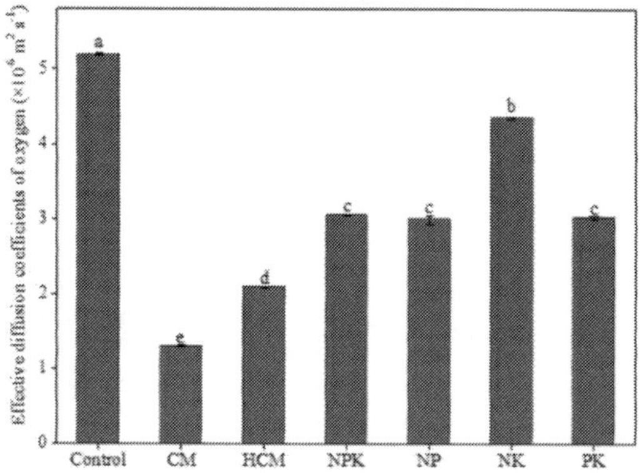

Fig. 1 The effective diffusion coefficient of oxygen (D) in different long-term (20 years) fertilization treatments. Vertical bars indicate the sd (n = 4). Different letters represent significant differences between treatments at $P < 0.05$.

3.2. Bacterial community composition

The 16S rRNA Illumina sequencing generated 517,660 high-quality sequences in total, with 73,951 sequences and 8372 unique OTUs per sample on average (OTUs are defined as sequences with 97% similarity), and the average read length was 225 bp. Eleven phylum-level groups were selected for the statistical analysis (Fig. 2). Of these, the most predominant phylum was *Proteobacteria* in all treatments, and accounted for 25.4−32.7% of the total abundance. *Actinobacteria*, *Bacteroidetes*, and *Acidobacteria* also constituted a large proportion of the total microbial abundance in all treatments and accounted for 17.1−21.4%, 8.4−23.4%, and 9.2−16.2% of the total abundance, respectively. Fertilization treatments presented lower relative abundance (RA) of *Bacteroidetes* and higher *Proteobacteria* and *Verrucomicrobia* than the Control. The RA of *Firmicutes* was augmented by 90.47% and 68.32%, respectively in the CM and HCM treatments but reduced by 52.47%−78.18% in the inorganic fertilization treatments. Relative to the Control treatment, the change of the RA of *Firmicutes* was mainly due to the variation in *Bacillales* in fertilizer-treated soil (Fig. 3). Nonetheless, the RA of *Acidobacteria* decreased slightly in the compost treatments (CM and HCM) but increased by 49.0% under NPK treatment and by 11.8−13.1% under unbalanced fertilization treatments relative to the Control.

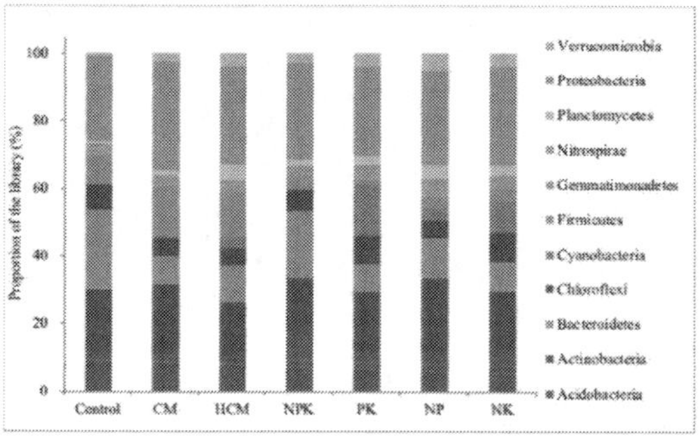

Fig. 2 Relative abundance (RA) of bacteria phyla in different long-term (20 years) fertilization treatments.

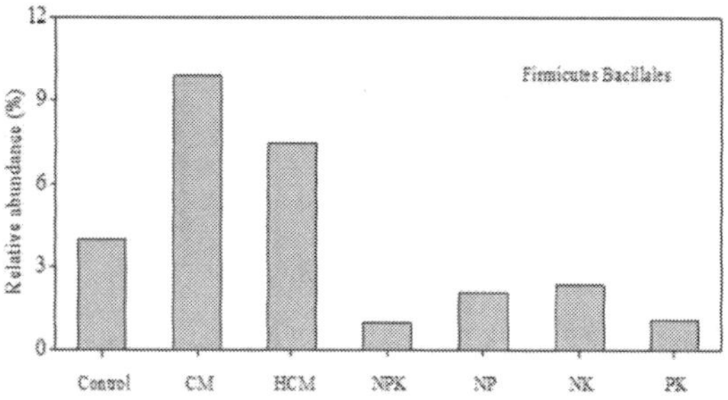

Fig. 3 Relative abundance (RA) of order Bacillales within phylum Firmicutes in different long-term (20 years) fertilization treatments.

For classes within phylum *Proteobacteria*, *Alpha-proteobacteria* augmented in the NPK and CM treatments relative to the Control (Fig. 4). The RA of *Beta-proteobacteria* augmented in all fertilization treatments except NPK. The RA of *Gamma-proteobacteria* augmented in the CM treatment while

https://doi.org/10.1051/e3sconf/202233801007

reduced in the other treatments. On the contrary, the RA of *Delta-proteobacteria* remained relatively stable in the CM treatment, but increased by 46.87%–74.33% in the other treatments. Finer taxonomic divisions revealed that the CM treatment presented the greatest RA of the order *Xanthomonadales* within *Gamma-proteobacteria* (Fig. 5).

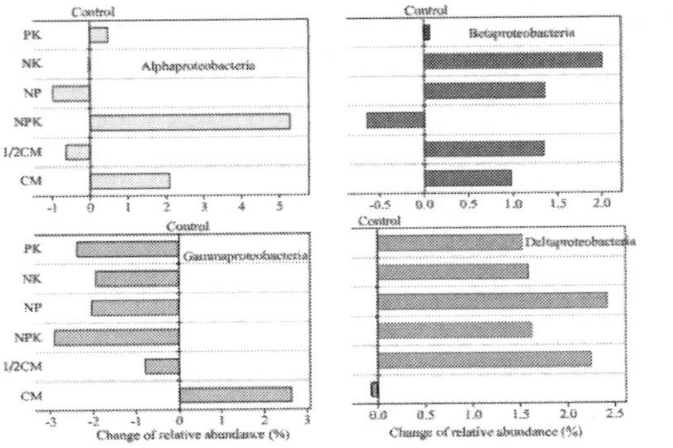

Fig. 4 Changes in the relative abundance (RA) of four classes of *Proteobacteria* (*Alpha-proteobacteria, Beta-proteobacteria, Gamma-proteobacteria*, and *Delta-proteobacteria*) in soil treated with compost and inorganic fertilizer application for 20 years compared with the Control.

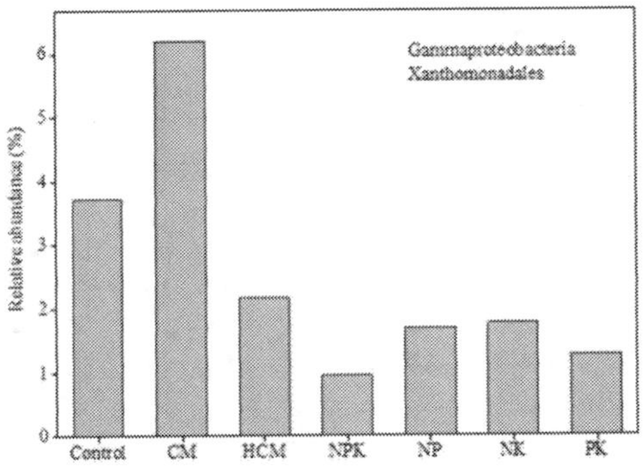

Fig. 5 Relative abundance (RA) of order *Xanthomonadales* within *Gamma-proteobacteria* in different long-term (20 years) fertilization treatments.

3.3. Relations between soil properties and microbial taxa

The SOC, SOC accumulation rate, carbohydrate content, and the total N were significantly ($P < 0.05$) correlated with the RA of *Firmicutes* and *Proteobacteria* (Fig. 6). The CCA ordination plots showed that the D was significantly ($P < 0.05$) related with the SOC, carbohydrate content, and SOC accumulation rate (Fig. 7). OTUs identified as *Mogibacterium* in the *Clostridiales* order, *Bacillus asahii* in the *Bacillales* order, and *Xanthomonadaceae* in the *Xanthomonadales* order were significantly related with the SOC accumulation rate, SOC, and carbohydrate content ($P < 0.05$), but a negative correlation was observed between the D and the above OTUs.

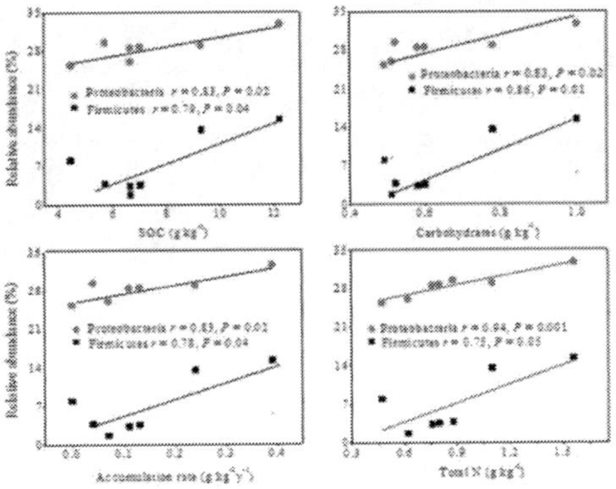

Fig. 6 Relation between the relative abundance (RA) of two bacterial groups, SOC, carbohydrate content, total N content, and organic C accumulation rate in different long-term (20 years) fertilization treatments.

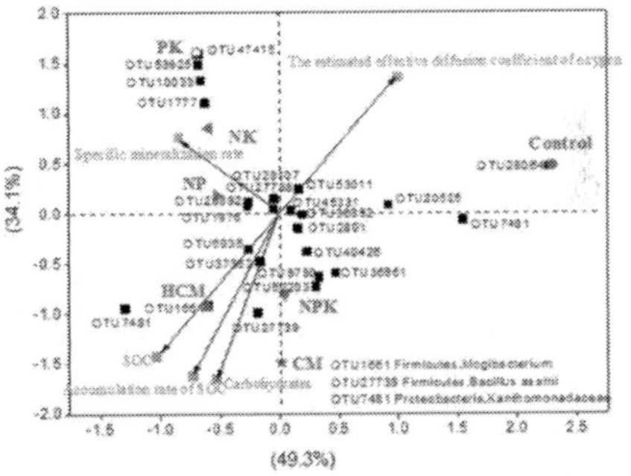

Fig. 7 Canonical correspondence analysis (CCA) illustrating the relation between microorganisms and some soil properties such as SOC, carbohydrate, accumulation rate of organic C, specific mineralization rate of organic C, and the effective oxygen diffusion coefficient at the OTU level.

4. Discussion

Proteobacteria and *Bacteroidetes* are generally considered to be copiotrophic taxa which likely flourish in soils as the availability of SOC increases. Our result showed that long-term fertilization enhanced the RA of *Proteobacteria* but reduced that of *Bacteroidetes* in soil relative to the Control (Fig. 2). However, an analysis of the finer taxonomic divisions revealed that the RA of order *Xanthomonadales* within *Gammaproteobacteria* increased only in the CM-treated soils, where the SOC (12.20 g C·kg^{-1}) was greater than the other treatments (Fig. 5). Similarly, in previous studies, *Xanthomonadales* were reported to be more plentiful in long-term N-fertilized treatment than the Control or unfertilized treatment when the SOC content was grerater than 12 g C·kg^{-1} [1]. More importantly, Li et al. [10] reported that the RA of *Xanthomonadales* increased with decreasing oxygen content of soil. Thus, we speculated that the SOC, particularly the effective oxygen diffusion coefficient, determined the growth of *Xanthomonadales* in our study. Our result showed that the Control treatment presented the highest abundance of *Bacteroidetes*. Similar to our findings, Li et al. [10] and Zeng et al. [2] also revealed that the abundance of *Bacteroidetes* decreased in soils treated with fertilizer (inorganic fertilizer combined with wheat straw or inorganic fertilizer alone). This may be because *Bacteroidetes* were not only positively correlated to availability of C or N but also negatively correlated with soil pH.

In contrast to *Bacteroidetes* and *Proteobacteria*, *Acidobacteria* can grow at low pH and utilize nutrient-poor and recalcitrant C substrates. In our study, *Acidobacteria* had the greatest RA in the NPK treatment, probably due to its relatively low pH. Although the HCM treatment presented lower pH than the NPK treatment, it had a higher SOC, consequently inhibiting the growth of *Acidobacteria* as members of this phylum favor oligotrophic conditions. In current study, the RA of *Firmicutes*, especially *Bacillus* spp., augmented by compost application but decreased following inorganic fertilizer treatment, which is in consistent with the results of the previous study [10]. Feng et al. [11] found that compost application not only increased the abundance of *Bacilli* significantly but also changed its composition, while NPK did not. It is likely that the soil environment established in the compost-treated soil provided a more suitable niche for the growth of indigenous *Bacillus* spp. [11].

We found that the RA of *Firmicutes* and *Proteobacteria* was significantly related with the SOC, carbohydrate content, and SOC accumulation rate (Fig. 6), in accordance with the results reported in previous studies. A major part of the identified anaerobic respiration genes have been allocated to the *Firmicutes*, *Proteobacteria*, and *Actinobacteria* phyla, which decomposed SOC at lower rates under anaerobic conditions than under aerobic conditions. In the present study, fertilization treatments, especially compost application, decreased the effective oxygen diffusion coefficient due to the changes in the pore systems and enhanced the RA of *Proteobacteria* and *Firmicutes*. Our results suggest that there was a gradual transition of SOC degradation from aerobic to anaerobic with increasing SOC [11]. In addition, *Actinobacteria*, *Bacteroidetes*, and *Verrucomicrobia* accounted for >70% of genes that were allocated to the three main groups of polysaccharide degradation (cellulases, endohemicellulases, and debranching enzymes). Thus, the significant decline in the abundance of *Bacteroidetes* in fertilized soils may have favored polysaccharide accumulation.

For finer divisions, we found that the *Mogibacterium*, *Bacillus* and *Xanthomonadaceae* showed positive correlations with the accumulation rate of SOC (Fig. 7). Previous researches have illustrated that the increase in the abundance of *Bacillus* significantly improved the activities of both lipase and polyphenol oxidase in soil, and then promoted soil organic matter to be transformed into humus, which is the main component of SOC. Thus far, however, how *Mogibacterium* and the *Xanthomonadaceae* family favor organic C accumulation remains to be understood and the function of these bacteria requires to be elucidated in future studies.

5. Conclusion

In conclusion, 20-year compost application was more favorable in augmenting the SOC content compared with inorganic fertilizer application. However, the Control treatment presented significantly greater D than the other treatments, especially in compost-treated soils. The soil bacterial community structure was altered by the shifts in soil properties between fertilization treatments. Fertilizer application decreased the RA of *Bacteroidetes* but augmented the RA of *Proteobacteria*. Compost application increased the RA of *Firmicutes* but inorganic fertilizer application decreased it. The enhancement of the RA of *Proteobacteria* and *Firmicutes* indicated degradation of SOC was gradually shrifted from aerobic to anaerobic with the application of fertilizers, especially in compost treatment, which would favor SOC accumulation. However, the significant reduction of the RA of *Bacteroidetes* in fertilized soils may have favored polysaccharide accumulation. At the genus levels, the RA of *Bacillus* spp. was higher in compost-treated soils, which could improve the conversion of soil organic matter into humus. This study aids in clarifying the impact of long-term organic and inorganic fertilization on bacterial community and its relation to organic carbon accumulation in a sandy loam soil.

References

1. K. Jangid, M.A. Williams, A.J. Franzluebbers, J.S. Sanderlin, J.H. Reeves, M.B. Jenkins, D.M. Endale, D.C. Coleman, W.B. Whitman, Relative impacts of land-use, management intensity and fertilization upon soil microbial community structure in agricultural systems, Soil Biol Biochem, 40 (2008) 2843-2853.
2. J. Zeng, X.J. Liu, L. Song, X.G. Lin, H.Y. Zhang, C.C. Shen, H.Y. Chu, Nitrogen fertilization directly affects soil bacterial diversity and indirectly affects bacterial community composition, Soil Biol Biochem, 92 (2016) 41-49.
3. Y. Ge, J.B. Zhang, L.M. Zhang, M. Yang, J.Z. He, Long-term Fertilization Regimes Affect Bacterial Community Structure and Diversity of an Agricultural Soil in Northern China, Journal of Soils and Sediments, 8 (2008) 43-50.
4. K.S. Ramirez, J.M. Craine, N. Fierer, Consistent effects of nitrogen amendments on soil microbial communities and processes across biomes, Global Change Biology, 18 (2012) 1918-1927.
5. M. Sapp, M. Harrison, U. Hany, A. Charlton, R. Thwaites, Comparing the effect of digestate and chemical fertiliser on soil bacteria, Applied Soil Ecology, 86 (2015) 1-9.
6. K.S. Ramirez, J.M. Craine, N. Fierer, Nitrogen fertilization inhibits soil microbial respiration

https://doi.org/10.1051/e3sconf/202233801007

regardless of the form of nitrogen applied, Soil Biol Biochem, 42 (2010) 2336-2338.

7. H.Y. Yu, W.X. Ding, J.F. Luo, R.L. Geng, A. Ghani, Z.C. Cai, Effects of long-term compost and fertilizer application on stability of aggregate-associated organic carbon in an intensively cultivated sandy loam soil, Biology and Fertility of Soils, 48 (2012) 325-336.
8. P. Puget, D.A. Angers, C. Chenu, Nature of carbohydrates associated with water-stable aggregates of two cultivated soils, Soil Biol Biochem, 31 (1999) 55-63.
9. M. Aachib, M. Mbonimpa, M. Aubertin, Measurement and prediction of the oxygen diffusion coefficient in unsaturated media, with applications to soil covers, Water Air Soil Pollut., 156 (2004) 163-193.
10. C.H. Li, K. Yan, L.S. Tang, Z.J. Jia, Y. Li, Change in deep soil microbial communities due to long-term fertilization, Soil Biol Biochem, 75 (2014) 264-272.
11. Y.Z. Feng, R.R. Chen, J.L. Hu, F. Zhao, J.H. Wang, H.Y. Chu, J.B. Zhang, J. Dolfing, X.G. Lin, Bacillus asahii comes to the fore in organic manure fertilized alkaline soils, Soil Biol Biochem, 81 (2015) 186-194.

https://doi.org/10.1051/e3sconf/202233801008

Research on Gas Drainage Laws of SRV-fractured Horizontal Wells in Different Types of Tight Gas Reservoirs

Xucheng Li [1], Jian Cao [1], Yajie Gao [1], Huiyan Zhao [1], Zhai Shuo [2, *]

[1] Northwest Sichuan Division, Petro China Southwest Oil & Gasfield Company, Jiangyou, Sichuan, China
[2] College of energy, Chengdu University of science and technology, Chengdu, Sichuan, China

Abstract. Horizontal well and large-scale hydraulic fracturing are the main technical means for tight gas development at present. However, tight gas reservoirs are characterized by strong heterogeneity, and different types of gas Wells have different production characteristics and pressure propagation laws. In view of the above problems, based on the physical characteristics and reservoir reconstruction evaluation of tight gas reservoir in GAS Reservoir A in Sichuan Basin, three types of reservoir hydraulic fracture models and numerical simulation models were generated by using numerical simulation method, and the production dynamic prediction and pressure wave propagation law were studied. The simulation results show that: (1) In the beginning of production, the deflated area is mainly hydraulic fracture reconstruction area, and the drainage radius of all kinds of gas Wells expands at similar speed; (2) When the drainage range is expanded in the untransformed area, the dimensionless drainage radius expansion speed of gas well is positively correlated with the reservoir physical property. The dimensionless drainage radius and drainage area of class I and II horizontal Wells are relatively faster, while that of Class III Wells is slightly slower.

Keywords: tight gas, horizontal well, dynamic prediction, drainage laws.

1. Introduction

Tight gas is one of the three major unconventional natural gas resources in the world, with abundant reserves. Efficient development of tight gas is of great significance for realizing green energy transformation. However, the density has the characteristics of low porosity, low permeability and low pressure. At present, the technology of long horizontal Wells and large-scale hydraulic fracturing is used for development. However, due to the poor physical properties of the reservoir, the economic benefits of tight gas development are reduced. Therefore, it is helpful to improve the development effect and economic benefits to carry out seepage law and production dynamic prediction and formulate a relative production management system.

In view of the strong heterogeneity of tight sandstone gas reservoir A in Sichuan Basin, this paper divides the reservoir into three types based on permeability, porosity and other parameters. Based on the established porosity and permeability model and the pressure improvement effect, the numerical simulation models of three types of reservoirs were established, and the production dynamic prediction was carried out, and the relationship between production and pressure drop spread and time of different types of reservoirs was analyzed. The research results of this paper can provide some help for differentiated management and reasonable well spacing evaluation of horizontal Wells in different types of reservoirs.

2. Construction of numerical simulation models for horizontal Wells in different types of reservoirs

Table 1. Basic parameters of different types of reservoir numerical simulation models

Parameter	Class I	Class II	Class III
The depth of the gas reservoir (m)	2000	2000	2000
Gas reservoir pressure (MPa)	20	20	20
The thickness of the reservoir (m)	15	20	25
Reservoir porosity (%)	12	10	8
Reservoir permeability (mD)	0.1	0.05	0.01
Gas saturation (%)	70	60	50
The grid size	10×10×1	10×10×1	10×10×1
The model size	3000×1 500×15	3000×1 500×20	3000×15 00×25
Perforation length of horizontal well (m)	800	800	800

The main development layer of A gas reservoir in Sichuan Basin is Jurassic Shaximiao Formation. Based on the

* Corresponding author: 2020050127@stu.cdut.edu.cn

development experience of CNPC and SINOPEC in Jurassic Shaximiao Formation, the reservoirs can be divided into three types.The physical parameters related to different types of reservoirs are shown in Table 1.

The development of tight gas in block A of Sichuan Basin mainly adopts the technology of horizontal well and large-scale hydraulic fracturing, in which the fracturing technology mainly selects multi-cluster perforation in stages and continuous sand addition of slickwater to form tight fractures in the reservoir, so as to improve the reservoir reconstruction effect. Based on the mathematical models of different types of reservoir permeability and the related parameters in Table 1, the combination of three kinds of typical Wells reservoir fracturing operation evaluation results of the MLF-P3D model, produce all kinds of corresponding hydraulic fracture reservoir model, and on the basis of hydraulic model with unstructured grid generation numerical simulation model, three kinds of reservoir numerical simulation model is shown in Figure 1.

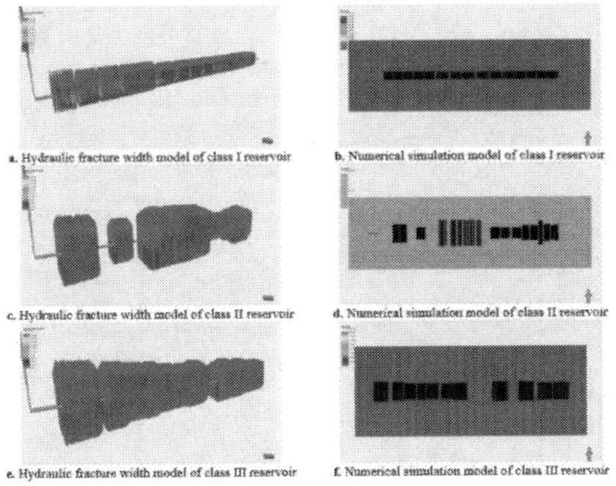

Figure 1. Hydraulic fracture width models and numerical simulation grid profiles of typical horizontal Wells in various reservoirs

3. Study on dynamic simulation and deflation law of horizontal Wells in different types of reservoirs

The numerical simulation model is used to simulate the horizontal production of different types of reservoirs, and the propagation characteristics of horizontal well pressure in different types of reservoirs are mastered.

3.1 Production forecast of different types of horizontal Wells

(1) Production prediction of horizontal Wells in Class I reservoirs

Based on the established production grid model, the production of typical Wells in class I reservoir was predicted. The wells were set to produce at a stable rate of $10\times10^4m^3/d$ and the 20-year development index was predicted. The production curve is shown in Figure 2. As can be seen from the figure, when the horizontal well of class I reservoir is produced at the rate of $10\times10^4m^3/d$, the stable production time is 3.8 years, and the estimated cumulative gas production at the end of the period is $2.69\times10^8m^3$.

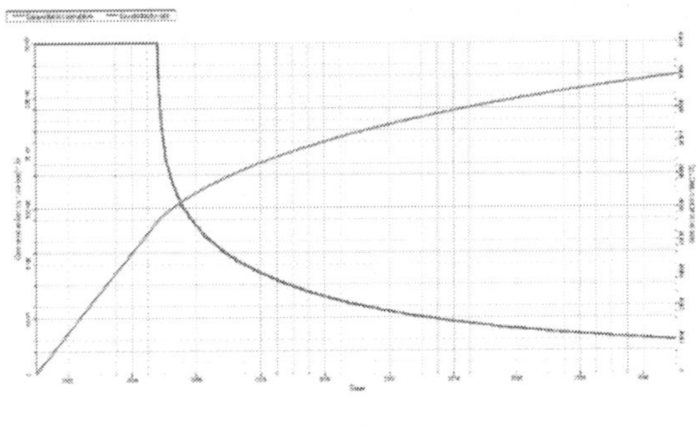

Figure 2. Prediction graph of typical well production curve of class I

Meanwhile, reservoir pressure distribution maps of different production times are obtained, as shown in Figure 3.

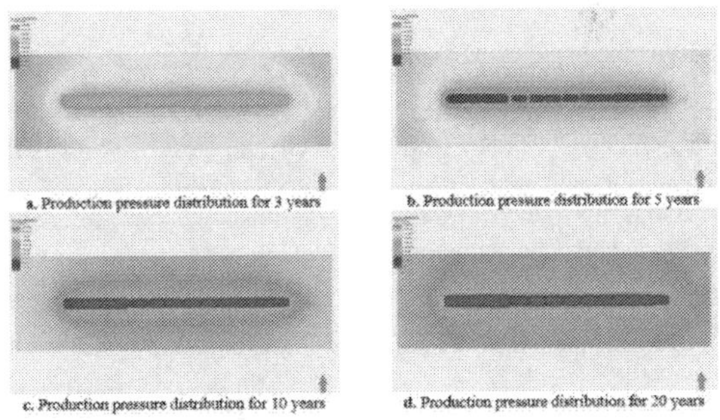

Figure 3. Class I typical wells reservoir pressure distribution of different production time

The dynamic simulation results show that the pressure drop of class I reservoir horizontal wells first reaches the outer boundary of the pressure fracture direction 90 days after production, then reaches the outer boundary of the well axis direction 18-0 days later, and spreads to the whole area 270 days after the pressure drop. At the same time, the equivalent dimensionless drainage radius and dimensionless drainage area of horizontal wells in class I reservoirs after transformation are shown in Figure 4. As can be seen from the figure, the equivalent dimensionless drainage radius rose rapidly at the initial stage, reaching 0.5 at 30 days of production and exceeding 0.7 at 90 days of production. The dimensionless drainage area of class I horizontal wells after transformation no longer increases linearly with time, but becomes slightly faster in the early stage and slower in the later stage.

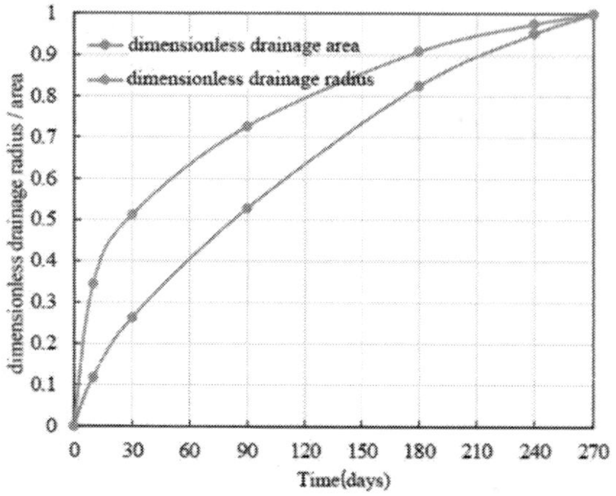

Figure 4. Class I of horizontal well after transforming the equivalent radius of dimensionless drainage and dimensionless drainage area change rule

(2) Class II horizontal well production forecasting reservoir

Based on the established production grid model, the production of horizontal Wells in class II reservoir is predicted. The well was set to produce at a stable rate of $10\times10^4m^3/d$, and the 20-year development index was predicted. The production curve is shown in Figure 5. As can be seen from Figure 5, when the horizontal well of class II reservoir is produced at the rate of $10\times10^4m^3/d$, the stable production time is 11 months, and the estimated cumulative gas production at the end of the period is $1.57\times10^8m^3$.

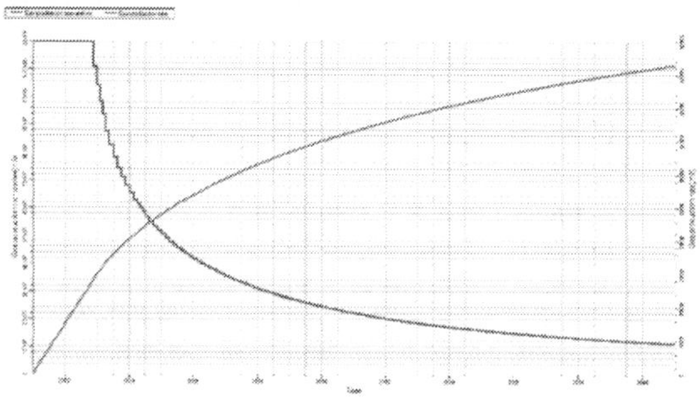

Figure 5. Class II typical wells production figure curve prediction

At the same time the reservoir pressure drawing of the different production time, as shown in Figure 6. The pressure drop of class II horizontal wells first reaches the outer boundary of the pressure fracture direction about 180 days after transformation, and then reaches the outer boundary of the well axis direction about 270 days later. The expansion rate of the drainage radius is slightly slower than that of class I wells.

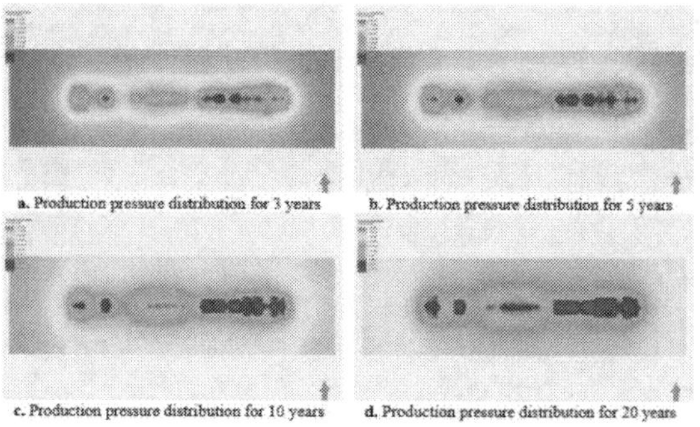

Figure 6. Class II typical wells reservoir pressure distribution of different production time

Changes of equivalent dimensionless drainage radius and dimensionless drainage area of class II horizontal wells after transformation. As can be seen from the figure, the equivalent dimensionless drainage radius rose rapidly in the initial stage, and the dimensionless drainage radius exceeded 0.5 at 50 days and 0.7 at 150 days. The dimensionless drainage area of class II horizontal wells after transformation increases rapidly with the early time, and basically increases linearly after 100 days, and the pressure drop spreads to the whole area for about 500 days.

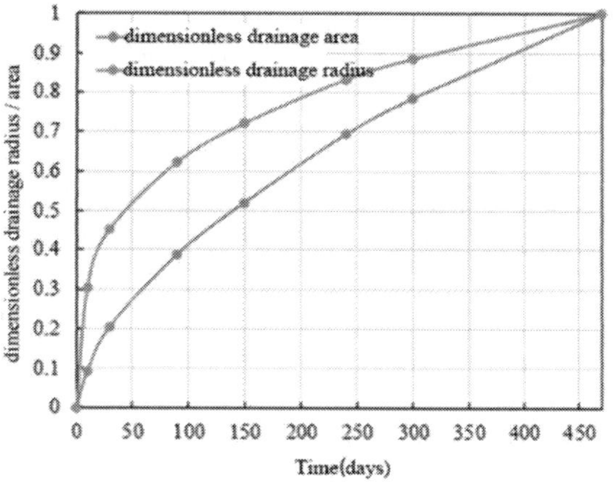

Figure 7. Changes of equivalent dimensionless drainage radius and dimensionless drainage area of class II horizontal wells after transformation

(3) Class III reservoir horizontal well production forecasting

Class III based on manufacturing grid model, reservoir horizontal well production forecast, set well with $5\times10^4m^3/d$ stable yield rate of production, Predict 20 years development, the production curve is shown in Figure 8. Can be seen from the diagram, the class III typical Wells at a rate of about $5\times10^4m^3/d$ production, stable yield of 2.9 years, Forecast the final tired gas $1.12\times10^8m^3$.

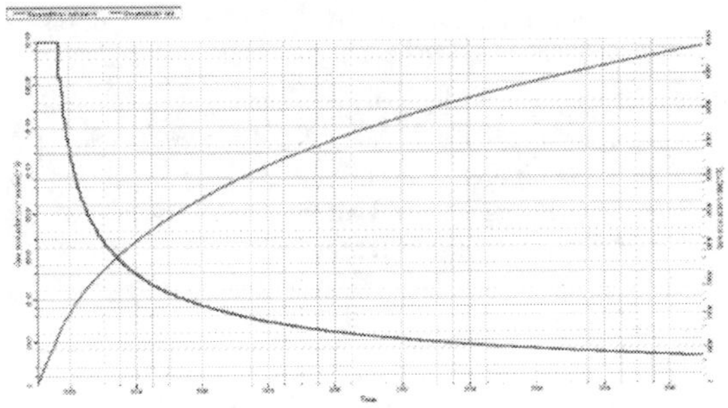

Figure 8. Class III typical wells production figure curve prediction

At the same time the reservoir pressure drawing of the different production time, as shown in Figure 9. Class III regularity of the frustrated radius horizontal well after transforming. Can be seen from the diagram, the class III pressure of horizontal well after about 360 days to reach outer boundary, compressive fracture direction to the shaft axis in 720 days, Frustrated radius expanding speed significantly slower than class I and II wells.

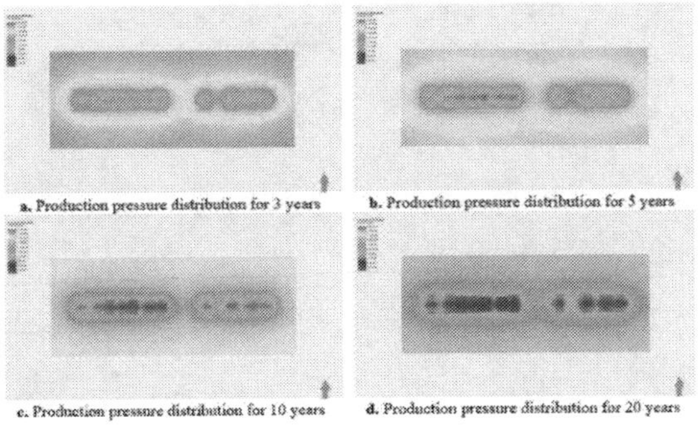

Figure 9. Class III typical wells reservoir pressure distribution of different production time

Figure for class II 3-2-16 horizontal well after transforming the equivalent radius of dimensionless drainage and dimensionless drainage area change rule. As can be seen from the diagram, the equivalent radius of dimensionless drainage early rise faster, to produce 50 days dimensionless drainage radius more than 0.5, 150 days radius of dimensionless frustrated over 0.7; Class II horizontal well after transforming dimensionless drainage area over time early increase quickly, basic linear increase after 100 days, pressure drop across the whole area of about 500 days.

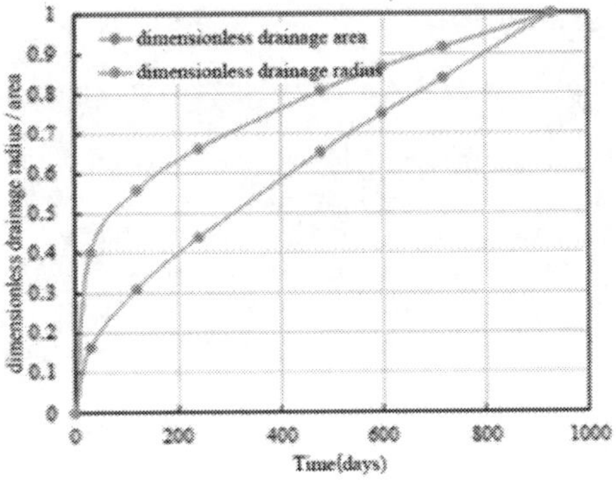

Figure 10. Class III horizontal well after transforming the equivalent radius of dimensionless drainage and dimensionless drainage area change rule

3.2 All kinds of horizontal well patterns discouraged

Figure 11 for different types of horizontal well after transforming the equivalent radius of dimensionless drainage and dimensionless drainage area of contrast. As you can see, all kinds of horizontal well in the early development of dimensionless drainage radius extended nearly, after a period of time, class I and class II horizontal radius of dimensionless drainage and drainage area is relatively fast, and class III well a bit slower than I, II class well.

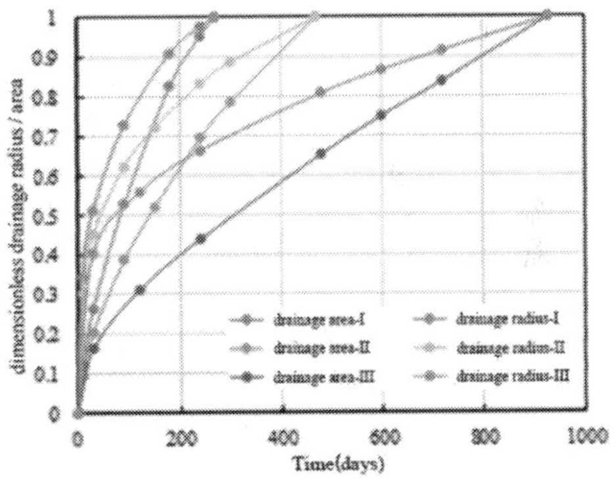

Figure 11. Different types of horizontal well after transforming the equivalent radius of dimensionless drainage and dimensionless drainage area of contrast

Table 2. Different types of gas reservoir pressure wave propagation time relates to the extent

Travel time / The pressure wave propagation distance	Class I (days)	Class II (days)	Class III (days)
SRV area	10	30	30
Outer boundary fracture direction	90	180	240
The horizontal axis outer boundary	180	270	360
Outer boundary reservoir	270	370	720
The all control area	300	500	900

https://doi.org/10.1051/e3sconf/202233801008

4. Conclusion

(1) In order to study the relationship between the variation law of reservoir drainage range and reservoir physical properties of fractured horizontal wells in tight gas reservoirs, a single well numerical simulation model was established for three types of reservoirs, and production performance prediction was carried out.
(2) In the early stage of development, the velocity of non-dimensional drainage radius expansion of all types of horizontal wells is close. After a period of time, the non-dimensional drainage radius and drainage area of class I and II horizontal wells are relatively fast, while class III wells are slightly slower than class I and II wells.

References

1. Shengli Li, Y.Zee Ma, Ernest Gomez. Importance of Modeling Heterogeneities and Correlation in Reservoir Properties in Unconventional Formations: Examples of Tight Gas Reservoirs[J].Journal of Earth Science, 2021, 32(04): 809-817.
2. Jie Wang,Fu-Jian Zhou.Cause analysis and solutions of water blocking damage in cracked/non-cracked tight sandstone gas reservoirs [J]. Petroleum Science, 2021, 18(01): 219-233.
3. CUI Mingming,FAN Aiping,WANG Zongxiu,GAO Wanli,LI Jinbu,LI Yijun.A Volumetric Model for Evaluating Tight Sandstone Gas Reserves in the Permian Sulige Gas Field,Ordos Basin,Central China [J]. Acta Geologica Sinica(English Edition), 2019, 93(02): 386-399.
4. Ya-Hao Huang,You-Jun Tang,Mei-Jun Li,Hai-Tao Hong,Chang-Jiang Wu,Ji-Zhen Zhang,Xiao-Lin Lu,Xiao-Yong Yang.Quantitative evaluation of geological fluid evolution and accumulated mechanism: in case of tight sandstone gas field in central Sichuan Basin [J]. Petroleum Science, 2021, 18(02): 416-429.
5. Yu-Liang Su,Jin-Gang Fu,Lei Li,Wen-Dong Wang,Atif Zafar,Mian Zhang,Wei-Ping Ouyang.A new model for predicting irreducible water saturation in tight gas reservoirs [J]. Petroleum Science, 2020, 17(04): 1087-1100.
6. SUN Hedong, OUYANG Weiping, ZHANG Mian, TANG Haifa, CHEN Changxiao, MA Xu, FU Zhongxin. Advanced production decline analysis of tight gas wells with variable fracture conductivity [J]. Petroleum Exploration and Development, 2018, 45(03): 472-480.
7. LI Mi, GUO Yinghai, LI Zhuangfu, WANG Huaichang, ZHANG Jingxia. Pore-Throat Combination Types and Gas-Water Relative Permeability Responses of Tight Gas Sandstone Reservoirs in the Zizhou Area of East Ordos Basin, China [J]. Acta Geologica Sinica (English Edition), 2019, 93(03): 622-636.
8. Atif Zafar, Yu-Liang Su, Lei Li, Jin-Gang Fu, Asif Mehmood, Wei-Ping Ouyang, Mian Zhang. Tight gas production model considering TPG as a function of pore pressure, permeability and water saturation [J]. Petroleum Science, 2020, 17(05): 1356-1369.
9. Liang Xue, Shao-Hua Gu, Xie-Er Jiang, Yue-Tian Liu, Chen Yang. Ensemble-based optimization of hydraulically fractured horizontal well placement in shale gas reservoir through Hough transform parameterization [J]. Petroleum Science, 2021, 18(03): 839-851.
10. Botao Lin, Han Meng, Jingjun Pan, Sen Chen. Porothermoelastic response of an oil sand formation subjected to injection and micro-fracturing in horizontal wells [J]. Petroleum Science, 2020, 17(03): 687-700.
11. Jiaxuan LIU, Xinchun SHANG, Weiyao ZHU. Investigation on nonlinear multi-scale effects of unsteady flow in hydraulic fractured horizontal shale gas wells [J]. Applied Mathematics and Mechanics (English Edition), 2018, 39(02): 181-192.
12. TANG Mingming, LU Shuangfang, LIANG Hongru, YAN Bihui, SHEN Shan.Study on the Fracturing Parameters and Productivity of Horizontal Wells [J] .Acta Geologica Sinica (English Edition), 2015, 89(S1): 321-323.

Performance evaluation of temperature-resistant nano-surfactants

Qunyi Wang [1], Yongbin Bi [1, 2], Tongfeng Cao [1], Yang Zhang [1], Dong Liu [1], Haiyan He [1], Xuena Zhang [1]

[1] Jidong Oilfield Company, PETROCHINA, China
[2] Northeast Petroleum University, China

Abstract. Surfactant flooding is a common technique in tertiary oil recovery. However, due to the high temperature of some reservoirs and the strong heterogeneity caused by their own geological conditions, the use of common surfactants in high-temperature reservoirs is limited. Temperature - resistant surfactants can reduce interfacial tension, improve conformance and increase oil washing efficiency In this paper, a temperature-resistant nano-type surface active JCN-001 was developed in the laboratory. By testing its particle size distribution, the experimental results can determine that the average particle size range of the system is 34.29nm, so that it can play a better role in low permeability reservoir recovery. Due to its unique nano properties, JCN at 0.2% concentration can still maintain a good effect at about 110, and the oil/water interfacial tension can reach 10-4nm /m, and can also reach ultra-low interfacial tension at high temperature, and the higher the temperature, the more significant the effect According to the changes of surface tension and oil-water interfacial tension, the critical micelle concentration was determined to be about 0.2%. The static adsorption experiments and dynamic adsorption experiments were carried out. The results show that the temperature resistant nano-surfactants have strong adsorption resistance and can effectively reduce the consumption of surfactants on rocks.

Key words: nanoparticles; Interfacial tension; Temperature resistant surface active agent; Enhanced oil recovery.

1. Introduction

As the conventional oil field has gradually entered the later period, the high temperature and other special oil and gas field development is increasingly wide attention by the researchers both at home and abroad. For example, shengli oilfield Jidong oilfield The hydrocarbon resources in tarim oilfield, such as the typical high temperature block is also considerable, because of its special geological conditions of reservoir itself, strong heterogeneity, reservoir temperature higher than 100 [1]. The effect of ordinary surfactants and polymers is not obvious under the condition of high temperature, and in the development process of water cone oil field, water cut rises fast and single-layer sudden phenomenon, serious uneven reserve utilization [2]. The function of nanomaterials provides a new perspective for the development of increasingly miniaturization and complex technology [3]. In recent years, surfactants have been widely used in the preparation and surface modification of composite nanomaterials and nanoparticles of different morphologies and sizes [4]. In order to realize the functionalization of nanomaterials Nano SiO2 exist a lot of surface, surface hydroxyl in the alkaline medium dissociative will happen so that SiO2 nanoparticles surface is negatively charged, and cationic surfactants hydrophilic head baseband has a positive charge [5]. Both can be spontaneously through the electrostatic force is united in wedlock, form large aggregates, the viscosity of the solution surface activity produces change [6], etc A kind of temperature resistant nano surfactant was developed by combining functional nanotechnology with surfactant, which can provide theoretical guidance for laboratory and field [7]. Ption to develop a reasonable development adjustment plan for complex block oil fields [8].

2. Experiments and methods

2.1 Materials and instruments

PDES/ODES negative - non-ionic surfactants; Nano silica SiO2 average particle size 155nm purity 99%; The experimental water is used to provide formation water for oilfield field, and the high speed mixer with a salinity of 2329mg/L. High temperature and high pressure aging reactor; Laser particle size analyzer; CNG interface tensiometer; Shz-22 Water bath constant temperature oscillator (Shanghai); Ld4-2 electric centrifuge (Jiangsu);

https://doi.org/10.1051/e3sconf/202233801009

Wcj-801 temperature-controlled magnetic agitator (Jiangsu); METTLER -PM200 1000 - Electronic balances (Switzerland) and different conventional glassware.

2.2 Particle size distribution

A temperature-resistant nano-surfactant with a concentration of 0.2% was prepared and synthesized in the laboratory. It was named JCN-001 and its particle size distribution was determined. Laser particle size analyzer was used in the experiment First, the sample container was cleaned, washed three times with anhydrated ethanol and then washed three times with the liquid to be tested. After cleaning, the liquid to be tested was dropped into the container to determine the particle size distribution. Experimental results showed that the average particle size of JCN-001 was 34.29nm, and the experimental results showed good dispersion as shown in the figure below.

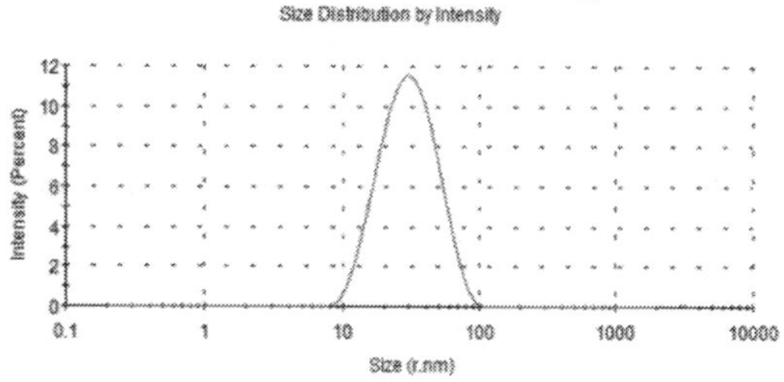

Figure 1. Particle size distribution of JCN-001 at 0.2% concentration

2.3 Measurement of oil-water interfacial tension

Interfacial tension (IFT) is a key parameter to measure the oil washing efficiency of foaming agents. In the order of 10-3Mn /m, it is considered to be an ultra-low grade [8]. At this time, the number of capillary tubes can be greatly increased and the oil displacement effect can be changed. Commonly used measurement methods include ring removal method, hanging plate method, rotary drop method and so on[9] .Under the action of centrifugal force and interfacial tension, the oil droplets suspended in aqueous solution are pulled into cylindrical shape. The shape is determined by the interfacial tension, and the shape is easy to be measured at equilibrium. Therefore, this method is convenient to measure the ultra-low interfacial tension [10].

Experimental steps:

1) Preparation of 0.2% jCN-0001 and common alkylbenzene sulfonate surfactant A;

2) Turn on the power source of CNG interfacial tension instrument and adjust the equipment temperature to 110 for preheating;

3) Moisten the sample tube once with the liquid to be tested, and then fill the sample tube;

4) Draw the crude oil provided by the site with a syringe, tilt the sample tube downward at a certain Angle, inject a small drop of crude oil into the sample tube to remove the small bubbles in the sample tube, button the tube cap, and install the sample tube into the rotary cylinder of the interface tensionometer for preheating for 5min;

5) Adjust the speed to 5000rpm and move the camera of the interface tension-meter to make the oil droplets move to the center of the screen for experimental observation;

(6) Start the interface tensionometer and calculate the instantaneous interfacial tension value through the program every 5min;

7) The measured data were plotted, and the lowest point was denoted as the lowest value of instantaneous interfacial tension.

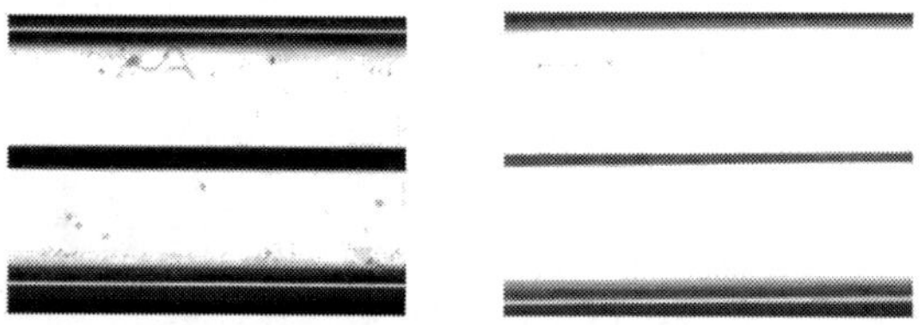

Figure 2. Oil-water interface tensile diagram of ordinary surfactant and nano-JCN-001 (temperature-resistant nano-surfactant at the back)

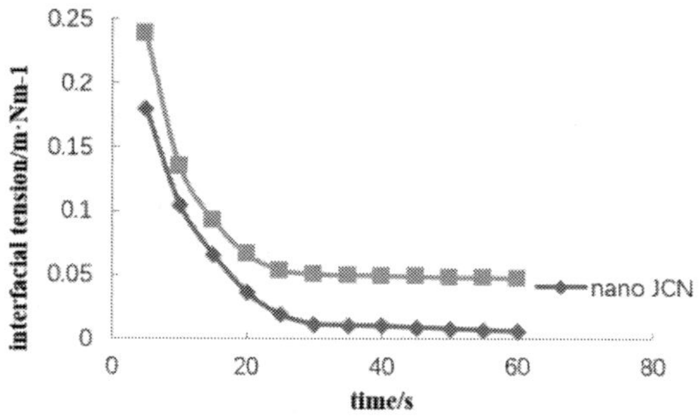

Figure 3. The oil-water interfacial tension of common surfactant A and JCN-001

Experimental results: The oil-water interface activity of surfactants has a great influence on the wettability and oil-washing effect of formation rocks changed by foaming agents.

The lower the oil/water interfacial tension of surfactants is, the better the oil/water interfacial activity of surfactants is. However, too low oil/water interfacial tension will also increase the difficulty of oil/water separation of surface produced crude oil. If other technologies are adopted to achieve oil/water separation, it will directly lead to the increase of economic cost in later stage.

At present, when the oil/water interfacial tension is in the range of 5×10-2~1×10-3 mN/m, the foaming agent not only has good oil/water interfacial activity, but also can guarantee the oil/water separation easily and reduce the production cost.

According to the oil-water interfacial tension test diagram, it can be clearly analyzed that compared with ordinary alkyl benzenesulfonic surfactant, the self-made nano oil displacement agent in this paper can achieve lower interfacial tension, and can also play a role in enhancing oil recovery under high temperature conditions.

2.4 Static adsorption experiment

In the process of oil displacement, the loss of surfactants due to sandstone or rock adsorption is very important, and the large amount of surfactant loss is one of the more difficult problems to solve [11], because it will directly affect the efficiency and cost of oil displacement Cause damage for detention surfactants in the formation of the main reasons are as follows [12]: first, when the surfactant into the formation, surface active agent and formation rock will occur, the solid-liquid interface adsorption phase behavior of this kind of undesirable makes surfactants was stagnant oil phase in the formation trap, [13] thus the surfactant adsorption phenomenon happened Second, the solubility of surfactants in the reservoir salinity water environment is poor, not fully dissolved can be deposited in the reservoir and lose the original effect of surfactants [14] .Therefore, the static adsorption loss experiment of surfactants and the adsorption loss experiment of surfactants in the process of dynamic oil displacement are important reference indexes. Through the comparative analysis of the static and dynamic adsorption loss experiment results, the influencing factors of the adsorption loss of surfactants in the process of oil displacement are studied [15].

Experimental steps: 300mL temperature resistant nano surfactant solution of 0.1%, 0.2%, 0.3%, 0.4% were prepared respectively, and the following experimental process was carried out:

(1) 300mL temperature resistant nano surfactant JCN-001 solution was taken, weighed 30g (80-120 mesh) oil sands were put into a 200mL triangular flask;

(2) Add 100g of temperature-resistant nano-type surfactant JCN-001 to the triangle flask sealed with plug and tape, put it into the high-temperature and high-pressure reactor, evenly shake it for 72h under 110, then remove it, centrifuge it at 4000r/min for 20min, take it out, the upper clarified liquid;

(3) The absorbance of the liquid after centrifugation was measured by ultraviolet spectrophotometer, and the concentration was obtained by using the standard curve formula. The concentration was denoted as one. The concentration after the first adsorption, and calculate the first adsorption amount according to the formula;

(4) Repeat the above experimental steps to calculate the adsorption capacity for the second and third time.

The static adsorption capacity is calculated as follows [16]:

$$A_i = [(\rho_0 - \rho_i)V]/m$$

$$A_n = \sum_{i=1}^{n} A_i$$

The experimental results: According to the shown in table 1, as the heat resistance nano surfactant concentration increasing, the single adsorption quantity and total adsorption capacity increased The highest adsorption quantity for the first time, the second adsorption capacity is low, basic unchanged for the third time the adsorption quantity By static adsorption experiment of rocks, the heat resistance of nano type surfactants in use process should choose low concentration.

Table 1. Static adsorption capacity at different concentrations

Original concentration (mg·L-1)	First adsorption (mg·L-1)	Secondary adsorption (mg·L-1)	Third adsorption (mg·L-1)	Cumulative adsorption capacity (mg·L-1)
1000	976.0056	982.0045	996.687	0.284562
2000	1965.6325	1982.5612	1996.9458	0.645214
3000	2946.6564	2941.6457	2986.9841	0.828612
4000	3960.1254	3962.1126	3982.2456	0.860576

3. Conclusion

A temperature-resistant nano-foam system was developed in the laboratory. By testing its particle size distribution, the experimental results can determine the average particle size range of the system is 34.29nm and the oil-water interfacial tension is measured at 110. The experimental results show that the nano-system can reach 10-4nm /m at high temperature, and the higher the temperature, the more significant the effect The static adsorption test shows that the temperature resistant nano surfactant JCN-001 has excellent adsorption resistance, and the optimal concentration is 0.2%.

References

1. He L, Luo J, Ding B, et al. Preparation and Properties of Nano Oil Displacement Agent for Low/Ultra-low Permeability Reservoir [J]. Oilfield Chemistry, 2018, 35(1): 81-84 and 90.
2. Lei Q, Luo J, Peng B, et al. Mechanism of expanding swept volume by nano-sized oil-displacement agent [J]. Petroleum Exploration and Development, 2019, 46(5):991-997.
3. Cheng Y, Zhao M, Zheng C, et al. Water-dispersible Reactive Nanosilica and Poly (2-acrylamido-2-methyl-1-propanesulfonic Acid Sodium) Nanoybrid as Potential Oil Displacement Agent for Enhanced Oil Recovery [J]. Energy & Fuels, 2017, 31(6):6345-6351.
4. Feng Q, Qu C, Zhang W, et al. Preparation and Performance Evaluation of Nano-Microsphere Oil Displacement Agent Suitable to Offshore Heavy Oil Field [J]. Journal of Liaoning Shihua University, 2019.
5. Zhang J H, Wang Y N, Wang X Y, et al. The performance evaluation of nano-micron microsphere for profile control and displacement agent in low permeability reservoir [J]. Iop Conference, 2016, 40:012020.
6. Harnoy G N. Enhanced oil recovery techniques using liposomes [J]. 2010.
7. Hendraningrat L, Torster O. Metal oxide-based nanoparticles: revealing their potential to enhance oil recovery in different wettability systems [J]. Applied Nanoscience, 2015, 5(2): 181-199.
8. Liu Q C, Liu Y J. Study on the Mechanism of Enhancing Oil Recovery by Molecular Film Displacement[C]// Advanced Materials Research. Trans Tech Publications, 2011:2135-2141.

https://doi.org/10.1051/e3sconf/202233801009

9. MD Bhavsar, Amiji M M. Polymeric nano- and microparticle technologies for oral gene delivery. [J]. Expert Opinion on Drug Delivery, 2007, 4(3):197-213.
10. Sun Q, Li Z, Li S, et al. Experimental study on interface properties and oil displacement efficiency of foams stabilized by SiO2 nanoparticles [J]. Journal of China University of Petroleum (Edition of Natural ence), 2016.
11. Cheng Y, Jing D U, Luo W, et al. Synthesis and properties of oil displacement agent nanosilica grafted poly-acrylmide/ 2-acrylamido-2-methyl-1-propanesulfonic acid sodium [J]. Chemical Research, 2017.
12. Sun Z G, Zhang J, Xia J H, et al. Development of two novel composite oil displacement agents based on petroleum sulfonate [J]. Journal of China University of Petroleum (Edition of Natural Science), 2007.
13. Li Q, Wei B, Lu L, et al. Investigation of physical properties and displacement mechanisms of surface-grafted nano-cellulose fluids for enhanced oil recovery [J]. Fuel, 2017, 207(nov.1): 352-364.
14. Jie H, Tang D, Zhang J. Research of the compatibility and oil displacement result of molecular deposition membrane agent and polymer [J]. Petroleum Geology and Recovery Efficiency, 2009.
15. Zhang L, Jing C, Khan N, et al. Efficient Preparation of Nano-Starch Particles and Its Mechanism of Enhanced Oil Recovery in Low-PermeabilityOil Reservoirs [J]. SPE Journal, 2020:1-14.
16. Zhang Z L, Wang C J . Research progress on new oil-displacing agent in extra-low-permeability reservoir in Yanchang oilfield [J]. Applied Chemical Industry, 2018.

Feasibility Study for Well pattern Encryption in Complex Fractured Block Reservoirs--Taking the Liu 90 South Fault Block in the Jidong Oilfield as an example

Qunyi Wang [1], Yongbin Bi [1,2], Tongfeng Cao [1], Yang Zhang [1], Dong Liu [1], Haiyan He [1], Xuena Zhang [1]

[1] Jidong Oilfield Company, PETROCHINA, China

[2] Northeast Petroleum University, China

Abstract. Jidong oilfield belongs to complex fault block reservoir, and the development has now entered into high water-cut stage. when using Well pattern encryption technology to stabilize production, it is necessary to study the feasibility of Well pattern encryption to ensure a better economic benefit. In this paper, we use theoretical analysis method, consider the influence of oil price on the calculation, improve the economic limit Well pattern density calculation formula, calculate the economic limit Well pattern density under different recovery rates, make recovery rate prediction for different Well pattern density scenarios by combining with Sherkachov's formula, and use the curve intersection method to determine the Well pattern density at the break-even point, so as to determine the economic feasibility of Well pattern encryption. The example calculations show that the use of well network encryption alone does not meet the development requirements of the Liu 90 South block and has no significant economic benefits, so a combination of two-three methods is needed to further improve the recovery rate. Numerical simulation prediction results show that the two-three combination method can improve the recovery rate by 14.54%, accumulate 28.88×10^4t of oil increase and increase revenue by 678,245,000 yuan.

Keywords: complex block reservoir; well network encryption; economic limit well network density; two-three combination.

1. Introduction

Jidong oilfield is a complex block oilfield and is now in the high water content development stage. Subsequent development adjustments usually take the form of well network encryption to improve the development level and economic efficiency. A large number of practices show that too small a Well pattern density leads to insufficient well control reserves, which will affect the development level of the field; too large a Well pattern density leads to high drilling investment, making the Well pattern encryption measures not economically efficient. Therefore, it is important to study the feasibility of Well pattern encryption to develop a reasonable development adjustment plan for complex block oil fields.

2. Applying Sherkachov formula to determine the relationship between well pattern density and recovery

2.1 Sherkachev formula

Whether the relationship between recovery factor and well pattern density is established correctly or not is related to the effect of infilling adjustment of well pattern. Most scholars have counted the relationship between recovery factor and well pattern density, and obtained the relationship between recovery factor and well pattern density, but most of these formulas lack practicability and universality 1. It was not until the 1960s that the Soviet scholar Serkachev, by compiling, analyzing and studying data from the end of oil field development, condensed Serkachev's formula to more accurately characterize the mathematical relationship between well type density and recovery rate 2.

$$E_R = E_D e^{(-a/f)} \tag{1}$$

 https://doi.org/10.1051/e3sconf/202233801010

where: ER is the ultimate recovery of the reservoir, % ; ED is the water displacement efficiency, % ; a is the Well pattern index, dimensionless quantity; f is the Well pattern density, *Port/km²*.

The variability of different oil fields is reflected in the variation of Well pattern index and Displacement efficiency in equation (1). The Well pattern index depends on factors such as formation connectivity, oil-water flow rate ratio, and non-homogeneous characteristics of the formation, and its value integrally reflects the characteristics of the field 3. Therefore, the key to the correct application of the Sherkachevformula is to determine the displacement efficiency and well pattern index that are consistent with the field reality.

2.2 Method for determining the Displacement efficiency and Well pattern index a

(1) Empirical formula method

The widely used empirical formulas include the empirical formula of the China National Petroleum Exploration and Development Institute, the Chen Yuanqian empirical formula, and the Yu Qitai empirical formula 4 5.

The Empirical formula of CNPC E&P Research Institute is shown in Table 1 6.

Table 1. Table of empirical formulas of CNPC E&P Research Institute

categories	Number of oil deposits	Fluidity / ($10^{-3}\mu m^2$/(mPa·s)$^{-1}$)	regression relation
1	13	300~600	$E_R = 0.6031e^{-}$
2	27	100~300	$E_R = 0.5508e^{-0.8}$
3	67	30~100	$E_R = 0.5227e^{-0.0}$
4	19	5~30	$E_R = 0.4832e^{-0.0}$
5	18	<5	$E_R = 0.4015e^{-0.18}$

(2) Actual data regression method

Taking the logarithm of both sides of equation (1), the following equation can be obtained.

$$\ln E_R = \ln E_D - a / f \tag{2}$$

On the right-angle coordinate axis, the actual production data are regressed according to Equation (2) using the inverse of the Well pattern density as the horizontal coordinate and the natural logarithm of the recovery rate as the vertical coordinate. The slope of the regression line is the Well pattern index a of the field, and the intercept is lnE_D.

(3) Relative permeability curve method

The Relative permeability data is first used to derive the oil Displacement efficiency, after which the Well pattern index in the Sherkachevformula is back-calculated using the current calibrated recovery of the field and the Well pattern density.

$$a = f \times \ln \frac{E_D}{E_R} \tag{3}$$

Jidong oilfield has accumulated a large amount of relative permeability data after more than 40 years of development, and the normalization of multiple relative permeability curves can represent the field characteristics and calculate the oil drive efficiency and well pattern index more accurately 7 8, so this method is used to calculate the oil drive efficiency and well pattern index in this study.

3. Method for determining the economic limit Well pattern density

3.1 Improved economic limit Well pattern density formula

Appropriate well pattern encryption can bring economic benefits to the oil field, and as the number of encrypted wells increases, the economic benefits of well pattern encryption measures first increase and then decrease until no economic benefits are generated 9. If the field reaches break-even after drilling an encrypted well, the Well pattern density of the field at that time is said to be the economic limit Well pattern density, and the average single well oil production under the economic limit Well pattern density is the economic limit single well oil production. To find the economic limit Well pattern density, it is only necessary to establish the input and output relationship of a single well based on the condition that the field reaches break-even 10.

$$[\frac{T_i}{T}(I_d + I_{sc}) + C_{wo}T_i](1 + R_{inj}) \geq (P_{oi} - P_c - P_{tax})R_{sp}(\sum Q_{oi}) \tag{4}$$

Where: T is the total forecast production time, year; I_d is the drilling investment, yuan; I_{sc} is the surface construction investment, yuan; C_{wo} is the oil and water well operation cost, yuan; T_i is the forecast production time of step i oil price, *a*; R_{inj} is the injection and extraction wells ratio, dimensionless; P_{oi} is the step i oil price, yuan/ton; P_c is the operation cost, yuan/ton; P_{tax} is the tax and management fee, yuan/ton; R_{sp} is the crude oil commodity rate, % ; $\sum Q_{oi}$ is the cumulative oil production of a single well, ton.

Equation (4) is a single-well input and output relationship equation established based on the net present value principle by considering the total cost and total income of a single well comprehensively 错误!未找到引用源。.

The actual situation varies widely from field to field, and the selection of economic parameters varies, but the form of equation (4) is constant, so equation (4) has universal applicability in oil fields.

Letting both sides of equation (4) take equal signs gives the economic limit of cumulative oil production per well at a step oil price.

$$(\sum Q_{oi})_{\min} = \frac{[\frac{T_i}{T}(I_d + I_{sc}) + C_{wo}T_i](1 + R_{inj})(1 + R_{inj})}{(P_{oi} - P_c - P_{tax})R_{sp}} \tag{5}$$

By combining the geological reserves, oil-bearing area and degree of crude oil recovery, the economic limit Well pattern density can be deduced for different recovery rates E_R.

$$f_{lim} = \frac{N(E_a - R_o)(1 + R_{inj})}{(\sum Q_o)_{lim} A} + f_{now} \quad (6)$$

Where: f_{lim} is the economic limit Well pattern density, *Port/km²*; N is the geological reserves of crude oil, tons; E_a is the given recovery rate, %; R_o is the degree of crude oil recovery, %; R_{inj} is the injection and extraction wells ratio; f_{now} is the original Well pattern density, *Port/km²*; A is the oil-bearing area of the reservoir, Km^2.

3.2 Curve intersection method to determine the economic limit Well pattern density

The equation (6) is processed to obtain the minimum recovery rate that must be achieved for economically efficient fields at different Well pattern densities.

$$E_{R min} = \frac{(f - f_{now})(\sum Q_o)_{lim} A}{N(1 + R_{inj})} + R_o \quad (7)$$

where: E_{Rmin} is the minimum recovery rate required for break-even at a Well pattern density f.
Recovery rate at Well pattern density f can be predicted from the Sherkachevformula.

$$E_R = E_D e^{(-a/f)} \quad (8)$$

The two curves are plotted on the same coordinates and the schematic is shown in Figure 1.

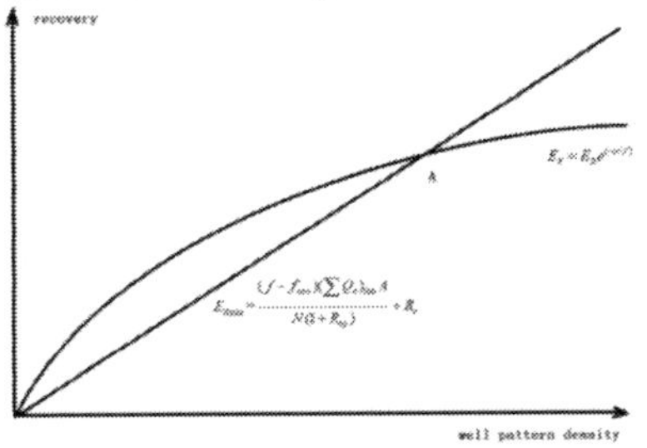

Figure 1. Curve intersection method to determine the economic limit Well pattern density

The two curves intersect at point A. The density of the Well pattern at the intersection point is the economic limit well pattern density. To the left $E_R > E_{Rmin}$, the output of the field is greater than the input, with economic benefits. To the right of the intersection point $E_R < E_{Rmin}$, there is no economic benefit, the Well pattern encryption scheme is economically unreasonable.

3. Application of the economic limit Well pattern density determination method in the Liu 90 South Fracture Block reservoir

3.1 Example calculations

The geological reserve of oil reservoir in Liu 90 South Fracture Block is 1,981,400 tons, Oil-bearing area is 1.2727km², using the five-point method of well placement, the number of injection and extraction wells ratio is 1:1, the current Well pattern density is 27.5 *port/km²*, the calibration recovery rate is 35.08%; single well drilling investment is 8,500,000 yuan, average surface construction costs is 850,000 yuan, single well average operating costs is 290,000 yuan/year, operating costs is 146 yuan/ton, tax and administration fee is 316 yuan/ton, and crude oil commodity rate is 1; step oil price P_{O1}= $45/bbl, T_1=2 years; P_{O2}=$50/bbl, T_2=2 years; P_{O3}=$60/bbl at T_3=11 years.
According to the formula (4) ~ (6) , the cumulative oil production and the economic limit well pattern density are calculated.
(1) Economic Limit Cumulative oil production of single well $\sum Q_{oi}$
Following equation (1), the cumulative oil production from a single well at the economic limit under the step oil price is calculated and the results are shown in Table 2.

Table 2. Calculation result of limit cumulative oil production of single well under the step oil price

Step oil price P_{oi}($/bbl)	45	50	60
Production time T_i (years)	2	2	11
$\sum Q_{oi}$ (million tonnes)	0.8321	0.5331	1.7062

(2) Economic limit Well pattern density f_{lim} at different recovery rates
On the basis of the calculated single well limit cumulative oil production, the required parameters were substituted according to equations (2) to (5) to calculate the economic limit Well pattern density under different recovery rate conditions, and the results are shown in Table 3.

Table 3. Calculated economic limit Well pattern density for a given recovery rate

Given recover y rate E_a (%)	20	25	30	35	40	45	50
f_{lim} (*Port/k m²*)	8.0 4	14.4 9	20.9 5	27.4 0	33.8 5	40.3 0	46.7 5

(3) Prediction of recovery rates at different Well pattern densities using the Sherkachevformula
The reservoir development information of the Liou 90 South Block is complete, and the Displacement efficiency of the block is 0.58 using relative permeability curve method, the current Well pattern density is 27.5 *Port/km²*, the calibrated recovery rate is 35.08%, and The value of the Well pattern index a was calculated as 13.83 using

 https://doi.org/10.1051/e3sconf/202233801010

Sherkachov's formula.

$$E_R = 0.58e^{(-13.831/f)} \quad (9)$$

Different Well pattern encryption schemes were considered for the reservoir and the final recovery was predicted using the Sherkachov formula and the results are shown in Table 4.

Table 4. Recovery at different well pattern density predicted by Sherkachov's formula

Well pattern density mouth (km^2)	7	12	17	22	27	32	37	42	47
Predicted recovery (%)	8.04	18.32	25.71	30.93	34.75	37.65	39.91	41.73	43.22

(4) Curve intersection method to determine the economic limit Well pattern density of oil fields

With the Well pattern density as the horizontal coordinate and the recovery rate as the vertical coordinate, the economic limit Well pattern density curves for different given recovery rates and the predicted recovery rate curves for different Well pattern scenarios are plotted respectively.

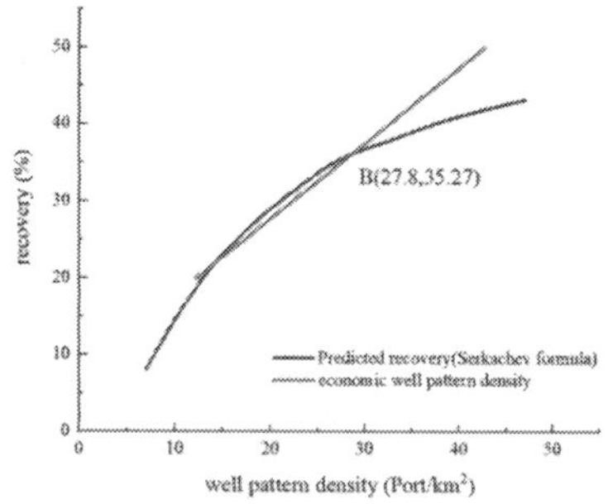

Figure 2. Curve intersection method to determine the economic limit Well pattern density

The curves in Figure 2 intersect at point B. Using MATLAB software, the coordinates of the intersection point are calculated as (27.8, 35.27), which means that the economic limit well network density of the field is 27.8 *Port/km²* and the predicted recovery rate of the field under this well pattern density is 35.27%. The current well network density is close to the economic limit well pattern density, and the well pattern encryption within a reasonable range has limited value to improve the recovery rate and poor economic benefits.

3.2 Recommended Measures

The economic limit well pattern density of complex fault block reservoir in South Liu 90 was determined to be 27.8 *Port/km²*. The analysis shows that the economic feasibility of well pattern infilling is not high, so it is suggested to adopt two-three combination method to enhance oil recovery. The Well pattern encryption scheme and chemical flooding scheme are designed according to the actual situation of the reservoir, and the development index is predicted by numerical simulation.

(1) Prediction of the effect of the two-three combination method to improve recovery

On the basis of studying the distribution of remaining oil in the target area, the well pattern is first optimized, then the binary system of cluster table is injected with an injection volume of 0.253 PV, and the subsequent development indexes are predicted by using CMG software. The results are shown in Fig. 3.

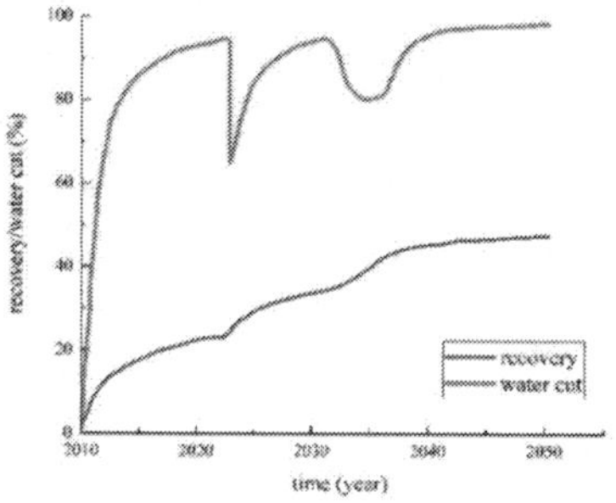

Figure 3. Development indexes of a two-three combination programme

The curve in Figure 3 shows that after the implementation of the two-three combination program, the recovery rate of the whole area reached 49.62%, the recovery rate improvement value was 14.54%, and the cumulative oil increase was 28.88×10^4t, which is a good development effect.

(2) Analysis of the economic feasibility of the two-three combination option

The mass concentration of both polymer and surfactant is 1500 mg/L. The unit price of polymer is 11,000 yuan/ton, and the unit price of surfactant is 20,100 yuan/ton. Considering all economic parameters, The calculation results of oilfield development index are shown in Table 5.

Table 5. Calculation of economic index

Well pattern encryption costs (yuan)	Chemical drive cost (yuan)	Measure revenue (yuan)	Input-output ratio
138797700	116693400	678245000	1:2.65

As can be seen from Table 5, the field revenue after the measures reached 67824.50 with an input-output ratio of 1:2.62. This indicates that the two-three combined measures can bring greater economic benefits to the Liu 90 South fault block, while the recovery rate improvement value reached 14.54% and the oil increase of 28.88×10^4t,

https://doi.org/10.1051/e3sconf/202233801010

which also meets the development requirements.

4. Conclusion

(1) The method of determining the economic limit well network density for complex block reservoirs is proposed. According to the input and output relationship in oilfield development, this paper considers more comprehensive economic parameters, improves the previous formula, innovatively derives the formula for the economic limit well network density under the step oil price, and combines the Sherkachov formula to determine the intersection of the two curves as the economic limit well network density of the oilfield.
(2) Taking the complex fault block reservoir of South Liu90 in Jidong Oilfield as an example, the feasibility of well network encryption is studied. The results show that the economic benefits in this block are not obvious if only well network encryption is used, so it is recommended to use two-three combination method to further improve the recovery rate. The Development Index of numerical simulation prediction shows that the two-three combination method can increase the recovery rate by 14.54%, accumulate 28.88×10^4t of oil and create economic benefits of 678245000 yuan. The method studied in this paper can provide a basis for the adjustment of the development scheme in the high water-bearing stage of complex block reservoirs, with simple calculation and high practicality.

References

1. Zhang W. Research on the calculation method of Well pattern density under the influence of comprehensive factors [D]. Changjiang University, 2012.
2. Hou Jianfeng,Hu Yafei,Liu Chang,Zhao Hui,Wei Tao. Method for determining economic limit and reasonable Well pattern density in water-driven reservoirs [J]. Xinjiang Oil and Gas, 2018, 14(03): 53-57+4.
3. Dou Zhidong, Li Shunying, Zhang Meiju, Wu Qiaoling, Zhang Huiqin, Chen Xiaoguang. Research and application of Sherkachov formula in Hu7 South Fracture Block [J]. Inner Mongolia Petrochemicals, 2013, 39(13): 129-130.
4. Geng Zhanli, An Guirong, Zhou Wensheng, Xu Jiafeng, Zhang Wei, Deng Jiuguo. Study on the relationship between Well pattern density and recovery rate in offshore thick oil fields [J]. China Offshore Oil and Gas, 2012, 24(03): 35-37.
5. Yu Q-T. A method for calculating reasonable and limiting Well pattern densities in water-driven sandstone reservoirs [J]. Petroleum Exploration and Development, 1986(04): 49-54.
6. Yu, Cheng-Long, Li, Hui-Min, Zhao, Min, Luo, Chi-Hui. Research on the calculation method of reasonable number of wells for Well pattern encryption in water-driven oil field [J]. Rocky oil and gas reservoirs, 2011, 23(01): 111-113.
7. Zhang Bengqiang, Xue Guoqing, Tang Mingguang, Wang Shuai, Chen Lin. Research on the evaluation method of extreme Well pattern density in offshore oil fields [J]. Natural Gas and Petroleum, 2019, 37(04): 67-72.
8. Zou Cunyou, Han Daquang, Sheng Haibo, Wang Ping, Zhang Aidong. Exploration of a method to establish the relationship between recovery rate and Well pattern density [J]. Oil and Gas Geology and Recovery, 2010, 17(04): 43-47+114.
9. Huang Jinshan. A new method for calculating economic limit Well pattern density in oilfield [J]. Oil and Gas Geology and Recovery, 2013, 20(03): 53-55+59+114-115.
10. Zhu Wenjuan, Yu Gaoming, Yan Weifeng, Zhang Na,Chai Junliang,Wang Delong. Determination of economic limit Well pattern density in oilfield [J]. Broken Block Oil and Gas Field, 2008(04): 66-67+75.
11. Zhang Shulin, Huang Yaoqin. Net present value method--a new method for calculating economic limit Well pattern density [J]. Geological Science and Technology Information, 2004(01): 78-80.

Research on Application and Benefits of Energy Storage Systems

Nana Li [1], Jing Wu [2], Qionghui Li [1], Jing Hu [1], Hao Fan [2], Bibin Huang [1]

[1] State Grid Energy Research Institute Co., Ltd., Beijing 102209, China
[2] State Grid Corporation of China, Beijing, 100017, China

Abstract. At present, Energy storage systems are widely used in power supply, power grid and end-users system. There have been extensive application explorations in most application scenarios in China, such as smoothing power fluctuation and output tracking of new energy sources, assisting conventional units to participate in frequency modulation, peak-shaving frequency modulation of the power grid, system standby, peak-valley arbitrage of the load side, as well as demand reduction. This paper firstly investigates the typical operation modes of energy storage applied to new energy consumption scenarios, and analyzes three important technical approaches in order to promote new energy consumption, such as energy storage to stabilize fluctuation, tracking output and peak load balancing. Secondly, to evaluate the economic benefits of energy storage allocation in new energy projects in different regions of China by using the self-developed software for economic analysis of new energy and comprehensive energy system; thereafter the strategic suggestions for energy storage allocation in different regions are proposed. The results show that it is economical for wind power owners to build Pumped Thermal Energy Storage (PTES) and it is even cheaper to purchase PTES by wind power owners than to build electrochemical energy storage (EES) batteries by users when the same conditions of energy storage applies. Owner-built and owner-allocated Photovoltaic (PV) power station is poor in economy. Under the same energy storage condition, when the allocated energy of 1MW PV power generation is less than 200 kW, EES is relatively more economical than PTES.

Key words: energy storage, new energy consumption, operation mode, economy measurement and calculation.

Introduction

Energy storage is an important component and key supporting technology of "internet plus" smart energy. With the development of electrochemical energy storage technology and cost reduction, energy storage has progressed rapidly in the application of end-user side, power grid side, grid-connected renewable energy, power auxiliary service and so on. From the perspective of energy storage scale, current energy storage projects in China mainly adopt PPES, followed by EES. According to the incomplete statistics of China Energy Research Society, CERS/Global Energy Storage Alliance (GESA), China Energy Storage Alliance (CNESA) global energy storage project library, by the end of 2020, the cumulative installed capacity of energy storage projects in China was 35.6GW, accounting for 18.6% of the global energy storage market, with a year-on-year growth of 9.8%. Among all EES technologies, the cumulative installed capacity of li-ion batteries is the highest with 2,902.4MW; molten salt thermal storage system ranked third, with a cumulative installed capacity of 520MW, up 23.8% year-on-year. From the distribution of energy storage applications, at present, the cumulative installed capacity of the power supply side of EES projects that have been put into operation in China is the highest, surpassing that of the user side for the first time. By the end of 2020, the cumulative scale of EES in China was 47.5%, 17.9% and 34.6% on the power supply side (including new energy generation side, combined auxiliary services of thermal power plants), the power grid side and the user side, respectively. Among EES projects newly put into operation in 2020, the installed capacity of new energy generation side projects takes the largest share, accounting for 50% [1-2].

This paper mainly studies the typical operation modes of energy storage used in new energy consumption scenarios, and analyzes three important technical approaches to promote new energy consumption, such as energy storage to stabilize fluctuations, tracking output and peak load balancing. On this basis, the self-developed economic analysis software of new energy and comprehensive energy system is used to conduct the economic benefit analysis of energy storage allocation in new energy

https://doi.org/10.1051/e3sconf/202233801011

projects in different regions of China; thereafter, the strategic suggestions for energy storage allocation in different regions are proposed.

2 Typical operation modes of energy storage to promote new energy consumption

Stabilizing fluctuation, tracking output and peak load balancing are three important technical approaches to improve the operation modes of new energy consumption. Inevitably, the large-scale centralized integration of new energy into the grid will bring many challenges to the operation and regulation of the power system. The inherent properties of new energy, such as randomness, fluctuation, and intermittence, are in urgent need of large-scale energy storage to realize smoothing and tracking to enhance the friendliness of new energy to the power grid [3].

2.1 Stabilizing fluctuation

Time scale and fluctuation amplitude are the limiting indicators of the system to the fluctuation of new energy power. Therefore, the selection of energy storage types should focus on the performance of power characteristics of the types on the time scale of fluctuation limiting indicators. Power transmission companies in various countries usually have different indicators of maximum power fluctuation for grid-connected wind farms on time scale, and the fluctuation requirements are shown in Table 1.

Table 1 Maximum power fluctuation requirements for grid-connected wind farms in different countries

Country	Company	Climbing rate standard		
US	FERC, WECC	ERCOT limits the 1-minute climbing rate to less than 10% of installed capacity.		
Canada	AESO	Less than 10% installed capacity in 1 minute		
Denmark	Eltra&Elkraft	Less than 5% installed capacity in 1 minute: adjustable from 10% to 100% per minute.		
Germany	E.ON EnBW	Less than 10% of installed capacity in 1 minute after startup		
UK	Soni	Less than 10MW in 1 minute and the 1-minute climbing rate not higher than 3 times of the average climbing rate in 10 minutes.		
Ireland	EITGRID	Less than 30MW within 1min and with 10min, and it can be operated according to the real-time climbing rate (1-30MW) required by power grid		
	ESBNG	Installed capacity < 100MW: Less than 5% of installed capacity within 1min (in any 15min period)	Installed capacity < 200MW: Less than 4% of installed capacity in 1min (in any 15min period)	Installed capacity > 200MW: Less than 2% of installed capacity in 1min (in any 15min period)
South Africa	RSA	Less than 50MW in 1min		
China	State Grid	Installed capacity < 30MW: Less than 3MW change within 1min; Less than 10MW change in 10min	30MW < installed capacity < 100MW: Less than 1/10 of the installed capacity within 1min; Less than 1/3 installed capacity within 10min	Installed capacity > 150MW: Within 1min, the change is less than 15MW; Less than 10MW change in 10min

Fluctuations of new energy power in different time scales will create different impacts on system standby, energy dispatching and safe operation, etc. and can be reduced by energy storage to stabilize fluctuations, thus improving the power quality of new energy grid. Taking the PV energy storage combined power generation as an example, the energy storage in the optical storage combined dispatching system controls the output of the energy storage system according to the set smooth range to stabilize the fluctuation of PV output, and achieves the goal of controlling the fluctuation of PV output within the specified range in multiple time scales. Taking a 50MW PV power station as an example, the output fluctuation rate within 10 minutes can be less than 10% by combined energy storage [4].

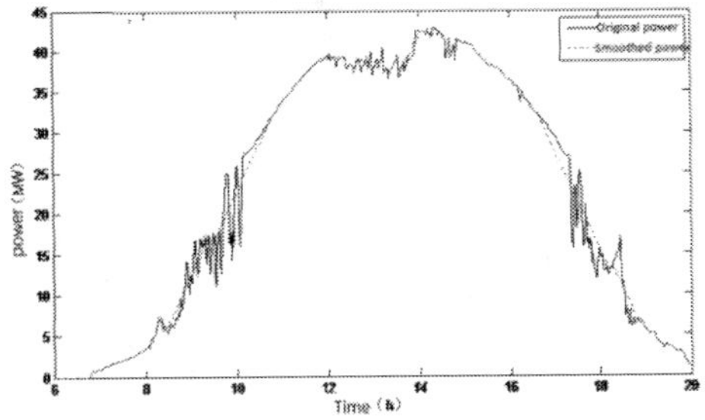

Figure 1 Smoothing fluctuation of PV (a)

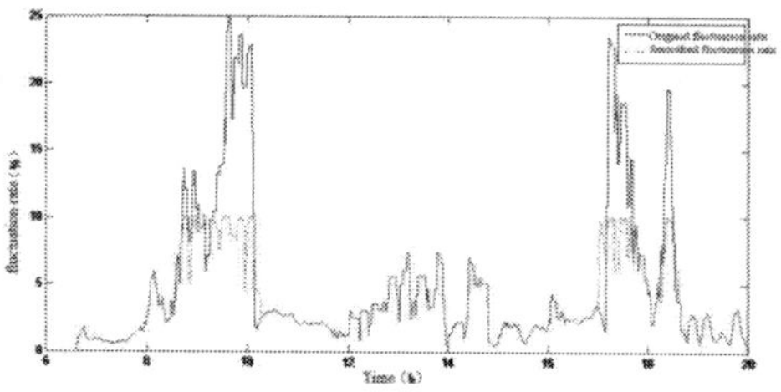

Figure 2 Smoothing fluctuation of PV (b)

The allocation of energy storage system to smooth out fluctuation requires comprehensive consideration including fluctuation limit indicators, characteristics of energy storage types, control methods of fluctuation smoothing control and energy management. The goal of the allocation is to minimize energy storage power and capacity while meeting system requirements. At present, the existing power and capacity allocation methods of energy storage systems are mainly based on theoretical analysis and simulation analysis. In general, an allocation method based on theoretical analysis is to analyze and extracts the characteristics of wind power fluctuation based on historical data at first instance, and follow by estimating the power and capacity of energy storage according to the characteristics of power fluctuation (such as maximum fluctuation, time scale, etc.). Whereas, an allocation method based on simulation analysis is generally based on massive typical wind power data. The existing fluctuation control and energy management methods are used to simulate and analyze the effect of the fluctuation control, and finally the minimum energy storage power and capacity required while meeting the fluctuation limit indicators are obtained.

2.2 Tracking output

In order to meet the stability of the output power of the combined power generation, tracking planned output is applied to ensure the actual output of the combined power generation system of new energy and energy storage as close as possible to the power generation plan curve based on the planned tracking error and energy state of energy storage through the charging and discharging of energy storage. According to the predicted output of new energy, the output of traditional units, the load demand, the operating state constraints and costs of each unit, the power grid dispatching body formulates the output curve of the new energy storage joint plan and sends it to new energy stations, which make coordinated control to track the output curve, which in fact, compensates the difference between the actual power of the combined power generation system and the planned curve in real time. At the same time, according to the feedback value of current battery power and battery remaining capacity, the maximum working capacity of the energy storage system is determined, and the information of the current allowable use capacity of the energy storage system and the current available maximum charge and discharge capacities are sent to the dispatching side, and requests the joint dispatching system to adjust the relevant control quantities. Figure 3 is a block diagram of the control strategy for tracking planned output. When the remaining capacity of the energy storage battery is close to overcharging, and the combined output is still higher than the planned value of power generation, a request for limiting power generation is sent to the combined dispatching system. When the remaining capacity of the energy storage battery is close to over discharging, and the combined output is still lower than the planned value of power generation, it sends the maximum working capacity of the energy storage system to the joint dispatching system, and requests the joint dispatching system to adjust the control strategy [5].

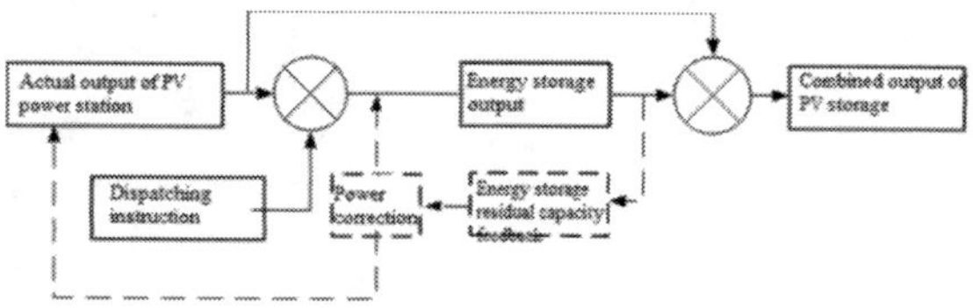

Figure 3 Control strategy for tracking planed output

2.3 Peak load balancing

New energy resources such as wind power and PV power have intermittent nature. Through the joint operation of energy storage and wind power or PV power, the electricity quantity of the new energy resources during the power-off period can be shifted in time, and the absorptive capacity of the system can be improved. When energy storage is operated in combination with wind power, energy storage absorbs the wind power output during the limited wind period and releases it during the non-limited wind power period, thus improving the profits of the joint system. The energy storage system discharges power when the wind power is lower than the power limit. At this stage, the energy storage system will be out of service after discharging the charged power, and it will not be put into use again until the upper limit of wind power output rises above the power limit again or the power limit is cancelled. When energy storage works in conjunction with PV, energy storage can store the excess power generated by PV during the day and release it to the load at night. When the energy storage is insufficient, it will supply power to the load by means of commercial power [6].

In the background of Energy Internet (EI), shared energy storage is a new-generation energy storage concept which has the advantages of wide distribution and flexible application and can effectively improve the stability characteristics of power grid and the absorptive capacity of new energy. Taking the Qinghai Shared Energy Storage project as an example, during the peak PV period from 10:00 to 16:00 on the same day, Longyuan Golmud PV Power Station and SDIC Huajing Golmud PV Power Station use the originally discarded PV power to charge the energy storage systems, reducing the discarded PV power and improving the absorptive capacity of the power systems for new energy; During the period of 19:00-21:00

https://doi.org/10.1051/e3sconf/202233801011

at night, the energy storage power stations discharge at a constant power, and the PV power stations and the energy storage power stations share the grid-connected power generation income of the energy storage power stations during this period.

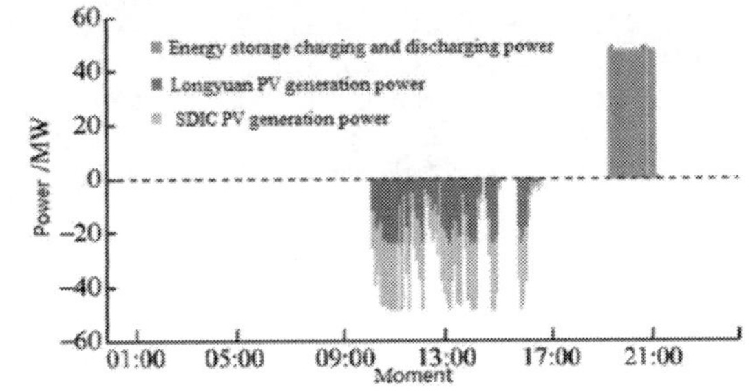

Figure 4 Charging and discharging operations of Qinghai Shared Energy Storage (a)

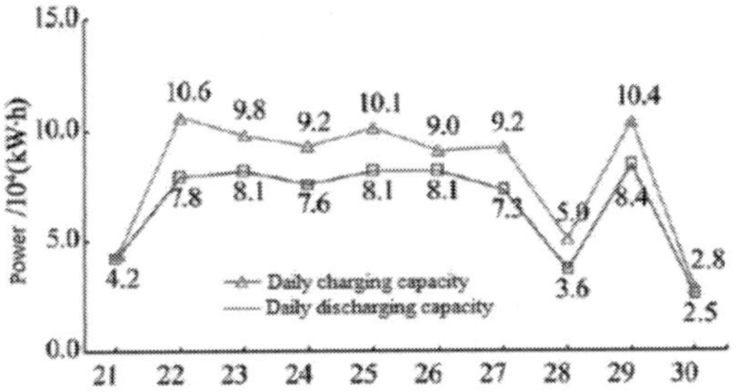

Figure 5 Charging and discharging operations of Qinghai Shared Energy Storage (b)

The principle for energy storage allocation of PV power plants is different from that of wind farms under peak load balancing, and wind power has higher requirements for energy storage capacity and duration. If a PV power station is equipped with the energy storage with 10% of its installed capacity and 4 hours of continuous discharge, the maximum PV abandonment rate can be reduced by 5%. For some wind farms that have been abandoned for a long period of time continuously, it is necessary to allocate an energy storage system with the installed capacity of about 20%, which requires higher duration of continuous discharging. If the complementary characteristics of wind power and PV power are comprehensively considered, the joint allocation of energy storage can appropriately reduce the demand for energy storage capacity [7-8].

3 Economic Analysis of "New Energy + Energy Storage"

3.1 New Energy and IES Economic Analysis software

The New Energy and IES Economic Analysis (NEIESEA) software is independently designed and developed by State Grid Energy Research Institute Co., Ltd., with completely independent intellectual property rights. The NEIESEA was designed and developed strictly in accordance with the standards of large-scale software projects, applying the object-oriented thought and the high-level language C++ to develop the core algorithms, and ensuring the encapsulation, inheritance and polymorphism of the software, and C# was used to develop the interface. The main functions of the NEIESEA include power supply (PV, wind power, natural gas, biogas, biomass), energy storage, energy network (power grid, heating network) and economic analysis of energy conversion equipment (heat pumps, electric boilers, ice storage). IES Economic Analysis; economic analysis of new energy in China. This paper uses NEIESEA software to analyze and evaluate the energy storage economy of new energy allocation [9-11].

3.2 Economic analysis of owner-built energy storage technologies

Owner-built energy storage is relatively cost effective. According to the investment cost of onshore wind power in each province in 2020 (average investment cost: RMB6,900/kW) and the benchmark power price of wind power in 2018 (connected to the grid before the end of 2020), investment cost of lithium iron phosphate battery: RMB1,900/kWh, calculated according to the assumption of being replaced twice on a 10-year and 20-year basis. If the wind farms are equipped with 10% lithium iron phosphate batteries for one hour (energy: 100 kWh), the national average internal rate of return (IRR) is 9.2%, and the IRR of projects in 21 provinces and regions including Fujian, Gansu, Liaoning, Sichuan, Jiangsu, Hubei, Tibet, Shandong, Anhui, Hunan, Heilongjiang, southern Hebei, Jiangxi, Beijing, Zhejiang, Shanxi, Tianjin, Yunnan, and Shanghai exceeds 8%. If the wind farms are equipped with 20% lithium iron phosphate batteries (energy 200) for one hour, the national average IRR is 8.6%, and the IRR of 19 provinces and regions including Fujian, Gansu, Liaoning, Sichuan, Jiangsu, Hubei, Tibet, Shandong, Anhui, Hunan, Heilongjiang, southern Hebei, Jiangxi, Beijing, Zhejiang, Shanxi, Tianjin, Yunnan, and Shanghai exceeds 8%. If the wind farms are equipped with 20% lithium iron phosphate batteries for 2 hours (10% lithium iron phosphate batteries for 4 hours) (energy 400 kWh), the national average IRR is 7.7%, and the IRR of projects in 14 provinces and regions including Fujian, Gansu, Liaoning, Sichuan, Jiangsu, Hubei, Tibet, Shandong, Anhui, Hunan, Heilongjiang, southern Hebei, Jiangxi, and Beijing still exceeds 8%. If the wind farms are equipped with 20% proportion of 4-hour lithium iron phosphate batteries (energy: 800 kWh), the national average IRR is 6.0%, and the IRR of projects in seven provinces and regions including Fujian, Liaoning, Gansu, Sichuan, Tibet, Jiangsu, and Hubei still exceeds 8%.

https://doi.org/10.1051/e3sconf/202233801011

Table 2 Economic comparison of owner-built energy storage of wind power owners

Energy storage allocation strategy			IRR	
Proportion of new energy installed capacity	Duration	Energy (1MW fan as an example)	National average	Number of provinces and regions higher than 8%
NA	NA	0	9.8%	22
10%	1 hour	100 kWh	9.2%	21
20%	1 hour	200 kWh	8.6%	19
10%	2 hours	200 kWh		
20%	2 hours	400 kWh		
10%	4 hours	400 kWh	7.7%	14
20%	4 hours	800 kWh	6.0%	7

Owner-built energy storage of PV power generation owners is less cost effective. According to the provincial centralized PV power investment cost in 2020 (average investment: RMB3,800/kW) and the benchmark PV power price in 2018, the investment cost of lithium iron phosphate battery system is 1,900 yuan/kilowatt-hour, which will be replaced twice after 10 and 20 years. If the PV power station is equipped with 10% lithium iron phosphate batteries for one hour, the national average internal rate of return is 6.6%, and the IRR of projects in Tibet, eastern Inner Mongolia, Shandong, northern Hebei, Shanxi, and Qinghai alone exceeds 8%. If the PV power station is equipped with 10% lithium iron phosphate batteries for 4 hours, the national average IRR is 4.3%, and the IRR of projects in all provinces is less than 8% [12].

Figure 3 Economic comparison of owner-built energy storage of PV power owners

Energy storage allocation strategy			IRR	
Proportion of new energy installed capacity	Duration	Energy (1MW PV as an example)	National average	Number of provinces and regions higher than 8%
NA	NA	0	7.5%	15
10%	1 hour	100 kwh	6.6%	6
20%	1 hour	200 kWh	5.7%	3
10%	4 hours	400 kWh	4.3%	0
20%	4 hours	800 kWh	2.4%	0

3.3 Economic analysis of energy storage capacity purchased by new energy owners

Purchased wind power PTES capacity is relatively cost effective. According to the investment cost of onshore wind power in each province in 2020 (average investment cost: RMB6,900/kW) and the benchmark power price of wind power in 2018 (connected to the grid before the end of 2020), the annual unit kilowatt cost for purchased pumped storage is RMB600 (energy: 6 kWh). If the wind farms buy pumped storage energy of 1.67% capacity (energy: 100 kWh), the national average IRR is 8.7%, and the IRR of projects in 17 provinces and regions including Gansu, Liaoning, Fujian, Sichuan, Jiangsu, Hubei, Shandong, Tibet, Anhui, Hunan, Heilongjiang, southern Hebei, Jiangxi, Beijing, Zhejiang, Tianjin, and Shanxi exceeds 8%. If 3.33% capacity (energy 200 kWh) pumped storage energy is purchased by wind farm, the national average IRR is 8.5%, and the IRR of projects in 16 provinces and regions including Gansu, Liaoning, Fujian, Sichuan, Jiangsu, Hubei, Shandong, Tibet, Anhui, Hunan, Heilongjiang, southern Hebei, Jiangxi, Beijing, Zhejiang, and Tianjin exceeds 8%. If the wind farm purchases 6.66% capacity (energy 400 kWh) pumped storage energy, the national average IRR is 8.2%, and the IRR of projects in 15 provinces and regions including Gansu, Liaoning, Fujian, Sichuan, Jiangsu, Hubei, Shandong, Tibet, Anhui, Hunan, Heilongjiang, southern Hebei, Jiangxi, Beijing, and Zhejiang exceeds 8%. If 13.34% capacity (energy 800 kWh) pumped storage energy is purchased by wind farm, the national average IRR is 6.9%, and the IRR of projects in 13 provinces and regions including Gansu, Liaoning, Fujian, Sichuan, Jiangsu, Hubei, Shandong, Tibet, Anhui, Hunan, Heilongjiang, southern Hebei, and Jiangxi still exceeds 8%.

Figure 4 Economic comparison of purchased energy storage by wind power owners

Energy storage allocation strategy		IRR	
Proportion of new energy installed capacity	Energy (1MW fan as an example)	National average	Number of provinces and regions higher than 8%
1.67%	100 kwh	8.7%	17
3.33%	200 kWh	8.6%	16
6.67%	400 kWh	8.2%	15
13.34%	800 kWh	7.4%	13

It is not economical to purchase PV PHES capacity. According to the provincial centralized PV power investment cost in 2020 (average investment cost: RMB3,800/kW) and the benchmark PV power price in 2018, if PV power stations purchase 10% capacity pumped storage energy storage, the national average IRR is 4.3%, and the IRR of each provincial project does not exceed 8%.

Figure 5 Economic comparison of purchased energy storage by PV owners

Energy storage allocation strategy		IRR	
Proportion of new energy installed capacity	Energy (1MW PV as an example)	National average	Number of provinces and regions higher than 8%
1.67%	100 kwh	5.6%	four
3.33%	200 kWh	5.3%	three
6.67%	400 kWh	4.9%	0
13.34%	800 kWh	4.3%	0

https://doi.org/10.1051/e3sconf/202233801011

It is therefore evident that self-construction and allocation of PTES for wind power owners are economically viable. Under the same energy storage conditions, it is economical for wind power owners to purchase PTES services than building EES batteries by themselves. Owner-built and owner-allocated PTES is not profitable and sustainable. Under the same energy storage condition, when the allocated energy of 1MW PV power generation is less than 200 kW, EES is relatively more economical than PTES.

4 Conclusion

The continuous development of energy storage technology and cost reduction drive growth of energy storage development in scale. Energy storage has diversified development trends in the fields of power grid side, power supply side, user side, power market and so on. This paper first studies the typical operation modes of energy storage applied to new energy consumption scenarios and analyzes three important technical approaches to promote new energy consumption, such as energy storage to stabilize fluctuation, tracking output and peak load balancing. Second, by using the self-developed software for economic analysis of new energy and comprehensive energy system, the economic benefits of energy storage allocation in new energy projects in different regions of China are analyzed, and the strategic suggestions for energy storage allocation in different regions are put forward. The results show that it is economical for wind power owners to build and Pumped Themes Energy Storage (PTES), and it is more economical to purchase PTES by wind power owners than to build electrochemical energy storage (EES) batteries by users under the same conditions of energy storage. Owner-built and owner-allocated PTES is less business viable. Under the same energy storage condition, when the allocated energy of 1MW PV power generation is less than 200 kW, EES is relatively more economical than PTES

Acknowledgments

This work was financially supported by the Pre-project of State Grid Corporation of China "Research on key issues of new energy development and consumption"

References

1. Xu Shouping, Li Xiangjun, Hui Dong. Overview of development status and demonstration application of large-scale electrochemical energy storage systems [J]. Electric Power Construction, 2013(7):8.
2. XU Shouping, LI Xiangjun, Hui Dong. Overview of development status and demonstration application of large-scale electrochemical energy storage system [J]. Electric Power Construction, 2013.
3. Mu Kai, Zha Hao, Liu Jia, et al. Research on comprehensive technical measures to promote large-scale new energy consumption [J]. Energy of China, 2017, 39(8):5.
4. Yang Junfeng, Zheng Xiaoyu, Hui Dong, et al. Capacity demand analysis of energy storage technology to promote the consumption of new energy in transmission-side power grid [J]. Energy Storage Science and Technology, 2018, v.7; No.36(04):158-164.
5. Hu Yang, Ma Xiyuan, Lei Bo, et al. Feasibility study on energy storage to promote new energy consumption in areas of China Southern Power Grid [J]. Southern Power System Technology, 2018, 12(9):9.
6. Sun Jie, Kang Yiran, Han Yongqiang, Zhang Xiulu, Jin Hongyang. Coordinated optimization models of grid energy storage in regional multi-energy systems considering new energy consumption [J]. Renewable Energy Resources, 2020, 38(11):6.
7. Bing Wang, Wang Nan, Li Na, et al. Study on the industrial policies of electrochemical energy storage for large-scale new energy grids [J]. Electrical & Energy Management Technology, 2021(4):6.
8. Sun Fengjie, Ma Jing, Xu Jiayin, et al. Economy of battery energy storage systems with different investors [J]. Battery Bimonthly, 2018, 48(2):5.
9. Wang Jiali. "Sword of Damocles" of new energy distribution and energy storage [J]. Energy, 2020(7):5.
10. Wang Jiali. Exploring new energy distribution and energy storage business model [J]. Energy, 2020(7):2.
11. Chen Minxi. Side A and side B of "new energy distribution and energy storage" [J]. China Power Enterprise Management, 2020(19):6.
12. Fan Baoji. Technical and economic analysis of China's new energy storage battery industry [D]. Journal of Jilin University, 2010.

E3S Web of Conferences 338, 01012 (2022)
ESMA 2021
https://doi.org/10.1051/e3sconf/202233801012

Fast prediction method of tight gas production based on segmented decline

Zhiqiang Fan [1], Kaifeng Wen [1], Tao Zhang [1], Tingting Jiang [1], Xiaoke Gong [1], Min Jing [2,*]

[1] The Research Center of Sulige Gas-field, Changqing Oilfield Company, CNPC, Xi'an, China
[2] College of energy, Chengdu University of science and technology, Chengdu, Sichuan, China

Abstract. The physical properties of tight gas reservoirs are poor. During the stable production period of gas wells, most of the recoverable reserves are produced in the declining stage. It is of great significance to accurately study the declining law of tight gas. However, tight gas production declines rapidly in the early stage and slower in the middle and late stages, and the single model fitting and prediction results have large errors. In view of the above problems, according to the production change characteristics of tight gas wells, the decline stage is divided into three stages, and a segmented production decline law analysis method is established. The research results show that the early production decline of tight gas wells is exponential decline, the relatively slow middle-term production decline belongs to depletion decline, and the late production decline belongs to linear decline. Based on the study of the law of production decline, a gas reservoir production prediction software was compiled, and the production variation characteristics of single wells and gas reservoirs under certain stable production requirements were studied.

1. Preface

Tight gas is one of the world's three largest unconventional natural gas resources, and it occupies an important position in the supply of natural gas energy. Due to the poor physical properties of tight gas reservoirs, the gas well enters a long decline production stage after a short stable production period. Most of the production of tight gas is produced in the decline phase. Research on the law of tight gas production decline is of great significance to the reasonable prediction of gas well production variation characteristics, EUR and the formulation of a reasonable development system.

The production decline period of tight gas wells has the characteristics of rapid decline in the early stage and slow decline in the middle and late stages. It is difficult to reasonably study the characteristics of gas well production changes using a single model. In response to the above problems, according to the tight gas production change characteristics, the tight gas decline stage is divided into three stages, and the segmented decline law analysis method is used to carry out the production decline research. Through example gas wells, the production variation characteristics of tight gas wells in different production stages are analyzed. Based on the production variation characteristics of tight gas, production prediction software is compiled to predict the production of tight gas reservoirs.

2. Variation characteristics of tight gas single well production

The production changes of gas wells during the production process show obvious two-stage characteristics. The early pressure drop is fast. This stage is in the early stage of instability, mainly based on the linear flow of fracturing fractures, and the pressure drop rate is large; the second stage is the natural continuous production stage, the pressure drop rate remains stable, the production decline is slow, and the gas well production begins to reach the level of reserves production.

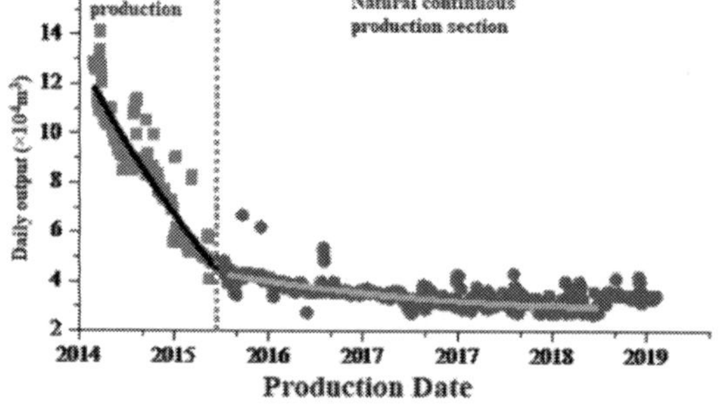

Figure 1. Division of production stages of tight gas wells

From the fitting results of actual production data of Well A (Figure 1), the three traditional decline models cannot

* Corresponding author: 2020050162@stu.cdut.edu.cn

fit well the production history of Well A, and the predicted annual gas production in the later stage of production is consistent with the actual value. Inconsistent, the annual gas production predicted by different declining methods is higher or lower.

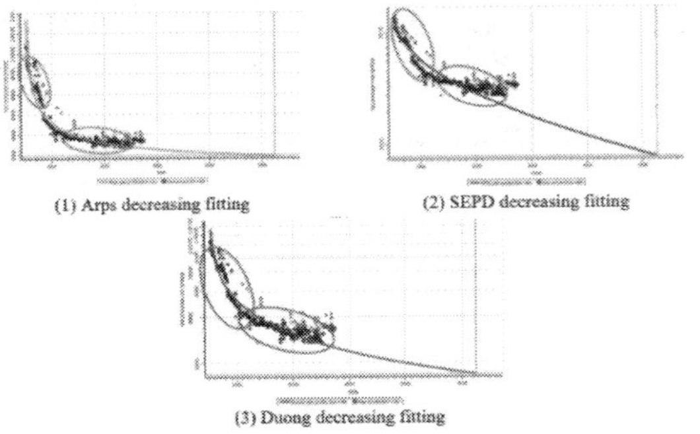

Figure 2. Fitting effects of different decreasing methods

It is imperative to carry out research on the law of stepwise decline in tight gas wells to reasonably predict the production of gas wells.

3. Stepwise decline model for tight gas wells

According to the seepage characteristics of tight gas wells and the production characteristics of gas wells, the life cycle of gas wells is divided into three stages: early stage, middle stage and late stage. In the first two stages, gas wells produced more than 80% of cumulative gas production. During the production process of gas wells, the first two stages of gas well management were emphasized, as shown in Figure 3. The staged evaluation of the decline rate change characteristics is a major feature of tight gas well production.

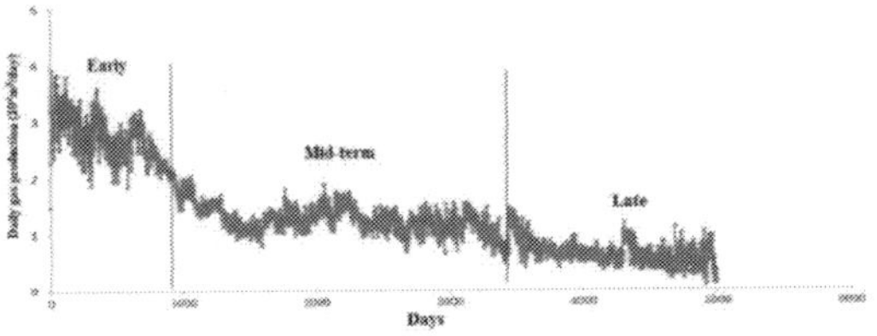

Figure 3. Schematic diagram of gas well life cycle division

In the early stage of production of tight gas wells, the production declines quickly, and the production time is 1-3 years. The initial production of gas wells is relatively high, the production declines quickly, and the decline rate is large. After multiple decline models are fitted, the early production meets the exponential decline model, but if the entire stage All using the exponential decline model, the later stage output of the model is much lower than the time output, which does not meet the characteristics of tight gas production, as shown in Figure 4.

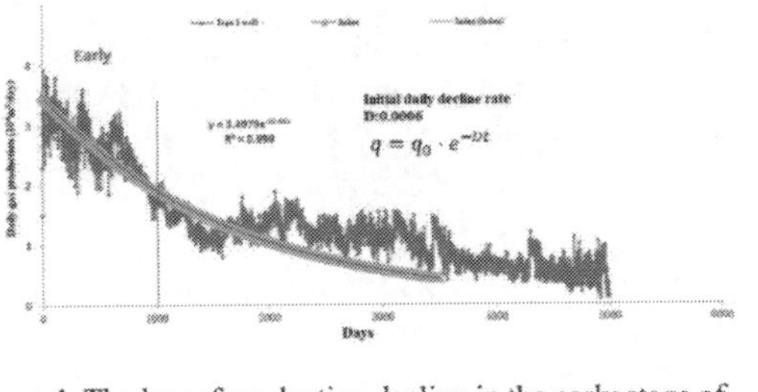

Figure 4. The law of production decline in the early stage of tight gas wells

After the gas well enters the mid-term, the decline rate slows down, the production lasts 4-10 years, and the relatively stable production phase begins for a long time, and the production pressure declines slowly. At this time, the decline rate change law conforms to the exhaustion decline, as shown in Figure 5.

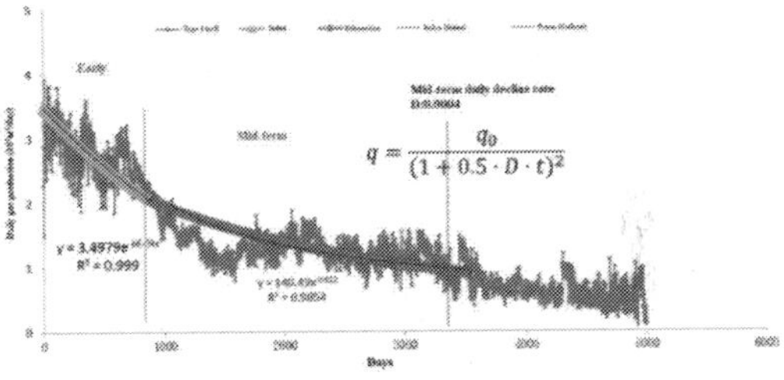

Figure 5. The law of mid-term production decline of tight gas wells

After the gas well enters the late stage, tight gas wells need indirect separation system or drainage gas recovery to obtain better productivity. The rate of gas well opening is less than 50%. If the early and mid-term decline model is used, the fitted production rate is higher than the actual gas production rate. . After analysis, it is recommended to use the change of annual gas production over time to evaluate the later decline rate, as shown in Figure 6. The prediction results show that the late decline law of tight gas wells conforms to the characteristics of the linear decline model.

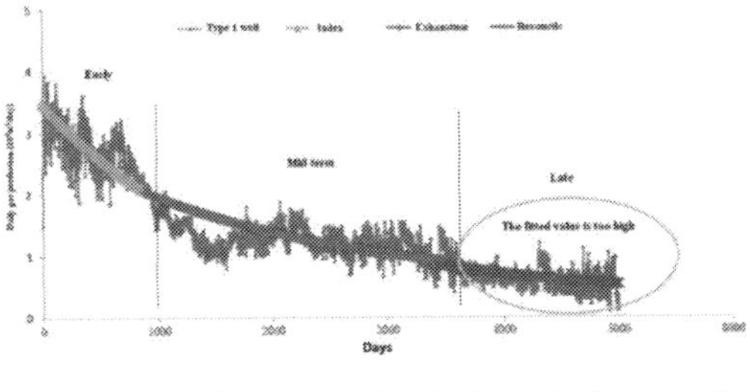

Figure 6. The law of late production decline of tight gas wells

4. Compilation of tight gas reservoir production prediction software

The production stability of tight gas wells is poor, so the mode of supplementing new wells is often used in the development of tight gas reservoirs to ensure that the gas reservoirs can produce stable gas production at a certain

 https://doi.org/10.1051/e3sconf/202233801012

scale. Therefore, on the basis of the study of tight gas well production decline law, the production forecasting software was compiled using VBA program to carry out the production forecasting work of a tight gas reservoir in China. The tight gas production forecast process is as follows:

1) Determine the number of development wells based on parameters such as geological reserves, gas-bearing area, reasonable well spacing, and production indicators;

2) Comply with the top-valley-bottom peak "bright spot" model of high-quality reservoir seismic response mode, and determine high-quality reservoir targets based on the strong peak reflection mode, deploy horizontal wells, and the horizontal section is perpendicular to the maximum horizontal principal stress direction, which is beneficial to the reservoir Transformation;

3) Determine the number of replacement wells for annual gas production based on the decline in gas wells and the production value of a single well;

4) Finally, according to the number of deployed wells, the gas field gas production change characteristics, cumulative gas production and production degree and other characteristic parameters are determined, and the block development potential prediction and development index prediction work are carried out.

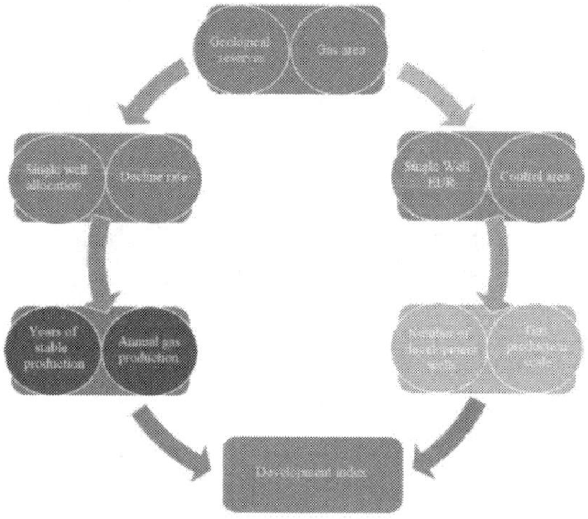

Figure 7. Key indicators deployment ideas

Enter the target scale, single well production allocation, single well stable production period, abandoned production, production start time, production end time, predicted age, gas-bearing area, single well control area, well construction rate, geological reserves and drilling in the software Number and other parameters. The gas production changes of a single well are calculated separately as shown in Figure 8.

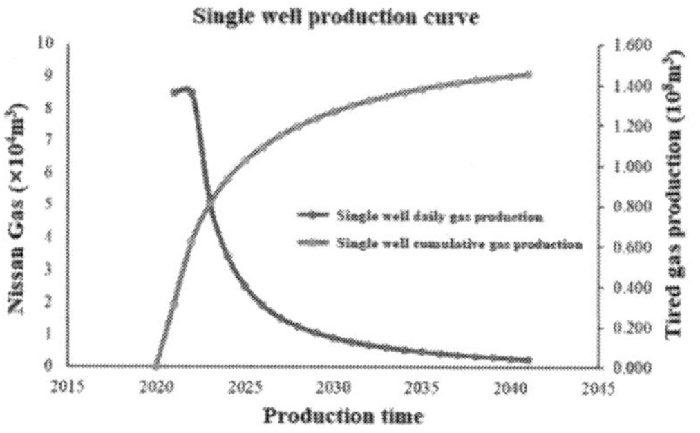

Figure 8. Predicted production curve

The tight gas reservoir has been producing stable production for 10 years with an annual output of 2.5 billion cubic meters. The gas production volume of the gas reservoir over the years and the production contribution of different types of gas wells are shown in Figure 9.

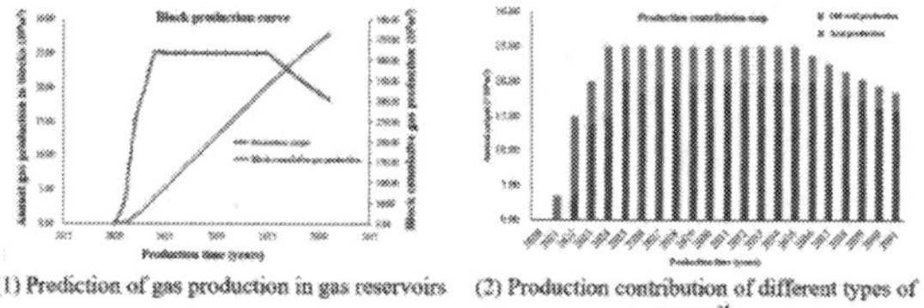

(1) Prediction of gas production in gas reservoirs (2) Production contribution of different types of gas wells

Figure 9. Block production and production contribution characteristics of different gas wells

Due to the rapid decline in production of tight gas wells, the decline rate of gas reservoirs is higher after the 10-year stable production period. In the process of gas reservoir development, with the increase in the number of wells, the contribution of old wells to gas reservoir production continues to increase.

5. Conclusion

(1) The production change of tight gas wells presents multi-stage characteristics, with rapid production decline in the early stage and slower production decline in the middle and late stages. The use of a single decline model to analyze the law of production decline has large errors.

(2) According to the production characteristics of tight gas wells, the production decline of tight gas wells is divided into three stages. The ARPS decline method can be used for fitting to better analyze the production decline characteristics of tight gas wells. The early decline of gas wells conforms to the exponential law, and the medium-term production decline conforms to failure. Decrease model, the law of late decline conforms to the linear decline model.

(3) According to the tight gas decline characteristics, the tight gas reservoir production prediction software was compiled using VBA, and the production change characteristics of a single well and the entire gas reservoir were predicted.

References

1. Chen Yuanqian, Fu Libing, Xu Jiaqian. Application and comparison of two types of production decline models in the prediction of shale gas wells and tight gas wells[J/OL]. Petroleum Geology and Recovery Efficiency: 1-6 [2021-11-23] .http://kns.cnki.net/ kcms/ detail/ 37.1359. TE. 20201210. 1720.002.html.
2. Chen Yuanqian, Fu Libing, Xu Jiaqian. Application and comparison of two types of production decline models in the prediction of shale gas wells and tight gas wells[J]. Petroleum Geology and Recovery Efficiency, 2021, 28(03): 84-89.
3. Li Yanzun, Bai Yuhu, Xu Bingxiang, Chen Ling, Dong Zhiqiang. The application of NARX neural network in the production performance prediction of tight gas wells [A]. Xi'an Shiyou University, Chengdu University of Technology, Shaanxi Petroleum Institute. 2020 Oil and Gas Field Exploration and Proceedings of Development International Conference[C]. Xi'an Shiyou University, Chengdu University of Technology, Shaanxi Petroleum Society: Xi'an Shiyou University, 2020: 8.
4. Wang Xilin. Research on productivity prediction of fractured horizontal wells in anisotropic tight gas reservoirs[D]. China University of Geosciences (Beijing), 2020.
5. Liang Yiwei, Wang Dong, Li Tingjun, Du Chao. Variation characteristics of Arps production decline index for tight gas wells[J]. Journal of Xi'an Shiyou University (Natural Science Edition), 2018, 33(02): 77-81.
6. Wei Yunsheng, Jia Ailin, He Dongbo, Wang Junlei, Han Pinlong, Jin Yiqiu. Development characteristics and development technology similarities and differences between shale gas and tight gas in China[J]. Natural Gas Industry, 2017, 37(11): 43-52.
7. Yang Zhen, Kong Lingfeng, Du Min, Zhao Chenhui. Economic evaluation of domestic tight sandstone gas development projects and fiscal and taxation support policy research[J]. Natural Gas Industry, 2016, 36(07): 98-109.
8. Wang Cai. Research on productivity calculation method for fractured gas wells in tight gas reservoirs[D]. China University of Geosciences (Beijing), 2016.
9. Hu Junkun, Gong Wei, Ren Ke. Analysis of key factors and countermeasures for China's tight gas development[J]. Natural Gas Technology and Economy, 2015, 9(06): 24-29+82.
10. Li Chen, Xia Chaohui, Wang Ping, Zhao Yixuan, Zhang Hongyan. Application of average decline index in tight gas reserve evaluation[J]. Special Oil and Gas Reservoirs, 2015, 22(02): 105-107+156.
11. Wang Xin, Qi Mei, Hu Yongle. Application of average model in production prediction of tight gas wells[J]. Science Technology and Engineering, 2015, 15(07): 173-176+180.
12. Gu Ning, Zhu Xueqian, Xing Liwen. Analysis of calculation methods for unconventional gas reserves[J]. Natural Gas and Petroleum, 2014, 32(06): 45-49+11.
13. Li Jiangfei, Fu Zhizhong, Zhang Huanzhi, Li Bo. Tight gas development and production prediction based on technological progress and engineering economic models [A]. Xi'an Shiyou University, Shaanxi Petroleum Institute, Xi'an Petroleum Service Industry Alliance. 2013 Oil and Gas Reservoir Monitoring And Management International Conference and Exhibition Proceedings[C]. Xi'an Shiyou University, Shaanxi Petroleum Institute, Xi'an Petroleum Service Industry Alliance: Xi'an Huaxian Network Information Service Co., Ltd., 2013: 7.
14. Qiu Zhongjian, Zhao Wenzhi, Deng Songtao. Development prospects and strategic significance of tight sandstone gas and shale gas in China[J]. China Engineering Science, 2012, 14(06): 4-8+113.
15. Yang Tao, Zhang Guosheng, Liang Kun, Zheng Min, Guo Bincheng. Global tight gas exploration and development progress and China's development trend forecast [J]. Chinese Engineering Science, 2012, 14(06): 64-68+76.

Simulation and analysis of force on connection of casing thread under alternating load of gas storage

Hanhua Song [1], Wei Tian [1], Chen Li [1], Zaishun Li [1], Lianlian Fan [1], Jian Lu [2] and Yufeng Gong [3,*]

[1] Oil and Gas Technology Research Institute of Changqing Oilfield Company
[2] Changqing Oilfield Company gas Field Development Division
[3] School of Energy, Chengdu University of Technology, Chengdu, China

Abstract. Underground gas storage as the main system of natural gas peak regulation, its construction demand continues to grow in the world. Different from other common oil and gas well strings, the service time of the gas storage string is longer and the service environment is worse, which poses a greater challenge to the integrity design of the string joint. In this paper, starting from the most important connection and sealing performance of the pipe string joint, aiming at the special threaded joint suitable for the gas storage pipe string, based on the analysis of the force and deformation of the gas storage pipe string, the joint connection strength and sealing performance of the pipe string joint under the axial load, internal and external pressure and long-term alternating load are considered. Based on the FINITE element model of VAM TOP special threaded joint, the deformation and sealing behavior of the joint under different composite loads were numerically simulated, and the variation law of joint connection stress and sealing contact pressure with load was obtained, and the most vulnerable failure position and the most dangerous working condition were analyzed.

1. Introduction

With the continuous growth of the demand for natural gas, the phenomenon of insufficient natural gas supply often occurs. In order to adjust the balance of natural gas supply and demand, it is necessary to use natural gas reserve system. At present, underground gas storage has become the most important way of natural gas storage and peak regulation in the world because of its advantages of high safety factor and large storage capacity [1-5]. Different from the common oil and gas well pipe string, the underground gas storage pipe string has been in service for more than 30 years, and the service environment is very bad. The alternating load caused by the long-term gas injection and production process poses a severe challenge to the design of pipe string, especially the design of pipe string joint. As the most critical part of the whole string, the joint of the string is also the weakest link, which can easily cause gas leakage due to failure [6-8].

There are two main reasons for the failure of underground gas storage pipe string joint: connection failure and sealing failure. Connection failure mainly includes the following forms :(1) trip failure (2) fracture failure (3) shear failure (4) over torsion failure. Seal failure refers to the gas leakage phenomenon of threaded joint due to various reasons such as machining accuracy, operation mode and working condition. In view of the above failures, it is necessary to study the connection and sealing integrity of threaded joint in order to maintain the operation safety of gas well in gas storage. The research methods of mechanical properties of threaded joints mainly include analytic method, full-size test method and finite element method.

2. Theoretical Basis

(1) Axial force calculation

In the early stage of production, the injection-production string is set inside the production tubing by a packer, and changes in the external extrusion pressure and internal pressure can be translated into axial force by the bulging effect or the piston effect. In the production process, the internal pressure in the string fluctuates and alternates with the frequent alternation of injection-production cycle, resulting in the change of external extrusion pressure and axial force. During gas injection and recovery, the formation volume expands or compacts the string in an axial direction. At the same time, the inner diameter of the pipe string varies, and the temperature, density, and flow rate of the pipe string fluctuate, which will impose additional axial load on the pipe string.

Therefore, the axial force of the gas storage pipe string is the sum of the superimposed axial force caused by dead weight, temperature effect, expanding diameter effect and ground stress during gas injection and production.

The axial tension generated by the dead weight of the tube body can be calculated by:

$$G = \rho_1 g(L - z) \qquad (1)$$

* Corresponding author: gongyufeng1995@stu.cdut.edu.cn

Where, ρl is the oil pipeline density, kg/m, L is the tubing length, m, z is the calculation point depth, m.

(2) Calculation of internal pressure strength

The internal compression strength of pipe string under combined load can be obtained by standard SY/T5322-2000:

$$p_{c_a} = p_{bo}\left[\frac{r_i^2}{\sqrt{3r_o^4+r_i^4}}\left(\frac{\sigma_a+p_0}{Y_p}\right)+\sqrt{1-\frac{3r_o^4}{3r_o^4+r_i^4}\left(\frac{\sigma_a+p_0}{Y_p}\right)^2}\right] \quad (2)$$

(3) Calculation of tensile strength

The gas storage pipe string still complies with the fourth strength criterion under the combined action of internal pressure, non-uniform external load and axial force, so the tensile strength of the pipe string under combined load is:

$$T_a = 10^{-3}\pi\left(P_i r_i^2 - P_0 r_0^2\right)+\sqrt{T_0^2+3\times10^{-6}\pi^2\left(P_i-P_0\right)^2 r_0^4} \quad (3)$$

Ta -- Triaxial tensile strength of pipe body, KN;
Pi -- Equivalent external pressure of tubing, MPa,
Po -- Tubing internal pressure, MPa,
Ri -- Tubing radius, cm;
Ro -- Outer tubing radius, cm.

(4) Calculation of compressive strength

Equivalent yield strength under axial force can be calculated by the following formula:

$$Y_{pa} = \left[\sqrt{1-0.75\left(\sigma_a / Y_p\right)^2}-0.5\left(\sigma_a / Y_p\right)\right]Y_{c_a} \quad (4)$$

Ypa -- Collapse pressure under axial tensile stress, MPa;
Yca -- Uniaxial collapse pressure, MPa;
σ a -- Axial stress, MPa;
Yp -- Pipe body yield strength, MPa.

Because of the working condition of gas storage, it is easy to collapse under combined load. Then the compressive strength of tubing under combined load is:

$$P_{ca} = P_{co}\left\{\left[1-\frac{3}{4}\left(\frac{\sigma_a+P_i}{Y_p}\right)^{0.5}-\frac{\sigma_a+P_i}{2Y_p}\right]\right\} \quad (5)$$

During gas recovery, axial pressure will be exerted on the tubing due to the decline of the inner layer of the well. At this time, the tubing compressive strength is:

$$P_{ca} = P_{co}\left\{\left[1-\frac{3}{4}\left(\frac{\sigma_a+P_i}{Y_p}\right)^{0.5}+\frac{\sigma_a+P_i}{2Y_p}\right]\right\} \quad (6)$$

3. Modeling process

The working environment of tubing is bad and the alternating load is large. Because the joint part itself is relatively weak, coupled with its sectional shape change, there is a high alternating stress, stress concentration is serious, is the most dangerous part of the force. The model established in this paper is shown in Figure 1 and Figure 2. V-038r, taper 1:4, elastic modulus E = 200GPa, Poisson's ratio = 0.3, density 7850kg/m3.

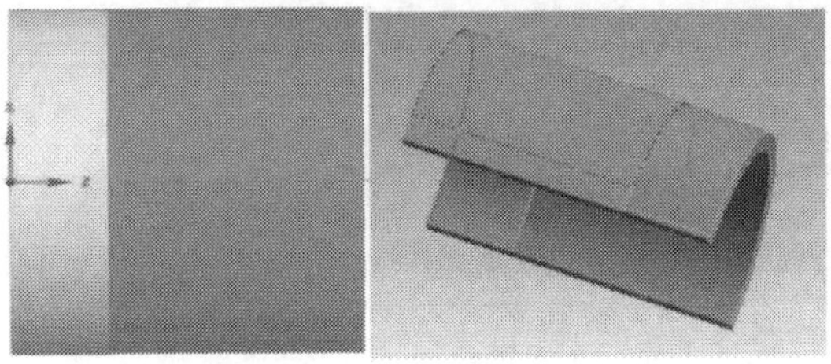

Figure 1. Model of thread connection

Set contact surface: Friction contact is used for the two geometers. There are 239320 nodes and 132,494 cells in the volume and contact grids.

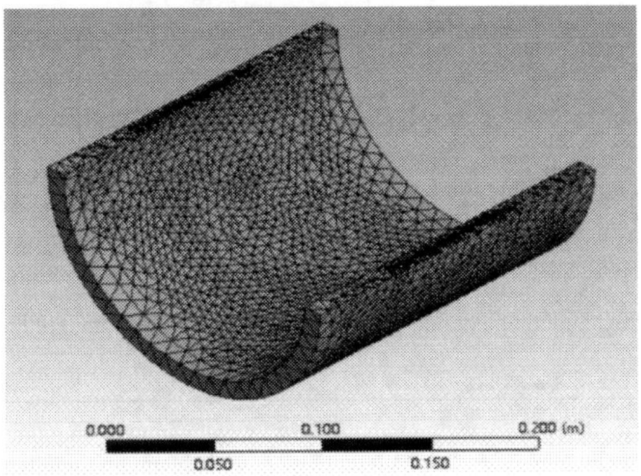

Figure 2. Meshing result diagram

Load added: The external extrusion force of the pipe string is 25MPa, the internal pressure is respectively set as 20/15/10mpa (pressure in different injection and production processes), and the axial tension is set as 10/20/30/40/50mpa (simulated axial loads are 99KN, 198KN, 297KN, 396KN and 495KN).

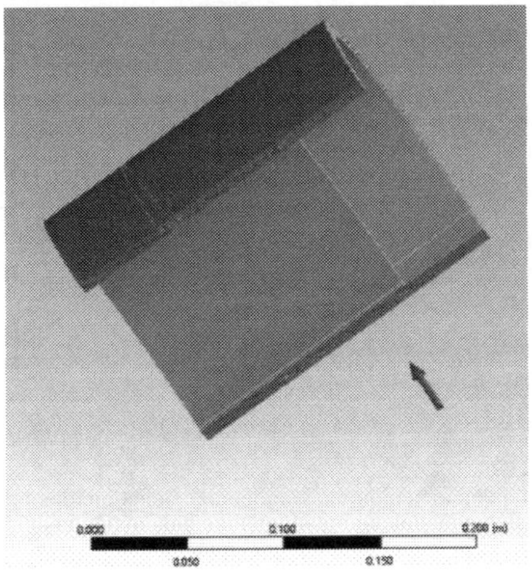

Figure 3. Schematic diagram of load loading

 https://doi.org/10.1051/e3sconf/202233801013

4. Discussion

Stress concentration occurs at the last thread of female thread, the maximum deformation is 3.0mm, the maximum equivalent stress is 584.8mpa, the contact compressive stress is very large, there is a risk of fatigue damage.

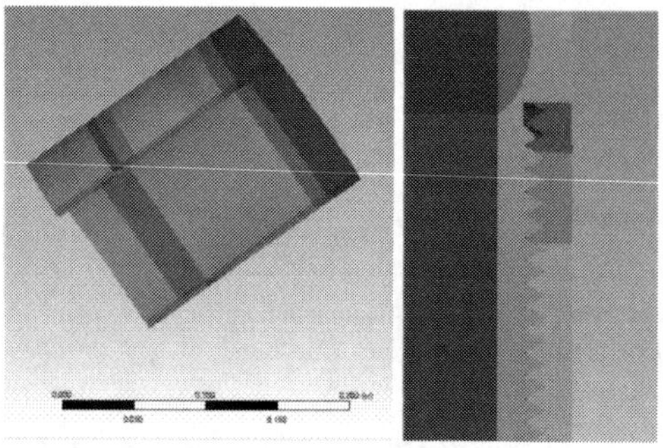

Figure 4. Stress analysis of thread connection

The stress concentration occurs at the last thread of female thread, the maximum deformation is 2.9mm, the maximum equivalent stress is 565.8MPa, the maximum deformation increases, but the maximum equivalent stress decreases.

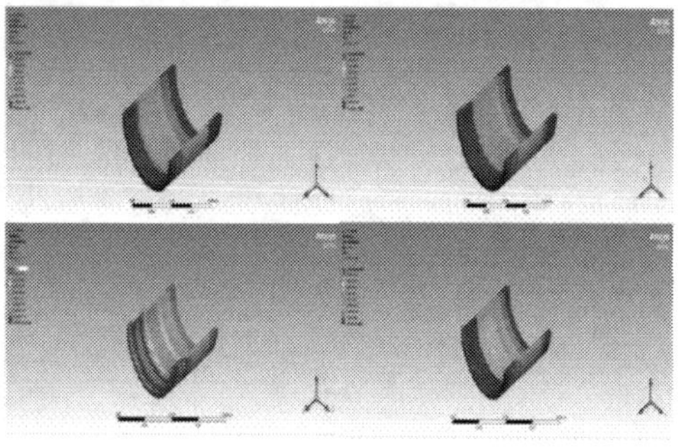

Figure 5. Strength analysis under different internal pressures (external pressure =30MPa, axial pressure =30MPa)

Under different internal compressive strength, the maximum strain is 3.41mm, the minimum strain is 2.51mm, the maximum stress is 668.62MPa, and the minimum stress is 488.23MPa.

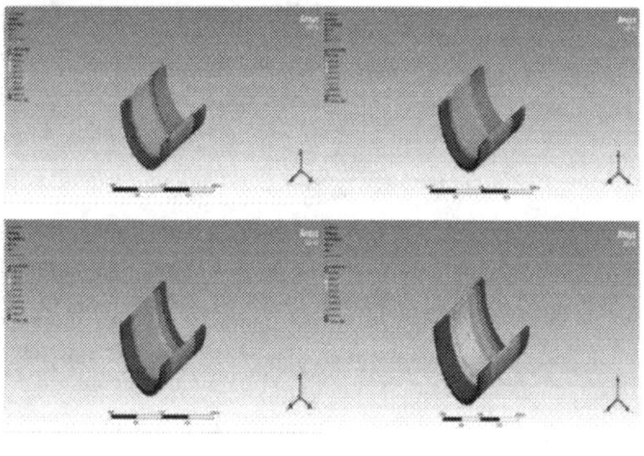

Figure 6. Strength analysis under different internal pressures (external pressure =30MPa, axial pressure =30MPa)

The maximum equivalent stress of 666.8mpa exceeds the thread connection limit stress, and the thread fatigue failure occurs.Two-dimensional binomial fitting was carried out, the fitting error R2=0.9947, and the fitting effect was relatively good.

$$P(Pout,Pin) = -403.2 + 44.89*Pout + 18.86*Pin -0.3409\ Pout2 -0.5999\ Pout * Pin$$

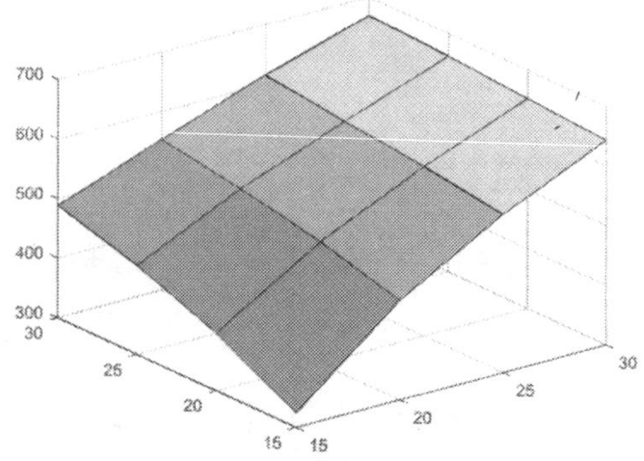

Figure 7. Schematic diagram of fitting 3D results

5. Conclusion

(1) Under the same external pressure, with the increase of internal pressure, the maximum strain increases gradually, the maximum stress increases gradually, and the limit life decreases.
(2) The thread connection needs to be considered, the lower part needs to check the compressive strength and extrusion strength. The upper part needs to be checked for axial tension.

References

1. Reitenbach, Viktor, et al. "Influence of added hydrogen on underground gas storage: a review of key issues."Environmental Earth Sciences. 73.11 (2015): 6927-6937.
2. Mazarei, Mehdi, et al. "The feasibility analysis of underground gas storage during an integration of improved condensate recovery processes."Journal of Petroleum Exploration and Production Technology. 9.1 (2019): 397-408.
3. ZHENG, Dewen, et al. "Key evaluation techniques in the process of gas reservoir being converted into underground gas storage."Petroleum Exploration and Development. 44.5 (2017): 840-849.
4. Davarpanah, Afshin, Mehdi Mazarei, and Behnam Mirshekari. "A simulation study to enhance the gas production rate by nitrogen replacement in the underground gas storage performance."Energy Reports. 5 (2019): 431-435.
5. Wang, Tongtao, et al. "Determination of the maximum allowable gas pressure for an underground gas storage salt cavern–A case study of Jintan,

China." Journal of Rock Mechanics and Geotechnical Engineering. 11.2 (2019): 251-262.

6. Liu, Jun, et al. "Nonlinear flow-induced vibration response characteristics of leaching tubing in salt cavern underground gas storage." Journal of Energy Storage. 41 (2021): 102909.
7. Wang, Tongtao, et al. "Safe distance between debrining tubing inlet and sediment in a gas storage salt cavern."Journal of Petroleum Science and Engineering. 196 (2021): 107707.
8. Bai, Mingxing, et al. "Well completion issues for underground gas storage in oil and gas reservoirs in China."Journal of Petroleum Science and Engineering. 171 (2018): 584-591.

Research on stimulation of injection and production capacity for single well in underground gas storage

Chen Li [1], Xiaoyong Wen [1], Zhihao Shen [1], Li Li [1], Peng Liu [2] and Hu Peng [3,*]

[1] Oil and Gas Technology Research Institute of Changqing Oilfield Company, China
[2] The Second Gas Production Plant of Changqing Oilfield Company, China
[3] School of Chengdu University of Technology, Chengdu, China

Abstract. Underground gas storage is the best choice for natural gas resource reserve and peak value. Storage capacity of underground gas storage and single well injection and production capacity are the key indicators of shaving capacity. This paper focuses on research of expansion of gas storage and the stimulation of injection and production capacity of single well of a basin in Western China. Firstly, based on the study of two-phase seepage law of gas and water, a numerical simulation model coupling high velocity non-Darcy effect and gas-water two phase seepage is established; Secondly, the influencing factors of single well injection and production capacity are analysed. Finally, acidizing can effectively improve the single well injection and production capacity of well. The numerical simulation result shows that the injection and production differential pressure is reduced by 70%, and gas injection and production volume are increased by 14.8% and 26.9%.

Key words: underground gas storage; seepage model; high velocity non-Darcy; numerical simulation.

1. Introduction

As a clean energy, natural gas is seriously uneven in distribution, and is easily affected by climatic conditions, civil consumption and other factors. Underground gas storage is the efficient measurement choice for natural gas resource reserve and peak value. Underground gas storage can be divided three types: depleted oil and gas fields, water bearing structures and salt caves. Underground gas storage can solve the problem of uneven urban gas consumption, which plays a important role for seasonal peak shaving. The capacity, safety and economy of underground gas storage are better than those of ground metal gas storage tanks.

Storage capacity is the gas volume corresponding to the movable gas of formation affected by pressure in the process of high-velocity injection and production. Storage capacity, single well injection and production capacity are key indicators of shaving. Improving the injection and production capacity of single well is an efficient measure for expansion of gas storage capacity. This paper focuses on the measures to improve the injection and production capacity of a single well in an underground gas reservoir reconstructed from a depleted gas reservoir in a basin in Western China. Firstly, numerical simulation model of single well in the basis of gas-water two-phase seepage is established. Secondly, the key factors affecting the injection and production capacity of a single well are analysed. The result of numerical stimulation shows that acidizing can effectively improve the injection and production capacity of a single well.

2. Numerical simulation model of single well

2.1 Physical model

A underground gas storage in western China is reconstructed from depleted gas reservoir, its lithology belongs to tight sandstone, and the micro fractures in the reservoir are not developed. In the process of gas reservoir injection and production, especially during gas supplying in winter, the influence of high velocity non-Darcy effect on gas seepage can not be ignored. When considering the high velocity non-Darcy effect and gas-water two-phase flow, the assumptions of the physical model of gas transport in reservoir are as follows:

(1) There are only two kinds of fluids in gas reservoir, natural gas and water, and the gas phase is insoluble in water phase;

(2) The compressibility coefficient of slightly compressible rock and water are constant, and gas is easily compressible;

(3) The effects of capillary force and gravity of two-phase are considered in the matrix system;

* Corresponding author: 201704010309@stu.cdut.edu.cn

 https://doi.org/10.1051/e3sconf/202233801014

(4) The influence of high velocity non-Darcy effect is considered in gas flow, and the water phase is Darcy seepage.

2.2 Mathematical model

(1) Seepage control equation

Based on the principle of mass conservation, the continuity equation of gas-water two-phase flow can be described as follow:

$$-\nabla\cdot\left(\rho_g v_g\right)+\delta_g q_g=\frac{\partial\left(\varphi\rho_g S_g\right)}{\partial\tau} \tag{1}$$

$$-\nabla\cdot\left(\rho_w v_w\right)+\delta_w q_w=\frac{\partial\left(\varphi\rho_w S_w\right)}{\partial\tau} \tag{2}$$

Where, φ is porosity, %; ρ_g, ρ_w are density of gas and water in reservoir pressure condition, kg/m^3; v_g and v_w are seepage velocity, m/s; s_g is gas saturation, %; s_w is water saturation; q_g and q_w are injection and production volume in micro element, injection is positive and recovery is negative (kg / (m^3·s)); δg and δw are well point function, at the well point δ=1, and at non well point, δg=0.

The influence of high velocity non-Darcy effect on gas transport in porous medias can't be ignored, in the process of gas injection and production of underground gas storage. According to Forchheimer equation, the expression of gas motion equation considering the influence of high velocity non-Darcy effect is shown as follows:

$$\nabla p=\frac{\mu_g}{K_g}\vec{v}_g+\beta\rho\vec{v}_g^{\,2} \tag{3}$$

In order to describe high velocity nonlinear seepage in porous medias, turbulence factor ξ is introduced in the motion equation. The expression of turbulence factor is as follows:

$$\xi=\frac{1}{1+\beta\rho\vec{v}_g K_g/\mu_g} \tag{4}$$

The following empirical formula of non-Darcy coefficient for multiphase flow β can be described as follow:

$$\beta=\frac{6.92\times10^{10}}{\left(KK_{rg}\right)^{0.5}\left[\phi\left(1-S_w\right)\right]^{1.5}} \tag{5}$$

Therefore, the motion equation of gas considering only considering the influence of high velocity non-Darcy can be rewritten as:

$$\vec{v}_g=-\frac{K_g\xi}{\mu_g}\nabla p \tag{6}$$

Then the governing equations of gas-water two-phase transport in the rock of underground gas storage are shown as:

$$\begin{cases}\nabla\cdot\dfrac{KK_{rw}}{\mu_w B_w}\left(\nabla p_w-\gamma_w\nabla D\right)+\delta_w q_w=\dfrac{\partial}{\partial\tau}\left(\dfrac{\varphi S_w}{B_w}\right)\\ \nabla\cdot\xi\dfrac{KK_{rg}}{\mu_g B_g}\left(\nabla p_g-\gamma_g\nabla D\right)+\nabla\cdot\dfrac{R'KK_{rw}}{\mu_w B_w}\left(\nabla p_w-\gamma_w\nabla D\right)+\delta_g q_g=\dfrac{\partial}{\partial\tau}\left(\dfrac{\varphi S_g}{B_g}+\dfrac{\varphi R'S_w}{B_w}\right)\end{cases} \tag{7}$$

Where D is vertical height below seepage datum, m.

Gas and water saturation satisfy the following equation:

$$S_g+S_w=1 \tag{8}$$

The capillary pressure satisfies the following equation:

$$p_c=p_g-p_w=f\left(S_w\right) \tag{9}$$

Where pc is capillary force between gas phase and water phase.

(2) Initial conditions

In the process of injecting gas into the underground gas storage, a certain time is selected as the initial time. It is necessary to determine the initial distribution of pressure and saturation at various points in the gas storage. Then, the distribution of pressure and fluid saturation in the gas storage at the initial time is shown as follows:

$$p_g(x,y,z)\big|_{\tau=0}=f_1(x,y,z) \tag{10}$$

$$S_w(x,y,z)\big|_{\tau=0}=f_2(x,y,z) \tag{11}$$

(3) Outer boundary condition

A underground gas storage is a closed sandstone gas reservoir without marginal and bottom water. Therefore, the outer boundary conditions can be written as follows:

$$\left.\frac{\partial p}{\partial n}\right|_{\Gamma}=0 \tag{12}$$

Where $\left.\dfrac{\partial p}{\partial n}\right|_{\Gamma}$ represents derivative of the pressure on the normal direction of outer boundary; Γ is the outer boundary of the gas reservoir.

(4) Inner boundary condition

When the well production rate is constant, Dirac function can be used to deal with the well point due to wellbore radius is particularly smaller than well spacing. The production of grid blocks can be expressed as:

$$q_g\left(i,j,k,t\right)=q_g\left(t\right)\delta\left(i,j,k\right) \tag{13}$$

Where δ(i, j, k) is Dirac function, which is equal to 1 when well is in the grid block, and equal to 0 when there are no wells.

When the bottom hole flow pressure is constant, the production in the grid block (wells in the grid block) is satisfied steady flow. According to Peaceman model, the production of wells in the grid block can be expressed as:

$$q_{\mathrm{g}} = \frac{2\pi K K_{\mathrm{rg}} h \alpha \xi}{\mu_{\mathrm{g}} B_{\mathrm{g}} \left[\ln\left(r_{\mathrm{e}} / r_{\mathrm{w}} \right) + s \right]} \cdot \left(p_{\mathrm{g}} - p_{\mathrm{wTg}} \right) \quad (14)$$

$$q_{\mathrm{w}} = \frac{2\pi K K_{\mathrm{rw}} h \alpha}{\mu_{\mathrm{w}} B_{\mathrm{w}} \left[\ln\left(r_{\mathrm{e}} / r_{\mathrm{w}} \right) + s \right]} \cdot \left(p_{\mathrm{w}} - p_{\mathrm{wfw}} \right) \quad (15)$$

Where h is effective thickness of gas reservoir, m); re is equivalent radius of grid block, m; S is skin factor; α is unit conversion factor, which is equal to 0.0864.

2.3. Numerical simulation model

Based on mathematical model of gas-water two-phase flow in gas storage, the solution of the numerical model can be deduced by finite difference method. The formation parameters of underground gas storage is shown in table 1.

Table 1. Parameters of reservoir for model construction

Parameters	Value	Parameters	Value	Parameters	Value
Reservoir pressure (MPa)	27.7	Temperature (K)	364	Porosity (%)	6.2
Permeability (mD)	3.8	Gas saturation (%)	68	Depth of reservoir (m)	2800
Length of reservoir (m)	2000	Width of reservoir (m)	1000	Thickness (m)	10.1

The relative permeability curve and rock compressibility coefficient curve used in the digital simulation process are shown in Figure 1.

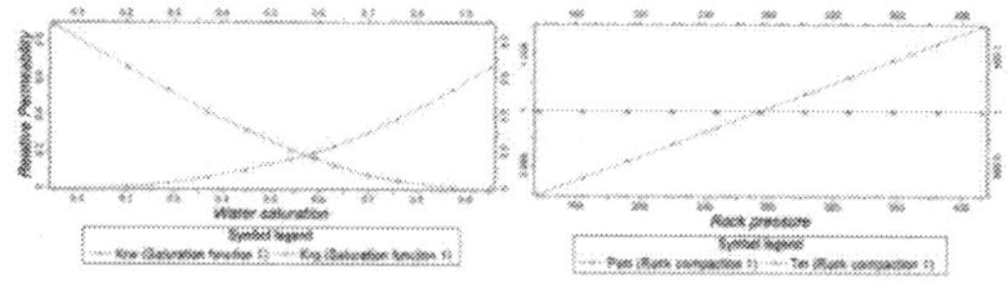

Figure 1. Relative permeability curve and reservoir compressibility for model construction

The numerical simulation model single well in underground gas storage is as shown in Figure.2, the horizontal section length is 1000m. The actual size of gas reservoir established in this paper is 2000m× 1000m× 100m, and the gas reservoir is divided into 42×24×1 grids.

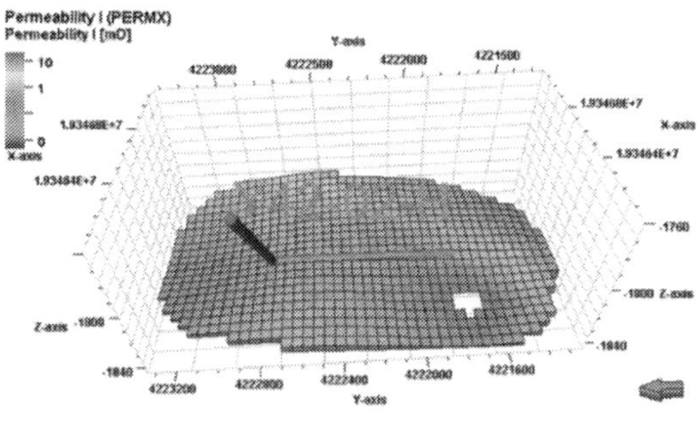

Figure 2. Numerical simulation model of single well in underground gas storage

3. Measurement of simulation

Figure 3 shows log-log plot of pressure and pressure derivative via time of pressure build up test of a gas well in the gas storage. The skin factor of the well is 5, indicating that there is existing high pollution near the wellbore.

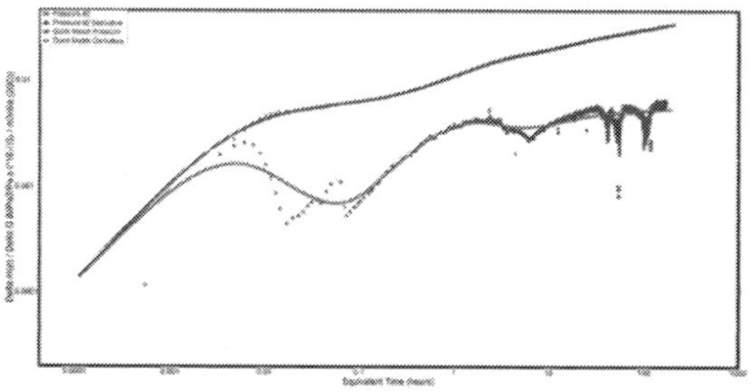

Figure 3. Double logarithmic curve of pressure and pressure derivative with. time

As shown in equation (14) and (15), the factors affecting the injection production capacity of gas wells including reservoir permeability, thickness, skin factor, wellbore radius, etc. For gas wells, the reservoir permeability and thickness can't be changed. Removing the pollution near the wellbore can improve the productivity of a single well. Acidizing is usually used for plug-release in the formation nearby wellbore. The purpose of acidizing is reducing skin factor to increase production capacity of gas well.

4. Result of numerical simulation

Acidizing can reduce skin factor of gas well, so the skin factors of acidized and none acidized gas wells in numerical simulation model are 0 and 3. The reservoir parameters used in simulation models are shown in table 1.The injection and production rate are respectively 33.64× 104m3/d and 60×104m3/D in the numerical simulation model, and simulation results are shown in figure 4 and 5. Figure 4 shows the bottom hole pressure and flow pressure in the process of injection and production. Simulation results shows that the pressure difference between reservoir pressure and flowing pressure is 5MPa for gas well without acidizing. After acidizing, pressure difference in the process of injection and production is reduced to 1.5MPa.

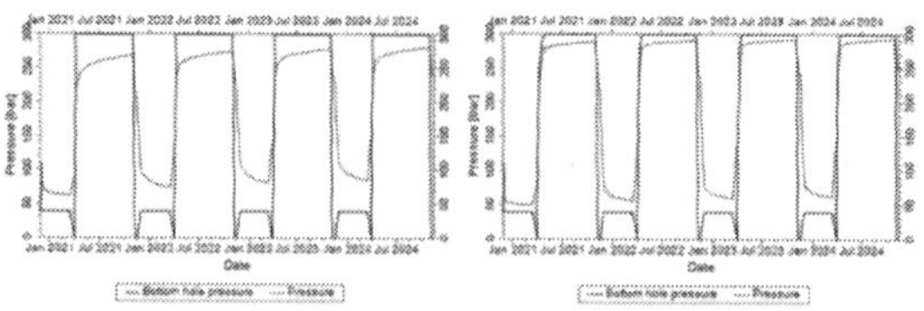

(1) gas well without stimulation (2) acidized gas well

Figure 4. Pressure difference between reservoir pressure and flowing pressure in the process of injection and production

Figure 5 shows the cumulative injection and production gas volume of acidized and none acidized gas well. The cumulative injection and production gas volume of the gas well without stimulation are $1.49\times10^8m^3$ and $4.95\times10^7m^3$, respectively. The cumulative injection and production gas volume of the acidized gas well are $1.71\times10^8m^3$ and $6.28\times10^7m^3$, respectively. After acidizing, the injection and production capacity are increased by 14.8% and 26.9% respectively.

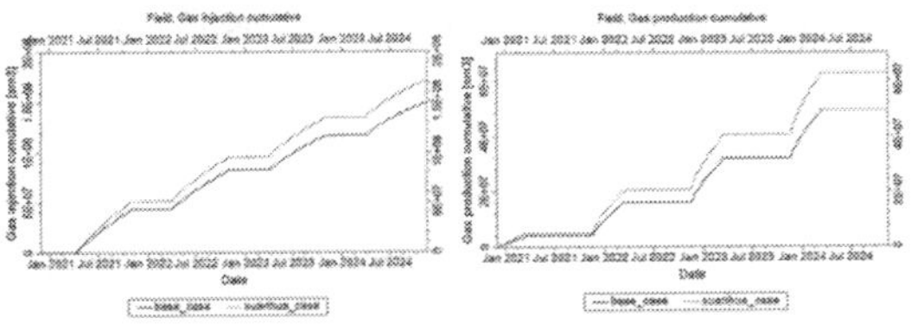

(1) cumulative injection gas (2) cumulative production gas

Figure 5. simulation results of cumulative injection production gas volume between acidized and none acidized gas well

5. Conclusion

(1) Based on multiphase seepage theory, a numerical simulation model considering high velocity non-Darcy effect and gas-water two-phase seepage is established.
(2) Acidizing is important measures to improve the injection production capacity of single wells in underground gas storage. After acidizing, the differential pressure in the process of injection and production of gas wells in underground gas storage are decreased by 70%, and the injection and production capacity increased by 14.8% and 26.9%.

References

1. Zhu S, Sun J, Wei G, et al. Numerical simulation-based correction of relative permeability hysteresis in water-invaded underground gas storage during multi-cycle injection and production[J]. Petroleum Exploration and Development, 2021, 48(1):190-200.
2. Wang T, Yan X, Yang H, et al. A new shape design method of salt cavern used as underground gas storage[J]. Applied Energy, 2013, 104(APR.):50-61.
3. Nagelhout A, Roest J. Investigating fault slip in a model of an underground gas storage facility[J]. International Journal of Rock Mechanics & Mining Sciences, 1997, 34(3-4):212.e1–212.e14.
4. Ma H, Yang C, Li Y, et al. Stability evaluation of the underground gas storage in rock salts based on new partitions of the surrounding rock[J]. Environmental Earth Sciences, 2015, 73(11):6911-6925.
5. Yang M, Guan B. Coupling model of underground gas-storage caverns and its application in engineering[J]. Chinese Journal of Rock Mechanics and Engineering, 2003.
6. Wang T, Yang C, Yan X , et al. Dynamic response of underground gas storage salt cavern under seismic loads[J]. Tunnelling and Underground Space Technology, 2014, 43(7):241–252.
7. Xin S. Optimum method for underground gas storage projects based on fuzzy comprehensive evaluation[J]. Acta Petrolei Sinica, 2006.

Synthesis of organic boron crosslinker for polyvinyl alcohol gel

Zhenhuo Zhang [1, 2], Haijun Liang [1, 2], Xiaolong Wei [3]

[1.] National Engineering Laboratory for Low-Permeability Oil & Gas Field Exploration and Development, Xi'an, Shaanxi, 710018, China;
[2.] Drilling & Production Engineering Technology Institute, CNPC Chuanqing Drilling Engineering Company Ltd., Xi'an, Shaanxi, 710018, China;
[3.] Changqing Downhole Technology Company, CNPC Chuanqing Drilling Engineering Co., Ltd., Xi'an city, Shaanxi 710021, China

Abstract. In this article, borax was used as the prime agent, and the organic boron that cross-linked agent was synthesized using adding sodium tartrate. The synthesis response shapes were optimized using unmarried factor way. The temperature opposition and crosslinking time of the fracturing fluid were used as the appraisal standards to decide the organic boron. The cross-linking agent's optimal synthesis statuses were measured, and the chemical and forcible holdings of the fracturing fluid after cross-linking with the polyvinyl alcohol-based liquid were measured.

Keywords: polyvinyl alcohol; fracturing fluid; organic boron; crosslinker.

1. Introduction

Fracturing is an significant measure to enhance gas recuperation and petroleum, raise petroleum yield and raise injection of water injection wells[1]. Its derivatives and tannin are the most usually applied thickeners for water-based that fractures operating fluids. They have good temperature resistance and strong viscosity-increasing ability, but it is difficult to break the fracturing fluid[2-4]. Water-insoluble affair and remaining colloidal flecks will the constitution to harm, decrease the proppant's conductivity, and the cost fluctuates greatly. Polyvinyl alcohol takes a definite thickening capability, and can compose a hydrogel using cross-linking response, which not only has traditional polymer's rheology fracturing fluid, masteries fluid cost, but also owns depressed price, convenient gel breaking and small harm to the reservoir. A appropriate crosslinking agent's arrangement is key to its application as a fracturing fluent thickener[5-7]. The organoboron that cross-links agent has the capability to crosslink with a hydroxyl band. Based on the fracturing fluent system of polyvinyl alcohol as a thickening agent, a appropriate organoboron that cross-linked agent was consequently synthesized by using altering the response temperature, response time[8-9].

2. Experimental

2.1 Materials

Polyvinyl alcohol (2488 flecks) industrial degree, borax, sodium potassium tartrate, sodium hydroxide are analytic degree.

2.2 Instrument

250ml three-necked flask, booster electrical mixer, electrical incessant temperature water bath, six-speed rotary viscometer (ZNN-D, Qingdao Camera plant) , complex rheometer, attractive stirrer, electronic balance, stopwatch.

2.3 Synthesis of organoboron crosslinker

Put a magnet in a 250 ml three-necked flask and add water. Put it in a attractive stirrer that is equipped with a condensing reflux instrument. After increasing the temperature to the response temperature, adapt the pH value, weigh the borax, add a three-necked flask, and stir to all the borax. Fade Away, add the ligand potassium sodium tartrate, and respond for a positive span of time to acquire an organic boron crosslinker.

3. The synthesis of organic boron is divided into two steps.

3.1 Hydrolysis reaction

$$Na_2B_4O_7 + 7H_2O \rightarrow 2Na^+ + 4B(OH)_3 + 2OH^-$$

$$B(OH)_3 + H_2O \Leftrightarrow B(OH)_4^- + H^+$$

https://doi.org/10.1051/e3sconf/202233801015

3.2 Complexation reaction

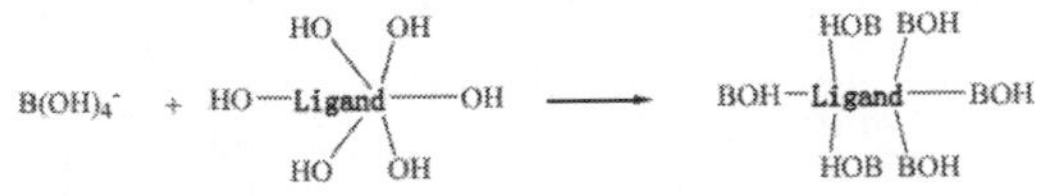

3.3 Physical and chemical properties evaluation of fracturing fluid

In thickener determination's instance, cross-linking temperature opposition and time are two significant performance indicators of whether the cross-linking agent is brilliant. The two indicators are used as the appraisal basis, and the Chinese petroleum and gas industry quality SY/T5107-2005 The performance appraisal approach of water-based that fractures fluid is an assessment approach, and the synthesis statuses are optimized.

3.4 Viscosity performance

The viscosity at $170s^{-1}$ varying temperature was evaluated by using complex rheometer.

3.5 Salt resistance

The evident viscosity of the cross-linked PVA that fractured fluid was assessed by using six velocity rotational viscometer, and the alteration of the evident viscosity at varying temperatures after adding varying salts was researched.

3.6 Suspended grit performance

Add 5g, 10g, 15g, 20g, 25g, 30g, 35g, 40g of sand to each of the eight beakers that contain polyvinyl alcohol that fractures fluid, stir equally, then pour into the measuring cylinder, and count with a stopwatch while pouring. Record the time demanded for the sand to locate at varying temperatures; use the ruler to evaluate the height of the sand that is taken in the cylinder and figure the sedimentation speed, after the sand sinks.

4. Results and discussion

From the literature, the polyvinyl alcohol foundation answer concentration was 2%, and the crosslinking proportion was 100:1. Borax in the shape of boric acid ions in aqueous answer can be rather varying from polyols beneath positive statuses. In this article, a unmarried ligand sodium tartrate is used to synthesize an organoboron that cross-links agent.

4.1 Effect of reaction temperature on organ boron crosslinking agent

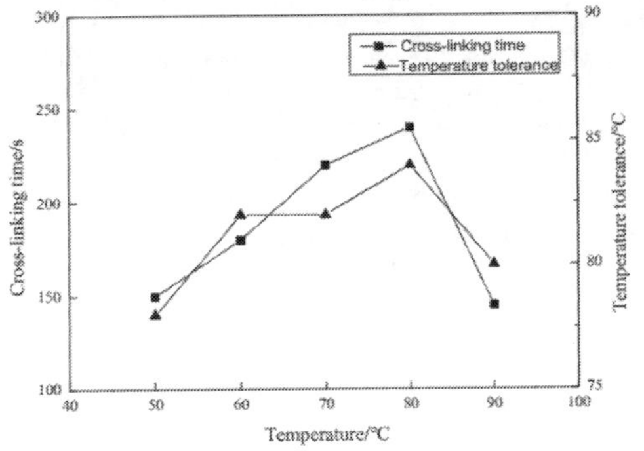

Fig. 1 Effect of reaction temperature on organoboron crosslinking agent

It can be seen from statue 1 that while the response temperature is depressed, organoboron's complexation is not complete, the borate ion is not entirely reacted, the crosslinking time is poor, and the temperature defiance is short. The temperature opposition and crosslinking time step by step grow and arrive in the optimal at 80 extents Celsius, as the response temperature builds up. If the temperature is excessively eminent, the chain connections will be split and the temperature defiance will be deteriorated, so the response temperature is picked to be 80°C

4.2 Effect of borax addition

Until experimental preliminary research and literature study, the set response statuses were 1.5% NaOH, 20% ligand, 4 h response time and 80°Creaction temperature. The quantity of borax was modified to research the synthesized organic boron crosslinker. The temperature resistance's influence and crosslinking the gel's time with polyvinyl alcohol was noticed. The experimental consequences are as follows:

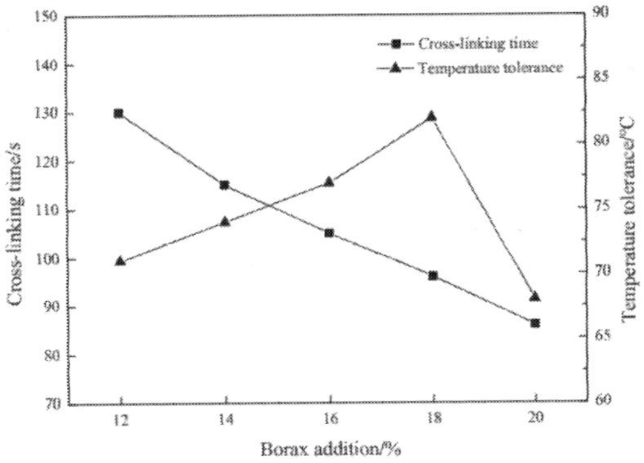

Fig. 2 Effect of borax addition on the performance of organoboron crosslinkers

Fig. 2 shows that as the amount of borax rises, the crosslinking time decreases, and the temperature resistance first rises and then decreases. While the quantity of borax is minor, the interaction degree with the ligand is less, the ligand encapsulates a bit of boron, and lento discharges, prolonging the crosslinking time, but cross-linking with polyvinyl alcohol to compose the fracturing smooth jelly's temperature defiance. Inadequate. Suppose the quantity of borax is inordinate, the unreacted borate responds with the cis- ortho-hydroxy band of the polyvinyl alcohol, the crosslinking time goes brief, and yet the phenomenon of "over-crosslinking" exists, and the temperature defiance is deteriorated. While the quantity of borax is 18%, the temperature defiance is excellent, getting 82°C.

4.3 Effect of Ligand on Organic Boron Crosslinking Agent

Other experimental statuses were unchanged, the quantity of ligand was merely varied, and the impact of cross-linking with polyvinyl alcohol on the temperature defiance of the crosslinking time and the fracturing fluid was researched.

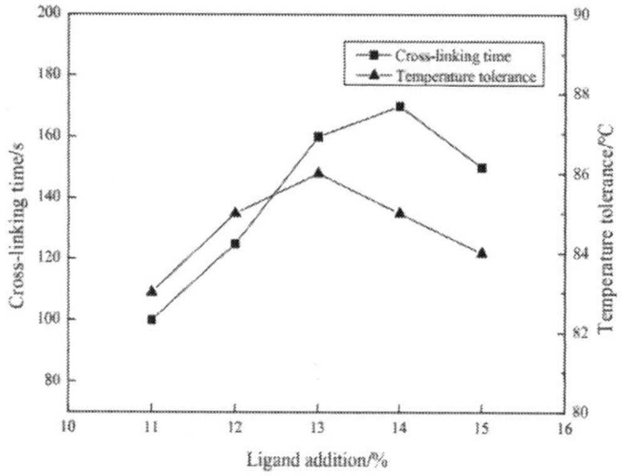

Fig. 3 Effect of ligand addition on the performance of organoboron crosslinkers

As the quantity of ligand growths, the crosslinking time growths, and the temperature opposition first builds up and then goes down. While the quantity of the ligand is minor, the crosslinking time is brief and the temperature opposition is not excellent. The addition quantity of the ligand grows, and the surplus ligand is wrapped outside the organic boron, which takes a shielding consequence on the complexation of the polyvinyl alcohol and the crosslinking agent. The consequence of the ligand addition sum of 13% is soundest in the above statue.

4.4 Effect of reaction time on organoboron crosslinking agent

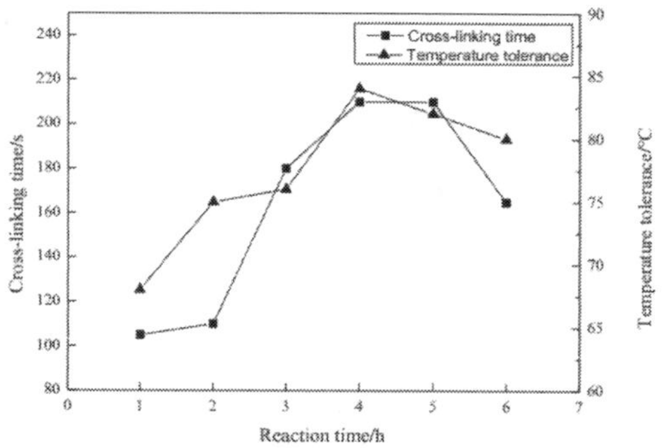

Fig. 4 Effect of reaction time on the performance of organoboron crosslinkers

While the response time is brief, the borate response in the crosslinking agent is not complete, the temperature defiance is not excellent, and the crosslinking time is poor. With the growth of response time, the temperature defiance and crosslinking time are bit by bit augmented. While the response time gets into 4-5h, the crosslinking time and temperature defiance are optimum.

4.5 Effect of NaOH Addition on Organic Boron Crosslinking Agent

To to upgrade borax's hydrolysis response, more borate ions are built in the answer, and the complexation response is speeded up. NaOH is overall added as a accelerator, and the accelerator has got small impact on the temperature defiance and crosslinking time. In this experimentation, the consequence of the stability of the organoboron that cross-linked agent was enquired into by using adapting the quantity of NaOH and other statuses.

Table 1. Effect of NaOH addition on the stability of crosslinker

NaOH addition/%	stability
0	stable
0.5	stable
1.0	a small amount of precipitation
1.5	There is a lot of precipitation
2.0	There is a lot of precipitation

With the increase of NaOH, the same time can be placed at room temperature, and the synthesized organic boron cross-linking agent will gradually precipitate out crystals. It is suitable to select 1.0% of NaOH.

 https://doi.org/10.1051/e3sconf/202233801015

4.6 Viscosity performance

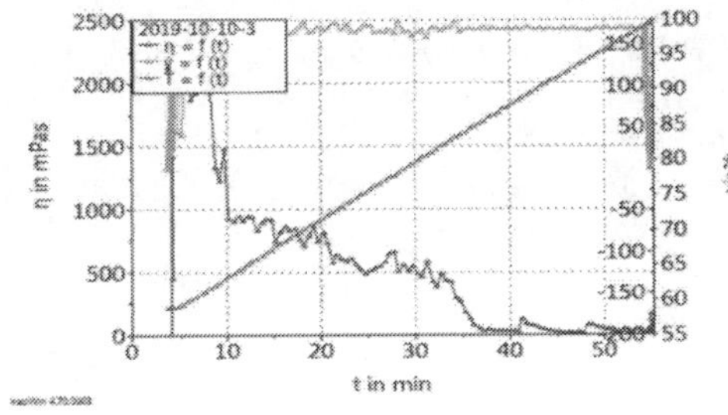

Fig. 5 Viscosity curve of polyvinyl alcohol fracturing fluid

With the complexity of fracturing, the depth of gas wells and oil is growing, so that the temperature opposition of fracturing fluids is greatly checked, and fracturing fluids with excellent thermal stability are demanded. As is visible from the above statue, the fracturing fluid's viscosity as a whole indicates a downward tendency, as the system's temperature goes up. Ahead of the temperature is up to 80°C, the viscosity declines considerably, after which the viscosity is yet falling, but the rate is reduced. While the system's temperature is lifted to 83°C, the viscosity is 53.3 mPa•s, which runs into the criteria of seam making and sand carrying, showing that the fracturing fluid takes more beneficial temperature opposition.

4.7 Salt resistance

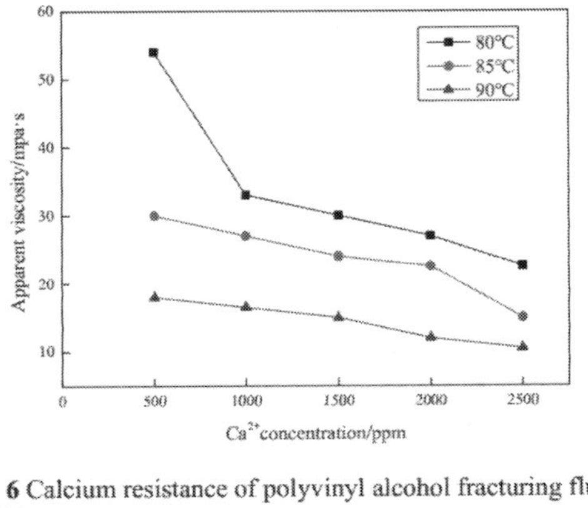

Fig. 6 Calcium resistance of polyvinyl alcohol fracturing fluid at different temperatures

According to Fig. 6, while the concentration of Ca^{2+} in the fracturing fluid at 80°C is 500-1000ppm, the fracturing fluid's evident viscosity goes down speedily. While the concentration of Ca^{2+} is 1000-2500ppm, the obvious viscosity of the fracturing fluid at 85°C falls down lento. While the concentration of Ca^{2+} in the fracturing fluid at 90°C is 500-1000ppm, the fracturing fluid's patent viscosity goes down lento with small alteration. It can be viewed that the stress fluid at 85°C and 90°C the fracturing fluid has got good salt defiance.

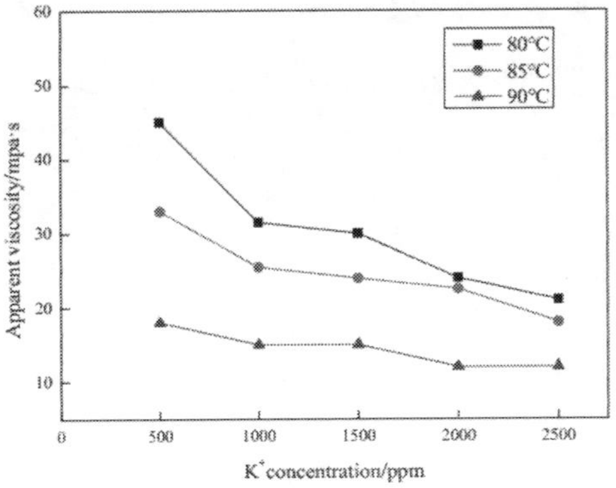

Fig. 7 potash resistance of polyvinyl alcohol fracturing fluid at different temperatures

from statue 7 that while the K^+ concentration of the fracturing fluid at 80°C is 500-1000ppm, the evident viscosity falls down speedily; while the K^+ concentration is 1000-1500ppm, the apparent viscosity virtually stays unchanged; when the K^+ concentration is 1500-2500ppm, the evident viscosity falls down speedily; while the K^+ concentration of the fracturing fluid at 85°C is 500-1000ppm, the evident viscosity goes down speedily; while the K^+ concentration is 1000-2500ppm, the obvious viscosity falls down lento; while the K^+ concentration of the fracturing fluid at 90°C, the patent viscosity goes down speedily. The evident viscosity alters little at 500 ~ 2500ppm, showing that the fracturing fluid at 90°C has got more excellent salty opposition.

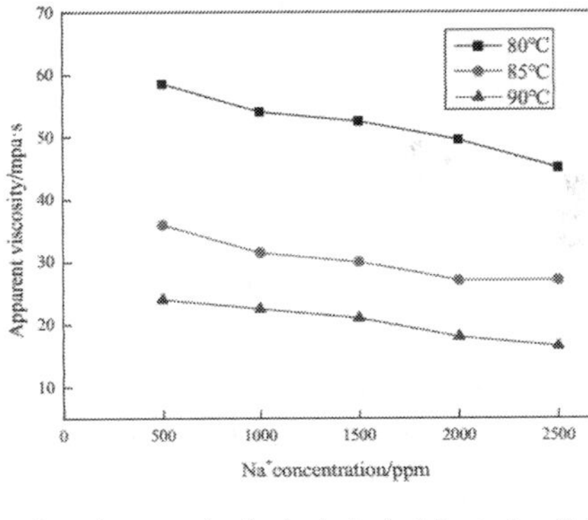

Fig. 8 salt resistance of polyvinyl alcohol fracturing fluid at different temperatures

According to Fig. 8, the Na^+ concentration of fracturing fluid at 80°C goes down step by step at 500-2500ppm, and the obvious viscosity goes down lento at 90°C and 85°C at 500-2500ppm. It can be viewed that the fracturing fluid at 90°C and 85°C has got more excellent salty opposition.

 https://doi.org/10.1051/e3sconf/202233801015

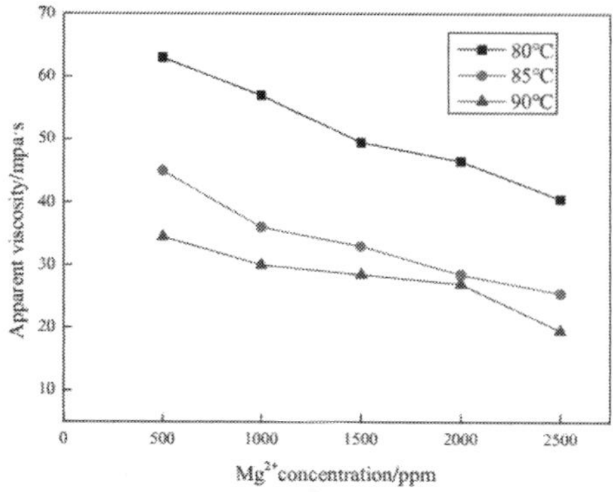

Fig. 9 Magnesium salt resistance of polyvinyl alcohol fracturing fluid at different temperatures

According to Fig. 9, the Mg^{2+} concentration of the fracturing fluid at 80°C step by step diminishes from 500 to 2500 ppm, and the obvious viscosity declines quickly while the concentration of Mg^{2+} in the fracturing fluid at 85°C is from 500 to 1000 ppm, and reduces from 1000 to 2500 ppm. The obvious viscosity of the fracturing fluent Mg^{2+} concentration at 90°C is not lento a lot modified at 500~2000ppm, and it diminishes speedily at 2000~2500ppm. It can be watched that the fracturing fluid at 90°C possesses more excellent salty opposition.

5. Conclusion

(1) The cross-linking agent's optimal synthesis statuses are as follows: response temperature 80°C, borax addition sum is 18%, ligand addition sum is 13%, response time is 4-5 h, and NAOH addition sum is 1%;
(2) The polyvinyl bromide that cross-links agent that is synthesized beneath the polyvinyl alcohol-based limpid cross-linked polyvinyl alcohol fracturing fluid and the optimum synthesis statuses take excellent temperature and shear defiance : the fracturing fluid is at a shear rate of 170 s-1 while the system is heated to 83°C, its viscosity is 53.3 mPa•s;
(3) The cross-linking time of the polyvinyl alcohol that fractures fluid after crosslinking of the organoboron that cross-links agent that is synthesized beneath the superlative synthesis statuses with the polyvinyl alcohol-based liquid is 220 s.

Acknowledgments

The work was supported financially by Shaanxi Provincial Key Research and Development Program (2019GY-136), Key Scientific Research Program of Shaanxi Provincial Department of Education (21JY035) and Youth Innovation Team of Shaanxi University. And we thank the work of Modern Analysis and Testing Center of Xi`an Shiyou University.

References

1. Yongwei SONG, Heru WANG. Using polyvinyl alcohol to improve the deacidification performance of titanium white waste acid: Pilot tests[J]. Waste Management, 2019, 87, p. 13-20
2. Xiaosen SHANG, Yunhong DING, Yonghui WANG. Rheological and Performance Research on a Regenerable Polyvinyl Alcohol Fracturing Fluid. [J]. PloS one, 2015, 10(12), P. 44-49
3. Siming YAN, Yongji WANG, Jia HE. Performance of the reproducible polyvinyl alcohol fracturing fluid system. [J]. Russian Journal of Applied Chemistry, 2015, Vol. 88 (11), p. 1884-1891
4. Yanping HOU, Kaiming LI, Haiping LUO. Using crosslinked polyvinyl alcohol polymer membrane as a separator in the microbial fuel cell[J]. Frontiers of Environmental Science & Engineering, 2014, 8(1), p. 137-143
5. Kyunghwan Yoon, Benjamin S. Hsiao, Benjamin Chu.High flux ultrafiltration nanofibrous membranes based on polyacrylonitrile electrospun scaffolds and crosslinked polyvinyl alcohol coating[J]. Journal of Membrane Science, 2009, 338(1-2), p. 145-152
6. Ashveen V. Nand, David R. Rohindra, Jagjit R. Khurma. Characterization of Genipin Crosslinked Hydrogels Composed of Chitosan and Partially Hydrolyzed Poly(vinyl alcohol)[J]. Polymers, 2013, 7(1), p. 402-410
7. Ruiyun Zhang, Wenyu Xu, Fuqing Jiang. Fabrication and characterization of dense Chitosan/polyvinyl-alcohol/poly-lactic-acid blend membranes[J]. Fibers and Polymers, 2012, 13(5), p. 571-575
8. Chang Suk Kong, Wan Suk Yoo, Kui Young Lee. Nanofiber deposition by electroblowing of PVA (polyvinyl alcohol)[J]. Journal of Materials Science, 2009, 44(4), p. 1107-1112
9. Shefali Mishra, R. Bajpai, R. Katare. On the mechanical strength of biocompatible semi-IPNs of polyvinyl alcohol and polyacrylamide[J]. Microsystem Technologies, 2008, 14(2), p. 193-198

Evaluation of temperature resistance of gelatinized modified starch drilling fluid

Wei Liu [1, 2], Mingming Zhu [3], Fan Fan [1, 2]

[1] National Engineering Laboratory for Low-Permeability Oil & Gas Field Exploration and Development, Xi'an, Shaanxi, 710018, China
[2] Drilling & Production Engineering Technology Institute, CNPC Chuanqing Drilling Engineering Company Ltd., Xi'an, Shaanxi, 710018, China
[3] Changqing Drilling Branch, CNPC Chuanqing Drilling Engineering Co., Ltd., Xi'an city, Shaanxi 710000, China

Abstract. This chapter evaluates and compares the indoor performance of different concentrations of non gelatinized starch and gelatinized starch in drilling fluid, gelatinized modified starch at 80°C, and then aged at high temperature. Taking the plastic viscosity (PV) and filtration loss (FL) as the main evaluation indexes, a formula with better performance was selected as the main additive and used as the follow-up study. At the same time, the inhibition of gelatinized starch in water-based drilling fluid was investigated.

Keywords: high temperature, modified starch, drilling fluid.

1. Introduction

Gelatinization is one of the basic physical and chemical properties in starch modification processing. With the heating of the starch suspension, the starch particles first start to absorb water and expand, and the volume becomes larger. Then the amylose molecules in the amorphous region are partially leached. After reaching a certain temperature, the starch particles suddenly expand rapidly, the starch particles lose birefringence, the crystal structure disintegrates, and continue to rise. The volume of the starch particles expands to dozens or even hundreds of times, The starch water suspension system finally becomes a translucent colloidal solution, which is the gelatinization of starch. The whole gelatinization process of starch can be roughly divided into three stages: the first is the reversible water absorption stage, in this reaction stage, only a small amount of water molecules enter the starch particles, and the particle volume expansion is very small; Then it enters the irreversible water absorption stage. In this process, a large amount of starch particles absorb water, the volume expands rapidly, the internal structural skeleton of starch is destroyed, some amylose molecules will leach out of the particles, the viscosity increases rapidly, and the transparency of starch solution also increases; The third is the particle disintegration stage, especially under the action of shear force, after the starch particles are broken and disintegrated, the starch molecules are finally dispersed in the solution [1].

The potato starch, corn starch and cassava starch used in this experiment showed irreversible water absorption in the process of fully heating with water, and the water molecules gradually entered the crystalline area in the starch particles. Some chemical bonds in starch molecules become unstable due to the increase of external temperature, which is conducive to the fracture of chemical bonds in starch molecules. With the breaking of these chemical bonds, the crystalline region in the starch particles gradually changes from the original closely arranged state to the loose state. In this process, the water absorption of the starch increases rapidly, and the volume of the starch particles expands rapidly. Its volume can expand to 50~100 times of the original volume, that is, the starch is modified by gelatinization; It can not only reduce viscosity in drilling fluid, but also effectively adjust the rheological properties of drilling fluid. The production method is simple, the synthesis technology is relatively mature, the source of raw materials is wide, and the cost is low. Gelatinized modified starch has the advantages of environmental protection, no pollution and easy degradation, and can be applied to environmental protection drilling fluid system.

2. Experiment

2.1 preparation of drilling fluid

Pre hydration of drilling fluid:350ml water+0.7g sodium carbonate+14g bentonite, 1600r/min, stirring for 120 minutes, aging under closed conditions for 1 day, ready for use.

https://doi.org/10.1051/e3sconf/202233801016

2.2 performance evaluation of starch drilling fluid

According to GB/t16783.1-2006, the plastic viscosity (PV, mPa•s), filtration loss (FL, ML) and other performance parameters of drilling fluids with different concentrations of cassava, potato and corn starch after hot rolling at different temperatures are evaluated. From four different amounts of starch selected in the experiment: 0.5%, 1.0%, 1.5% and 2.0%, the amount with the best temperature resistance (low filtration) and good lubricity (low plastic viscosity) was selected as the experimental standard of gelatinization modification [2,3].

2.3 comparative analysis of performance characteristics of starch gelatinized modified drilling fluid

The starch with the best performance was used as the experimental standard of gelatinization modification, and the starch: distilled water = 1:4 was mixed and stirred Gelatinized starch was prepared by fully gelatinizing in a water bath at 80°C for 5 minutes. It was added to the drilling fluid solution, stirred at 1600r/min for 120 minutes, and aged under closed conditions for 1 day. This paper mainly evaluates the plastic viscosity, filtration loss and other performance parameters of three starch gelatinized modified drilling fluids after hot rolling at different temperatures, and selects the gelatinized starch with the best temperature resistance.

2.4 linear expansion rate of Bentonite

According to sy-t6335-1997, the inhibition performance of distilled water, KCl solution with the same concentration and gelatinized starch drilling fluid treatment mud with the best temperature resistance are evaluated respectively, the expansion amount of bentonite of drilling fluid treatment mud at different times is evaluated, compared with distilled water and KCl solution, and the expansion rate is calculated according to the expansion amount to draw the curve .

3. Results and Discussion

3.1 Characterization of starch

Different concentrations of potato, corn and cassava starch were added to the fresh water base mud at room temperature. The plastic viscosity PV(mPa•s), dynamic shear YP(PA), apparent viscosity AV(mPa•s), filtration loss FL(ML) and other performance parameters of the treated mud at room temperature were tested. When 0.50% ~ 2.0% cassava starch was added, compared with 4% fresh water base mud, the filtration loss decreased with the increase of starch dosage, The plastic viscosity basically did not change with the increase of the amount of starch, which was 3mPa•s. when 2.0% cassava starch was added, the filtration rate decreased to 28ml; When 0.50% ~ 2.0% potato starch was added, compared with 4% fresh water base mud, the filtration loss decreased with the increase of starch dosage, and the plastic viscosity basically did not change with the increase of starch dosage, which was 3mPa•s. when 2.0% potato starch was added, the filtration loss decreased to 20.6ml. When 0.50% ~ 2.0% corn starch was added, compared with 4% fresh water base mud, the filtration loss decreased with the increase of starch dosage, and the plastic viscosity basically did not change with the increase of starch dosage, which was 3mPa•s. when 2.0% corn starch was added, the filtration loss decreased to 20.6ml. Through the screening of three kinds of starch, it was found that when 2% potato and corn starch were added, the performance was better, among which 2% corn starch had the best performance, the filtration loss was reduced to 20.6ml and the plastic viscosity was 3.5mPa·s. In conclusion, through the performance evaluation of drilling fluid with three different types and different concentrations of starch, it is found that compared with 4% fresh water base mud, the three starch treated mud can increase the apparent viscosity and plastic viscosity of drilling fluid, reduce the filtration loss and increase the friction coefficient Tg of sliding block. This is because the starch added at room temperature is still small particles without gelatinization modification and does not form polymer glue [4-6].

Table 1. Results of treated pulp with different starch concentrations at room temperature

Mud	consumption/ %	PV /mPa•s	YP /Pa	AV /mPa•s	YP/PV /Pa/mPa•s	G10s Pa	G10min Pa	FL mL	tg
Base mud	/	3.0	0.50	3.50	0.167	0.50	0.25	33.0	0.0963
Base mud + cassava starch	0.50%	3.0	0.50	3.50	0.167	0.50	0.25	31.0	0.1228
	1.00%	3.0	0.50	3.50	0.167	0.50	0.25	29.8	0.1763
	1.50%	3.0	0.50	3.50	0.167	0.50	0.25	28.8	0.2217
	2.00%	3.0	0.50	3.50	0.167	0.50	0.25	28.0	0.1763
Base mud + potato starch	0.50%	3.0	0.25	3.25	0.167	0.75	0.50	27.2	0.1051
	1.00%	3.0	0.50	3.50	0.167	0.50	0.50	25.6	0.1405
	1.50%	3.0	0.50	3.50	0.167	0.50	0.50	23.8	0.2217
	2.00%	3.5	0.25	3.75	0.083	0.50	0.50	20.6	0.1763
Base mud + corn starch	0.50%	3.0	1.00	4.00	0.330	0.50	0.50	26.8	0.1139
	1.00%	3.0	1.00	4.00	0.330	0.75	0.50	24.8	0.1405
	1.50%	3.0	1.00	4.00	0.330	0.50	0.50	24.0	0.1564
	2.00%	3.5	0.25	3.75	0.083	0.50	0.50	20.6	0.1763

Compared with 0.5% ~ 2.0% treated pulp at room temperature, after aging at 130 ℃ for 16 hours, the filtration of 0.5% cassava starch treated pulp decreased by 76.77% and the plastic viscosity increased by 1.66 times; The filtration of 0.5% potato starch treated pulp decreased by 69.12%, the plastic viscosity increased by 0.5 times, the filtration of 0.5% corn starch treated pulp decreased by 80.59%, and the plastic viscosity increased by 1 time. The filtrate loss of 1.0% cassava starch treated pulp decreased by 46.3%, and the plastic viscosity increased by 1.83 times; The filtrate loss of 1.0% potato starch treated pulp decreased by 68.75%, and the plastic viscosity increased by 1.5 times; The filtration of 1.0% corn starch treated pulp decreased by 82.26%, and the plastic viscosity increased by 2 times. The filtrate loss of 1.5% cassava starch treated pulp decreased by 42.36%, and the plastic viscosity increased by 3 times; The filtration loss of 1.5% potato starch treated pulp decreased by 74.79%, and the plastic viscosity increased by 2.83 times; The filtration of 1.5% corn starch treated pulp decreased by 90% and the plastic viscosity increased by 2.5 times. The filtrate loss of 2.0% cassava starch treated pulp decreased by 48.57%, and the plastic viscosity increased by 4.83 times; The filtration of 2.0% potato starch treated pulp decreased by 90.29%, and the plastic viscosity increased by 2.83 times; The filtration of 2.0% corn starch treated pulp decreased by 68.93%, and the plastic viscosity increased by 2.83 times. The results showed that the comprehensive properties of 2.0% corn starch were the best at 130°C, the filtration of 2.0% corn starch treated pulp was 2ml and the plastic viscosity was 12MPa·s.

Table 2. Results of starch treated pulp with different concentrations at 130 °C

model	consumption/ %	PV /mPa•s	YP /Pa	AV /mPa•s	YP/PV /Pa/mPa•s	G10s Pa	G10min Pa	FL mL	tg
Base mud + cassava starch	0.50%	8.0	0.75	8.75	0.094	0.50	0.50	7.2	0.5206
	1.00%	8.5	1.50	10.00	0.176	0.50	0.50	16.0	0.4663
	1.50%	12.0	2.00	14.00	0.167	0.75	0.50	16.6	0.4348
	2.00%	17.5	2.75	20.25	0.157	1.00	0.75	14.4	0.3839
Base mud + potato starch	0.50%	4.5	1.00	5.50	0.220	0.25	0.25	8.4	0.3541
	1.00%	7.5	0.75	8.25	0.100	0.25	0.25	8.0	0.3443
	1.50%	11.5	1.50	13.00	0.130	0.50	0.50	6.0	0.3443
	2.00%	11.5	3.75	14.25	0.330	0.75	0.50	5.6	0.3839
Base mud + corn starch	0.50%	6.0	2.50	8.50	0.420	1.00	0.75	5.2	0.1317
	1.00%	9.0	2.00	11.00	0.220	1.00	1.00	4.4	0.1493
	1.50%	10.5	3.25	13.75	0.310	0.75	0.75	2.4	0.1673
	2.00%	12.0	3.00	15.00	0.250	1.25	1.25	2.0	0.1763

Compared with 0.5%~2.0% treated pulp at room temperature, after aging at 140°C for 16 hours, the filtration of 0.5% cassava starch treated pulp decreased by 73.55% and the plastic viscosity increased by 1.67 times; The filtration of 0.5% potato starch treated pulp decreased by 55.89%, the plastic viscosity increased by one time, the filtration of 0.5% corn starch treated pulp decreased by 69.4%, and the plastic viscosity increased by 1.17 times. The filtrate loss of 1.0% cassava starch treated pulp decreased by 39.6%, and the plastic viscosity increased by 2.42 times; The filtration loss of 1.0% potato starch treated pulp decreased by 44.53%, and the plastic viscosity increased by 1.67 times; The filtration loss of 1.0% corn starch treated pulp decreased by 61.29%, and the plastic viscosity increased by 1.67 times. The filtrate loss of 1.5% cassava starch treated pulp decreased by 37.5%, and the plastic viscosity increased by 3.83 times; The filtrate loss of 1.5% potato starch treated pulp decreased by 56.3%, and the plastic viscosity increased by 3.33 times; The filtration of 1.5% corn starch treated pulp decreased by 66.67%, and the plastic viscosity increased by 3.17 times. The filtration of 2.0% cassava starch treated pulp decreased by 46.43%, and the plastic viscosity increased by 5 times; The filtration loss of 2.0% potato starch treated pulp decreased by 52.43%, and the plastic viscosity increased by 3.29 times; The filtration loss of 2.0% corn starch treated pulp decreased by 63.11%, and the plastic viscosity increased by 4.71 times. It is concluded that the comprehensive performance of corn starch is the best at 140°C. Although the filtration of 2% corn starch treated pulp is only 7.6ml, its plastic viscosity is 20MPa·s, which is obviously high, poor lubricity and weak practicability. After hot rolling at 140°C, the temperature resistance, filtration reduction and lubricity of the three Starch Treated pulps decreased significantly.

Table 3. Results of starch treated pulp with different concentrations at 140 °C

model	consumption/ %	PV /mPa•s	YP /Pa	AV /mPa•s	YP/PV /Pa/mPa•s	G10s Pa	G10min Pa	FL mL	tg
Base mud + cassava starch	0.50%	9.5	0.5	10.0	0.21	1.00	1.00	10.4	0.3057
	1.00%	10.5	1.5	12.0	0.24	1.00	1.00	17.0	0.3153
	1.50%	14.5	0.5	15.0	0.21	1.50	1.00	18.0	0.2962
	2.00%	18.0	2.5	20.5	0.25	2.00	1.50	15.0	0.4040
Base mud + potato starch	0.50%	6.0	1.0	7.0	0.25	0.50	0.50	12.0	0.2867
	1.00%	8.0	3.0	11.0	0.13	0.50	0.50	11.2	0.3057
	1.50%	13.0	2.0	15.0	0.23	0.75	0.50	10.4	0.3346
	2.00%	15.0	1.5	16.5	0.53	1.00	0.75	9.8	0.3443
Base mud + corn starch	0.50%	6.5	2.5	9.0	0.54	1.50	1.00	8.2	0.3640
	1.00%	8.0	2.0	10.0	0.25	0.50	0.50	9.6	0.3346
	1.50%	12.5	4.0	16.5	0.32	0.75	0.50	8.0	0.3839
	2.00%	20.0	7.0	27.0	0.35	1.50	1.00	7.6	0.4142

In conclusion, the following conclusions can be drawn through the characterization of the concentration gradient properties of the three starches: The best starch content of 0.5%, 1.0%, 1.5% and 2.0% was 2%, which was used as the standard of subsequent gelatinization modification experiment. The highest temperature resistance of the three starches without gelatinization modification can only reach 130°C, and corn starch and potato starch are better than cassava starch in temperature resistance, filtration reduction and lubricity, among which corn starch is the best.

3.2 Comparative analysis of gelatinization properties of three kinds of starch

It can be seen that the filtration loss of the three gelatinized starch treated slurries decreases significantly during the temperature rise from room temperature to 110°C, and gradually increases at 110 ~ 150°C. The temperature resistance, filtration reduction and lubricity of the gelatinized corn starch drilling fluid system are better than those of potato and cassava starch treatment agents. The temperature resistance and lubrication of the three gelatinized starch treated slurries after hot rolling at 140°C The performance of fluid loss reduction and lubricity are significantly reduced, so the high temperature resistance can only reach 130°C. The lubricity of 2% gelatinized corn starch treated pulp is obviously better than that of corn starch treated pulp without gelatinization modification at the same concentration, but the temperature resistance and filtration reduction need to be further improved by adding other modifiers.

https://doi.org/10.1051/e3sconf/202233801016

Table 4. Results of three starch 2% gelatinized pulps at different temperatures

Temperature °C	model	PV /mPa•s	YP /Pa	AV /mPa•s	YP/PV /Pa/mPa•s	G10s Pa	G10min Pa	FL mL	tg
25	potato	6	1.5	7.5	0.25	0.50	0.50	15.0	0.1584
	Corn	2	1.0	3.0	0.50	0.25	0.25	5.6	0.1405
	cassava	2	1.5	3.5	0.75	0.25	0.25	17.0	0.1228
90	potato	9	3.5	12.5	0.39	0.50	0.50	6.0	0.2126
	Corn	5	3.0	8.0	0.60	0.25	0.25	5.6	0.2217
	cassava	4	1.5	5.5	0.35	2.00	2.00	5.8	0.2586
110	potato	14	3.5	18.0	0.25	1.00	1.00	5.6	0.2401
	Corn	9	3.0	10.0	0.33	0.50	0.50	5.2	0.2493
	cassava	6	3.0	9.0	0.50	1.00	1.00	5.5	0.1944
130	potato	19	3.5	22.5	0.18	1.00	1.00	11.2	0.1763
	Corn	13	3.0	16.0	0.23	0.50	0.50	7.0	0.4142
	cassava	7	4.0	11.0	0.57	0.50	0.50	9.0	0.4348
140	potato	17	1.0	18.0	0.06	1.00	1.00	16.0	0.1584
	Corn	10	2.0	12.0	0.20	0.50	0.50	14.0	0.1405
	cassava	6	2.0	8.0	0.33	0.50	0.50	18.0	0.1317
150	potato	20	4.0	24.0	0.20	2.50	2.00	15.0	0.1584
	Corn	14	4.0	18.0	0.29	2.00	2.00	16.0	0.1495
	cassava	10	6.0	16.0	0.60	1.50	1.00	19.0	0.1317

3.3 Linear expansion rate of Bentonite

The inhibitor in the drilling fluid system mainly plays the role of stabilizing the wellbore and is one of the important treatment agents of water-based drilling fluid [7]. In the experiment, 2% potassium chloride inhibitor with low cost and good environmental protection performance was selected for comparative experiment, and 2% gelatinized corn starch with the best temperature resistance was selected to verify the inhibition. The linear expansion rate of bentonite with the same dosage of two inhibitors was evaluated.

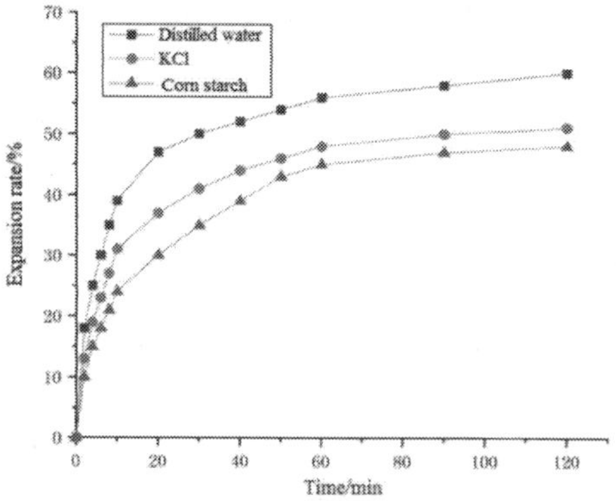

Fig. 1 Effect of 2% gelatinized corn starch solution on linear expansion rate of bentonite

The influence of the two treatment slurries on the linear expansion rate of bentonite is shown in Fig. 1. It can be seen from Fig.1 that the expansion rate of bentonite tablet after 2h in distilled water is 59.23%; The swelling rate of bentonite tablet after 2h in gelatinized corn starch treated pulp is 46.68%, and the inhibition effect of 2.0% potassium chloride treated pulp with the same concentration is the second. The experiment shows that gelatinized corn starch has a certain inhibition effect on the hydration and dispersion of bentonite, because the crystal forming area in starch particles changes from the original closely arranged state to the loose state, The water absorption of starch increases rapidly. Starch is a hydrocarbon polymer with many hydroxyl groups in its branched chain, which will combine with clay molecules due to van der Waals force, so as to reduce the dispersion and expansion of clay particles; It can be seen that gelatinized corn starch can inhibit the expansion of bentonite [8-9].

4. Conclusion

(1) Through the characterization of the concentration gradient properties of the three kinds of starch, it can be concluded that the best concentration of the four different starch concentrations of 0.5%, 1.0%, 1.5% and 2.0% is 2%. The high temperature resistance of the three kinds of starch without gelatinization modification can only reach 130°C, among which corn starch is better than potato and cassava starch in temperature resistance, filtration reduction and lubricity.
(2) Through the performance evaluation of three kinds of gelatinized starch treated mud, it is selected that the gelatinized corn starch gelatinized drilling fluid has better performance. After aging at room temperature for 24 hours, the temperature resistance and filtration reduction of the three gelatinized starch treated pulps were not obvious. After hot rolling at 90°C, 110°C, 130°C, 140°C and 150°C, the performance was evaluated. The results showed that the filtration loss of the three gelatinized starch treated slurries decreased significantly from room temperature to 110°C, and gradually increased at 110 ~ 150°C. The temperature resistance, filtration reduction and lubricity of the gelatinized corn starch drilling fluid system were better than those of the gelatinized potato and cassava starch treated slurries, However, the highest temperature resistance can only reach 130°C, and its lubricity is significantly better than that of corn starch treated pulp without gelatinization modification at the same concentration. It is necessary to further optimize and improve the temperature resistance by adding other modifiers [10].
(3) Through the linear expansion rate experiment of bentonite, it is concluded that the gelatinized corn starch can inhibit the hydration expansion of bentonite and inhibit the hydration dispersion of bentonite. Its inhibition effect is stronger than fresh water mud and slightly stronger than 2% KCl solution. The inhibition of the system can be improved by adding other suitable environmental friendly modifiers.

Acknowledgments

The work was supported financially by Shaanxi Provincial Key Research and Development Program (2019GY-136), Key Scientific Research Program of Shaanxi Provincial Department of Education (21JY035) and Youth Innovation Team of Shaanxi University. And we thank the work of Modern Analysis and Testing Center of Xi`an Shiyou University.

https://doi.org/10.1051/e3sconf/202233801016

References

1. R.J. Zhang, Y. Bai, Y. Sun, W.C. Du, C.S. Pu, J. Zhang, G. Chen, Preparation of ammonium-oleic salts and evaluation as shale swelling inhibitors in water-based drilling fluid, Tenside Surfactants Detergents, 58 (2021) 311-316.
2. W.J. Ni, W.L. Wang, Q.C. Wang, W.C. Du, G. Chen, Modification and application of waste shaddock peel as a green additive for water-based drilling fluid, Journal of Biobased Materials and Bioenergy, 15 (2021) 380-384.
3. W.C. Du, X.Y. Wang, T.F. Bi, Man Liu, J. Zhang, G. Chen, Synthesis and inhibitive mechanism of a novel clay hydration inhibitor for water-based drilling fluids, Materials Science-Medziagotyra, 27 (2021) 128-142.
4. X.X. Liu, L. Gao, Q.C Wang, W.C. Du, X.F. Gu, J. Zhang, G. Chen, Evaluation and application of PEG as lubrication in water based drilling fluid for horizontal well in Sulige Gas Field, Polymer International, 70 (2021) 83-89.
5. Materials Research; Universidad del Zulia Researchers Update Current Study Findings on Materials Research (Modified Starch as a Filter Controller in Water-Based Drilling Fluids), Journal of Technology, 12 (2020) 97-113.
6. Z.H. Wang, Design and New Product Development of Drilling Fluid chemicals. Northwest University Press, Xi'an, 2006, pp. 210-212.
7. J.J. Xiao, H.G. Zeng, J. Han, Z.W. Sun, Y. Zhao, Application of high temperature resistant and environment-friendly drilling fluid in Henan Oilfield, China Petroleum and chemical industry standards and quality, 41 (2021) 47-58.
8. F.T.G. Dias, R.R. Souza, E.F. Lucas, Influence of modified starches composition on their performance as fluid loss additives in invert-emulsion drilling fluids, Fuel, 140 (2015) 140-152.
9. Y. Kong, Z. Yang, Z.F. Wang, X.H. Yang, Study on modification of starch and its application in drilling fluid, Energy Weekly News, Applied chemical industry, 11 (2016) 78-93.
10. W.Y. Guo, B. Peng, Synthesis and characterization of starch-graft-polyacrylamide copolymers and their application as filtration control agents in drilling fluid, Journal of Vinyl and Additive Technology, 4 (2012) 261-263.

E3S Web of Conferences **338**, 01017 (2022)
ESMA 2021
https://doi.org/10.1051/e3sconf/202233801017

Study on CO_2 Emission Characteristics of China VI Heavy Duty Diesel Engine

Mingzhi Zhang, Mingshi Chen, Fengbin Wang, Mingqiu Gao, Tieqiang Fu

CATARC Automotive Test Center (Guangzhou) Co. Ltd. Guangzhou 511300, China

Abstract. CO_2 emission control is of great urgency, and the decrease of heavy-duty diesel engines' CO_2 emission is one of the significant methods to reduce CO_2 emission. This paper uses a full-flow constant-volume dilution sampling system to experiment on the China VI heavy-duty diesel engine in order to measure CO_2 emissions under WHTC and WHSC cycles and different loads, with studying the instantaneous emissions characteristics of CO_2, post-processing effects on CO_2 emissions, influence factors of CO_2 emissions. The study found that the CO_2 emissions before the post-treatment of the WHSC cycle are 37% higher than that of the WHTC cycle, while emissions of CO_2 are 3.45% higher than that before post-treatment. Simultaneously, cold start increases the CO_2 emissions of the heavy-duty diesel engines by more than 1%. Post-treatment still increases the CO_2 emissions of heavy-duty diesel engines by 3.5%. In addition, CO_2 emissions have different trends with power at different speeds. CO_2 emissions get an incremental within 600rpm and 900rpm, which gradually becomes slower until it reaches the peak, as engine power increases; the CO_2 emissions initially increase, followed by a decrease, and then continue to increase within 1000rpm and 1400rpm; the CO_2 emissions are almost not affected by the speed within 1500rpm and 1900rpm.

Keywords: CO_2; China VI; Heavy Duty Diesel Engine; Emission Characteristics.

1. Introduction

The United Nations made a summary in October 2018, greenhouse gas emissions must be reduced by about half within 12 years.Only in this way is there the chance of maintaining the limit of global warming at 1.5°C [1] [2]. The contribution of CO_2 to the greenhouse effect accounts for about 50% of all greenhouse gases [3]. Since 2000, China's carbon emissions began to grow rapidly [4], which have reached 10.251 billion tons by 2000, and China have become the largest CO_2 emission country in the world (27.92%) [5]. On September 22nd, 2020, China proposed in the Seventy-fifth United Nations General Assembly: "Strive to reach the peak of CO_2 emissions before 2030, and strive to achieve carbon neutrality before 2060" .The "14th Five-Year Plan" clearly stated that reduce CO_2 emissions by 18% in the next 5 years. Therefore, it is imminent to reduce CO_2 emissions.

According to the 2014 National Greenhouse Gas List, the greenhouse gas of energy activities emits 9.559 billion tons of carbon dioxide equivalent, which is the largest source of greenhouse gas emissions in China, accounting for 77.7% of total greenhouse gas emissions. Greenhouse gas emissions of transportation are 820 million tons of carbon dioxide equivalent, accounting for 8.6% of greenhouse gas emissions of energy activities and 6.7% of the country's total greenhouse gas emissions. Road transportation energy accounts for 84.1% of transportation greenhouse gas emissions, while medium and heavy commercial vehicles account for 47.1% of road transportation greenhouse gas emissions. Moreover, Forward Industry Research Institute sorted out "China Automobile Low Carbon Action Plan Research Report 2020", which showed that diesel fuel vehicles have the highest carbon emissions in unit mileage of vehicles with different fuel types in 2019, reaching 281.9g/km. In addition, the GB17691-2018 "Limits and Measurement Methods for Emissions from Diesel Fueled Heavy-Duty Vehicles (CHINA VI)", clearly stated that the specific requirements on CO_2 emissions would be suitable for publication, and stipulated that the engine standard cycle emission test should measure the CO_2 emissions of the engine, moreover, record the CO_2 specific emission value and the fuel consumption specific fuel consumption value of the cycle. Therefore, it is essential to study the CO_2 emission characteristics of heavy-duty diesel engines based on the China VI emission standards.

This paper studies via the following three points:

1) The instantaneous emission characteristics of CO_2 in the China VI Standard Cycle WHTC and WHSC.

2) The post-treatment route of China VI is EGR + DOC + DPF + SCR + ASC [6], but this technical route will convert conventional pollutants into CO_2 [7]. Therefore, the emission differences before and after post-treatment

 https://doi.org/10.1051/e3sconf/202233801017

are compared and analyzed, and analyze whether the CO_2 converted by other pollutants via the post-treatment route can be ignored at the current stage.

3) The influence law of different factors such as engine power, speed, excess air coefficient, etc. on CO_2 emissions of heavy-duty diesel engines are studied and analyzed.

2. Experimental Methods

The China VI emission standard recommends using full-flow dilution for emission test, moreover, constant-volume dilution sampling is closer to the actual application scenario where exhaust gas are discharged into the air in comparison with direct sampling [8]. Therefore, this experiment adopts the HORIBA full-flow constant-volume dilution sampling system. As shown in Fig.1, the diluted air is sampled after being mixed with the exhaust gas in the dilution channel through the filter unit, and the gas analyzer analyzes to obtains the measurement result.

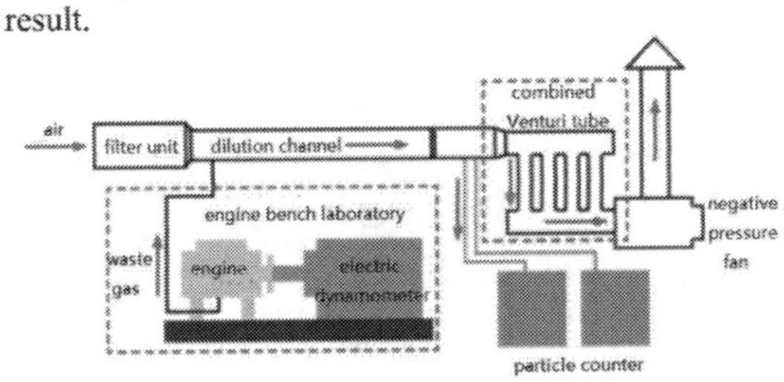

Fig. 1 HORIBA full-flow gas circuit diagram

WHTC and WHSC experiments were carried out based on China VI standards, the CO_2 emissions of original machine and post-treatment back end were measured, the experiment were repeated ten times and the results of the ten experiments were compared and analyzed.

In order to study the influencing factors of CO_2 emissions of China VI heavy-duty engines, the CO_2 emissions under stable working conditions were measured. Experiments were carried out based the China VI emission standards: (1) set the idle speed as the first working condition speed, and 0Nm as the first working condition torque; (2) first, keep the working condition speed unchanged and increase torque based on the 100Nm interval until the throttle is increased to 100%; (3) then increase the engine speed base on the 100rpm interval, and repeat step (2) until the speed reaches the maximum speed. At each working condition point, the bench data and the emissions of various pollutants are recorded based on point distance, and each point distance is recorded as the average value within 10s.

2.1 Experimental equipment

The experimental bench includes: AVL engine dynamomete, AVL 740 fuel consumption meter, AVL puma operating system, AVL air flow meter, Horiba gas analyzer, inlet air conditioning, full room air conditioning, intercoole and coolant temperature control system, PR3 oil return pressure control system, the specific parameters are shown in Table 1.

2.2 Experimental engine and fuel

The engine selects a heavy-duty diesel engine, which meets the test requirements of GB17691-2018 "Limits and Measurement Methods for Emissions from Diesel Fueled Heavy-Duty Vehicles (China VI)". The engine parameters are shown in Table.2.

The engine fuel selects China VI commercial diesel, the fuel information is shown in Table.3.

Table 1. Parameters of experimental equipment

experimental equipment	equipment model	equipment measurement range	accuracy
dynamometer	AVL ASM 3000/1.8-4.5	speed: 0-4500r/min torqoe: 0-3000Nm; power: 0-560kW	torque: ±0.3%F.S speed: ±1rpm
fuel consumption meter	AVL 740MF	(0-150)kg/h	≤±2% of flow setting value
air flow meter	AVL FLOWSONIXTM Air 150	20-1400 kg/h	/
direct sampling gas analyzer	HORIBA MEXA-ONE-DC-OV-OVN-25H	CO0-5000 ppm CO_2:0-20vol% NO/NOx:0-100000 ppm	Within 1.0%(Range≥155ppm)or Within 2.0%(Range≤155ppm)
xicai gas analyzer	HORIBA MEXA-ONE-DC-OV-OVN-35H	CO(L):0-5000 ppm CO_2:0-6vol% NO/NOx:0-5000 ppm	Within 1.0%(Range≥155ppm)or Within 2.0%(Range≤155ppm)

Table 2. Parameters of engine

number of cylinders	Displacement(L)	intake way	rated power (Kw)/speed (rpm)	maximum torque (Nm)/speed (rpm)	fuel requirement
6	12.94	charge inter-cooling	430/1900	2600/1000-1400	0# China VI fuel

Table 3. Parameters of fuel

cetane number	cetane number index (Rating)	density (15°) (kg/m³)	density (20°) (kg/m³)	total aromatics (m/m)	kinematic viscosity (40°) (mm²/s)
52.0	49.2	840.9	835.4	21.4%	3.974

3. Experimental Results and Analysis

3.1 Research on the characteristic of CO_2 instantaneous emission

The China VI standard stipulates that the instantaneous test cycle WHTC and the steady-state test cycle WHSC are used for engine test. Therefore, this paper studies the characteristics of CO_2 instantaneous emission of WHTC and WHSC cycles.

As shown in Fig.2, the CO_2 concentration of WHTC cold and hot start cycles is between 0-40000ppm, and the peak value is between 1200-1500s. As shown in Fig.3, the CO_2 concentration of WHSC cycle is between 0-110000ppm, and the peak value is much higher than that of WHTC cycle.

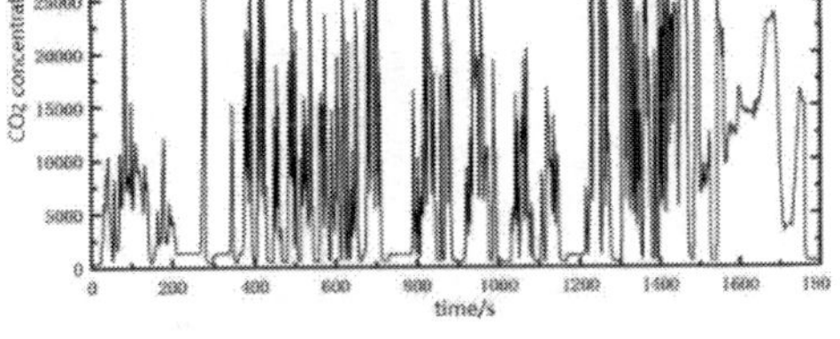

(a) WHTC cold start cycle

 https://doi.org/10.1051/e3sconf/202233801017

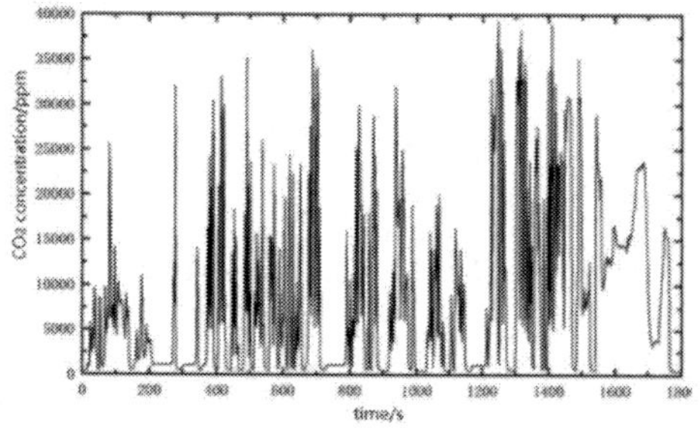

(b) WHTC hot start cycle

Fig. 2 CO_2 instantaneous emission trend of WHTC cycle

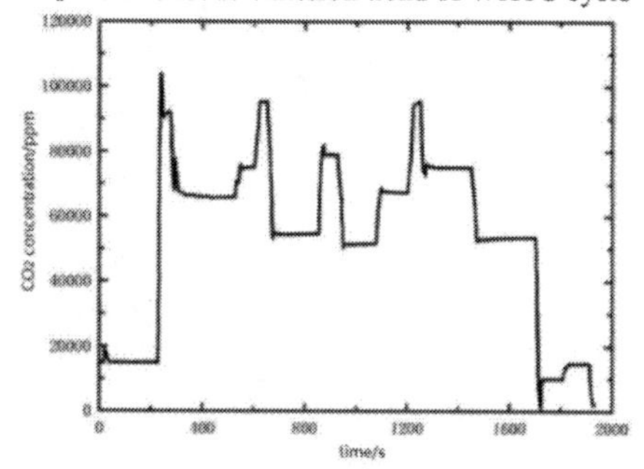

Fig. 3 CO_2 instantaneous emission trend of WHSC cycle

3.1.1 Contrast studies of WHTC and WHSC cycle emission

The instantaneous emission mass is calculated by the original concentration and exhaust mass flow of pollutants arranged based on conversion time. The instantaneous value of the whole cycle is integrated, and in order to obtain the pollutant mass emission, the integration is multiplied by the ratio of exhaust component to exhaust density, as shown in equation (1) [9].

$$m_{gas} = u_{gas} \times \sum_{i=1}^{i=n} c_{gas,i} \times q_{mew,i} \times \frac{1}{f} \ (unit: g / test) \quad (1)$$

In the equation, u_{gas} is the ratio of exhaust component density to exhaust density; $c_{gas,i}$ is the instantaneous concentration of exhaust component, ppm; $q_{mew,i}$ is the instantaneous exhaust mass flow, Kg/s; f is the sampling frequency, Hz; n is the number of tests.

As shown in Fig.4, at the front of the engine post-treatment, the CO_2 of the WHSC cycle engine tops 37131g, and the WHTC cycle tops 26177g. After averaging the results of ten experiments, the CO_2 emissions of WHSC cycle are 37% higher than weighted CO_2 emissions of WHTC cycle in hot and cold states, and the CO_2 specific emissions of WHSC cycle are 3.45% greater than weighted CO_2 emission of WHTC cycle in the cold and hot states, as shown in Fig.5. Because the WHSC cycle is the steady-state cycle, the combustion in the cylinder is fuller.

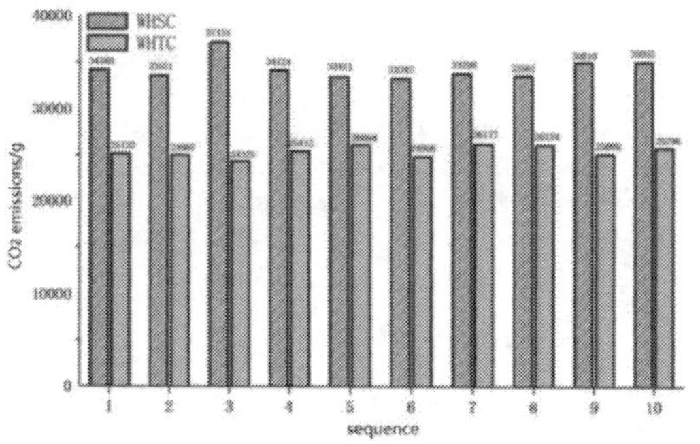

Fig. 4 comparison of CO_2 emissions of WHSC and WHTC cycles at the front of post-treatment

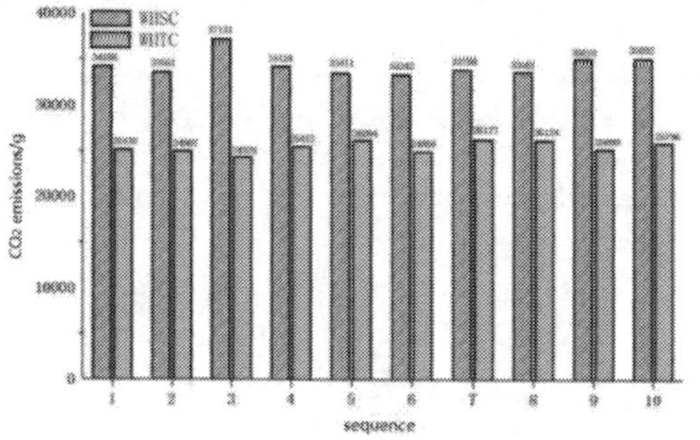

Fig. 5 comparison of CO_2 specific emissions of WHSC and WHTC cycles at the front of post-treatment

3.1.2 The impact of cold start condition on CO_2 emissions of heavy-duty diesel engines

As shown in Fig.6, at the front of the engine post-treatment, the CO_2 emissions of WHTC in cold state are 1.09% larger than that in hot state, which suggests that cold start condition will increase CO_2 emissions of heavy-duty diesel engines. Because the combustion is not full during cold start, however, the increase of fuel injection quantity plays a decisive role and causes the increase of CO_2 emissions.

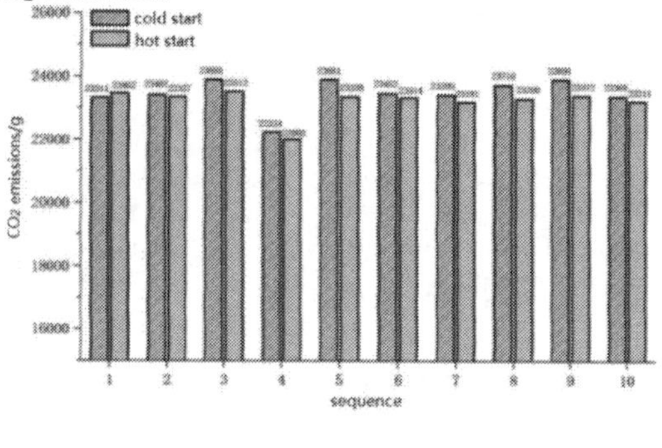

Fig. 6 comparison of CO_2 emissions of WHTC cycle in hot and cold states at the front of post-treatment

3.2 The impact of post-treatment on CO_2 emissions

As shown in Fig.7, the CO_2 specific emissions after post-treatment are 3.5% larger than that before post-treatment on average. Because DOC oxidizes unburned HC to CO_2.

 https://doi.org/10.1051/e3sconf/202233801017

Moreover, DOC oxidizes the diesel fuel injected into the exhaust pipe with released heat, which increases the temperature of the DPF. And the carbon in DPF can react with oxygen to generate CO_2. In addition, the hydrolysis reaction of urea in SCR can also generate CO_2 [10]. This post-treatment technology of heavy-duty diesel engine increases CO_2 emissions while reducing conventional pollutants.

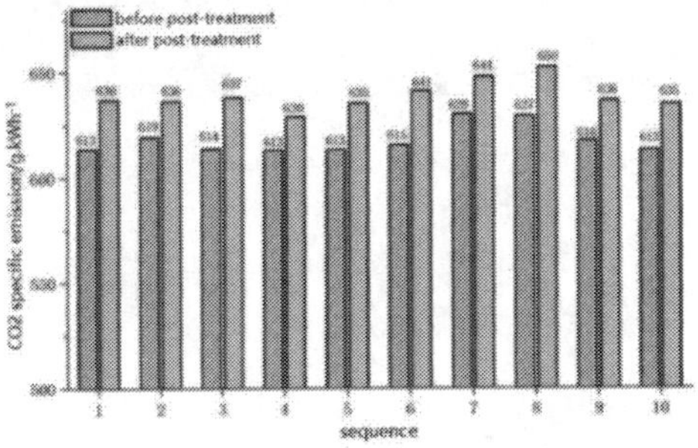

Fig. 7 comparison of CO_2 specific emissions before and after post-treatment

3.3 The impact of different factors on CO_2 emissions of heavy-duty diesel engines

3.3.1 The impact of power and speed on CO_2 emissions of heavy-duty diesel engines

As shown in Fig.8, the CO_2 emission concentration of engine is in the range of 2000-11000ppm. In the range of 600rpm-900rpm, the CO_2 emission concentration can reach 11000ppm at 200KW, while in the range of 1000rpm-1400rpm, the CO_2 emission concentration can reach maximum value at 300KW, and in the range of 1500rpm-1900rpm, the CO_2 emission concentration can reach maximum value at 400KW. Since CO_2 emissions show varied laws in different speed ranges, it is necessary to study separately.

As shown in Fig. 8(a), when the engine speed is between 600rpm-900rpm, CO_2 emissions increase with the increase of engine power, but the increasing trend gradually becomes slower and does not increase until it reaches the peak value. Moreover, at the same power, the higher the speed, the smaller the CO_2 emissions. As the load increases, the amount of fuel injection quantity increases, resulting in the rise of CO_2 emissions. However, due to the increase of the load, the oxygen concentration will decrease and the fuel injection duration will increase, so the reaction time of the fuel injected later is shorter with the result that the combustion is not full. Therefore, under the combined effect of the fuel injection quantity, the increasing trend of CO_2 emissions is gradually slowing down. Moreover, the higher the speed, the shorter the mixing and combustion time, and the combustion is not easily full, so the CO_2 emissions are smaller.

As shown in Fig. 8(b), when the engine speed is between 1000rpm-1400rpm, CO_2 emissions increase steadily and the differences of CO_2 emissions at different speeds are not obvious before 90KW. But between 90KW and 130KW CO_2 emissions start to decline, and then continue to rise. Meanwhile the higher speed, the smaller the CO_2 emissions. Therefore, there are two turning points between 1000rpm-1400rpm: the turning point A from increase to decrease and the turning point B from decrease to rise. Turning points A are relatively close at different speeds, and there is no obvious law. Turning points B shift below and behind as the speed increases. Namely, the greater the speed, the greater the reduction of CO_2 emissions and the wider the reduced power range.

As shown in Fig.8(c), when the engine speed is between 1500rpm-1900rpm, the development law of CO_2 emissions is similar to that of 1000rpm-1400rpm. However, the changing curves of CO_2 emissions with power at different speeds basically coincide. Therefore, the CO_2 emissions of the engine are less affected by the speed between 1500rpm and 1900rpm.

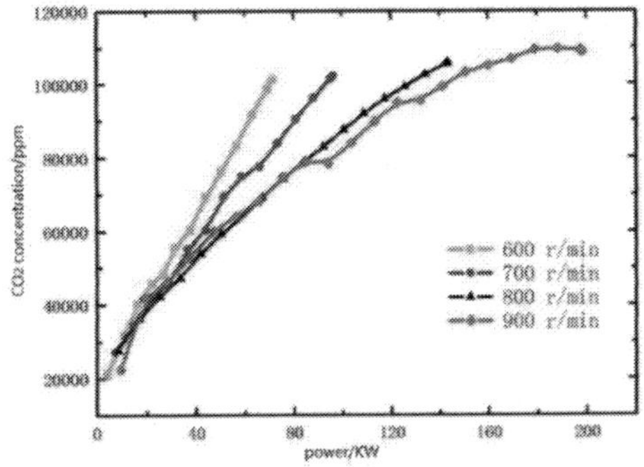

(a) 600rpm-900rpm

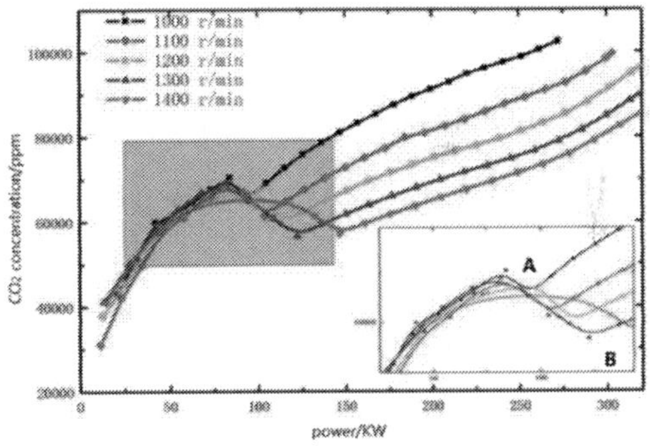

(b) 1000rpm-1400rpm

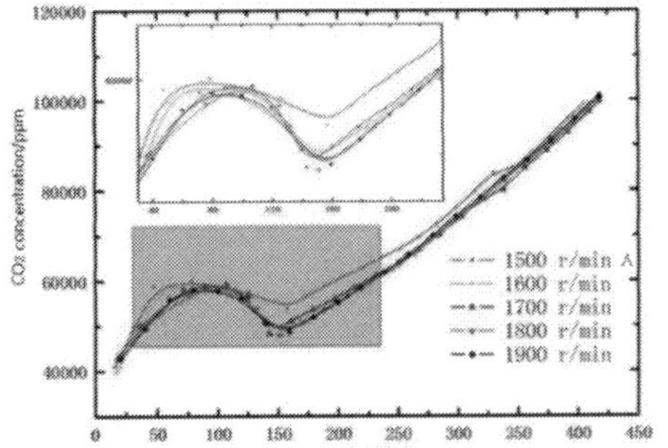

(c) 1500rpm-1900rpm

Fig. 8 the relationship between CO_2 and power and speed

https://doi.org/10.1051/e3sconf/202233801017

In order to avoid the influence of differences of ECU control strategy on the above laws, namely, the influence of the differences of fuel injection quantity at different loads on the above laws, compare the CO_2 emissions and the fuel consumption with power of heavy-duty diesel engines in three speed ranges. As shown in Fig.9, the fuel injection quantity of this engine increases linearly with the increase of power, but CO_2 emissions with power still have turning points within 1000rpm-1400rpm and 1500rpm-1900rpm. Therefore, in the 600rpm-900rpm, fuel consumption plays a leading role in CO_2 emissions, in the 1000rpm-1400rpm and 1500rpm-1900rpm, in addition to the impact of fuel consumption on CO_2 emissions, load also has an impact on CO_2 emissions, its influence mechanism will be studied as the content of the next stage.

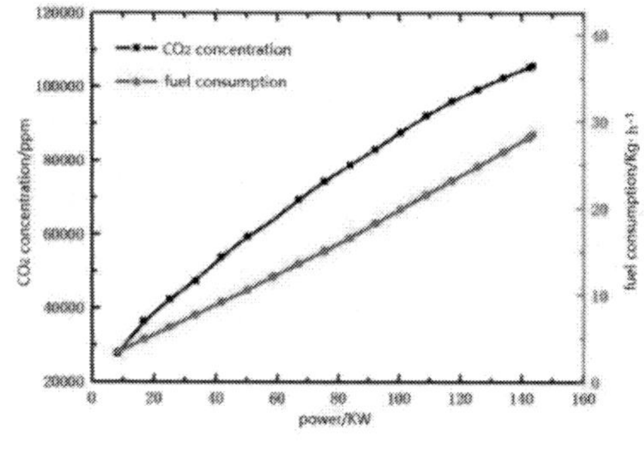

(a) 600rpm-900rpm

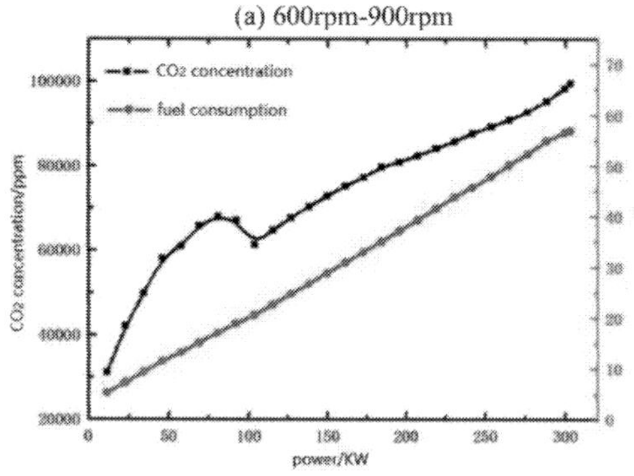

(b) 1000rpm-1400rpm

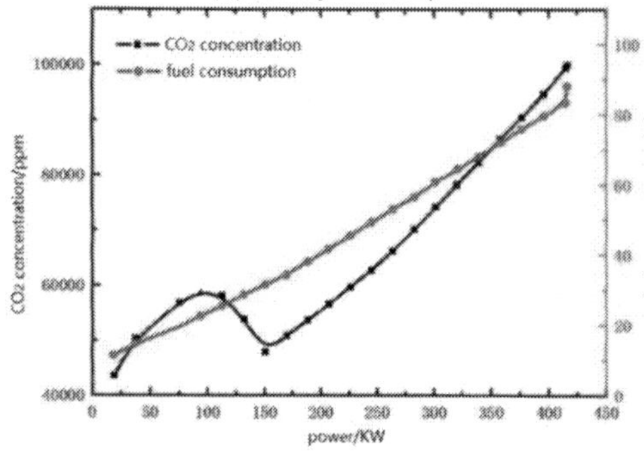

(c) 1500rpm-1900rpm

Fig. 9 CO_2 emission and fuel consumption change with power

4 Conclusion

This paper carries out experiments on the China VI heavy-duty diesel engine with full-flow constant-volume dilution sampling system, measuring the CO_2 emissions of the WHTC and WHSC cycles and different loads of engine, after processing the data. The following conclusions are drawn:

(1) At the front of engine post-treatment, the CO_2 emissions of the engine WHSC cycle are 37% higher than the weighted CO_2 emissions of WHTC cycle in the cold and hot states. Moreover, the CO_2 specific emission of engine WHSC cycle are 3.45% greater than the weighted CO_2 specific emission of WHTC cycle in the cold and hot states.

(2) At the front of engine post-treatment, the CO_2 emissions of WHTC in cold state are 1.09% larger than that in hot state. Therefore, cold start conditions will increase CO_2 emissions of heavy-duty diesel engines.

(3) The CO_2 specific emission after post-treatment are 3.5% larger than the CO_2 emissions before post-treatment on average.

(4) When the engine speed is between 600rpm-900rpm, CO_2 emissions increase with the increase of engine power, but the increasing trend gradually becomes slower and does not increase until it reaches the peak value. Moreover, at the same power, the higher the speed, the smaller the CO_2 emissions. When the engine speed is between 1000rpm-1400rpm, CO2 emissions increase steadily and the differences of CO2 emissions at different speeds are not obvious before 90KW. But between 90KW and 130KW CO2 emissions start to decline, and then continue to rise. Meanwhile the higher speed, the smaller the CO2 emissions. So the greater the speed, the greater the reduction of CO_2 emissions and the wider the reduced power range. When the engine speed is between 1500rpm-1900rpm, the development law of CO_2 emissions is similar to that of 1000rpm-1400rpm. However, the changing curves of CO_2 emissions with power at different speeds basically coincide. Therefore, the CO_2 emissions of the engine are less affected by the speed between 1500rpm and 1900rpm.

References

1. Science-Geoscience; New Geoscience Findings from T. Schneider and Colleagues Discussed (Possible Climate Transitions From Breakup of Stratocumulus Decks Under Greenhouse Warming)[J]. Science Letter, 2019.
2. Wang Xieqin. Greenhouse Effect and Emission Reduction of Greenhouse Gases[J]. Natural Gas Technology, 2008(06):53-58+79-80.
3. Qi Yuchun, Dong Yunshe. Emission of Greenhouse Gases from Energy Field and Mitigation Countermeasures in China[J]. Scientia Geographica Sinica, 2004(05): 528-534.
4. Liu Qiang, Liu Jiaqi, He Huaiyu. Research Advances on Concentration Change of Greenhouse Gases and

Their Source & Sink[J]. Advances in Earth Sciences, 2000(04):453-460.

5. Wang Feng, Wu Lihua, Yang Chao. Driving Factors for Growth of Carbon Dioxide Emissions During Economic Development in China[J]. Economic Research Journal, 2010, 45(02): 123-136.
6. Lan Zulong. Technical Analysis of China VI Emission Post-treatment of Heavy-Duty Vehicle Diesel Engines[J]. Technology and Market, 2020, 27(03): 78-80.
7. Zhang Qinjun, Hou Feiyue, Ren Xiyang, Jie Yanmeng, Shi Zhili. Introduction to Technical Route of the Sixth Post-Processor of Heavy Diesel Vehicle[J]. Automobile Applied Technology, 2019(15): 193-194.
8. Xu Xiaohua, Zhang Tao. The Effects of Sampling Methods on the Emission Test Results for Diesel Engines[J]. Small Internal Combustion Engine and Motorcycle, 2020, 49(01): 67-72.
9. Ministry of Ecology and Environment, etc., GB18352.6-2016, " Limits and Measurement Methods for emissions from Light-dutyVehicle (China 6).
10. Lan Zulong. Technical Analysis of China VI Emission Post-treatment of Heavy-Duty Vehicle Diesel Engines[J]. Technology and Market, 2020, 27(03): 80.

https://doi.org/10.1051/e3sconf/202233801018

Full life-cycle economic evaluation of integrated energy system with hydrogen storage equipment

Yuqiong Zhang[1], Qiang Zhao[1], Jindi Ao[2], Zhaozhen Wang[2], Yuqing Wang[2,*]

[1] China Electric Power Research Institute, Beijing 100192, China
[2] North China Electric Power University, Baoding 071000, Hebei Province, China

Abstract. Hydrogen energy storage, as a new type of energy storage with zero carbon emission, multi-energy federal reserve and combined supply, has a good development prospect in the integrated energy system. Based on the integrated energy system with hydrogen storage equipment, this paper proposes the operation mechanism of the integrated energy system with hydrogen storage equipment in the environment of electricity market and carbon market. On this basis, considering the time value of money, the life-cycle economic evaluation model of the integrated energy system with hydrogen storage equipment is constructed. The model is applied to calculate the investment benefit of a community integrated energy system with hydrogen storage equipment in the whole life cycle. The result of an example shows that the integrated energy system with hydrogen storage equipment is of good economic benefits.

Key words: Hydrogen Storage; Integrated Energy System; Electric Hydrogen Production; Full Life-cycle; Economic Evaluation

1. Introduction

In the context of "carbon peaking", "carbon neutral" and large-scale new energy applications, hydrogen energy storage has the characteristics of zero carbon emission,multi-energy federal reserve and combined supply, which help improve the utilization rate of new energy and the stability of power system operation[1]. In the integrated energy system, the use of hydrogen storage instead of traditional battery storage can not only supply hydrogen fuel to fuel cell vehicles and support the transformation of electrified transportation, but also convert electricity into natural gas with hydrogen as a carrier in a clean and efficient manner, realizing electrical synergistic operation and complementary transformation [2]. At present, the integrated energy system with hydrogen storage equipment is technically feasible, but whether can it generate considerable economic benefits in the market environment and its economic viability are worthy of in-depth study and exploration.

At present, a series of research on investment decision-making of integrated energy system containing hydrogen storage has been carried out at home and abroad. Literature [3] analyzes the economy of hydrogen production, storage and transmission from renewable energy by using the levelized hydrogen cost analysis model. Literature [4] puts forward the optimal allocation model of hydrogen energy storage units in the park integrated energy system with the optimization objectives of investment and operation cost and carbon emission. Literature [5] constructs a multi-objective programming model of electric thermal hydrogen integrated energy system considering uncertainty with the goal of minimizing economic cost and maximizing wind and solar energy consumption rate. In reference [6], aiming at minimizing the economic cost and potential cost of daily chemical system, a family comprehensive energy system planning model based on hydrogen energy storage is constructed. To sum up, most of the existing studies focus on the cost analysis of comprehensive energy systems containing hydrogen storage, and few studies analyze the income composition of such comprehensive energy systems in the market environment and calculate the economic benefits in the whole life cycle.

In summary, this paper proposes the operation mechanism of the integrated energy system with hydrogen storage equipment in the environment of electricity market and carbon market and establishes a model to evaluate the life-cycle economic benefits of the integrated energy system with hydrogen storage equipment, and then takes a community-based integrated energy system with hydrogen storage equipment as an example to calculate whether the integrated energy system with hydrogen storage equipment is economically feasible.

* Corresponding author: wangyuqingncepu@foxmail.com

https://doi.org/10.1051/e3sconf/202233801018

2. Integrated energy system architecture and operation mechanism with hydrogen storage equipment

The integrated energy system with hydrogen storage equipment includes wind turbines, photovoltaics, cogeneration units, electrolytic cells, hydrogen storage tanks, hydrogen refueling stations, fuel cell vehicles, methanation devices, natural gas networks, gas boilers and other equipment. The system architecture is such as As shown in Figure 1.

The electrical load in the integrated energy system is supplied by wind turbines, photovoltaic and cogeneration units.When the electric energy generated by the fan and photovoltaic cannot meet the demand, the cogeneration unit will supplement the electricity; when the electric energy generated by the fan and photovoltaic has surplus in addition to the electricity sold, the surplus electric energy is electrolyzed into hydrogen through the electrolytic cell and stored in the hydrogen storage tank, the hydrogen refueling station provides hydrogen for fuel cell vehicles.When there is a surplus of hydrogen, the methanation unit is started to convert the surplus hydrogen into methane and input into the natural gas network.The heat load is mainly supplied by cogeneration units, and gas boilers are used as supplementary heat sources.

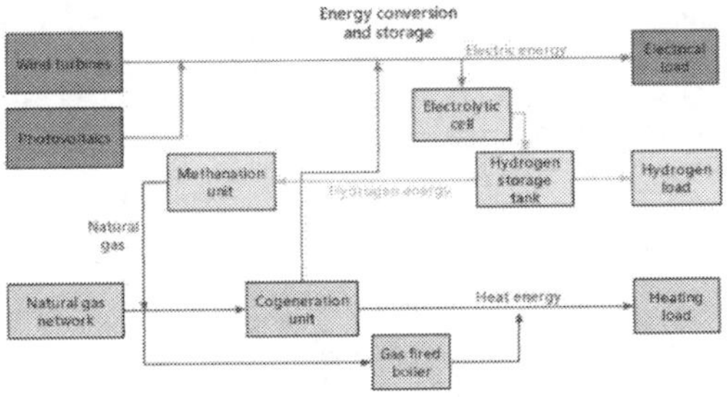

Fig 1 Architecture diagram of an integrated energy system with hydrogen storage equipment

3. Cost benefit analysis of integrated energy system with hydrogen storage equipment

3.1 Cost analysis

Assuming that the financial cost and facility exit cost are not considered, the life cycle cost of the integrated energy system including hydrogen storage equipment mainly includes investment cost, operation and maintenance cost and production cost. The investment cost includes the purchase, construction and installation costs of wind power, distributed photovoltaic, cogeneration units, electric hydrogen production, methane production units, gas-fired boilers, hydrogen storage tanks and other equipment; Operation and maintenance costs include repair costs, personnel salaries and welfare expenses; Production costs include fuel, water, etc.

3.2 Revenue analysis

In the environment of electricity market and carbon market, the integrated energy system with hydrogen storage equipment can supply electric energy, hydrogen energy, thermal energy and methane to users, and its carbon emission reduction can participate in carbon trading. Therefore, the life cycle income of the integrated energy system including hydrogen storage equipment mainly includes energy sales income, carbon emission reduction income and other income. Among them, energy sales revenue includes power supply revenue, hydrogen supply revenue, heating revenue and methane sales revenue. Carbon emission reduction revenue includes carbon emission reduction revenue from renewable energy power generation and carbon emission reduction revenue from methane production. As renewable energy, wind and light can obtain carbon emission reduction income by participating in the carbon emission reduction market. Compared with traditional coal chemical methane production, hydrogen production by electricity can reduce carbon emissions in methane production, so it can also obtain carbon emission reduction income. Other income includes equipment residual value recovery income, etc. The cost income composition of comprehensive energy system including hydrogen storage equipment is shown in Table 1.

4 Life cycle economic evaluation model of integrated energy system with hydrogen storage equipment

4.1 Life cycle NPV calculation model of integrated energy system with hydrogen storage equipment

Considering the time value of funds, the calculation of life cycle economic benefits of comprehensive energy system including hydrogen storage equipment is shown in formula (1).

$$NPV = \sum_{t=1}^{n} \frac{\left(R_t - \left(C_{t,2} + C_{t,3}\right)\right)}{\left(1+r\right)^t} - C_1 \qquad (1)$$

Where, NPV is the present value of the net economic benefits of the comprehensive energy system with hydrogen storage equipment in the whole life cycle; n is the estimated service life of the project; t represents year t; R_t is the economic income of the integrated energy system in year t; C_1 is the investment cost for the construction of integrated energy system; $C_{t,2}$ is the operation and maintenance cost of the integrated energy system in year t; $C_{t,3}$ is the production cost of the integrated energy system in year t; r is the discount rate.

Table 1. Cost income composition of comprehensive energy system including hydrogen storage equipment

Cost and revenue category		Concrete content
Life cycle cost	Investment cost	Wind power
		Distributed photovoltaic
		CHP
		Electric hydrogen production
		Methane production unit
		Gas fired boiler
		Hydrogen storage tank
	Operation and maintenance cost	Repair cost
		Personnel salary
		Welfare funds
	Production costs	Fuel cost
		Charge for water
Life cycle revenue	Energy sales revenue	Power supply revenue
		Hydrogen supply revenue
		Heating revenue
		Methane sales revenue
	Carbon emission reduction revenue	Carbon emission reduction revenue from renewable energy power generation
		Carbon emission reduction revenue from methane production
	Other revenue	Equipment salvage value recovery revenue

4.2 Life cycle cost calculation model of integrated energy system with hydrogen storage equipment

(1) Investment cost of integrated energy system with hydrogen storage equipment

The investment cost of integrated energy system including hydrogen storage equipment mainly consists of seven parts: the purchase and installation cost of wind power equipment, distributed photovoltaic equipment, cogeneration equipment, electric hydrogen production equipment, methane production unit, gas-fired boiler and hydrogen storage tank. The calculation is shown in equation (2).

$$C_1 = C_f + C_p + C_c + C_e + C_m + C_g + C_h \tag{2}$$

Where, C_f , C_p , C_c , C_e , C_m , C_g and C_h are the investment costs of wind power equipment, distributed photovoltaic equipment, CHP Cogeneration Equipment, electric hydrogen production equipment, methane production unit, gas-fired boiler and hydrogen storage tank respectively. The investment cost of each equipment is directly related to the system scale, and the specific relationship is shown in equations (3) - (9).

$$C_f = U_f \times I_f \tag{3}$$

$$C_p = U_p \times I_p \tag{4}$$

$$C_c = U_c \times I_c \tag{5}$$

$$C_e = U_e \times I_e \tag{6}$$

$$C_m = U_m \times I_m \tag{7}$$

$$C_g = U_g \times I_g \tag{8}$$

$$C_h = U_h \times I_h \tag{9}$$

Where, U_f , U_p , U_c , U_e , U_m , U_g , U_h are the unit cost of each equipment; I_f , I_p , I_c , I_e , I_m , I_g , I_h are the installed capacity of each equipment.

(2) Operation and maintenance cost of integrated energy system with hydrogen storage equipment

The operation and maintenance cost of integrated energy system with hydrogen storage equipment is calculated as shown in equation (10).

$$C_2 = \sum \lambda C_i \alpha_i \tag{10}$$

Where, λ is the formation rate of fixed assets, C_i is the investment cost of class I equipment, and α_i is the freight rate of class I equipment.

(3) Production cost of integrated energy system with hydrogen storage equipment

The production cost of integrated energy system with hydrogen storage equipment is mainly composed of fuel and water. The calculation are shown in equation (11) - (13).

$$C_3 = C_u + C_w \tag{11}$$

$$C_u = Q_u P_u \tag{12}$$

$$C_w = Q_w P_w \tag{13}$$

Where, Q_u and Q_w are the annual gas consumption and water consumption of the integrated energy system respectively, P_u and P_w are the natural gas price and water price respectively.

4.3 Life cycle income calculation model of integrated energy system with hydrogen storage equipment

Life cycle income R mainly consists of six parts: power supply income R_e, hydrogen supply income R_h, heating income R_t, methane sales income R_m, carbon emission reduction income R_c and residual value recovery income R_s .The calculation is shown in equation (14).

$$R = R_e + R_h + R_t + R_m + R_c + R_s \tag{14}$$

(1) Power supply income of integrated energy system with hydrogen storage equipment
The power supply income is determined by the electricity sales (MWh) and the electricity sales price (yuan / MWh). The calculation is shown in equation (15).

$$R_e = Q_e P_e \tag{15}$$

Where, Q_e is the electricity sales; P_e is the selling price.
(2) Hydrogen supply income of integrated energy system with hydrogen storage equipment
Hydrogen supply revenue is determined by hydrogen sales volume (ton) and hydrogen sales price (10,000 yuan / ton). The calculation is shown in equation (16).

$$R_h = Q_h P_h \tag{16}$$

Where, Q_h is the hydrogen sales volume; P_h is the selling price of hydrogen.
(3) Heating income of integrated energy system with hydrogen storage equipment
The heating revenue is determined by the heat sold (MWh) and the heat sold price (yuan / MWh). The calculation is shown in equation (17).

$$R_t = Q_t P_t \tag{17}$$

Where, Q_t is the selling heat; P_t is the selling price.
(4) Methane sales revenue of integrated energy system with hydrogen storage equipment
Methane sales revenue is determined by methane sales volume (ton) and methane price (10000 yuan / ton). The calculation is shown in formula (18).

$$R_m = Q_m P_m \tag{18}$$

Where, Q_m is the sales volume of methane; P_m is the price of methane.
(5) Carbon emission reduction revenue of integrated energy system with hydrogen storage equipment
Carbon emission reduction revenue consists of carbon emission reduction revenue from renewable energy power generation and carbon emission reduction revenue from methane production, which is determined by carbon emission reduction (ton) and carbon price (yuan / ton). The specific relationship is shown in equations (19) - (21).

$$R_c = R_g + R_y \tag{19}$$

$$R_g = Q_g F_g P_c \tag{20}$$

$$R_y = Q_y F_y P_c \tag{21}$$

Where, Q_g and Q_y are respectively the annual power generation of renewable energy and the annual production of methane; F_g and F_y are carbon emission factors of electric power production and carbon emission factors of coal chemical industry to methane; P_c is the carbon price.
(6) Residual value recovery income of integrated energy system with hydrogen storage equipment
The residual value recovery income is determined by the investment cost and the residual value recovery rate. The calculation is shown in equation (22).

$$R_s = C_1 \beta \tag{22}$$

Where, β is residual value recovery.

5. Analysis of algorithms

In order to measure the economics of an integrated energy system with hydrogen storage equipment, this paper takes a community-based integrated energy system with hydrogen storage equipment as an example and conducts a full life-cycle cost-benefit calculation of an integrated energy system with hydrogen storage equipment participating in carbon trading.

5.1 Basic data

This integrated energy system with hydrogen storage equipment has a construction period of 1 year, an operation period of 20 years, a discount rate of 7.5%, a fixed asset formation ratio of 95%, a salvage recovery rate of 5% and a depreciable life of 15 years.

Table 2. Data sheet on investment costs and O&M costs

Equipment Type	Unit construction cost (million yuan/Mw)	Installed capacity (Mw)	O&M rate (%)
Wind energy	350.00	0.60	1.00
Distributed PV	950.00	2.10	1.00
CHP Combined Heat and Power	160.00	4.70	2.00
Electric hydrogen production	930.00	2.90	2.00
Methane production unit	470.00	1.90	1.00
Gas boiler	120.00	1.10	2.00
Hydrogen storage tank	128.73	7.20	2.00

Table 3. Data sheet on production costs and revenues

Specific categories of production costs and revenues	parameters
Natural gas price (Yuan/Nm³)	3
Water price (yuan/ton)	3.15
Annual electricity sales (Mwh)	8957.1
Annual heat sales (Mwh)	5277.9
Annual hydrogen sales (tons)	22.70
Annual methane sales (tonnes)	45.69
Annual carbon emission reductions (tonnes)	4403.19
Sale price of electricity (yuan/Mwh)	800
Heat selling price (Yuan/Mwh)	330
Hydrogen sales price (million yuan/ton)	7
Methane selling price (million yuan/ton)	0.6
Carbon price (yuan/ton)	100

5.2 Results of the economic assessment

Substituting the data from Tables 2 and 3 into the integrated energy system with hydrogen storage equipment full life-cycle economics measurement tool, yields the financial indicators shown in Table 4.

Table 4. Financial indicators of integrated energy system with hydrogen storage equipment (million yuan)

Financial indicators	Parameters
Initial investment cost	76.06
Annual operation and maintenance costs	1.18
Annual production costs	2.64
Annual sales revenue	10.77
Annual carbon reduction revenue	0.44
Net present value (NPV)	0.12
Internal rate of return (%)	7.52%
Static payback period (years)	11.29
Dynamic payback period (years)	20.95

As can be seen from Table 4, the total initial investment cost is 76.06 million yuan, the annual operation and maintenance cost is 1.18 million yuan, and the annual production cost is 2.64 million yuan the annual sales revenue is 10.77 million yuan, and the annual carbon reduction revenue is 0.44 million yuan. The net present value is 0.12 million yuan, the internal rate of return is 7.52%, the static payback period is 11.29 years, and the dynamic payback period is 20.95 years. The NPV is greater than 0, the IRR is greater than the base rate of return, and the project is economically viable.

5.3 Sensitivity analysis

This section performs a sensitivity analysis on the economics of an integrated energy system with hydrogen storage equipment, and measures the impact on the NPV of the project when the price of hydrogen, the price of methane, the price of carbon, the cost of electric hydrogen production equipment, the cost of hydrogen storage equipment, and the cost of methane production equipment fluctuate in the range of -10% to 10% for each individual factor. The results of the analysis are shown in Figure 2. The results show that the NPV of the project is sensitive to the cost of electric hydrogen production equipment, the price of hydrogen followed. The cost of hydrogen storage equipment, the cost of methane production equipment, the price of carbon and the price of methane have a relatively small impact on the NPV of the project. The three items with the greatest sensitivity to NPV are all related to hydrogen, indicating that the cost of hydrogen production, hydrogen storage and the price of hydrogen sales are very important in the integrated energy system with hydrogen storage equipment which will have a large impact on the economics of the integrated energy system with hydrogen storage equipment. Therefore, with the development of technology, the cost of hydrogen storage decreases or the price of carbon is considered to increase while the economic benefits of integrated energy systems with hydrogen storage equipment will also increase.

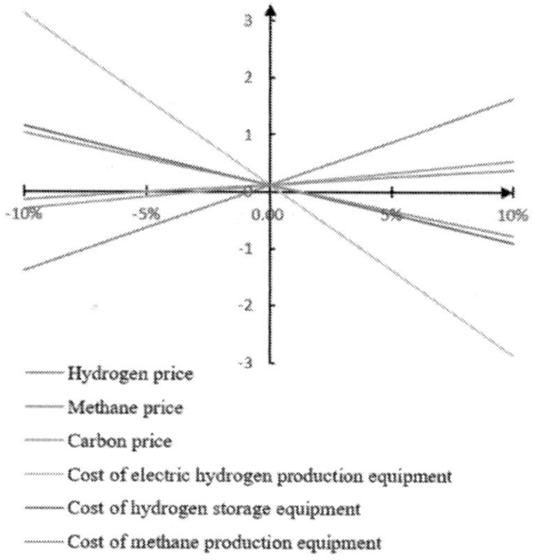

Fig 2 Sensitivity analysis of an integrated energy system with hydrogen storage equipment (million yuan)

6 Conclusion

In this paper, a community-based integrated energy system with hydrogen storage equipment is used as the research object, and a life-cycle economic evaluation model of the integrated energy system with hydrogen storage equipment is established. Under the premise of considering the time value of money, the evaluation system is measured in terms of NPV, IRR, payback period and other indicators. The calculation results yields that the integrated energy system with hydrogen storage equipment can generate investment benefits and has investment significance.

Acknowledgements

This paper is supported by the National Key Research and Development Program (2018YFB1503101).

https://doi.org/10.1051/e3sconf/202233801018

References

1. Liu Daobing, Yuan Ye, Li Shichun, Cao Hongji, Jin Zitong, Bao Zhiyang. Review on capacity allocation of renewable energy system using hydrogen energy storage [J]. Electrical Measurement & Instrumentation, 2021, 32(07): 1-14.
2. Li Guojun, Yuan Tiejiang, Sun Yima, Chen Guangyu, Shengwei Mei. Life cycle economic evaluation of wind power-hydrogen energy storage and coal chemical multi-energy coupling system [J]. Transactions of China Electrotechnical Society, 2017, 32(21): 132-142.
3. Huang Xuanxu, Lian Jijian, Wai Shum, Ma Chao. Economic analysis of large-scale hydrogen energy supply chain in China [J]. Southern Energy Construction, 2020, 7(02): 1-13.
4. Xiong Yufeng, Chen Laijun, Zheng Tianwen, Si Yang, Shengwei Mei. Optimal allocation of hydrogen storage in comprehensive energy system of low-carbon park considering the coupling characteristics of electricity and heat [J]. Electric Power Automation Equipment, 2021, 41(09): 31-38.
5. Hou Hui, Liu Peng, Huang Liang, Xie Changjun, Zhang Ruiming. Integrated energy system planning of electricity, heat and hydrogen considering uncertainty [J]. Transactions of China Electrotechnical Society, 2021, 36(S1): 133-144.
6. Wang Yibo. Research on optimization of household comprehensive energy system based on hydrogen storage [D]. Beijing Jiaotong University, 2020.

Optimization of hot-press process and structural characterization of PF Camellia oleifera cake adhesive

Xiao Hu [1,3], Rui Zeng [2,§], Yuyuan Li [4], Jinghua Zhou [5], Xi Li [4], Yong Wang [6], Xiang Li [2], Dong Wang [2,*]

[1] Forestry College of Guangxi University, Nanning, Guangxi Province, China
[2] Hunan Airbluer Environmental Protection Technology Co., Changsha, Hunan Province, China
[3] Hunan Association of Environmental Improvement, Changsha, Hunan Province, China
[4] Institute of Subtropical Agroecology, Chinese Academy of Sciences, Changsha, Hunan Province, China
[5] Anxiang County Agricultural and Rural Bureau, Changde, Hunan Province, China
[6] Institute of Forest Products and Industry, Hunan Academy of Forestry, Changsha, Hunan Province, China

§Contributed equally to this work

Abstract: In this paper, the result based on the techniques of indoor wood adhesive of Camellia oleifera cake and manufacturing of manmade board suggests that the most appropriate condition of preparation this adhesive is that the solid content is 50%, the reaction temperature is 50 ℃, the reaction time is 40min, the dosage of PF resin prepolymer accounts for 50 percent. The pH of the reaction medium is 10 and the dosage of SDBS is 1%. The proper conditions hot pressing process of PF Camellia oleifera cake adhesive for bonding plywood are the hot pressing temperature is 120 ℃, and the hot pressing time is 0.7min/mm (42 s / mm), the gluing amount is 120g / ㎡, and the hot pressing pressure is 1.1MPa. The average water-resistant bonding strength of the plywood prepared under this condition is 0.79mpa, which meets the requirements of class II plate in the national standard GB / T 9846.3-2004. The emission of formaldehyde is 0.38 mg / L, which meets the requirements of class E0 plate in the national standard GB 18580-2001. What's more, the cost is the lowest among all the techniques.

Key words: Camellia oleifera cake adhesive, hot pressing technique, bonding strength, manmade board.

1. Introduction

Board making technique is a vital step in examining the performance of adhesive. Better hot pressing technique can not only achieve a good quality of the product but also can improve manufacturing efficiency. What's more, it can reduce equipment wear and energy consumption and save cost[1]. Therefore, seeking for best hot pressing technique has already become the most important technique in applying and spreading the new wood adhesive[2]. Under the best technique, PF- Camellia oleifera cake adhesive has lots of advantages such as high bonding strength, good water resistance, less cost and E0 standard of formaldehyde emission. However, compared with commonly used urea formaldehyde resin, higher temperature is needed when pressing plywood with it. （135 ~ 140℃） this temperature is higher than that of urea formaldehyde resin for 20-30℃[3].this is because the composition of PF Camellia oleifera cake adhesive contains PF resin, protein, tannin that have reaction activity and some polymers formed by them. When these compositions need solidification, they require high activation energy[4-6].At present, there are a few studies and reports about the curing at low temperature of vegetable protein, tannin and adhesive prepared with them. However, we can find many literatures about raising curing speed and decreasing curing temperature[7-9]. Therefore, Na2CO3 is used as curing agent[10]. To achieve rapid curing at low temperature, we add Na2CO3 in the preparing the PF-Camellia oleifera cake adhesive. And then we study the effect of hot pressing temperature, hot pressing time, amount of glue and hot pressing pressure on the bonding performance of adhesive.

2. Resources and methods

2.1 Resources

Camellia oleifera cake protein: after drying and crushing, we make the protein pass through the 140 ~ 160 mesh sieve. Then we use Soxhlet extraction device to add petroleum ether to remove grease and dry it out at low temperature. Take 100g of degreased Camellia oleifera cake powder, then add 4000ml of 70% ethanol aqueous solution, adjust the pH of the solution to 8 - 11, then perform ultrasonic extraction in a water bath at 30 ~ 60 ℃,

* Corresponding author: wd195@qq.com

https://doi.org/10.1051/e3sconf/202233801019

and filter the product after a period of time to obtain the filtrate.

Then we carry out the second and third time extraction at the ratio of 100 grams residue: 4000ml ethanol aqueous solution. Then merge all the filtrate together and let it sit overnight. Then filter it again. Extract the supernatant at the speed of 4000r/min for 10 minutes. Then adjust the supernatant to the Isoelectric point with 20% HCl. When the precipitation is stable, freeze it and dry it out. Finally, we get camellia oleifera cake protein.

PF-camellia oleifera cake adhesive: add some distilled water to the glass reaction vessel. When the temperature raises to 30-60°C, adjust the pH of the solution to 8 with 20% Sodium hydroxide aqueous solution. Then add the powder of camellia oleifera cake at the speed of 10 ~ 20grams/min. the pH should be kept stable during the process of 20-60minutes' high speed stirring. Finally, when the reaction is completed, we should cool down the container and take out the product. Then we get the camellia oleifera cake adhesive.

Other reagents such as: NaOH, HCl, Na2CO3: analytical pure, Sinopharm Chemical Reagent Co., Ltd

Poplar veneer:fast-growing poplar in Northeast， The moisture content is 8 ~ 11% ， size: 300mm×300mm×1.6mm， Wen an, He bei。

2.2 Experimental instruments

Varian 300 superconducting nuclear magnetic resonance instrument: Varian Technology Co., Ltd;

Tensor27 Fourier transform infrared spectrometer: Bruker company, Germany;

Dsc-60 / 60A differential scanning calorimeter: Shimadzu company, Japan;

PHS-3B multifunctional pH meter: Shanghai Precision Scientific Instrument Co., Ltd;

Jj-1 precision booster electric mixer: Jintan Kejian Instrument Co., Ltd;

3856 experimental hot press: American Carver company;

Wdw50d microcomputer controlled electronic universal testing machine: Jinan Shijin Group Co., Ltd.

3. Methods for experiment

3.1 Preparation for PF—Camellia oleifera cake

Add an appropriate amount of PF - Camellia oleifera cake adhesive into plastic containers. then add30 percent Na2CO 3 aqueous solution.(solid Na2CO 3 that accounts for the whole solution) stir the solution until it even. Then stir it with glass rod evenly under high shear. In this way we get well-prepared adhesive.

3.2 Gel time test

Take 4 grams prepared adhesive into a test tube.(be cautious not to make the sample adhere to the tube wall) then insert a piece of thin wire into the tube. When the temperature of methyl silicone oil in the short neck flask reaches the required temperature (130 °C, 140 °C), then put the test tube with iron wire into it. Then instantly start the stop watch. During this period, the temperature of the methyl silicone oil should be kept unchanged. The liquid surface should be lower than the surface of methyl silicone oil for 20mm. adhesive turns solid with constant stirring. Until the stir rod can't be lifted up suddenly, stop the stopwatch and set down curing time. Do the parallel experiment 3 times for each sample. the difference in parallel experiments shouldn't exceed 5 seconds. Then get the average of 3 valid results. The result is accurate to one second.

3.3 Preparation of plywood

Apply the Camellia oleifera cake(content of Na2CO3 accounts for 2% of the total quality.) to the poplar veneer. Then prepare 3-layers plywood according to the conditions in the table1.

Tab.1 Factors and levels of the orthogonal experiment

Level	Hot-press temperature(°C)	Hot-press time	Glue spread/single side	Hot-press pressure
1	110	2	120	0.9
2	120	3.5	140	1.1
3	130	5	160	1.3

3.4 Test for water resistant adhesive strength

Use the standard test of class II panels in "GB / T 17657-4.15-1999 test method for physical and chemical properties of wood-based panels and veneered wood-based panels"

4. Results and analysis

4.1 Optimization of hot pressing process parameters

Orthogonal experimental design has many advantages such as: less times of experiments, representativeness. This method also can show the main factor among the complex factors and analyze rules that how each factor affects the index. Therefore, we take this method to carry out this experiment. Optimize the hot pressing process of PF- Camellia oleifera cake with the catalyst of Na2CO3 through studying some impacts on the water resistant adhesive strength of conditions like hot pressing temperature, hot pressing time, unit pressure and gluing amount.

4.1.1 Orthogonal test scheme

According to the studied rules in literatures and process in factories, apply the orthogonal table with 3 levels and 4 factors L9 （34） in this experiment. The scheme is shown in figure 1

4.1.2analysis of the results in orthogonal test

(1) the influence on strength of water resistance of hot pressing temperature.

Hot pressing temperature have a direct influence on bonding performance of adhesive, hot pressing parameter

 https://doi.org/10.1051/e3sconf/202233801019

and efficiency. It is an important factor to ensure the level of curing.

It can be concluded form the figure1 that with the rising of temperature, bonding strength of the plywood rises up consistently. When the hot pressing temperature is 110°C, the bonding strength of PF- Camellia oleifera cake is 0.34MPa, which doesn't meet the required national standard of the class II plywood (≥0.7MPa) . because the hot pressing temperature is so low that it doesn't reach the curing temperature(128°C), the adhesive layer is loose and is not water resistant. With the rising of hot pressing temperature, The temperature gradient of the surface core layer of slab increases, which contributes to the heat conduction from surface to the core. And this increase can achieve complete curing of the adhesive between surface and core of the slab. Furthermore, this can also promote strengthening the bonding property on the surface between adhesive layer and veneer. The hot pressing temperature is higher, the permeability can be better, which makes the glue nail and intermolecular force easier to get. What's more, the rising temperature is helpful to polymerization of phenolic hydroxymethyl groups with active groups such as protein and tannin in PF-camellia oleifera cake gum and and deep crosslinking at the interface between polymer and binder. Therefore, when the hot pressing temperature rises to 130°C, the bonding strength rises from less than 0.7MPa to 0.78MPa. it means that bonding plywood is turned into qualified products meeting the requirements of class II plywood standard.

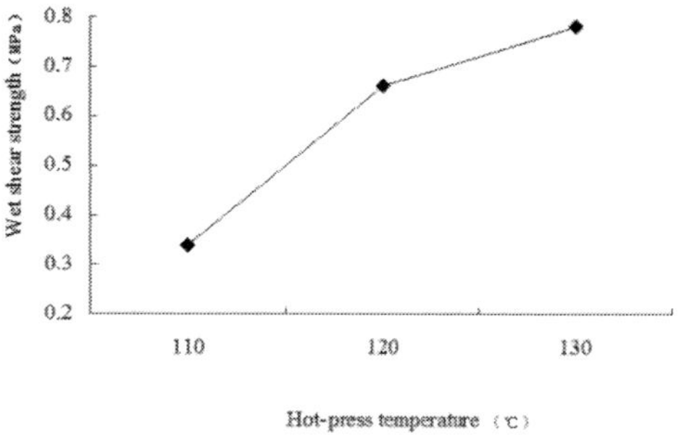

Fig. 1 Wet shear strength of plywood prepared by PF modified oil-tea based adhesive under different hot-press temperature

Higher strength can be gotten if the hot pressing temperature continues rising up. However,

If the temperature is too high, it can cause excessive vapor pressure in the board, which can lead to bubbling and other quality defects during pressure relief. Besides, high temperature will degrade some chemical compositions in wood , so the bonding property will be impacted it. there will be deformation and discoloration in plywood. What's more, higher temperature causes more energy consumption. In this way, the cost of adhesive-making and plywood-bonding is higher.

(2) the effect on bonding strength and water resistance of hot pressing time.

It can be concluded from range analysis in table 2 and visual trend chart in table 4 that among 4 factors in hot pressing, the effect on bonding strength of hot pressing is the most notable. The time of hot pressing depends on growth rate of adhesive layer temperature, slab thickness, curing rate of adhesive layer and water removal rate. With the longer hot pressing time, bonding strength of adhesive increases suddenly at the beginning and then rises up slowly. When the hot pressing time is 2minutes, the bonding strength is 0.29MPa. When the hot pressing time is extended to 3.5min and 5min respectively, the corresponding bonding strength increases to 0.71mpa and 0.77mpa respectively.

Tab. 2 Results and range analysis of orthogonal experiment

NO.	Hot-press temperature	Hot-press time (min)	Glue spread/ single side (g/m^2)	Hot-press pressure (MPa)	Wet shear strength (MPa)
1	110	2	120	0.9	0.11
2	110	3.5	140	1.1	0.54
3	110	5	160	1.3	0.38
4	120	2	140	1.3	0.41
5	120	3.5	160	0.9	0.64
6	120	5	120	1.1	0.93
7	130	2	160	1.1	0.36
8	130	3.5	120	1.3	0.95
9	130	5	140	0.9	1.03
Mean 1	0.34	0.29	0.65	0.59	
Mean 2	0.66	0.71	0.67	0.61	
Mean 3	0.78	0.77	0.46	0.56	
Range	0.44	0.48	0.21	0.05	

In PF - Camellia oleifera cake gum, PF component and polymer cross-linking with it play an important role in wet shear strength of adhesive. Because PF component has hydroxymethyl group with high reactivity, at specific curing temperature, the longer hot pressing time is, the more completely adhesive cures, which contributes to forming of water-resistant structure. The extension of hot pressing time will make the adhesive in the board have high curing rate, which can let the plywood free from bubbling. However, hot pressing time shouldn't be excessive. Otherwise, it leads to over curing of adhesive on the surface of board and degradation of wood cellulose macromolecules, which weakens bonding strength. According to the range analysis, the difference between the mean value 2 and the mean value 3 is very tiny, and both meet the requirements of class II board in the national standard. According to the comprehensive relation between hot pressing time and cost, the proper hot pressing time should be 3.5 minutes in this experiment.

(3) effect on wet shear strength of glue applied

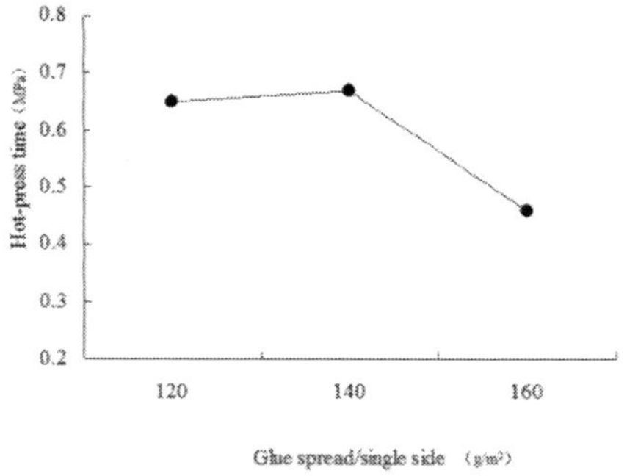

Fig. 2 Wet shear strength of plywood prepared by PF modified oil-tea based adhesive under different glue spread

Figure2 shows effect on wet shear strength of glue applied. Proper amount of glue makes the adhesive layer thin and even. This lessens the applied adhesive to economize. What's more, it lessens stress concentration. So that it can improve the aging resistance of bonded joints.

It can be found from table-2 and figure-3 that with the increase of the amount of applied glue, bonding strength rises slowly then goes down suddenly. This is because with the increase of glue spread, the bonding surface between glue and veneer increases, too. Therefore, the combination between wood and adhesive is more compact and firm and the mechanical properties of plywood is enhanced. When glue spread goes up from 120g/m2 to 140g/m2 bonding strength turns from 0.65MPa to 0.67MPa. the mean values are almost the same. It means that when the glue spread is 120 ~ 140, it has little influences on bonding strength. When the amount rises to 160g/m2, bonding strength decreases on the contrary. This is because that with the constant increase of glue spread, the adhesive layers will be uneven and the thickness isn't same. There are great differences in properties among different parts of the board due to lack of adhesive. The property of the whole board will be lessened. Take all analysis into consideration, glue spread should be 120 ~ 140g/m2 .

(4) the effect on wet shear strength of plywood hot pressing pressure

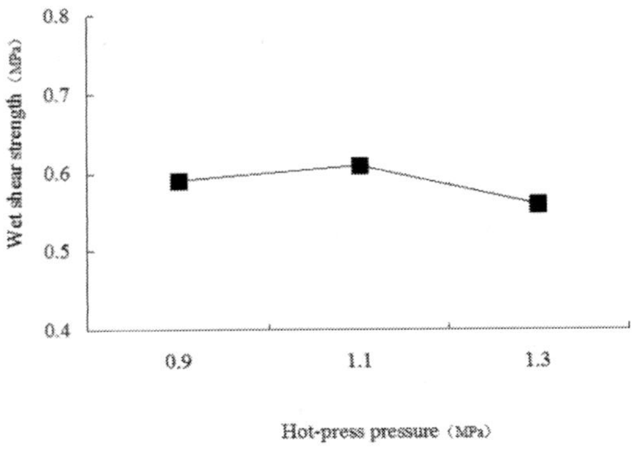

Fig. 3 Wet shear strength of plywood prepared by PF modified oil-tea based adhesive under hot-press pressure

It can be concluded from table2 and 3 that hot pressing pressure has the least impact on bonding strength. Figure 4 shows that when the pressure rises up from 0.9MPa to 1.1MPa. bonding strength rises up slowly. When the hot pressing pressure reaches 1.1MPa, bonding strength reaches the maximum, 0.61MPa. when the pressure rises to 1.3MPa, bonding strength decreases. To make the board-adhesive-board layers combine with each other closely. We need to increase the pressure of slab during bonding. Then let some adhesive infiltrate into holes so that bonding quality will be good enough. Proper pressure compacts the slab tightly and accelerates the uniform diffusion of glue liquid and make the liquid penetrate into the wood, so that the adhesive can wet the surface of plywood better and reduce the gap of adhesive layer and increase the cohesion of glue layer molecules. Because of poor fluidity permeability of PF-camellia oleifera cake gum, higher hot pressing pressure is helpful to the improvement of flow ability and the amelioration of adhesive layer structure of adhesive.

Additionally, with some pressure, active groups in PF-camellia oleifera cake gum can react with hydroxyls on the surface of wood or generate firm glue nail in the holes inside the wood. So that bonding strength of adhesive is enhanced. However, when the pressure is beyond the proper value, it will cause higher consumption of energy during hot pressing and over-penetration of adhesive into the wood that lead to lack of adhesive in the adhesive layer. Finally bonding strength is lessened. Because of much fine powder of cake in the PF-camellia oleifera cake, only if the pressure is high enough while hot pressing, then the adhesive and wood can be compacted completely. Therefore, in this experiment, the proper hot pressing pressure is 1.1MPa.

4.1.3 working out the best hot pressing process of PF-camellia oleifera cake gum

Given that properties meeting the national standard and the least cost are two premises, we have taken plenty of factors into consideration and we have analyzed hot pressing process obtained by orthogonal test to conclude better conditions of hot pressing of PF-camellia oleifera cake gum. The factors include hot pressing temperature, hot pressing time , glue spread, and hot pressing pressure. The hot pressing temperature is 130 °C, the hot pressing time is 0.7min/mm (42s / mm), the gluing amount is 120g / m2, and the hot pressing pressure is 1.1MPa. these conditions above are better ones we have obtained. Prepare the plywood under these conditions and then test bonding strength. We can clear that the wet shear strength of PF- camellia oleifera cake gum is 1.01MPa. this value is far beyond 0.7MPa, which is the minimum strength value of class II plate required in national standard. But in this process, hot pressing temperature is significantly higher than urea formaldehyde resin adhesive. (110 ~ 115°C) Remaining other parameters unchanged, we decrease hot pressing temperature and further optimize this process to adapt to the production conditions in factories. Values in tab.3 are wet shear strength of plywood under different hot-press temperatures of plywood. In this table, we can clear that decrease of hot-press temperature can lead to decrease of wet shear strength, but when the temperature reaches 120°C, wet shear strength of prepared plywood is 0.79MPa. This value still meets the required wet shear strength of class II plywood in national standard. Therefore, given that hot-press temperature in the second process is similar to that of urea formaldehyde resin adhesive, we select this process to be the optimum hot pressing process of PF-camellia oleifera cake adhesive. Repeatedly examine the bonding strength, we conclude that the mean value of bonding strength is 0.79MPa. The coefficient of variation of each bonding strength is less than 2%,which means that the optimum hot-press process is highly stable and reliable.

Tab. 3 Wet shear strength of plywood under different hot-press processes

process	Hot-process conditions				Wet shear strength (MPa)
	Hot-press temperature (°C)	Hot-press time (s/mm)	Glue spread (g/m^2)	Hot-press pressure	
1	110	42	120	1.1	0.43
2	120	42	120	1.1	0.79
3	130	42	120	1.1	1.01

5. Discussion and conclusion

(1) adding some Na2CO3 can promote instant curing at low temperature while preparing PF- camellia oleifera cake adhesive. Compared with PF- camellia oleifera cake adhesive, the adhesive catalyzed by Na2CO3 has higher ΔH. this means that the latter adhesive performs curing reaction more violently and completely. When the dosage of Na2CO3 is 2%, it can accelerate quick curing effect on PF- camellia oleifera cake adhesive at its best.

(2) DSC analysis of the curing characteristics of the adhesive shows that protein, tannin and other active components in PF- camellia oleifera cake adhesive perform cross-linking reaction with PF resin structural unit while curing. Water resistant structural system in PF- camellia oleifera cake adhesive is built by polycondensation reaction performed by structural components of PF resin and active components such as protein and tannin and chemical reaction of each active structure in PF resin and Camellia oleifera cake.

(3) optimize hot-press process of PF- camellia oleifera cake adhesive catalyzed by Na2CO3 with orthogonal experimental design method. Then it can be concluded that among the four parameters of hot-press process, the time of hot pressing affects the result the most significantly. On the contrary, hot-press pressure has a least influence on the result. Increasing the hot-press temperature can raise wet shear strength of plywood; the optimal hot-press process is as follows : Hot-press temperature is 120℃, hot-press time is 0.7min/mm (42 s/mm) 、glue spread is120g/m2, hot-press pressure is 1.1MPa; under these conditions, average wet shear strength of prepared plywood is 0.79 MPa, which meets the national required standard for class II plate in GB / T 9846.3-2004.

Acknowledgements

This work was financially supported by the Special funds for construction of innovative provinces in Hunan Province (high-tech industry science and technology innovation leading program, No.2020GK4094), National Key Research and Development Program for International Science and Technology Cooperation Projects (No.2017YFE9135300).

References

1. A. X. Luo, Y. H. Liu. Study on water resistance of soybean-based wood adhesives. Agricultural Products Processing, 2006, 6: 15 ~ 18;
2. J. Y. Gu. Adhesives and Coatings. Beijing: China Forestry Press, 1999, 49 ~ 87;
3. D. B. Fan, J. Z. Li, Z. L. Lu. Thermal behavior and gluing plywood properties of low molar ratio urea-formaldehyde resins with different curing agents. China Adhesives, 2006, 15(12): 1~5;
4. C. M. Ding, Q. P. Song, L. L. Wang. Development of orthogonal corn starch adhesives. Chemistry and Adhesion, 2002(6):265 ~ 266;
5. Experimental Design Group, Department of Mathematics, Peking University. Orthogonal test method. Beijing: Science Popularization Press, 1981, 21 ~ 43;
6. D. B. Fan, T. F. Qin, F. X. Chu. A New Interior Plywood Adhesive Based on Oil-Tea Cake. Advanced Materials Research, 2011, 194-196 (4): 2183 ~ 2186;
7. H. Lei, A. Pizzi, P. Navarrete, et al. Gluten Protein Adhesives for Wood Panels. Journal of Adhesion Science and Technology, 2010, 24 (15): 1583 ~ 1596;
8. G. A. Amaral-Labat, A. Pizzi, A. R. Gonçalves, et al. Environment-friendly Soy Flour-based Resins without Formaldehyde. Journal of Applied Polymer Science, 2008, 108 (1): 624 ~ 632;
9. D. B. Fan, J. Zh. Li, J. M. Chang, et al. Chemical Structure and Curing Behavior of Phenol–Urea–Formaldehyde Cocondensed Resins of High Urea Content. Journal of Adhesion Science and Technology, 2009, 23 (9): 1787 ~ 1797;
10. G. VÁZQUEZ, F. LÓPEZ-SUEVOS, A. VILLAR-GAREA, et al. 13C-NMR Analysis of Phenol-urea-formaldehyde Prepolymers and Phenol-urea-formaldehyde-tannin Adhesives. Journal of Adhesion Science and Technology, 2004, 18 (13): 1529 ~ 1543.

Preparation of cellulose-based cationic adsorbents and their removal of Pb (II) from water

Xiao Hu [1,3], Rui Zeng [2,§], Weidong Xie [3], Zhixin Hu [2], Yuyuan Li [4], Dong Wang [2], Xiang Li [2,*]

[1] Hunan Association of Environmental Improvement, Changsha, Hunan Province, China
[2] Hunan Airbluer Environmental Protection Technology Co., Changsha, Hunan Province, China
[3] Forestry College of Guangxi University, Nanning, Guangxi Province, China
[4] Institute of Subtropical Agroecology, Chinese Academy of Sciences, Changsha, Hunan Province, China

§Contributed equally to this work

Abstract: Industrial production is a double-edged sword, which not only brings convenience to human beings, but also does some harm to the environment. Water pollution, especially heavy metal pollution, has become a major environmental problem. In this paper, ionization reagent was prepared and attached to cellulose to obtain Cell-IA.The cationic Cell-IA was selected to evaluate the adsorption properties of PBII. The effect of the adsorbent on the actual sewage treatment was studied and whether the adsorbent could be applied in practice was determined.

Keywords: Cellulose; Heavy metal ion; Pb(II); Chemical modification.

1. Introduction

Modern industry has brought much convenience to the world. However, at the same time, inevitably, it has also done much harm to our environment. In the process of industrial procedure, not only the gaining of resources but also the emission of industrial waste would be harmful to the surrounding. Among the various environmental problems, water pollution is rather serious. Especially the pollution caused by heavy metal ion. Too much heavy metal ion will cause a series of trouble. The excess of heavy metal ion in the water will endanger fishes and shrimps and if it becomes more serious, it may lead to the death of these creatures. Then it will destroy the ecosystem in the water. What's more, this can damage the health of people due to the accumulation of these heavy metal ions. Therefore, removing the heavy metal ions and recycling those recyclable ions have been the concerned and studied issues.

Heavy metal waste water is produced widely. Exploitation and smelting of the metal mine mainly produces heavy metal in water. What's more, some industries like electrolysis and chemical industry could also leave some heavy metal in to the water. Such as waste water containing copper and mercury that is discharged from chemical fertilizer plants and waste water containing mercury and lead discharged from chemical plants both can be victims. The water polluted by heavy ions keeps the features such as it is long-term poisonous and difficult to degrade. It may even be absorbed and accumulated by our bodies from food chain. This accumulation can cause various diseases and dysfunction and seriously destroy our health in the end. The main sorts of metal that cause pollution include Cu, Ni, Hg, Pb, Cd, Cr and so on. The Minamata disease that happened in Japan in 1960s was caused by the excess of mercury in rivers.

The lead is a part of heavy metal. It has high density and strong ductility. It can't be easily degraded in surrounding. It also has highly potential toxicity to our lives and environment. Therefore, the lead is a strong pollutant, too. The lead ions taken in by people would invade their nerve tissue and damage their brains. It may lead to death if it is worsen. Lead and its compounds both contain toxicity. What's more, besides strong oncogenicity, they would do harm to immune system and urinary system after being absorbed by people. Industrial wastewater containing lead, lead deposition in the atmosphere and the dissolution of lead mineral are the main sources of lead in water.

At present, to deal with heavy metal wastewater, we may use chemical method, physical treatment method and biological treatment method. The chemical method would be taken when the concentration of the heavy metal ions is too high in the water. Such as oxidation-reduction method and coagulation method. Adsorption method is often taken by us, too. It is more efficient to remove the heavy metal in the water in this way. Furthermore, costing would be reduced when the cheap cellulose is used to be the adsorption material.

Cellulose, as a important composition of the cell walls, can be found widely. What's more, it is recyclable.

* Corresponding author: 815523642@qq.com

https://doi.org/10.1051/e3sconf/202233801020

Because of its biodegradability, it almost does no harm to the environment. It can be processed to be a kind of sorbent through the modification of cellulose so that we can remove the heavy metal in the water. This adsorption material would keep some advantages such as less costing and larger specific area after turning into an adsorption material by chemical modification. This measure that we prepare the cellulose adsorption material would cost less and have higher removal rate. This means has bright applying prospect so it has become the focus of researchers.

2. Materials and methods

2.1 Instruments and reagents

Deionized water is used in this experiment and other chemical reagents and instruments which are made use of are shown in the figure 1 and 2 below.

Tab.1 Main reagents

Names of reagents	purity	Names of manufacturers
Diethyl iminodiacetic acid	98 %	Beijing Lianhe Technology Co., Ltd
Epichlorohydrin	Analytical pure	Aladdin
Dioxane	98 %	Aladdin
NaOH	Analytical pure	Tianjin kemio Chemical Reagent Development Center
K_2CO_3	Analytical pure	Tianjin kemio Chemical Reagent Development Center
HCl	Analytical pure	Tianjin kemio Chemical Reagent Development Center
$Pb(NO_3)_2$	Analytical pure	Aladdin

Tab.2 Instruments and models

Names of instruments	models	Names of manufacturers
Precision acidity meter	PHS-25C	Shanghai Haozhuang Instrument Co., Ltd
Vacuum drying oven	DZF-6050	Beijing Zhongke Environmental Test Instrument Co., Ltd
Analytical balance	AUW220D	Shimadzu
Variable speed multipurpose oscillator	HY-2	Jiangsu Jintan Youlian Instrument Research Institute
Mechanical agitator	RW20	IKA
Precision three purpose thermostatic water tank	HH420-2B	Shanghai Binglin
Nuclear magnetic resonance instrument	Bruker Avance III	Bruker

2.2 The preparation of resources

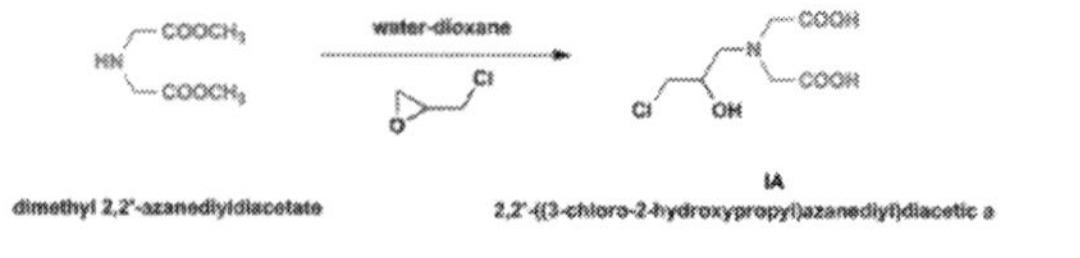

Fig.1 The composition route of IA

The preparation of IA, the ionizing reagent has been completed. detailed steps are shown below: firstly, weigh 15.0 grams of dimethyl iminodiacetic acid then put it into a double neck bottle whose volume is 150 ml. then add the mixed reagent of water and dioxane(the ratio is 1:1). After stirring the reagent for 30 minutes, add 10.0 grams of epichlorohydrin. They will react for 24 hours in the condition of 30 degree Celsius . then when the reaction is over, filtration is needed. Then we will get the precipitate. Then we need to wash it for 3 times with deionized water and dry out it in the condition of 60 degree Celsius. Finally, we will get the IA that we want 13.25 grams.

Tab.3 The results of characterizing the IA's structure through NMR are shown below.

Compound	^{1}H NMR, δ (ppm) 500 MHz, (DMSO-d_6)	^{13}C NMR, δ (ppm) 125 MHz, (DMSO-d_6)
IA	3.75 (m, 1H), 3.69 (dd, J = 10.9, 4.2 Hz, 1H), 3.52 (dd, J = 10.9, 5.5 Hz, 1H), 3.46 (s, 4H), 2.75 (dd, J = 13.6, 5.4 Hz), 2.67 (dd, J = 13.6, 6.4 Hz)	174.3, 72.1, 58.4, 53.8, 48.8, 36.4

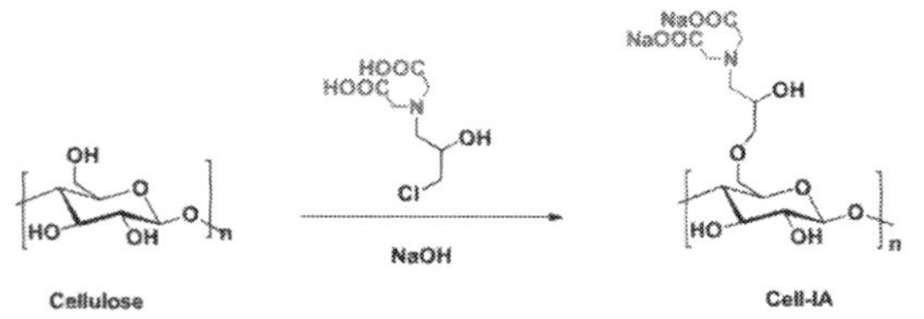

Fig.2 Composition routine of Cell-IA

The composition routine of Cell-IA is shown in the figure 2. The detailed steps are as follows: firstly, weigh 3.0 grams of cellulose and then add it into the 15% (w / V) NaOH aqueous solution. This reaction will last for 2 hours with mechanical stirrer at 80 ° C. and then, add some IA aqueous to the cellulose. It will take 10 hours to complete this reaction at 80 ° C.

The product needs to be centrifuged after the reaction is over. Then wash the solid with water for twice and next, wash it with absolute ethanol for once. The final step is to freeze and dry out the product and the modified cellulose IA will be done.

 https://doi.org/10.1051/e3sconf/202233801020

2.3 The modified material's ability to absorb Pb(II)

2.3.1 The effect on the absorption of the content of the Cell-IA

Take 20 ml of Pb (II) solution with a concentration of 200 mg L-1. Add it to a 50 ml triangular flask. And then add 0.5 – 3 G L-1 adsorbent cell IA. Adjust the pH to 5.0. start the adsorption at the room temperature. Filter the mixture after 12 hours' adsorption. Then measure the content of Pb(II) in the remaining solution. And then calculate the amount and efficiency of the adsorption. Finally, evaluate the effect of the content of Cell-IA. We need to perform three parallel experiments in each group and repeat three times.

2.3.2 Effect of solution pH on Pb (II) adsorption

Take 20 ml of 200 mg L-1 Pb (II) solution, add it into a 50 ml triangular flask, then add 0.04 g of Cell-IA to the triangular flusk. Adjust the solution pH to 1.0-6.0. adsorb it for 12 hours at room temperature. Then filter the product. Then determine the content of Pb(II) in the remaining solution. Then work out the removal rate of Pb(II). Finally, evaluate the effect of solution pH on Pb(II) adsorption. We also need to perform 3 parallel experiments in each group and repeat for 3 times.

2.4 The norm of performance evaluation

This experiment regards the adsorption capacity and removal rate of Pb(II) in the solution as the norm of adsorption performance. Take 20mg composed Cell-IA and place it into 25ml conical flask. Then add 20 mL 200 mg L-1 Pb(II) solution. Shake at a constant temperature of 200 rpm at 20 ° C for 3 hours. Suction filtration is after the reaction. Take some filtrate accurately from the flask. Dilute it and then determine the content of Pb (II) in solution by atomic spectrophotometry. Then, we can calculate the adsorption capacity (QE) and removal rate by formula 2-1 and formula 2-2.

$$q_e = \frac{(C_0 - C_e)V}{W} \qquad (2-1)$$

$$\text{Removal rate}(\%) = \frac{C_0 - C_e}{C_0} \times 100\% \qquad (2-2)$$

In the formula, qe is adsorption capacity (mg g-1) ; C0 and Ce are the Content of Pb(II) (mg L-1) before and after the adsorption. V is the volume of the solution (L) ; W is the content of sorbent (g) .

3. Result and analysis

3.1 The effect of the content of Cell-IA on Pb(II) adsorption

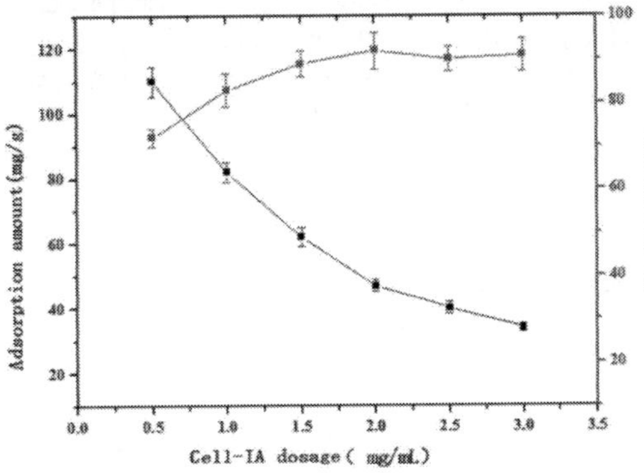

Fig.3 The effect of the content of Cell-IA on Pb(II) adsorption

In the specific condition, the result of the effect of the content of Cell-IA on Pb(II) adsorption is shown in the figure 3.

We can conclude from this figure that when the content of Cell-IA rises from 0.5g L-1 to 2.0 g L-1 , the removal rate of the Pb(II) rises from 71 percent to 92 percent consistently. This is because the increase of dosage of the Cell-IA brings more adsorption sites, which are helpful to adsorption. When the dosage is beyond 2 g L-1 , its effect on removal rate isn't so obvious like before. Perhaps this is because when the concentration of Pb(II) in the water is low, Pb(II) has lower probability of touching the activated sites. So in the later researches, we keep the dosage of the Cell-IA at 2 g/L.

3.2 The effect of solution pH on adsorption of Pb(II)

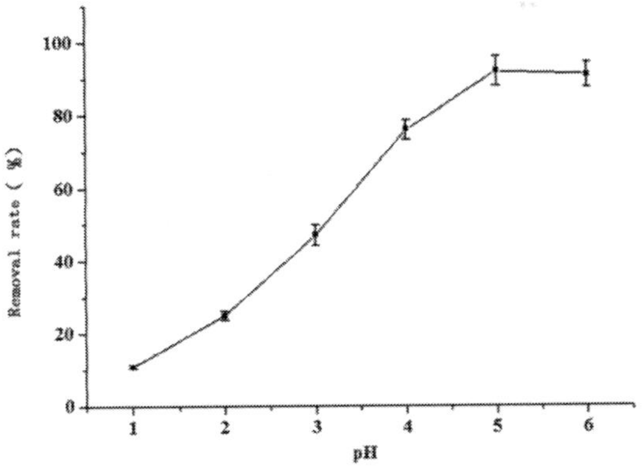

Fig.4 The effect of solution pH on adsorption of Pb(II) by Cell-IA

The pH also plays an important role in adsorption process. when the pH is between 1.0 and 6.0, the performance that Cell-IA removes the Pb(II) is shown in the figure 4.

When the solution pH ranges from1.0 to 5.0, removal rate of Pb(II) increases from12 % to 93 %.when the solution pH is 6.0, the removal rate of Pb(II) is almost the same as the rate in pH 5.0. removal rate can change in different pH condition, it may because: when the pH is low, the concentration of H+ in the reagent is high, which may occupy plenty of activated sites. This will have an influence on adsorption of Pb(II), so with the increase of pH, Cell-IA can remove more Pb(II) when the pH is under 5.0, Pb in the solution is in the form of Pb2+ when the pH is near 6.0, Pb in the solution is in the form of Pb(OH)+, this may influence performance of the sorbent, Cell-IA.

4. Outcome and discussion

When the dosage of Cell-IA increases from 0.5 g L-1 to 2.0 g L-1, the removal rate of Pb(II) by Cell-IA increases from 71 % to 92 %, when the dosage of Cell-IA is beyond 2 g L-1, there is no obvious effect on Pb(II).when the solution pH ranges from1.0 to 5.0, the removal rate of Pb(II) increases from 12 % to 93 %. When the pH is 6.0, removal rate of Pb(II) is almost the same as that in the solution of pH 5.0.

Cellulose is a sort of recyclable resource which can be found widely. It is economical and environmentally friendly. We can prepare sorbent that is applied in adsorbing heavy metal ions by modifying cellulose material and adding some functional groups with good adsorption performance. If we use this prepared sorbent to remove the heavy metal in the water, we will get higher removal rate and less cost, which is in advance in processing heavy metal wastewater. In recent years, more and more people focus on this field. With further studies, I believe that cellulose adsorption material can play a more and more important role in fighting against heavy metal wastewater.

Acknowledgements

This work was financially supported by the Special funds for construction of innovative provinces in Hunan Province (high-tech industry science and technology innovation leading program, No.2020GK4094), National Key Research and Development Program for International Science and Technology Cooperation Projects (No.2017YFE9135300).

References

1. Q. Mei. Hazards of heavy metal wastewater and its treatment. Trace elements and health research, 2004, 21(4):54-56.
2. S. Luo, X. Xu, G. Zhou, et al. Amino siloxane oligomer-linked graphene oxide as an efficient adsorbent for removal of Pb(II) from wastewater. Journal of Hazardous Materials, 2014, 274(12):145.
3. K. K. Wang, S. Zhu, T. Zheng, et al. The history of arsenic in China. Studies in the history of natural sciences, 1982, 1(2):115-126.
4. M. Li, Y. L. Lin. Urban environmental lead pollution and its impact on human health. Environmental Monitoring Management and Technology, 2006, 18(5):6-10.
5. S. Li, H. P. Cha, Z. L. Fan. Current status and prospect of lead-containing wastewater treatment technology. Chemical Progress, 2011, 30(S1): 336-339.
6. K. Guo. Preparation and performance of magnetic adsorption materials based on amphoteric microcrystalline cellulose. Suzhou University, 2015.
7. Y. Wang, S. D. Lv, X. Li, et al. Progress and Prospects of Arsenic Removal in Water. Environmental Science and Technology, 2010, 33(9):102-107.
8. Y. Jiang, C. J. Huang, H. Pang, et al. Advances in cellulose-based ionic adsorbents. Chemical Bulletin, 2008, 71(12):891-899.
9. F. Ma. Modification of wheat straw and its cellulose and mechanism of Pb(II) and As(V) adsorption in water. Northwest Agriculture and Forestry University, 2017.
10. S. T. Zhai. Research progress and prospects of chemical modification of cellulose. Urban Construction Theory Research:Electronic Edition, 2015(1).
11. Tiryaki, B, Yagmur, E, Banford, A, et al. Comparison of activated carbon produced from natural biomass and equivalent chemical compositions. [J]. Journal of Analytical & Applied Pyrolysis, 2014, 105(5):276-283.
12. L. P. Yang, X. K. Ouyang, L. Y. Yang, et al. Study on the adsorption of lead ions in aqueous solution by bamboo lignocellulose. Journal of Zhejiang Ocean College (Natural Science Edition), 2014(1):97-100.
13. Z. M. Wu, Study on the purification of lead in polysaccharide system by sulfhydryl modified cellulose. Dalian:Dalian University of Technology, 2012.
14. F. L. Zhang, Preparation of sulfated cellulose and its adsorption of heavy metal ions. Jinan:Qilu University of Technology, 2016.
15. J. Li, B. Q. Zhen, Research progress on the treatment of heavy metal wastewater by adsorption method. Chemical Progress, 2016,33(2):207-213.

https://doi.org/10.1051/e3sconf/202233801021

Parameter optimization of acid fracturing in ultra-deep fault zone carbonate reservoir

Yudi Geng [1], Jun Zhou [2,*]

[1] Research Institute of Petroleum Engineering, Sinopec Northwest Oil field Company, Urumqi, Xinjiang, China
[2] Sinopec Research Institute of Petroleum Engineering, Beijing, China

Abstract. The characteristics of fracture development are complex in Shunbei area. The natural fracture development is different between different fault zones and in different locations of the same fault zone. Not all natural fractures can be activated during acid fracturing, and not all natural fractures can contribute to well productivity after acid fracturing. The use of natural fractures can not only improve the seepage capacity of the reservoir, but also improve the well productivity. Therefore, the influence of artificial fracture on the opening and fracture conductivity maintenance of natural fracture is studied, and finally the acid fracturing roceand parameters based on the change of natural fracture are formed.

1. Fracture distribution in fault zone

The distribution of large fault zones is dense and complex in the Shunbei region, which is a ultra-deep carbonate reservoir in Tarim Basin. There are great differences in the internal structure of large fault zones, and the characteristics of fracture development are complex. The natural fracture development is different between different fault zones and in different locations of the same fault zone.

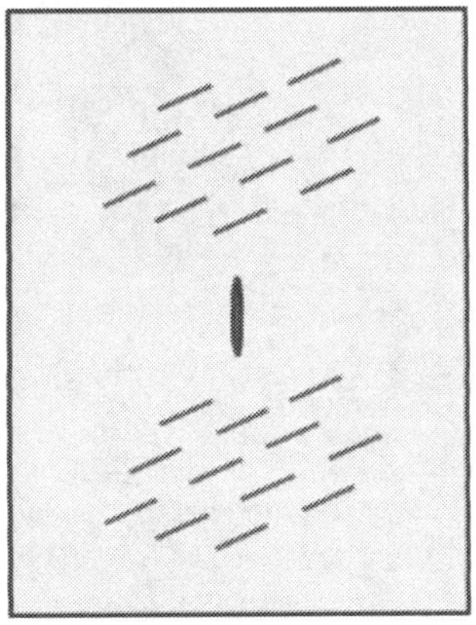

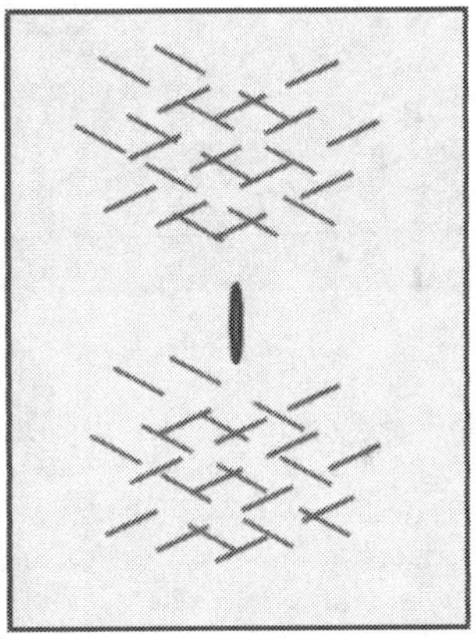

Figure 1. Two intersecting modes of artificial fracture and natural fracture.

According to the internal distribution characteristics of the large fault zone, the surrounding area of the large fault zone can be divided into central fracture zone and induced fracture zone. In the central fracture zone, the stress concentration changes greatly, the rock fracture is seriously broken, and the fracture is dense. In the induced fracture zone, the stress dispersion is small, the rock fragmentation is weak, and the fractures are sparse. In the process of acid fracturing, artificial fractures may pass through the central fracture zone with dense fractures and the induced fracture zone with sparse fractures.

Due to the influence of stress changes in the fault zone, there must be stress inversion in the area near the fault, and the distribution of fractures around the fault should be staggered or reticulated with high fracture density. However, the fractures far away from the fault zone are less affected by stress changes, and the fracture direction distribution is single and the fracture density is smaller.

* Corresponding author: zhoujun.sripe@sinopec.com

 https://doi.org/10.1051/e3sconf/202233801021

According to the fracture characteristics of natural fractures at different distances from the fault zone, two intersecting modes of artificial fracture and natural fracture are proposed: (1) Artificial fracture intersects with a single mode natural direction. (2)Artificial fracture intersects with two modes natural directions (Fig.1).

2. Analysis of regional reconstruction technology of fault zone

According to the above distribution characteristics of natural fractures near the fault zone, the XFEM extended finite element model was established. As shown in Figure 2, the natural fracture is in the state of intersection, and the artificial fracture approaches the natural fracture at a certain Angle. The smaller the Angle between natural fracture and artificial fracture, the more easily artificial fracture is captured by natural fracture, and continue to expand along the direction of maximum principal stress.

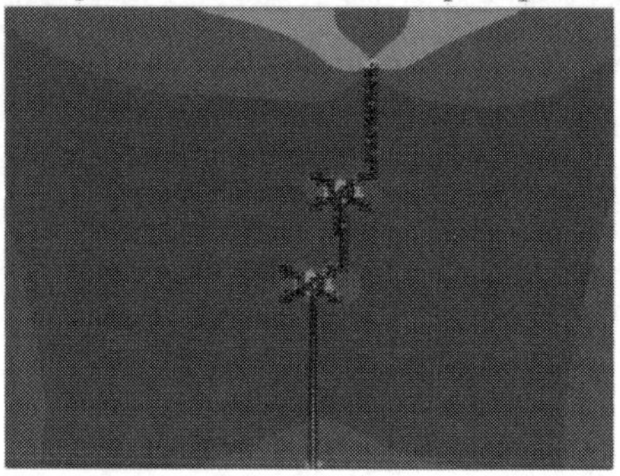

Figure 2. Artificial fractures communicate two kinds of intersecting natural fractures.

Due to the length and height of natural fractures in real reservoirs, artificial fractures are more likely to directly intersect with natural fractures when approaching them. In this case, the model can be simplified as the intersection between artificial fracture and one of the intersecting natural fractures. After the first natural fracture is opened, another natural fracture intersects with the natural fracture communicated by artificial fracture. Therefore, the natural fractures that have been communicated can be regarded as artificial fractures at this time, and the first natural fracture that has been communicated continues to communicate with the second natural fracture. This intersecting pattern creates a more complex hydraulic fracture system. Figure 3 shows the intersection simulation of artificial fracture and single kind natural fracture.

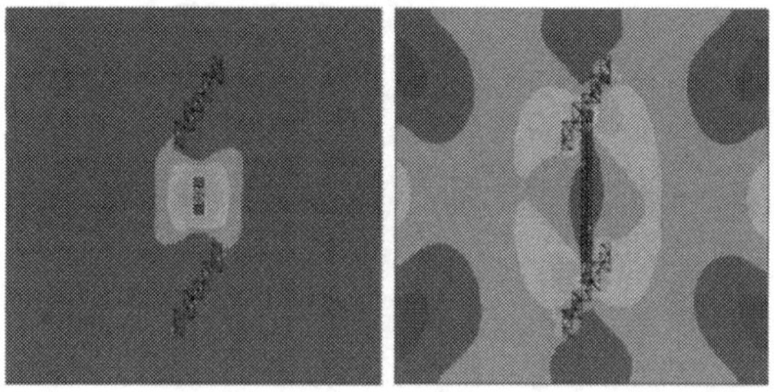

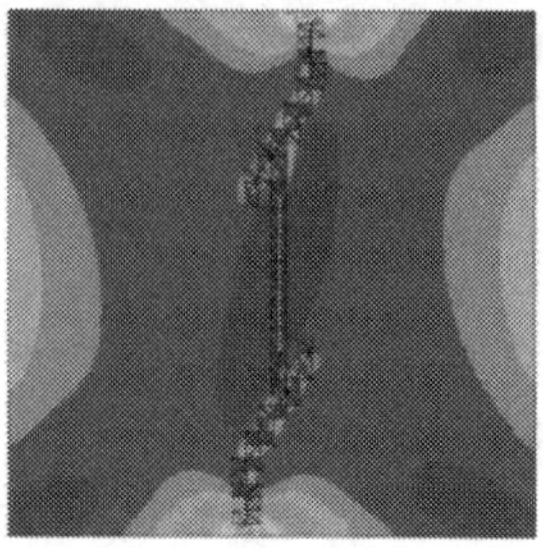

Figure 3. Artificial fractures communicate with single natural kind fractures.

Natural fractures can be extended by artificial fractures. The extension of natural fracture is due to the stress concentration at the tip of artificial fracture. The stress difference increases at the stress concentration position of artificial fracture tip. Under the condition of the increase of stress difference, the shear stress value on the wall of natural fracture increases and leads to the opening and extension of natural fracture (Fig.4).

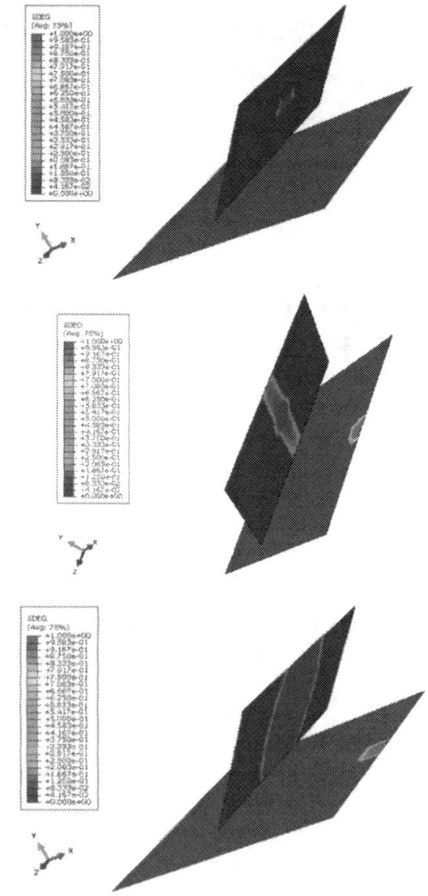

https://doi.org/10.1051/e3sconf/202233801021

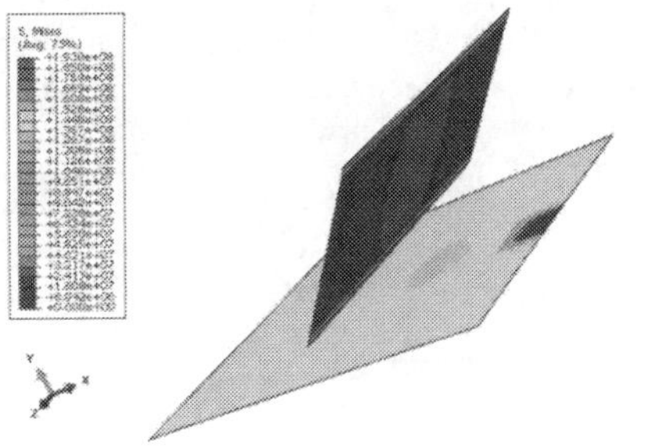

Figure 4. Natural fractures open under the interference of artificial fractures.

In the process of artificial fracture propagation, although the filtration loss of working fluid is increased to a certain extent under the action of acid, the action of acid can change the mechanical properties of formation rock and increase the propagation distance of artificial fracture. The proper use of acid changes the mechanical properties of the formation rock, allowing artificial fractures to communicate with a wider range of reservoirs (Fig.5).

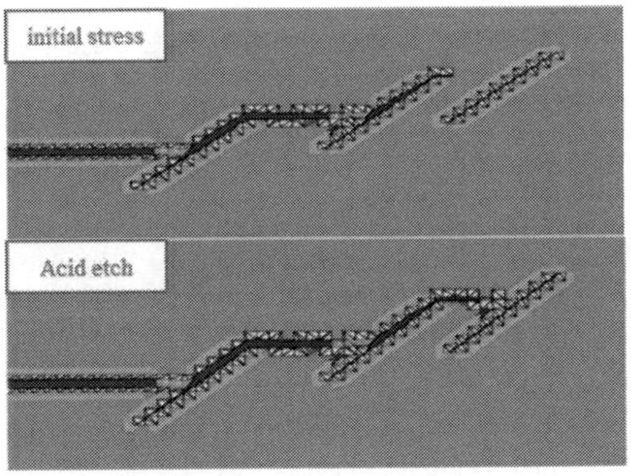

Figure 5. Effect of acid on communication distance.

First, high-viscosity fracturing fluids should be used to open the formation before acid is used, because acid reduces the range of artificial fracture-induced stress interference. Under the action of fracturing fluid, artificial fractures continue to expand. Under the action of induced stress of artificial fractures, natural fractures near artificial fractures are opened. At the same time, the intersection of artificial fractures and natural fractures can also open some natural fractures.

Weak acid or low acid concentration should be added after natural fractures near artificial fractures are opened. Under the pressure of the injected fluid, the acid filtrates into the formation near the fracture for preliminary dissolution of the formation. Under the action of acid, Poisson's ratio and Young's modulus of rock near artificial fractures will decrease in different degrees, which is conducive to the communication of more natural fractures when artificial fractures intersect with natural fractures. When the artificial fracture expands to a certain scale, conventional acid is injected to dissolve the formation on a large scale. At this time, the acid plays a role of forming dissolution fractures with certain conductivity.

3. Organization of the Text

3.1 Liquid scale optimization

In the process of reservoir stimulation, the scale of fluid has a decisive influence on the scale of stimulation volume. Under the same injection parameters of the model, different injection time can represent different liquid injection scales. The longer injection time, the farther the artificial fracture extension distance, and the larger the sweep range of stress concentration zone at the tip of artificial fracture extension. In the area swept by the stress concentration zone at the artificial fracture tip, most natural fractures will open, so the larger the fluid size, the better.

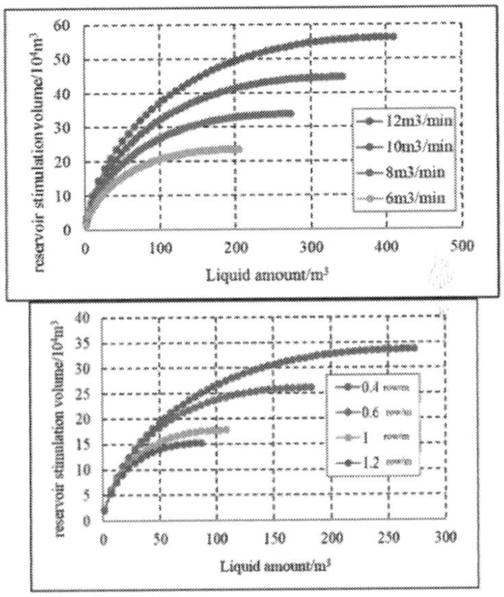

Figure 6. Reservoir communication volume with different acid amount.

According to the volume model established by the natural fracture communication mode in the study area, the reservoir communication volumes under different construction fluid volumes under different pumping rate and different fluid volumes under different natural fracture densities are analyzed, as shown in Figure 6. Due to the high degree of fracture development near the fault zone, the volume of reservoir stimulation volume during conventional fracturing is limited. It can be seen from the stimulation volume simulation, within the range of formation and wellbore conditions, the pre-fracturing fluid of 400m^3 can achieve better stimulation effect.

3.2 Pumping rate optimization

It is known that in the in-situ stress field, the pumping rate is 6m^3/min and the viscosity is 100mPa•s, and the angle range of the artificial fracture can open the natural fracture is 0°~55° (Fig.7). The pumping rate optimization study found that 60° natural fractures should be opened under the formation conditions in the study area, and it is recommended that the pumping rate during construction should be greater than 10m^3/min.

https://doi.org/10.1051/e3sconf/202233801021

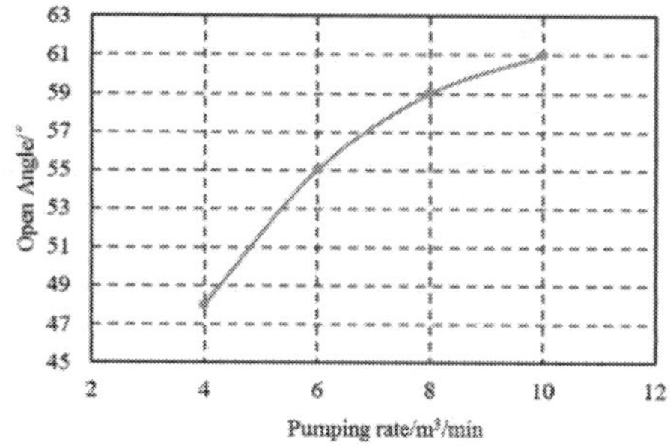

Figure 7. Effect of pumping rate on artificial fracture opening natural fracture.

3.3 Optimization of liquid viscosity

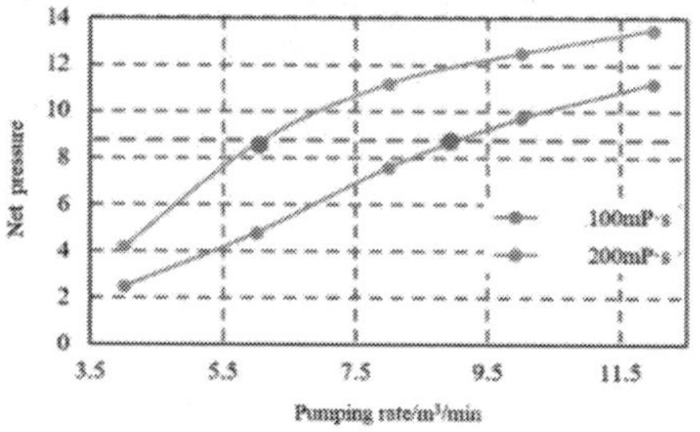

Figure 8. Net pressure under different pumping rate and viscosity.

When the pumping rate is 6m³/min, the corresponding viscosity is 200MPa•s. The Angle between the natural fracture and the maximum horizontal principal stress in the study area ranges from 30° to 60°. The net pressure required for the intersection and communication of the 60° natural fracture is about 9MPa, the liquid pumping rate is 9m³/min, the net pressure reaches 9MPa, and the liquid viscosity is 100mPa•s (Fig.7). The liquid pumping rate is 6m³/min and the net pressure reaches 9MPa. The required liquid viscosity is 200mPa•s. In the actual construction, if the pumping rate is higher, the viscosity can be appropriately reduced and the natural fractures with an approaching Angle of 60° can be opened.

4. Conclusion

(1) In the area near the fault zone, artificial fractures continue to expand under the action of high viscosity fracturing fluid, and natural fractures near artificial fractures are opened under the action of induced stress induced by artificial fractures. At the same time, natural fractures are opened by the intersection of artificial fractures and natural fractures.

(2) After natural fractures near artificial fractures are opened, weak or low-concentration acids are added. Under the action of acid, Poisson's ratio and Young's modulus of rock near artificial fractures will decrease in different degrees, which is conducive to the communication of more natural fractures when artificial fractures intersect with natural fractures.

(3) When the artificial fracture expands to a certain scale, conventional acid is injected to dissolve the formation on a large scale. At this time, the acid plays a role of forming dissolution fractures with certain conductivity. The retardance acid was used as the pre-acid to etch the distal fractures, and the crosslinked acid system with a viscosity greater than 200mPa•s was used as the main acid to etch the fractures, and the acid pumping rate should be greater than 10m³/min as the fracturing fluid.

Acknowledgments

This work was financially supported by NSFC Basic Research Program on Deep Petroleum Resource Accumulation and Key Engineering Technologies (U19B6003), Project of the ministry of science and technology of Sinopec (P20064-3).

References

1. Wang S.B. Key techniques for improving the length of acid corrosion fractures in Leikoupo gas reservoir in Weatern Sichuan. Southwest Petroleum University.
2. Zhang Z.W. Research on Spatial Evolution Law of Acid Etching Fractures in Carbonate Rocks. Chengdu University of Technology.
3. Huang W.Q. Research on factors influencing effective carbonate fracture volume caused by acid fracturing. Chengdu University of Technology.
4. Shen Y.X, Feng Z.C, Zhou D, et al. Study on numerical simulation of effect on natural fractures to hydraulic fracture propagation in shale reservoirs. Coal science and technology,2021,49(8):195-202.
5. Sheng G.L, Huang L.Y, Zhao H, et al. Integrated Simulation Approach for Fracture Network Propagation and Gas Flow in Shale Gas Reservoirs. Journal of Southwest Petroleum University（Science & Technology Edition）,2021,43(5):84-96.
6. Zhu H.Y, Song Y.J, Xu Y, et al. Four-dimensional in-situ stress evolution of shale gas reservoirs and its impact on infill well complex fractures propagation. Acta Petrolei Sinca, 2021, 41(9):1224-1236.
7. Xiong J, Liu J, Wu J, et al. Fracture propagation law and fracability evaluation of the tight reservoirs. Natural GasGeoscience, 2021, 32(10): 1581-1591.

https://doi.org/10.1051/e3sconf/202233801022

Study on the difference of pore structure characteristics between the main oil reservoir and the second oil reservoir in Daqing Oilfield

Hongda Teng*

Research Institute of Exploration and Development of Daqing Oilfield Company Ltd., Heilongjiang Daqing, China.

Abstract. In order to study the difference of pore structure characteristics between the second oil reservoir and the main oil reservoir in Daqing oilfield, the pore structure characteristic parameters of core were characterized by routine mercury injection experiment. The results show that the average pore radius of the main reservoir ranges from 5.24μm to 12.50μm, the sorting coefficient ranges from 1.14 to 3.08, the median saturation pressure ranges from 0.04MPa to 0.27MPa, and the maximum median radius can reach 15μm. The permeability is high and the displacement pressure is low. The average pore radius of the second type reservoir is in 2.21μm~9.03μm, the sorting coefficient is 2.70~4.77, the median saturation pressure is 0.076MPa~5.148MPa, the maximum radius is only 5μm, and the permeability is low and the displacement pressure is high. It is important to clarify the difference of reservoir pore structure characteristics for efficient reservoir development.

1. Introduction

Pore structure of reservoir rock is characterized by influencing reservoir fluid reservoir capacity and oil and gas resources are the main factors, especially the multiphase fluid in the reservoir seepage features, in addition to its place of temperature and pressure conditions and the interaction between rock and fluid (wetting, adsorption, etc.), more important is related to the microscopic pore structure characteristics of the reservoir. Clear, therefore, the reservoir pore radius, the radius of the median, sorting coefficient and permeability, expulsion pressure 2 kinds of microscopic pore structure characteristics of the reservoir rock and its distribution, is to increase the crude oil recovery factor and the key to reservoir development effect, to the sustainable development of oil field implementation, eventually improve the economic benefits of oilfield has very important practical significance[1-3].

2. Routine mercury injection experiment

A total of 398 rock samples from 19 Wells in the second and main oil reservoirs of daqing placanticline were selected for routine mercury injection experiments, of which 231 are the main oil reservoirs and 127 are the second oil reservoirs. The main oil layer is putaohua oil layer and the second oil layer is Saertu oil layer. These cores were subjected to conventional mercury injection to collect pore structure characteristic parameters.

2.1 Characteristic analysis of core capillary pressure curve

Capillary pressure curve of rock samples comprehensively reflects pore size and connectivity controlled by larynx. Morphological characteristics of capillary pressure indicate different pore structures of samples. Is closely related to the permeability of capillary pressure curve, as the permeability from large to small, capillary pressure curve from lower left direction on successive arrangement, the greater the permeability, capillary pressure curve, the convex to the lower left corner, and the horizontal axis parallel flat long, shows that the micro pore structure is good, throat size, the greater the uniform pore throat, the lower the expulsion pressure[4]. On the contrary, for the sample with low permeability, the capillary pressure curve is far away from the horizontal axis. The farther away from the horizontal axis, the flat segment gradually decreases, and the worse the microscopic pore structure is, the lower the permeability is, and the higher the displacement pressure is. The length of gentle section indicates that the laryngeal radius is large and the proportion of the large laryngeal radius is large.

Figure 1 shows the capillary pressure curves of the main and secondary oil zones in two Wells. It can be seen that the capillary pressure curve of the main oil reservoir is close to the lower left, and there is a gentle section, indicating that the main oil reservoir has high permeability, large pore radius, a large proportion of large pores, good pore throat sorting, and low capillary pressure[5]. The capillary pressure curve of the second

* Corresponding author: 523411995@qq.com

 https://doi.org/10.1051/e3sconf/202233801022

type oil reservoir is far away from the horizontal axis. Compared with the main oil reservoir, the flat section is smaller, the permeability is lower, the pore-throat sorting is not good, and the displacement pressure is higher.

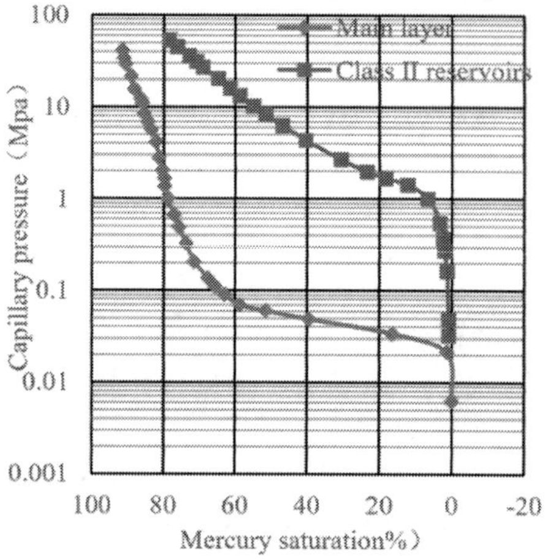

（a）The well 1

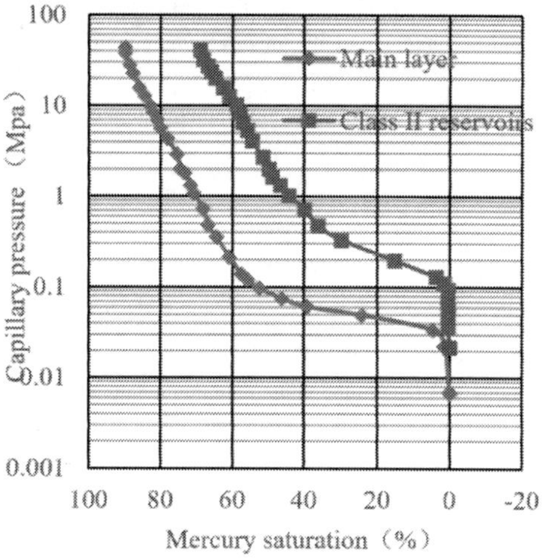

（b）The well 2

Figure 1. Capillary pressure curves of main and secondary reservoirs

2.2 Comparative analysis of pore structure parameters and permeability

The parameters describing pore structure characteristics can be divided into three categories: pore radius characteristic parameters, pore throat distribution characteristic parameters and pore throat connectivity characteristic parameters. Representative parameters are selected to evaluate the pore structure characteristics of the main and second-class oil reservoirs[6]. Table 1 shows the range of pore structure parameters of the main and second-class oil reservoirs.

Table 1. Pore structure parameters of main and secondary oil reservoirs

Category	Characteristic parameters of pore structure	Major reservoir	The second class reservoir
Pore radius characteristic parameters	Maximum pore radius(μm)	11.70~20.90	6.25~17.60
	Mean pore radius(μm)	5.24~12.50	2.21~9.03
	Median pore radius(μm)	2.90~16.60	0.15~9.34
Pore throat distribution characteristic parameters	Sorting coefficient	1.14~3.08	2.70~4.77
	The mean radius(μm)	4.40~13.33	1.34~8.73
	Relative sorting coefficient	0.14~0.88	0.41~3.048
	Homogeneous coefficient	0.35~0.61	0.23~0.51
Pore throat connectivity characteristic parameters	Expulsion pressure(MPa)	0.02~0.06	0.035~0.118
	Maximum mercury intake saturation(%)	83.59~99.20	64.60~98.01
	The median pressure(MPa)	0.04~0.27	0.076~5.148
	Characteristic structural parameter	0.35~6.59	0.117~0.961

(1) Mean pore radius

It can be seen from Table 1 that the average pore radius of class II oil reservoir ranges from 2.21μm to 9.03μm. The average pore radius of the main reservoir ranges from 5.24μm to 12.50μm. Figure 2 shows the relationship between average pore radius and permeability of the main reservoir and the secondary reservoir. It can be seen that the average pore radius of the main reservoir is 12.50μm, while the average pore radius of the second type reservoir is 9.03μm, so it can be seen that the main channel of the second type reservoir fluid flow is small[7]. There is a strong regularity between the average pore radius and permeability. With the increase of permeability, the average pore radius of the reservoir increases, and the average pore radius of the main oil layer is larger than that of the second oil layer, so the seepage channel of the main oil layer is larger than that of the second oil layer.

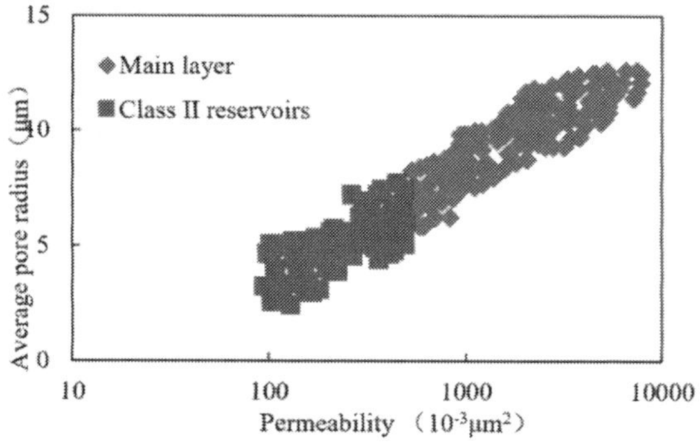

Figure 2. Relationship between average pore radius and permeability

(2) Sorting coefficient

The sorting coefficient is used to describe the distribution and concentration degree of pore-throat. The smaller the value is, the more uniform the pore-throat distribution is. Otherwise, the pore-throat distribution is worse. It can be

https://doi.org/10.1051/e3sconf/202233801022

seen from Table 1 that the sorting coefficient of the main oil reservoir ranges from 1.14 to 3.08, and that of the second oil reservoir ranges from 2.70 to 4.77. It can be seen that the pore throat distribution of the main oil reservoir is uniform, while the sorting of the second oil reservoir is relatively poor.

(3) Saturation median pressure

The size of median saturation pressure can indicate the size of oil and gas productivity. The higher the median saturation pressure is, the denser the reservoir rock is and the worse the permeability is. The lower the median saturation pressure is, the better the percolation ability of fluid in the reservoir is, and the higher the productivity is. For the main oil reservoir, the median saturation pressure ranges from 0.04MPa to 0.27MPa, while for the secondary oil reservoir, the median saturation pressure ranges from 0.076MPa to 5.148MPa. It can be seen that the secondary oil reservoir has poor seepage ability.

(4) Correlation between porosity and permeability

The permeability and porosity of 398 rock samples were statistically analyzed. Figure 3 shows the relationship curve between permeability and porosity of the main and secondary oil reservoirs. It can be seen that there is a strong correlation between porosity and permeability[8]. As the permeability increases, the porosity increases. The permeability of the second type oil layer is smaller than that of the main oil layer, and the porosity is small, indicating that the second type oil layer has poor reservoir physical properties.

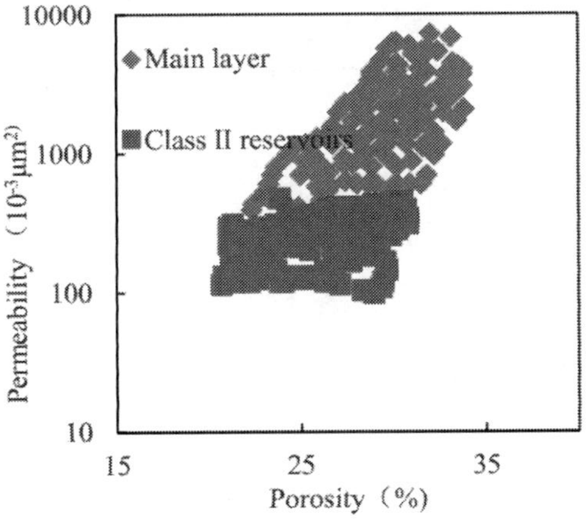

Figure 3. The relationship between permeability and porosity of main and secondary oil reservoirs

(5) Relationship between median pore radius and permeability

Figure 4 shows the relationship between the median pore radius and permeability of the main and secondary oil reservoirs. It can be seen that the median radius of the main oil reservoir is up to 15μm, while the median radius of the secondary oil reservoir is only 5μm. Therefore, the main channel of fluid flow in the second type oil reservoir is small. The regularity between the median radius and permeability is very strong. With the increase of permeability, the median pore radius increases and the permeability increases. There is a good correlation between the median pore radius and permeability, which is in the form of Y = AxB with a high correlation coefficient above 0.9.

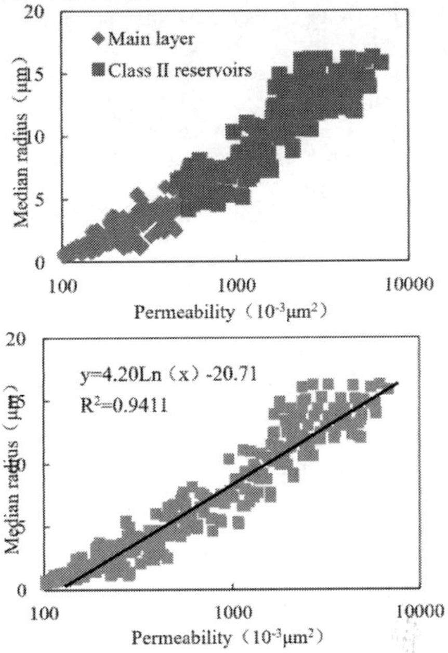

Figure 4. The relation curve between the median radius and permeability of the main reservoir and the secondary reservoir

(6) Relationship between drainage pressure and permeability

The relationship between permeability and displacement pressure in Figure 5 shows that high permeability and low displacement pressure of the main oil reservoir indicate good rock permeability. The larger the maximum pore radius is, the better the reservoir performance is. On the contrary, the second type reservoir has low permeability, and the higher the displacement pressure, the worse the reservoir performance.

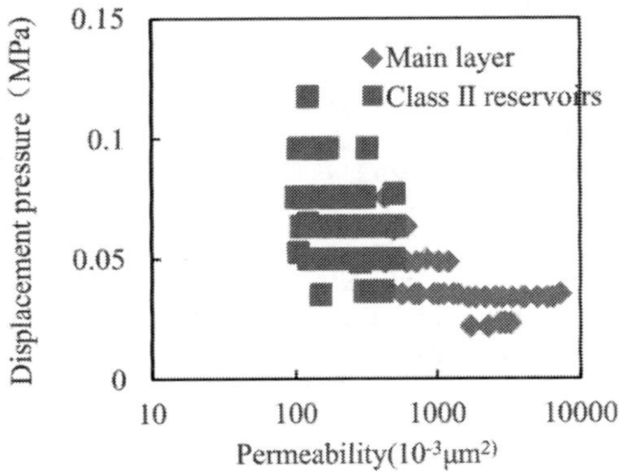

Figure 5. Relationship curve of displacement pressure and permeability between main and secondary oil reservoirs

3. Conclusion

(1) According to the conventional mercury injection test data, the capillary pressure curve of the main oil reservoir is close to the lower left and has a gentle section, indicating that the main oil reservoir has high permeability, large pore radius, a large proportion of large pores, good pore-throat sorting, and low capillary pressure. The capillary pressure curve of the second type oil reservoir is far away from the horizontal axis. Compared with the main oil reservoir, the flat section is smaller, the permeability is lower, the pore-throat sorting is not good, and the displacement pressure is higher.

(2) The average pore radius of the main oil reservoir ranges from 5.24μm to 12.50μm, and that of the second oil reservoir ranges from 2.21μm to 9.03μm. The sorting coefficient of the main oil reservoir ranges from 1.14 to 3.08, and that of the second oil reservoir ranges from 2.70 to 4.77. The pore throat distribution of the main oil reservoir is uniform, while the sorting coefficient of the second oil reservoir is relatively poor. The median saturation pressure of the main oil reservoir ranges from 0.04MPa to 0.27MPa, while the median saturation pressure of the second oil reservoir ranges from 0.076MPa to 5.148MPa. The second oil reservoir has poor seepage ability. The median radius of the main oil reservoir is up to 15μm, while the median radius of the second oil reservoir is only 5μm, and the correlation coefficient is higher than 0.9. The main oil reservoir has high permeability, low displacement pressure and good rock permeability. The larger the maximum pore radius, the better the reservoir performance. On the contrary, the permeability of the second type reservoir is low, and the higher the displacement pressure is, the worse the reservoir performance is.

References

1. Wang Zheng.Study on classification of medium and low porosity and permeability reservoirs based on fractal characteristics [J] Marine geological frontier, 2021,37 (11): 78-84.
2. Liao Hai Water characteristic curve model of salinized soil based on pore structure [D] Northwest University of agriculture and forestry science and technology, 2021.
3. Xie Mingying, Dai Zong, Luo Donghong, Li Hailong, Tang Fang, Tu Zhiyong, Zhu Jian, Wang Chenchen A new method for residual oil characteristic analysis of heavy oil reservoir based on micron CT scanning displacement experiment [J] Unconventional oil and gas, 2020,7 (05): 102-107.
4. Shan Changan, Zhang Tingshan, Liang Xing, Hu Ranran, Zhao Weiwei Nano pore structure characteristics of high rank coals of vitrinite rich and inertinite rich formations [J] Journal of petroleum, 2020,41 (06): 723-736.
5. Song xinglei Study on the control mechanism of micro pore structure of tight sandstone reservoir on tight oil occurrence [D] Xi'an University of petroleum, 2020.
6. Pei zhansong, Zhu Yan Influence of diagenesis on different micro pore structure characteristics in Sazhong Development Zone [C] Proceedings of 2019 International Conference on oil and gas field exploration and development, 2019:2204-2209.
7. Zhu Haihua, Zhang Tingshan, Zhong Dakang, Li yaoyu, Zhang Jingxuan, Chen Xiaohui Binary pore structure characteristics of tight sandstone reservoir [J] Petroleum exploration and development, 2019,46 (06): 1220-1228.
8. Han Jin, Sun Wei, Bai yunyun, Zhang Qian, fan Xiujiang Study on fluid seepage characteristics and influencing factors of oil displacement efficiency of low permeability reservoir based on real sandstone micro water displacement experiment: taking Chang 6 reservoir of wangpanshan in Jiyuan oilfield as an example [J] Geological science and technology information, 2018,37 (06): 89-95.

Effect of pyrolysis temperature on adsorption and degradation of THI and IMI by biochar

Siyao Wang, Hongbo Peng*

College of modern agricultural engineering, Kunming University of Science and Technology, Kunming 650500, China

Abstract. In order to explore the effects of biochar prepared at different pyrolysis temperatures and different solid-liquid ratios on the adsorption and degradation of thiacloprid and imidacloprid in biochar, three biochar were prepared by oxygen pyrolysis with sawdust and as raw materials at 300, 500 ℃ and 600 ℃ respectively. The effects of biochar on the adsorption degradation of thiacloprid and Imidacloprid in biochar were studied. The results showed that the addition of biochar could significantly increase the soil pH, available phosphorus and organic carbon content, and reduce the soil H / C. The addition of biochar significantly improved the adsorption of thiacloprid and imidacloprid, and the adsorption capacity increased with the increase of biochar pyrolysis temperature. Biochar with different pyrolysis temperatures had different effects on the degradation of thiacloprid and imidacloprid. The strong adsorption capacity of high temperature biochar system reduces the chemical degradation rate of thiacloprid and imidacloprid. Proper solid-liquid ratio can avoid the waste of adsorbent and achieve the optimal utilization rate. Therefore, the types and properties of biochar should be fully considered when using biochar to repair pesticide contaminated soil.

key word: Biochar; THI; IMI; adsorption; degradation

1. Introduction

Imidacloprid, also known as mimimidine, is a new nitromethylene insecticide. Its chemical name is 1-6-chloro-3-pyridylmethyl-N-nitroimidazol-2-ylideneamine)
Imidacloprid has a strong effect on insect nicotinic acetylesterase receptor, destroys the normal conduction of insect central nerve, and causes the rapid death of insect nerve paralysis. It has the characteristics of ultra-high efficiency and broad spectrum. The results of field efficacy test showed that imidacloprid had strong knockdown ability, rapid effect, significant control effect and long duration against black tailed leafhopper, planthopper (rice brown planthopper, gray Planthopper and white backed planthopper), aphid (cotton aphid and peach aphid) and thrips. It also had certain control effect on whitefly, rice borer, rice negative mud insect and rice weevil, and its performance was better than buprofezin, permethrin, Pirimicarb Fenitran and furbutan. In addition, imidacloprid has low toxicity to environmental organisms and low dosage, so it has a wide application prospect[1-4]. Imidacloprid contains nitroso, nitroguanidine, cyanamide and other pharmacokinetic groups. The neurotoxic substituent of imidacloprid is its nitroimine [5-7].

In recent years, pesticides have played an important role in controlling crop diseases and pests, but their extensive and inefficient use has led to serious soil pollution problems and toxic effects on most organisms, resulting in potential risks to agricultural soil and human health. The pharmacophores containing = N-NO_2, = NCN and = C (H) NO_2 are important molecular characteristics of neonicotine pesticides. These highly electronegative pharmacophores can selectively identify the cationic binding sites on insect unique nicotinic acetylcholine receptors (nAChRs), but not with vertebrate nicotinic receptors α four β 2 subunit (α four β 2 nAChRs)[8,9].

The main insecticidal mechanism is to act on the insect nervous system and its surrounding nerves to keep the insect excited, paralyze and die. Because there is no cross resistance between neonicotine insecticide and conventional insecticide, it has been widely used in crop planting. Only about 5% of its active components are absorbed by crops, and the unabsorbed parts enter into human body, soil and other media. The concentration detected in the environment is μ g/L~mg/L[10]. In 2014, the global pesticide market sales were US $18.82 billion, while the share of neonicotine pesticides exceeded 25%. Neonicotine pesticide is frequently detected and widely used. Its impact on soil pollution and food safety has attracted extensive attention of researchers.

At present, a variety of technologies have been used to reduce the potential risk of soil pollution caused by pesticides, such as chemical redox and bioremediation, but these technologies have problems such as high cost and complex treatment [11]. On January 1, 2019, China

* Corresponding author: 673483508@qq.com

began to implement the law of the people's Republic of China on the prevention and control of soil pollution, which puts forward higher requirements for soil pollution and remediation. Therefore, in order to reduce the absorption and transfer of pesticides in crops and ensure food safety, it is urgent to seek economic and effective remediation technologies for pesticide contaminated soil. Compost and biochar are common remediation agents for fixing or transforming pesticides [12], while biochar is considered as an environmental remediation agent for adsorbing and degrading pollutants to reduce the risk of soil pollution. It is obtained by pyrolysis of biomass under anoxic and low temperature (< 700 ℃) [10]. Because biochar has large specific surface area and porous structure, it has strong adsorption capacity for heavy metals and pesticides in soil. The rich active oxygen-containing functional groups on the surface of biochar will transfer electrons and have high active oxygen generation ability, so as to promote its degradation of pesticides. Moreover, persistent free radicals on the surface of biochar or highly active small molecular free radicals induced by dissolved organic matter in biochar can directly oxidize and degrade p-nitrophenol, and these free radicals may directly degrade pesticides.

After biochar is applied to the soil, it will interact with dissolved organic matter (DOM), minerals and other components in the soil, block surface pores and reduce pesticide adsorption sites, thus affecting the adsorption of pesticides on biochar. It is found that the addition of biochar can improve the adsorption of imidacloprid, atrazine and isoproturon in soil system, However, due to the specific surface area and organic carbon of the mixed system of biochar and soil The actual value of organic carbon (OC) content is lower than the theoretical value, resulting in its actual adsorption capacity being lower than the theoretical adsorption capacity. Therefore, the adsorption capacity of biochar for pesticides in soil may be overestimated, which needs to be verified by more research data. Biochar remediation also has advantages and disadvantages for the microbial degradation of pesticides in soil. Previous studies have shown that biochar can improve the biodegradation of pesticides in soil. Soil microenvironment, improve soil microbial abundance, and then improve the degradation rate of pesticide microbial degradation. Firstly, due to the strong adsorption of biochar on pesticides, the utilization of pesticides by microorganisms and plants is reduced, which inhibits the microbial degradation of pesticides, and the inhibition increases with the increase of biochar dosage. Secondly, the degradable organic matter from the surface of biochar can promote the growth of microorganisms, but the strong adsorption of biochar reduces the utilization of such substances by microorganisms. The above differences in the effects of different biochar on microbial degradation of pesticides may be related to the pyrolysis temperature, raw materials, dosage and soil type of biochar, which needs further research.

2. Material and method

2.1 Material

The biomass wood sample used in this study was from Kunming University of science and technology. Technical-grade imidacloprid (IMI , 98.5%) and thiacloprid (THI , 97%) were purchased from the Aladdin Reagent Co., Ltd. (Shanghai, China). The basic properties of the two pesticides are listed in Table 1. Other chemicals and solvents were at least of analytical grade and used without further purification, except that the acetonitrile was chromatography pure. Ultra- pure (UP) water (18.2 MΩ·cm) was used to prepare all chemicals.

Table 1. Physicochemical properties of IMI and THI.

Compound	Molecular	Molecular weight	Water solubility /mg·L^{-1}	lg K_{ow}	pK_a	Molecular structure
Imidacloprid	$C_9H_{10}ClN_5O_2$	255.66	510	0.57	0.01±0.10	
Thiacloprid	$C_{10}H_9ClN_4S$	252.72	185	1.3	0.01±0.10	

Note: Kow data are taken from the PubChem datebase of Biotechnology Information(NCBI); Koc Organic carbon adsorption coefficient; pKa acidity coefficient.

2.2 Preparation of biochar

A lignin-rich biochar was used in this study. Wood was air-dried, ground, and passed through 100 mesh (0.15 mm) sieve. The dried feedstocks were charred at 300 ,500 and 600 °C for 4 h in a closed 300-mL ceramic crucible with a cap under oxygen-limited conditions in a muffle furnace. The produced biochars were ground to pass through 100 mesh (0.15 mm) sieves and stored in 40-mL glass jars.

2.3 Adsorption experiments

Batch adsorption equilibrium method was used in adsorption experiment. The specific steps were as follows : 80 mg, 40 mg, 8 mg and 4 mg biochar were weighed respectively in 4 mL EPA sample bottle (with a cover with Teflon gasket), and then 4 mL 10 mg/L IMI and THI solution containing 5 mmol·L-1 NaCl and 200 mg·L-1 NaN3 were added. Cover the cover tightly, shake well and place in 25 ± 1 °C shaker to avoid light oscillation, oscillation speed 150 r·min-1. After oscillation for 144 h, the sample bottle was taken out and centrifuged at 3500 r·min-1high-speed centrifuge for 10 min. The supernatant was analyzed by HPLC after passing 0.45 μm water filter membrane. Repeat 2 times per treatment.

2.4 Degradation experiments

This experiment only studied the chemical drop of IMI and THI. After 144 h, the liquid in 4 mL flask was extracted completely, and 4mL acetonitrile solution was added each time. After shaking well, it was placed in a 25 ± 1 °C shaker to avoid light oscillation, and the oscillation speed was 150 r·min-1. After oscillation for 3 h, the sample bottle was taken out and centrifuged at 3500 r·min-1 high-speed centrifuge for 10 min. The supernatant was removed and determined by HPLC after passing 0.45 μm organic membrane. The extraction recoveries were above 90 %. The above solvents are pure chromatographic grade.

3. Results and discussion

3.1 Effect of pyrolysis temperature on adsorption and degradation of THI and IMI by biochar

The adsorption results of thiacloprid and imidacloprid in biochar are shown in Figure 1. As shown in Figure 1, it shows that the adsorption of thiamethoxam by biochar system is mainly multi-layer adsorption[23]. After adding biochar, the adsorption capacity of thiacloprid and imidacloprid was improved. The addition of biochar could significantly improve the adsorption capacity of soil for thiacloprid and imidacloprid, and the improvement degree of adsorption capacity increased with the increase of pyrolysis temperature of added biochar. The se of thiacloprid and imidacloprid in high temperature biochar system is higher than that in low temperature biochar system, which indicates that high temperature biochar has stronger adsorption capacity for thiacloprid and imidacloprid in soil. This is because during the high-temperature pyrolysis of sawdust, with the increase of pyrolysis temperature, the specific surface area of biochar increases, the degree of aromatization deepens and the surface hydrophobicity increases, which provides the possibility for biochar to adsorb pesticides[26]. Liu Jiannan et al. [27]also found that with the increase of pyrolysis temperature, the larger the specific surface area, the more adsorption sites can be provided on the surface of biochar, so the adsorption capacity of thiacloprid and imidacloprid on high-temperature biochar is strong. In addition, high temperature pyrolysis makes biochar contain more aromatic carbon and high specific surface area, so that thiacloprid and imidacloprid are adsorbed on biochar through hydrophobic distribution, pore filling, hydrogen bonding, p (n) - π and π - π electron donor acceptor interaction. The strong adsorption capacity in the high-temperature biochar system leads to the reduction of the concentration level of available nitrogen and soluble organic carbon. At the same time, this adsorption may compete with pollutant molecules for high-energy adsorption sites on the biochar surface or block micropores and mesopores[29], so as to reduce the adsorption sites of thiacloprid and imidacloprid. However, for the 300 °C biochar system, the release of available nitrogen, phosphorus and soluble organic carbon on the biochar surface changed its surface properties and improved the adsorption of thiacloprid and imidacloprid[31]. The adsorption of thiacloprid and imidacloprid by biochar still improved the adsorption capacity of soil due to biochar remediation, and the degree of improvement increased with the increase of biochar pyrolysis temperature. Therefore, the strong adsorption capacity of biochar to thiacloprid and imidacloprid can play an important role in reducing their mobility in soil.

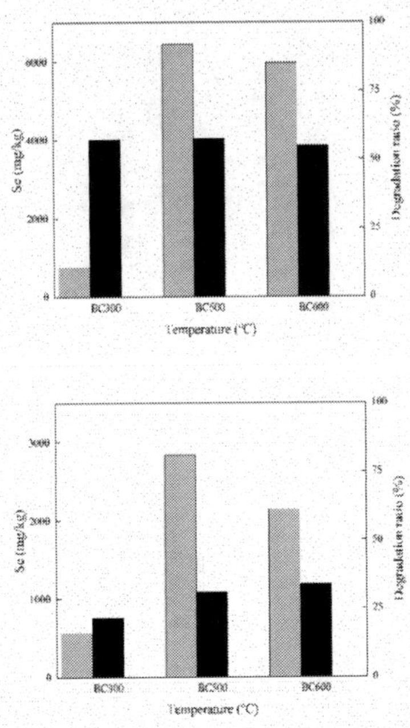

Figure 1. Adsorption and degradation of THI (left) and IMI (right) by biochar at different temperatures.

3.2 Effect of solid-liquid ratio on adsorption and degradation of THI and IMI by biochar

The experiment of solid-liquid ratio is mainly to explore the relationship between the input amount of adsorbent and the removal efficiency of thiacloprid and imidacloprid. If the input amount of adsorbent is too small, the amount of thiacloprid and imidacloprid can not be effectively removed. On the contrary, it will form a waste of resources and cause unnecessary economic losses. In order to fully improve the utilization of adsorbent, we did solid-liquid ratio experiment. The experimental results are shown in Figure 2、3 and 4.

As can be seen from Fig. 2、3 and 4, in the initial stage, the removal efficiency increases with the increase of adsorbent dosage. When the solid-liquid ratio reaches a certain value, even if the input of adsorbent increases, the adsorption capacity of thiacloprid and imidacloprid basically maintains a certain value without significant increase. When the solid-liquid ratio of biochar at 300 °C reaches 1:100, the removal efficiency is almost the highest, and there is no increase. According to the highest removal efficiency and cost-effectiveness, the best solid-liquid ratio is 1:100. At the same time, the best solid-liquid ratio of biochar at 500 °C and 600 °C is 1:1000.

 https://doi.org/10.1051/e3sconf/202233801023

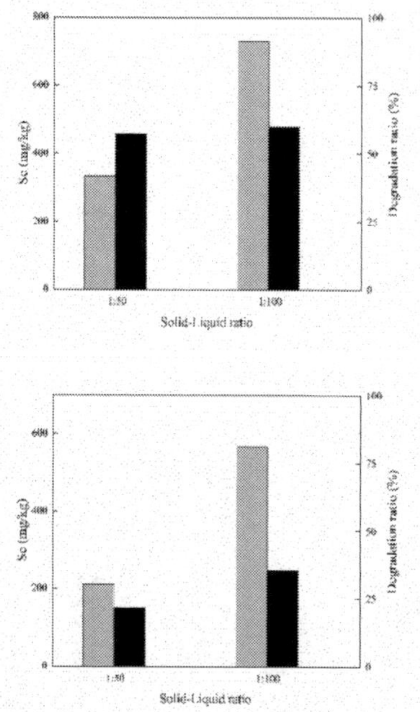

Figure 2. Adsorption and degradation of thiacloprid (left) and imidacloprid (right) by biochar at 300 °C under different solid-liquid ratio

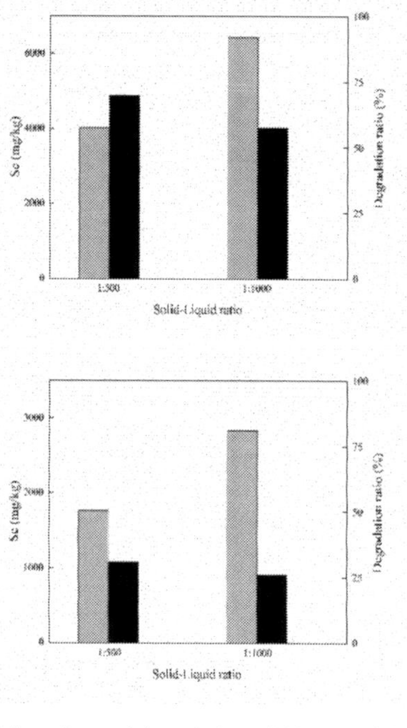

Figure 3. Adsorption and degradation of thiacloprid (left) and imidacloprid (right) by biochar at 500 °C under different solid-liquid ratio

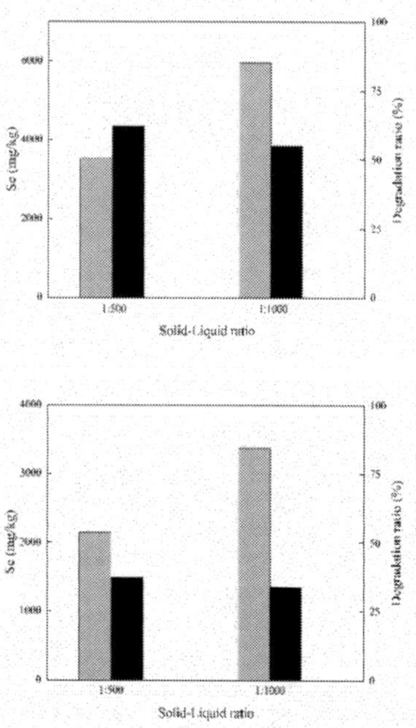

Figure 4. Adsorption and degradation of thiacloprid (left) and imidacloprid (right) by biochar at 600 °C under different solid-liquid ratio

3.3 Adsorption and degradation mechanism of THI and IMI under biochar

Other studies have pointed out that for the adsorption of thiacloprid and imidacloprid by the same biochar, the adsorption of biochar at 500 ° C is higher than that of biochar at 300 ° C. Compared with 300 ° C biochar, 500 ° C biochar has relatively fewer polar functional groups, higher aromaticity and stronger hydrophobicity. Therefore, it is speculated that hydrophobicity plays a dominant role in the adsorption of thiacloprid and imidacloprid on biochar, and there may also be adsorption mechanisms such as pore filling, π - π electron donor receptor and hydrogen bond, which affect the adsorption of thiacloprid and imidacloprid. Some studies have also shown that the adsorption of thiacloprid and imidacloprid on biochar will increase with the increase of organic carbon content; The study also pointed out that when the complex adsorbs hydrophobic organic pollutants, hydrophobicity is the dominant mechanism controlling its adsorption. In conclusion, the adsorption mechanism of thiacloprid and imidacloprid on biochar is mainly hydrophobic and π - π effect.

The - OH peak at 3420 cm-1 and the aromatic - C = C peak at 1610 cm-1 of sawdust biochar decreased significantly with the decrease of temperature (Fig. 5), indicating the infrared characteristics of thiacloprid and imidacloprid before and after adsorption on biochar at 300 ° C, 400 ° C and 500 ° C. It was found that the - OH peak at 3420 cm-1 of thiacloprid and imidacloprid adsorbed complex was not different from the original complex, However, the aromatic-C = C peak of the complex adsorbed by thiacloprid and imidacloprid at 1610 cm-1 is

 https://doi.org/10.1051/e3sconf/202233801023

much lower than that before the corresponding reaction. The - COOH of biochar may form a π electron conjugated system with its aromatic ring. Through p / π - π interaction with the benzene ring of thiacloprid and imidacloprid, phenanthrene interacts strongly with the complex. In addition, thiacloprid and imidacloprid can be directly combined with the aromatic components of biochar through π - π interaction. Of course, the contribution of aliphatic components to the adsorption of thiacloprid and imidacloprid can not be ignored. In conclusion, the adsorption mechanisms of thiacloprid and imidacloprid on biochar are mainly hydrophobic, p / π - π and π - π.

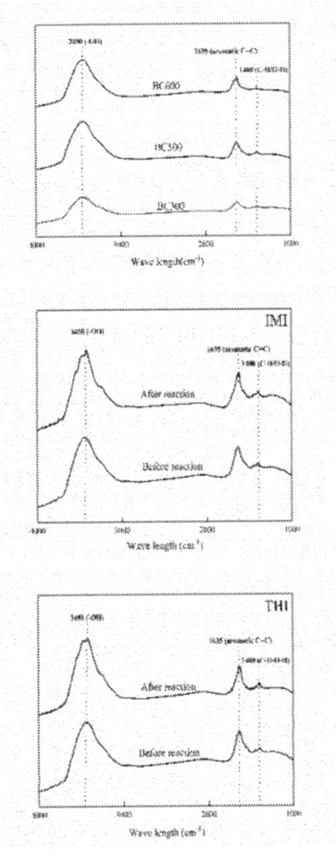

Figure 5. FT-IR

4. Conclusion

(1) Adsorption of thiacloprid and imidacloprid on biochar system biochar at different pyrolysis temperatures affects the adsorption and degradation of thiacloprid and imidacloprid by affecting the physical and chemical properties of biochar.
(2) Thiamethoxam has relatively high chemical degradation rate in high temperature biochar system, but relatively low in low temperature biochar system. Biochar enhanced the adsorption and degradation of thiacloprid and imidacloprid by increasing the content of organic carbon.
(3) At the same temperature, large solid-liquid ratio does not necessarily have strong adsorption and degradation ability. Biochar has a certain adsorption capacity and will not continue to adsorb after reaching saturation. Therefore, it is very important to find an appropriate solid-liquid ratio.

References

1. Chen, LG Determination of imidacloprid in rice by molecularly imprinted-matrix solid-phase dispersion with liquid chromatography tandem mass spectrometry[J]. J CHROMATOGR B, 2012, 2012,897(-): 32-36.
2. Pandiselvi S, Sathiyanarayanan S, Ramesh A Determination of Spirotetramat and Imidacloprid Residues in Cotton Seed, Lint, Oil and Soil by HPLC UV Method and their Dissipation in Cotton Plant[J]. Pesticide Research Journal, 2010, 22: 168-173.
3. Iqbal, S., Uddin, et al. Extraction, Cleanup, and Chromatographic Determination of Imidacloprid Residues in Wheat[J]. BULLETIN OF ENVIRONMENTAL CONTAMINATION AND TOXICOLOGY, 2012:
4. Li Y, Yang L, Yan H, et al. Uptake, translocation and accumulation of imidacloprid in six leafy vegetables at three growth stages[J]. Ecotoxicology and Environmental Safety, 2018, 164: 690-695.
5. Michlig M P, Julieta M, Pacini A C, et al. Determination of imidacloprid in beehive samples by UHPLC-MS/MS[J]. Microchemical Journal, 2018, 143: S0026265X18303278-.
6. Wang S W, Zeng G F, Liu Y P, et al. Determination of Thiacloprid,Spirotetramat and Its Metabolites Residues in Litchi and Longan by High Performance Liquid Chromatography-Tandem Mass Spectrometry[J]. Journal of Instrumental Analysis, 2019:
7. Min, Huang, Xinxian, et al. A liquid chromatography with tandem mass spectrometry method to simultaneously determinate chlorpyrifos, imidacloprid and imidacloprid metabolites in wheat[J]. Journal of separation science, 2019:
8. Angioni A, Porcu L, Pirisi F LC/DAD/ESI/MS method for the determination of imidacloprid, thiacloprid, and spinosad in olives and olive oil after field treatment[J]. Journal of Agricultural & Food Chemistry, 2011, 59(20): 11359-11366.
9. Auteri D, Arena M, Barmaz S, et al. Neonicotinoids and bees: The case of the European regulatory risk assessment - ScienceDirect[J]. Science of the Total Environment, 2017, 579(feb.1): 966-971.
10. Mommaerts V, Reynders S, Boulet J, et al. Risk assessment for side-effects of neonicotinoids against bumblebees with and without impairing foraging behavior[J]. Ecotoxicology, 2010, 19(1): 207-215.
11. Wu B, Cheng G, Kai J, et al. Mycoextraction by Clitocybe maxima combined with metal immobilization by biochar and activated carbon in an aged soil[J]. Science of the Total Environment, 2016, 562(aug.15): 732-739.

https://doi.org/10.1051/e3sconf/202233801023

12. Richard, S., Quilliam, et al. Life in the 'charosphere' – Does biochar in agricultural soil provide a significant habitat for microorganisms?[J]. Soil Biology and Biochemistry, 2013, 65(1): 287-293.
13. Deng J H, Gao L Y, Zhou W W, et al. Adsorption characteristics and mechanisms of Cd2+ in biochar derived fromvetiver grass under different pyrolysis temperatures[J]. Journal of Agro-Environment Science, 2018:
14. Charisma, Lattao, Xiaoyan, et al. Influence of Molecular Structure and Adsorbent Properties on Sorption of Organic Compounds to a Temperature Series of Wood Chars[J]. Environmental Science & Technology: ES&T, 2014, 48(9): 4790-4798.
15. Liu J N, Feng J M, Dan L I, et al. The adsorption of Cd~(2+) and Zn~(2+) in aqueous solutions by dairy manure and walnut shell biochar[J]. Journal of Agro-Environment Science, 2019:
16. Ren G, Teng Y, Ren W, et al. Pyrene dissipation potential varies with soil type and associated bacterial community changes[J]. Soil Biology and Biochemistry, 2016:
17. Ke, Sun, Mingjie, et al. Impact of Deashing Treatment on Biochar Structural Properties and Potential Sorption Mechanisms of Phenanthrene[J]. Environmental Science & Technology, 2013:

 https://doi.org/10.1051/e3sconf/202233801024

The Key Application Technology of Desulfurized Gypsum in Dry-Mixed Mortar

Guangxu Fang *, Jin Pan, Rui Ma, Huan Wang, Jipeng Wang

Changji State Product Quality Inspection Institute ChangJi XinJiang 831100 China

Abstract. In this paper, in view of the problem of low early and late strength of dry-mixed mortar prepared by cement-fly ash-slag powder composite cementing system, the ratio of mixing fly ash and slag powder to replace cement is 70%. To study the effect of desulfurization gypsum (FGD) on improving the activity of the system. The results show that adding desulfurized gypsum, which accounts for 6% to 8% of the total mass of the cementitious material, has no adverse effect on the workability and can significantly improve the compressive resistance of the slurry. Strength and tensile bonding strength, shrinkage rate is reduced by more than 10%, and the ability to resist carbonization is improved to make the mortar volume more stable.

Key words: Desulfurized gypsum, dry-mix mortar, fly ash, slag powder.

1. Introduction

Ready-mixed mortar is one of the key projects implemented in China in recent years. Although mineral admixtures such as fly ash and slag powder have been widely used in dry-mixed mortars, mortars mixed with fly ash and slag powder, especially mortars mixed with large amounts of fly ash and slag powder, have obvious early mechanical properties Reduction seriously restricts the large-scale application of fly ash and slag powder in mortar. Desulfurized gypsum is an industrial by-product gypsum obtained after flue gas desulfurization in coal-fired or oil-fired power plants [1]. Its main components and physical and chemical properties are basically the same as natural gypsum, with higher purity and smaller particle size. Since desulfurized gypsum contains water with a mass fraction of about 10%, it also contains impurities such as fly ash, organic carbon, calcium carbonate, calcium sulfite, and soluble salts composed of sodium, potassium, magnesium sulphate or chloride. Therefore, the application of desulfurized gypsum is subject to certain restrictions, and a large amount of desulfurized gypsum is discarded and stored. This article proposes to use desulfurized gypsum as a modifier of the cement-fly ash-slag powder composite cementing system in a large amount of fly ash-slag powder dry-mix mortar to stimulate the activity of fly ash and slag powder, thereby the idea of improving the performance of dry-mixed mortar, and researching related issues through experiments.

2. Experimental Design

2.1 Raw materials

Two types of fly ash are used: coarse fly ash from Zhengzhou Taixiang Thermal Power Co., Ltd. and low-calcium fly ash from Luoyang Power Plant [2]. The coarse fly ash of Zhengzhou Taixiang Thermal Power Co., Ltd. is ground to the specified time with a standard laboratory ball mill and divided into four types: undisturbed fly ash, ground fly ash (milled for 10 minutes), and ground fly ash (Grinding for 20min), grinding fly ash (grinding for 30min). The chemical properties of fly ash are shown in Table 1. The flue gas desulfurization gypsum adopts Zhengzhou Taixiang Thermal Power Co., Ltd., with a water content of 10.5%; it is dried in an oven at 60°C for use in the laboratory.

Table 1. Chemical composition of raw materials

Material name	CaO	SiO_2	Al_2O_3	Fe_2O_3	K_2O	Na_2O	SO_3	MgO	Loss
cement	60.01	22.21	5.51	2.88	0.80	0.08	2.50	2.60	3.21
Zhengzhou undisturbed fly ash	1.20	60.00	26.00	5.00	0.78	0.40	0.45	0.40	5.50
Luoyang Fly Ash	0.80	57.50	30.00	5.20	0.66	0.41	0.38	0.45	3.60
Flue gas desulfurization gypsum	33.70	3.93	2.47	0.45	0.39	0.19	43.27	1.52	14.05

2.2 Method design

Test specimen preparation and basic performance tests such as consistency, water retention, setting time, tensile bonding strength, compressive strength and shrinkage are

* Corresponding author: 471268185@qq.com

all carried out with reference to "Test Methods for Basic Performance of Building Mortar" (JGJ/T70-2009), using a mortar mixer Stir, the stirring time is not less than 180s, and the tensile bond strength, compressive strength and shrinkage test block are cured according to the standard. Add water to the corresponding composite gelling system mortar according to the specified consistency, mix and form uniformly (the test mold is a compressive strength test mold), remove the mold after 24 hours, and cure it in a standard curing room to the specified age, and terminate it with anhydrous ethanol for hydration, perform the following treatments on the sample after 3 days of hydration: 1) X-ray diffraction (XRD) sample and scanning electron microscope (SEM) sample. Crush the sample, select a slurry without artificial sand under an optical microscope for SEM observation, and grind the remaining slurry for XRD testing. 2) Samples for pore structure analysis [3]. The sample is broken up, the samples containing artificial sand and the slurry without artificial sand are selected under an optical microscope, and the number of the slurry is half, mixed evenly, and then the pore structure is analysed.

2.3 Experimental protocol

The experimental study of the cement-fly ash-desulfurized gypsum mortar system has explored the composition of cement, FA, and FGD through experiments [4]. The cement content is initially set at 10%-20% of the cementitious material, and FA is added. The amount is 10% to 60%, and the FGD is 20% to 70%; methyl cellulose ether is blended at 0.1% of the mass of the cementing material; polypropylene hybrid fibre is blended at 0.4% of the mass of the cement; aggregate the mixing amount is 3 times the mass of the cementitious material (1:3 mortar), and the water-binder ratio is uniformly adopted at 0.5. The specific coordination ratio is shown in Table 2.

Table 2. Test mix ratio of mortar

No.	Cement	FA	FGD	Sand	Water	MC	Fibber
1	0.10	0.60	0.30	3	0.50	0.1%	0.4%
2	0.10	0.45	0.45	3	0.50	0.1%	0.4%
3	0.10	0.30	0.60	3	0.50	0.1%	0.4%
4	0.15	0.60	0.25	3	0.50	0.1%	0.4%
5	0.15	0.45	0.40	3	0.50	0.1%	0.4%
6	0.15	0.30	0.55	3	0.50	0.1%	0.4%

3. Results

3.1 The influence of Portland cement on the consistency of mortar

Figure 1 shows the effect of Portland cement content change on the consistency of desulfurized gypsum-based mortar. It can be seen that as the amount of cement increases, the consistency of the mortar shows a linear increase trend [5]. The consistency of the desulfurized gypsum-based mortar without cement (reference mortar) is 63mm; when the cement content is 10%, the mortar consistency increases significantly to 85mm; when the cement content is 20%, the mortar consistency increases to 102mm; When the cement content is 30%, the consistency of the mortar reaches 110mm, an increase of 75%. This shows that cement can significantly increase the consistency of desulfurized gypsum-based mortar and improve the fluidity of desulfurized gypsum-based mortar; and as its content increases, the consistency of the mortar gradually increases and the fluidity gradually improves.

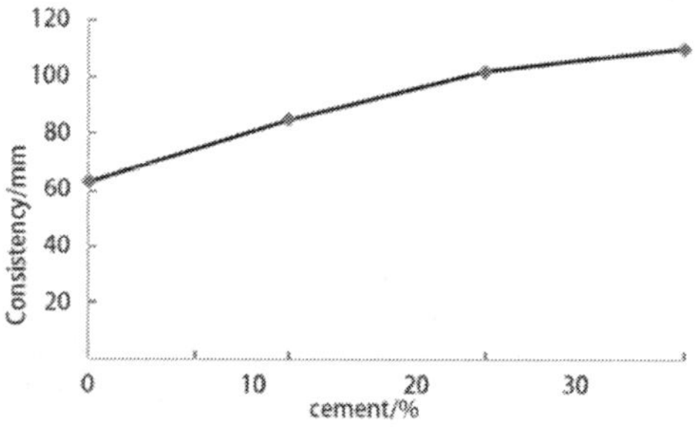

Figure 1. The effect of cement content change on the consistency of sulphurised gypsum-based mortar

3.2 The influence of FGD on the performance of cement-fly ash-slag powder composite cementitious system mortar

For the freshly mixed mortar mixture, when it reaches the specified consistency (90-100mm), compared with the sample without FGD, when FGD is added to the cement-fly ash-slag powder composite cementing system, the unilateral mortar is Water consumption and water retention have been reduced, but the change is not big; the change of setting time is more complicated. With the increase of FGD, the single-mixed fly ash gradually shortens, and the maximum shortens 30min; the single-mixed slag powder gradually increases, the maximum extension 40min; the two-compound mixed first lengthened and then shortened, and the change was within ±20min. For hardened mortar paste, compared with samples without FGD, after FGD is mixed into the cement-fly ash-slag powder composite cementing system, the early and late compressive strength and tensile bonding strength of the mortar are both There are varying degrees of change [6]. When fly ash is mixed alone: FGD does not significantly improve the early compressive strength of the mortar, and too high a content will reduce its early compressive strength, but the compressive strength and tensile bonding strength of the mortar in the later period will be significantly improved; compared with single-mixed powder Compared with coal ash, when it is mixed with slag powder only: FGD improves the compressive strength of mortar in the early stage, but its later compressive strength and tensile bonding strength are less improved; compared with single-mixed fly ash or slag powder, the two When compounding: FGD significantly improves the compressive strength of the mortar in the early and late stages, and the increase rate of tensile bonding strength is equivalent to that of single-mixed slag powder; the increase rate of the early and late compressive strength and tensile bonding strength of the mortar reaches the maximum At the same time, the best content of desulfurization gypsum is 6%.

3.3 The influence of Portland cement on the bulk density of mortar

Figure 2 shows the effect of Portland cement content change on the freshly mixed bulk density and 28d hardened bulk density of desulfurized gypsum-based mortar. It can be seen that after adding cement, the volume density of the freshly mixed desulfurized gypsum-based mortar has increased [7]. The volume density of the new benchmark mortar is 2010kg/ m^3; when the cement content is 10%, the volume density of the fresh mortar is 2098kg/m3; when the cement content is 20%, the volume density of the fresh mortar is 2060kg/ m^3; the cement content is at 30%, the volume density of the freshly mixed mortar significantly increases to 2102kg/ m^3. With the change of cement content, the volume density of fresh mix fluctuates within the range of 50kg/ m^3. This shows that the incorporation of cement will increase the volume density of the freshly mixed desulfurized gypsum-based mortar, but the influence of the change in its mixing amount is relatively small.

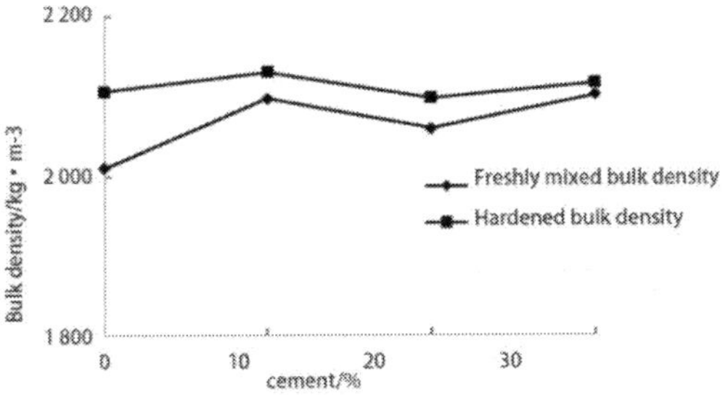

Figure 2. The influence of cement content change on the bulk density of desulfurized gypsum-based mortar

The 28d hardened bulk density of desulfurized gypsum-based mortar changes with the increase of cement content and the trend is similar to that of freshly mixed bulk density [8]. When the cement content is 10%, the hardened bulk density is 2131kg/ m^3, which is a slight increase of 25kg/ m^3 compared to the benchmark mortar; the hardened bulk density of the mortar with cement content of 20% is slightly reduced to 2099kg/ m^3; the cement content is 30% The hardened bulk density of the mortar increased to 2117kg/ m^3. With the change of cement content, the hardening volume density changes within 30kg/ m3. This indicates that the change of cement content has a relatively small effect on the hardened bulk density.

3.4 SEM image

In this experiment, scanning electron microscopy (SEM) and scanning electron microscopy (SEM) were carried out on the cementitious material according to the mixing ratio of cement: fly ash: desulfurized gypsum=30:50:20 (mass ratio) and water-binder ratio of 0.3. X-ray diffraction (XRD) analysis, the results are shown in Figures 3 and 4.

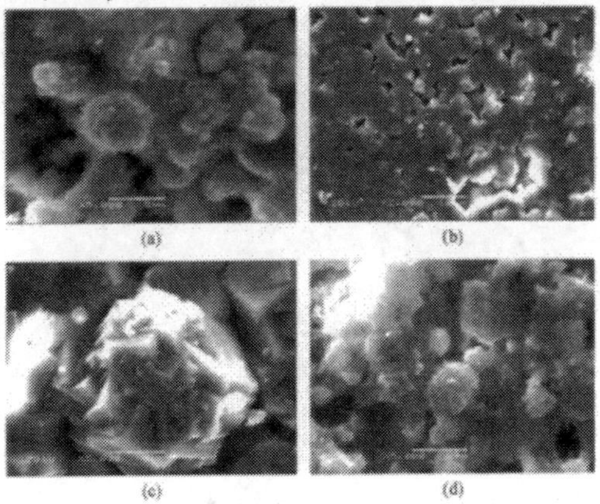

Figure 3. SEM image of hardened gel material

Figure 3(a) is the SEM image of the 3d hardened body of Luoyang low-calcium fly ash (Class II undisturbed ash). It can be seen from Figure 3(a) that there is a small amount of needle-like hydration products between the particles, and the structure is very Loose, the wheel angles of spherical fly ash particles and lump gypsum particles are clearly visible; Figures 3(b) and 3(c) are SEM images of 38d hardened body of Luoyang low-calcium fly ash (level II undisturbed ash). From Figures 3(b) and 3(c), it can be seen that the particles are irregular and the structure is loose as shown in Figure 3(b); a large amount of plate-like gypsum products or low-sulphur hydrated sulphur are deposited on the surface of spherical fly ash particles [9]. The calcium aluminate product is shown in Figure 3(c). The main elements of the plate-like substance are calcium, sulphur, oxygen and a small amount of silicon and aluminium according to the energy spectrum analysis; Figure 3(d) is the 3d hardening mixed with ground fly ash (Class II) The SEM image of the body, as can be seen from Figure 3(d): there is a certain amount of needle-like hydration products between the particles, the structure is looser, but denser than 3(a), spherical fly ash particles and lump gypsum The wheel angle of the particles is not clear. The XRD analysis of the cementitious material (Figure 4) shows that the cementitious material mixed with undisturbed ash and ground ash contains ettringite crystals and gypsum crystals in 3d and 28d hardened bodies; the cemented material mixed with fine ash 28d hardened body The obvious increase of the baseline of the XRD pattern indicates the formation of a large amount of gel.

https://doi.org/10.1051/e3sconf/202233801024

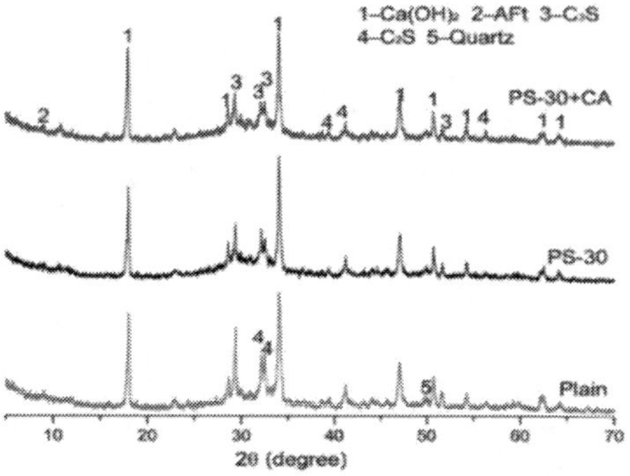

Figure 4. XRD pattern of hardened cementitious material

4. Conclusion

In a large amount of fly ash-slag powder dry-mix mortar, desulfurized gypsum not only directly stimulates the activity of fly ash and slag powder, but also accelerates fly ash and slag powder by promoting the hydration of cement the hydration reaction. Large-volume fly ash-slag powder dry-mixed mortar is a new type of green building material with excellent performance. It can not only effectively use industrial waste gas desulfurized gypsum, but also further promote the utilization of fly ash and slag powder, and reduce cement The consumption, energy saving and consumption reduction have achieved remarkable results, and the application prospects are broad, which are in line with the national circular economy strategy.

References

1. Liu Yin, Wang Haoyu, Guo Hao, et al. Research on optimization and performance of high-volume fly ash filling materials. Mining Research and Development, 40(3) (2020) 56-62.
2. Wang Chenxia, Liu Jun, Cao Fubo, et al. Experimental study on slag-fly ash recycled concrete under the coupling effect of freeze-thaw-carbonization. Building Structure, 50(15) (2020) 45-49.
3. Xie Tianyi, Lou Zongke, Huo Yizhen, et al. The effect of fly ash and slag on the fluidity and mechanical properties of channel lining mould bag concrete. Agricultural Research in the Arid Areas, 37(2) (2019) 74-79.
4. Wu Yonghua, Hu Yubo, Nan Feng, et al. The effect of fly ash on the corrosion resistance of alkali-activated slag cementitious materials with hydrochloric acid. Bulletin of the Chinese Ceramic Society, 38(4) (2019) 15-22.
5. Jiao Xuemei, Qin Can, Gong Jingwei, et al. Analysis of hydration heat release of ordinary Portland cement-based cementitious material system with large amount of mineral admixtures. Hydropower, 45(11) (2019) 10-18.
6. Huai Jianfeng. Analysis of the influence of fly ash and ceramsite on concrete road performance. Comprehensive utilization of fly ash, 15(1) (2019) 57-60.
7. Li Bing, Wei Sha, Zheng Yiwen. Preparation and performance of desulfurized ash-based semi-light dry-mixed mortar. Non-metallic Minerals, 43(1) (2020) 15-20.
8. Wang Yan, Tong Yueping, Zhang Shaohui, et al. Effect of nano-clay on the properties of high-volume fly ash mortar. Industrial Construction, 50(2) (2020) 47-58.
9. Huang Qian, Tang Shuai, Chen Yibo, et al. The effect of nano-SiO2 on the properties of high-volume fly ash cement. Non-metallic Minerals, 43(2) (2020) 17-28.

Seismic imaging and recognition technology of medium and shallow channel sand body

Dongna Wang*

PetroChina Jidong Oilfield company, Tangshan, Hebei 063004, China

Abstract. The fine characterization of channel sand body is a complex system engineering. The longitudinal superposition relationship of channel is complex, the sandstone thickness is thin, and the lateral changes of lithology and physical properties are obvious. It is necessary to carry out the research on the integration of processing and interpretation and seismic geology. The key technologies of seismic high-resolution pre stack and post stack inversion of medium and shallow channel sand bodies with "improved HHT point spectrum whitening" and "weak sidelobe wavelet structure" as the core and "azimuth well control inversion modeling" and "Cauchy regularization high-resolution inversion" as the core have been formed through experimental research.

key word: Channel sand; seismic high-resolution imaging processing; pre stack inversion; post stack inversion.

1 Introduction

The poor imaging, low resolution and low signal-to-noise ratio of existing seismic data in middle and shallow layers make it impossible to effectively resolve the thin-layer (5-10 m) channel sand deposited in the river phase in middle and shallow layers, low coincidence rate predicted by reservoir inversion and paradoxically prominent well shock. Pilot investigations were conducted to form the key techniques for high-resolution imaging of meso shallow channel sand body earthquakes with cores of " improved HHT point spectrum albinism " and " weak paravalved daughter wave construction ", and for high-resolution pre stack and post stack inversions with cores of " azimuthal well controlled Inversion Modeling " and ""Corsi regularized high-resolution inversion "[1].

2 Key technology

2.1 Improved HHT point spectrum whitening technology Key technologies

HHT point spectrum whitening technology is the key technology of post stack high-resolution processing. It includes three parts: time spectrum effective information extraction technology, high-frequency information optimization technology and fractal amplitude preserving technology[2]. The basic idea of HHT point spectrum whitening is shown in Figure 1.

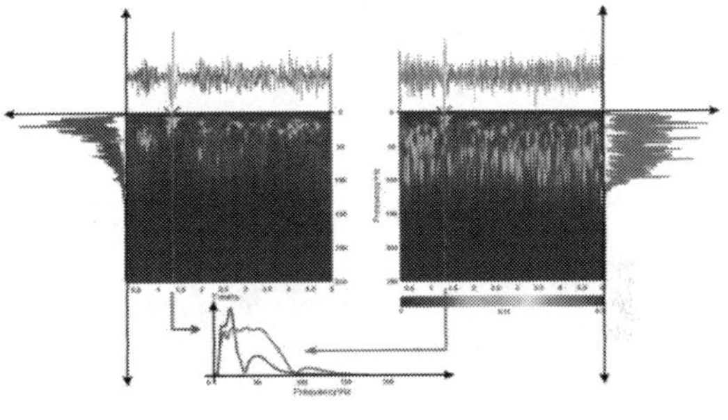

Fig. 1 Schematic diagram of HHT point spectrum whitening principle
(blue on the left - before high-resolution processing, red on the right - after high-resolution processing)

2.2 Construction of weak sidelobe wavelet

Seismic wavelet refers to the signal with stable waveform and length of about 60-100ms formed after the pulse function excited by the source propagates for a period of time through geodetic filtering[3], resulting in wavelet distortion, especially the thin-layer tuning effect caused by wavelet sidelobe is the inevitable cause of error. In this study, a weak sidelobe mexh seismic wavelet (weak sidelobe Mexican Hat seismic wavelet) is constructed The construction method considers the influence of the sidelobe of the seismic wavelet on the seismic data processing link, considers the signal-to-noise ratio of the seismic section and the effective frequency band range to

* Corresponding author: wangdongna@petrochina.com.cn

construct the wavelet, and designs the wavelet with the minimum sidelobe amplitude under the constraint of the effective frequency band width. It is of great value to improve the resolution and fidelity of seismic data. Through seismic high-resolution imaging processing, the resolution and amplitude retention of medium and shallow seismic data in matouying area are effectively improved. After high-resolution processing, the main frequency is increased from the original 15Hz to 26hz, the effective bandwidth[4] is expanded from the original 8-25hz to 5-45hz, and the longitudinal resolution is increased from the original 44m to 18m, which lays a foundation for the identification of thin channel sand bodies (as shown in Figure 2).

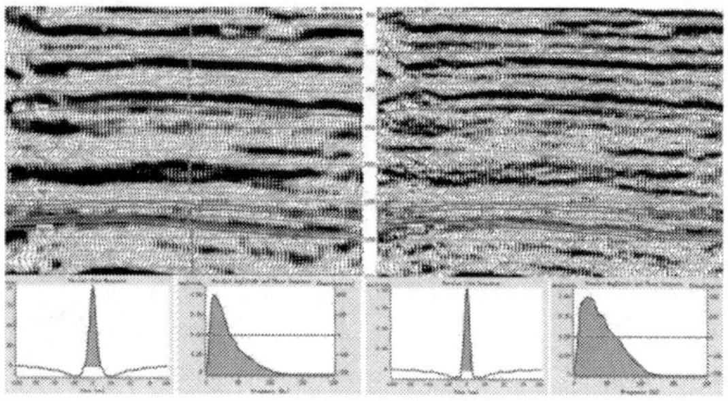

Fig. 2 cross section before (left) and after (right) high resolution processing of HHT point spectrum whitening (left - original profile, wavelet and spectrum, right - high resolution processing profile, weak sidelobe wavelet and spectrum)

2.3 Azimuth well control Inversion Modeling Technology

The logging data is broadband information in the vertical direction and has high resolution, which can accurately describe the detailed characteristics of the formation, but the horizontal distribution is relatively scattered [5]. It is necessary to match the constraints of each well to each seismic trace according to a certain weight. If geostatistical inverse distance weighted inversion modeling is applied, it will cause "bull's eye effect" (as shown in Figure 3), which is not conducive to the lateral fidelity of prestack seismic inversion. Azimuth constraints are introduced, and the shielding effect between wells is fully considered, so that the well can be extrapolated further and the modeling conforms to the sedimentary law.

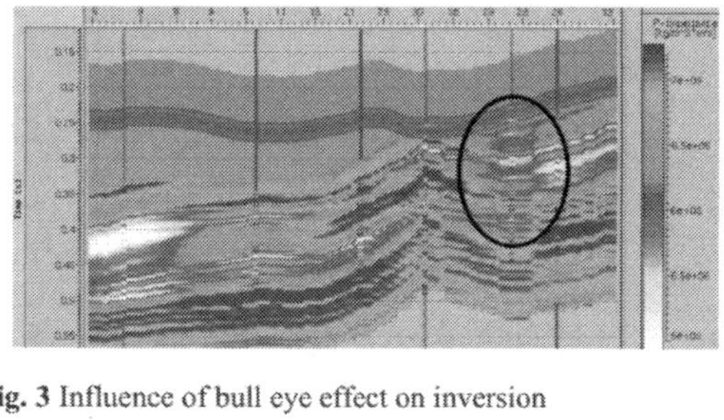

Fig. 3 Influence of bull eye effect on inversion

2.4 Cauchy regularization high resolution inversion technique

Compared with the existing Gaussian adaptive regularization, the Cauchy regularization high-resolution inversion technology proposed in this research has the following advantages: ① the Gaussian distribution of the existing algorithm belongs to the "short tail" distribution, and the inversion results are mainly concentrated near the mean value, and the overall effect is relatively smooth; Cauchy distribution has the characteristics of "long tail" and constitutes a sparse constraint. Compared with Gaussian distribution, the vertical resolution of inversion is higher. ② The block diagonal element of Gaussian regularization parameter is constant, and the block diagonal element of Cauchy regularization parameter changes adaptively[6]. Therefore, Cauchy regularization can produce different constraint coefficients for model parameters of different layers, further eliminate the statistical correlation between the three parameters, and improve the stability of prestack inversion.

3 Application examples

The high-resolution pre stack and post stack seismic inversion of medium and shallow channel sand body with high-precision logging modeling and constraint method[7], azimuth well control inversion, Cauchy regularization high-resolution inversion, shear wave prediction and multi angle joint inversion as the core has improved the prediction accuracy and resolution of medium and shallow channel sand body reservoir in Matou camp area, and the clear imaging of thin channel sandstone, The 3-5M thin channel sand reservoir is effectively identified [8]. By combining with the drilling data, the reservoir coincidence rate exceeds 90%, which lays a foundation for the characterization of thin channel sand body (as shown in Fig. 4).

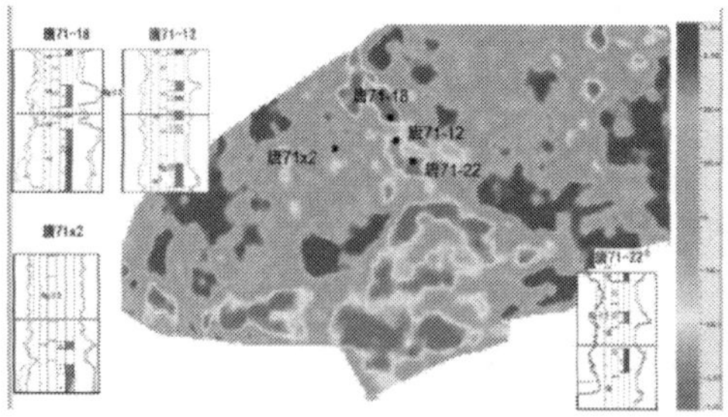

Fig. 4 distribution of medium and shallow channel and prediction of channel sand reservoir

The research results are applied to expand from the main structure to the structural wing, predict and depict the favorable river channel, and provide reliable support for the next drilling. As shown in Figure 5, the upper figure shows the river channel distribution and favorable river channel sand body prediction predicted by using the new processing data. Through the deployment and drilling of well T 71-39 and well T 71-35, thick oil layers were also drilled at the structural wing, which confirmed the amplitude preservation of the new data and the accuracy of river channel sand body prediction. The lower figure shows the data of traditional high-resolution processing, with great contradictions between well earthquakes and wells, It is difficult to identify the river distribution and boundary [9].

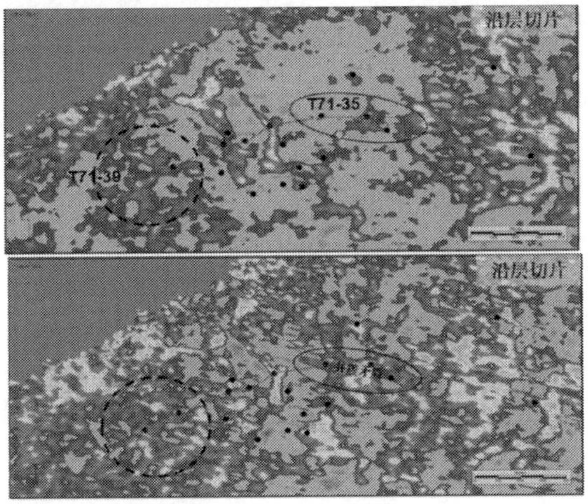

Fig. 5 channel distribution and channel sand reservoir prediction at the wing of matouying
(Upper: prediction chart of this key problem solving data, lower: prediction chart of previous key problem solving data)

4 Conclusion

This paper presents an integrated scheme of seismic data processing and interpretation based on geological targets. The seismic high-resolution imaging processing technology of medium and shallow channel sand body with "HHT point spectrum whitening high-resolution processing and weak sidelobe wavelet shaping" as the core has been formed, which improves the vertical resolution of medium and shallow seismic data and maintains the horizontal resolution, laying a seismic imaging foundation for the identification of thin interbedded channel sand body; Through the dynamic interpretation of sedimentary evolution based on standard layer, the dynamic evolution of channel sand body is recognized and characterized with high resolution.
Through the research and promotion of integrated processing and interpretation technology, it has effectively supported the construction of high-efficiency and high-quality production capacity in Nanpu Sag, greatly improved the exploration and development effect of mature exploration areas, and has reference significance for tapping the potential of similar seismic and geological conditions.

References

1. Zoeppritz K. Reflection and Propagation of Seismic Seismic Waves [J]. Gottinger Nachrichten, 1919(1). 66-84.
2. Stockwell RG , Mansinha L, Lowe R P. Localization of the complex spectrum : thestransform [J] . IEEE Transactions on Signal Processing, 1996, 44(4): 998-1001.
3. Roberts A. Curvature attributes and their application to 3D interpreted horizons [J]. First Break, 2001, 19(2): 85-100.
4. CASTAGNA J P, SMITH S W. Comparison of AVO indicators: A modeling study [J]. Geophysics, 1993, 59(59): 1849-1855.
5. ALEMIE M W. Regularization of the AVO inverse problem by means of a multivariate Cauchy probability distribution [D], 2010.
6. DOWNTON J. Seismic parameter estimation from AVO inversion [M]. Ph D, University of Calgary, 2005.
7. Brossier R , Stéphane Operto, Virieux J . Velocity model building from seismic reflection data by full-waveform inversion [J]. Geophysical Prospecting, 2014, 63(2): 354-367.
8. utton, S.P., and Loucks, R.D. 2010. Diagenetic controls on evolution of porosity and permeability in lower Tertiary Wilcox sandstones from shallow to ultradeep (200–6700 m) burial, Gulf of Mexico Basin, U.S.A.: Marine and Petroleum Geology, v.27, p.69–81.
9. Bennion D B, Thoma F B, Imer D. (2000). Low Permeability Gas Reservoirs and Formation Damage -Tricks and Traps. SPE, 59753. DOI: 10.2118/59753-MS.

Controlling factors of matrix acidizing potential of low permeability clastic reservoir in faulted lacustrine basin

Ningning Xu [1, 2,*], Yongshi Wang [3], Shoupeng Zhang [2], Bo Li [2], Zhengwei Fang [2]

[1] Postdoctoral Scientific Research Station, Sinopec Shengli Oilfield Company, Shandong Dongying 257000, China
[2] Research Institute of Petroleum Exploration and Development, Sinopec Shengli Oilfield Company, Shandong Dongying, 257022, China
[3] Sinopec Shengli Oilfield Company, Dongying 257000, Shandong, China

Abstract: Based on constant rate mercury injection experiment, casting thin section identification, scanning electron microscope observation, clay mineral X-ray and rock specific surface area analysis, the controlling factors of matrix acidizing potential of low-permeability sandstone reservoir in fault depression lacustrine basin were determined from three aspects: pore filling, throat filling and pore-throat combination characteristics. It is concluded that provenance controls the plane partition of reservoir pore fillings. Burial depth controls the longitudinal zoning of key filling material in reservoir throat. The difference of rock structure in sedimentary facies - microfacies controlling zone leads to the change of pore-throat assemblage pattern. The matrix acidizing scheme of low permeability sandstone reservoir in fault depression basin can be formulated according to the law of "provenance zoning, buried depth zoning and being controlled by microfacies in zone", and the implementation scheme of pre-acid, main acid and post-acid can be put forward respectively. This method can effectively promote the integration process of exploration and development of low permeability clastic reservoir in mature exploration area.

Keywords: low permeability; matrix acidization; pore-throat structure; Bonan Sag; faulted lacustrine basin; integration process of exploration and development.

1. Introduction

In recent years, the increasing demand for oil and gas exploration and production has led to a shift in direction and focus towards unconventional oil and gas resources. Among them, low permeability clastic reservoir is the most widely distributed, most deeply studied and most realistic. At the same time, the integration of exploration and development has gradually become an important concept and policy to improve oil and gas productivity for mature oil and gas fields in the middle and later stage of development. The low permeability clastic reservoirs of continental lacustrine distributed in the Neogene of Bohai Bay Basin have gradually changed from reserve to dominant resource type. Low permeability reservoirs in fault depression basins are characterized by diverse provenance, large burial depth and diverse sedimentary facies, which make the reservoir structure and type complex[1-7]. At the same time, the low-permeability reservoir has a small pore throat radius, and the types and crystal shapes of the impurity base and cement filled are diverse, leading to prominent water-sensitive and fast-sensitive characteristics[8-11], which seriously affects the later mining and development.

Matrix acidification is one of the most commonly used stimulation treatments. Matrix acidification is the solution or dissolution of pore-throat filling material on the basis of ensuring the basic structure of rock, thus increasing reservoir permeability. Therefore, for matrix acidizing of low permeability sandstone reservoir, the integrated thinking of exploration and development is how to establish the connection between reservoir geology, development geology and oilfield chemistry. How to define and evaluate the potential of matrix acidizing transformation of low permeability sandstone reservoir from the perspective of reservoir geology, and evaluate the reservoir by the transformable ability, and then put forward that the targeted acidizing liquid system is the work that needs to be completed at present.

At present, the fluid system used for matrix acidification of sandstone reservoirs is more based on empirical conclusions. From the original acidizing formula guide in 1983[12] to the acidizing formula Guide in 2001[13], reservoir evaluation is mainly based on permeability, reservoir mineralogical composition (feldspar, clay minerals, etc.) and other parameters. Different parameters are isolated from each other, and the research methods and achievements of reservoir geology cannot be reflected. Therefore, how to use the research method of reservoir geology to analyze and evaluate the transformation potential of reservoir matrix acidification, and to clarify its main control factors and control mode is the key of the

* Corresponding author: 418048012@qq.com

https://doi.org/10.1051/e3sconf/202233801026

research. The low permeability clastic reservoir in the northern bonan sag of Jiyang Depression is selected to analyze and summarize the controlling factors and control modes of matrix acidizing potential.

2. Controlling factors of acidizing potential of low permeability sandstone matrix

The characteristics of low permeability sandstone reservoir in continental faulted lacustrine basin are complex and diverse. It is concluded that these geological characteristics are determined by three factors: (1) the provenance controls the plane partition of reservoir pore fillings (calcite, andolomite, siliceous and pyrite, etc.); (2) Burial depth controls the longitudinal zonation of reservoir throat fillers (kaolinite, illite, chlorite and mixed layer minerals, etc.) and (3) the rock structure differences (sorting, rounding, contact mode, etc.) within the sedimentary facies - microfacies control zone, and leads to the change of pore-throat assemblage mode (Fig. 1).

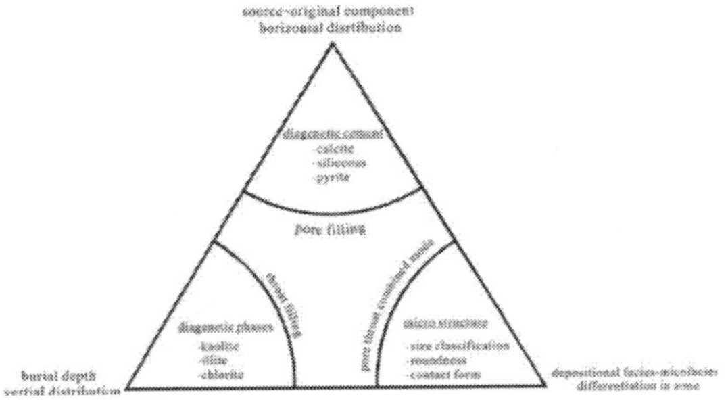

Fig.1 Controlling factors of matrix acidizing potential of low permeability reservoir

2.1 Provenance controls the plane partition of pore fillings

The differentiation of pore and throat radius is obvious in low permeability sandstone reservoir. The relatively developed pore types include primary intergranular pore, intergranular residual pore, intragranular dissolved pore, intergranular dissolved pore and fracture pore. The pore fillings mainly include the original sedimentary complex and the types of diagenetic alteration (such as gray matter complex recrystallization), siliceous cementation in early diagenetic stage and calcite - andolomite cementation in middle diagenetic stage.

First, the aim of matrix acidification of sandstone is to chemically remove or dissolve minerals from the pore throat. The original deposits and alteration products are usually argillaceous or gray complexes, and often contain clay components and adsorbed iron. At the same time, after a long time of compaction, they often appear as relatively dense occurrence state. Therefore, the acidizing effect of hydrochloric acid or soil acid in common use is relatively general, so for pore filling, matrix acidizing pays more attention to the diagenetic and cementation minerals in it. Secondly, compared with the throat (radius < 5 μm), the pores are filled with authigenic minerals formed in the diagenetic stage. Because the pore space is larger, it is easier for the fluid to crystallize out minerals. The cemented rock forming minerals in the pores are significantly affected by the original particle composition of the reservoir and the early synsedimentary fluid. By comparing different provenance areas in the study area, it is found that the types of reservoir pore fillings are obviously controlled by provenance.

2.2 Burial depth controls the longitudinal zoning of clay mineral assemblage pattern in reservoir throat

The throat radius of low permeability sandstone reservoir is less than 5 μm, and the filling minerals are mainly illite, Aemon mixed layer and chlorite. Montmorillonite or chloritic coatings are most easily formed on the surface of particles during the sedimentation-transport process and in the codeposition period. During the syndepositional and early diagenetic stages, the particles began to contact with each other in the form of point, point and line, and this envelope became one of the earliest filling types of larynx. In the early diagenetic stage, the diagenesis type of reservoir is early siliceous cementation. Reservoir porosity before early diagenesis was about 39%, and after compaction, it decreased by 20%~30% to 10%~15%. After diagenesis, porosity varies within a small range. This suggests that compaction, porosity reduction and diagenesis during early diagenesis largely determine the type of filling in the throat (< 5 μm).

According to the results of previous studies, the laryngeal types mainly include pore shrinkage part, variable section contraction part, flaked - curved flaked laryngeal and bundle - shaped laryngeal. The first three are the results of different degrees of contact between particles, bundle throat mainly refers to the microscopic channels in the intergranular complex. Therefore, rock transport and deposition, synsedimentary and early diagenetic stages are the main causes of the formation of throat filling types. Among them, different types of clay mineral original envelope and late diagenetic variation, and early siliceous cements formed in synsedimentary and early diagenetic stages are the main types of throat filling. Because of the variety of clay mineral types, crystal shape and complex sensitivity characteristics, it has become the most important object in matrix acidification.

Clay minerals, especially in sandstone reservoirs, undergo a series of complex diagenetic evolution. Different basins have relatively stable evolution patterns in different layers. The evolution of clay minerals in sandstone reservoirs of the 4th Member of Shahejie formation in Jiyang Depression is a conventional montmorillonite - Illite mixed layer and kaolinite - chlorite/illite evolution model. There are different assemblage patterns of clay minerals in different provenances and layers at different depths.

2.3 Sedimentary facies-microfacies control rock structure difference leading to the change of pore-throat combination model.

Provenance and burial depth control the pore and throat filling material of sandstone reservoir, and the size, connectivity and combination pattern of pore and throat space are also very important aspects to evaluate the acid solution reconstruction potential of reservoir. Burial depth has an influence on it, but the influence is universal, and the reservoir is subjected to the same compaction intensity within the same burial depth range. The real difference of pore throat spatial pattern in low permeability sandstone reservoir is sedimentary facies - microfacies. Because of reservoir at the beginning of the diagenetic process, transportation, deposition and consolidation of the rock structure elements including grain size, sorting, psephicity, contact between particles, as well as the mechanical or chemical differentiation of primitive components such as particles and the differences of the type and content of mixed base, makes the reservoir showed significant difference.

The sedimentary facies of low permeability sandstone in the study area mainly include fan delta, turbidite fan and nearshore subaqueous fan. The sedimentary environments of the three facies types are quite different, which makes them have different rock structure characteristics. The combination of provenance, depth and sedimentary facies and microfacies control the plane partition of diagenetic cementation, the longitudinal zonation of clay mineral assemblage model and the pore throat space configuration. As a result, the low permeability sandstone reservoir has a different specific surface area.

3. Conclusion and Enlightenment

(1)Taking Bonan Sag as an example, a "ternary" control model of matrix acidizing potential of low-permeability sandstone reservoir in faulted lacustrine basin was proposed, that is, the plane partition of pore fillers (calcite, dolomite, siliceous and pyrite, etc.) controlled by provenance; Burial depth controls the longitudinal zonation of key filling materials (kaolinite, illite, chlorite and mixed layer minerals) in the reservoir throat and the rock structure differences (sorting, rounding, contact mode, etc.) in the sedimentary facies - microfacies control zone, and leads to the change of pore-throat assemblage pattern.

(2) Based on the "three-step" control mode of reservoir matrix acidizing potential, according to the law of "provenance zoning, buried depth zoning and microfacies control within the zone", matrix acidizing can take a "three-step" plan formulation process. Firstly, the modification method (acid pressure or acidification) and the type and concentration of pre-acid were determined according to the plane partition characteristics of pore fillings caused by the difference of provenance. Secondly, the type and concentration of main acid were determined according to the longitudinal zonation of key fillings in throat caused by burial depth. Finally, it is adjusted according to the difference of pore throat conFiguration patterns caused by sedimentary facies and microfacies in sand group or single sand body acid system.

Acknowledgments

This work was financially supported by China Postdoctoral Science Foundation Funded Project (Project No.2019M662438).

References

1. Zhang Shuncun, Chen Lihua, Zhou Xinxian, et al. Sedimentary model of the Permian sandy conglomerate in the footwall of the Kebai Fault, the Junggar Basin[J]. Oil & Gas Geology, 2009, 30(06):740-746.
2. Zheng Zhan, Wu Shenghe, Xu Changfu, et al. Lithofacies and reservoirs of allluvial fan in the Lower Keramay Formation in the block-6 of Karamay oilfield,the Junggar Basin[J]. Oil & Gas Geology, 2010, 31(04):463-471.
3. Huang Huicai, Liu Kai. Discussion on the present situation and problems of water flooding development in the conglomerate reservoir of Yanjia oilfield[J]. Nei Jiang Science & Technology, 2009, 30(4): 91-92.
4. Zhang Jing, Wang Weifeng, Rong Qihong, et al. Deep-Water Turbidite Fan Deposits and Relation to Hybrocarbon of the Upper Sha-4 of Shahejie Formation at Yong-55 Block in Dongying Sag[J]. Journal of Jilin University (Earth Science Edition) , 2007, 37 (03): 519-524.
5. Zhang Shuncun, Jiang Huan, Zhang Lei, et al. Genetic Analysis of the High Quality Reservoir of Triassic Baikouquan Formation in Mabei Region, Junggar Basin[J]. Acta Sedimentologica Sinica, 2014, 32 (06): 1171-1180.
6. Shao Hongmei, Liu Zhaojun, Wang Cheng, et al. Diagenesis and pore evolution of deep sandstone in north of Songliao Basin[J]. Global Geology, 2005, 24(01): 58-62.
7. Wang Tinghao, Yan Deyu, Huang Wenhui, et al. Characteristics of conglomerate reservoir of Kexia Formation in Liuzhong area of Karamay oilfield[J]. Journal of Northeast Petroleum University, 2014, 38(3): 31-41.
8. Soeder D, Randolph P. Porosity, permeability, and pore structure of the tight Mesaverde Sandstone, Piceance Basin, Colorado. SPE Formation Evaluation [J], 1987, 2(2): 129-136.
9. Reinicke A, Rybacki E, Stanchits S, et al. Hydraulic fracturing stimulation techniques and formation damage mechanisms—Implications from laboratory testing of tight sandstone– proppant systems[J]. Chemie der Erde - Geochemistry, 2010, 70(S3):107-117.

https://doi.org/10.1051/e3sconf/202233801026

10. Li Daopin. Introduction to development of low permeability oil fields[J]. Petroleum Geology and Oilfield Development in Daqing, 1997, 16 (3):33-37.
11. Jiang Lingzhi, Gu Jiayu, Guo Binchegn. Characteristics and Mechanism of Low Permeability Clastic Reservoir in Chinese Petroliferous Basin[J]. Acta Sedimentologica Sinica, 2004, 22(1): 13-18.
12. Crowe C, Masmonteil J, Thomas R. Trends in matrix acidizing. Oilfield Review [J], 1992, 4(4): 22-40.
13. Kalfayan L J, Metcalf A S. Successful Sandstone Acid Design Case Histories: Exceptions to Conventional Wisdom[C]. 2000.

Main controlling factors and models of tight oil accumulation in Zhaoyuan area

Yanhua Fu

No.10 Oil Production Plant of Daqing Oilfield Co., Ltd., Heilongjiang Daqing 163000, China

Abstract: The study block opens up with the already found oil reservation, through the comprehensive analysis to seismic, well logging, well log and core data, collate and stipulate the system of fault, and then make sure the oil source fault; Meanwhile we make use of Geo-Office and Jason multiply technology, to launch micro faces and single sand body spread research. The result shows that, the study block mostly have 4 kinds of oil reservation: fault-lithologic, fault block, fault-screened and lithologic reservoir, the main target layer is Fuyu oil layer of Quantou Formation 3 and 4 part , the reservation and spread of oil is mainly controlled by the distance to the oil source, the space spread which is coordinated to form transportation system by fault concentrated belt and sand body, the high fault block trap. The oil reservation mainly exist in the internal part of fault concentrated belt and the sand body nearby, all in all the spread feature shows that the oil stays above and the water keeps low , and the formations which includes oil becomes less and less from the downstructure location to the updip ; The major period for hydrocarbon accumulation is the late period of the Mingshui Formation deposition; Here are the modes of the oil transformation and reservation : the oil goes downward and flow backward and transforms into Fuyu formation, which origins from the source rocks of Qingl member in Sanzhao depression, under the abnormal pressure through the source fault , and then the oil in Fuyu formation of Sanzhao depression transforms to study block under the affect of floatage along the two fault concentrated belt which was linked up by the sand body , at the upstructure location lithology or fault aligns with lithology forms the trap which keeps together to oil reservation .

Keywords: Master control factor; reservoir modes.

1. Introduction

The research block is located in the northern Songliao Basin. The target layer is the Fuyu reservoir of the third and fourth member of Quantou Formation, which shows good exploration prospects and one of the important replacement areas for reservoir increase and production. Through the anatomy of the reservoirs have been found and combined with the accumulation conditions, analysis of the research block oil and gas distribution and accumulation process, summarizes control the main controlling factors of hydrocarbon accumulation in the study blocks, It is of great significance to establish the corresponding hydrocarbon accumulation mode for the strategic deployment of oilfield exploration and development.

2. Geological background of oil field

The study block is located on the nose structure in the wings of a terrace. The main extension direction of the structure is NNE, and the overall performance is a monocline structure dipping in the NW direction. The block is on the slope of transition from depression to inversion tectonic belt, and the inversion strength is characterized by "strong in the east and weak in the west, strong in the south and weak in the north" [1-3]. In the area, the main oil-bearing strata are Cretaceous, and the oil-bearing strata are mainly distributed in Fuyu reservoir of the third and fourth member of Quantou Formation.

3. Reservoir type and oil distribution

The oil field types and productivity characteristics of the block are analyzed. There are four types of reservoirs in this area: fault-lithologic, fault block, fault-screened and lithologic reservoir. Fault-lithologic and fault block reservoirs are the most, mainly distributed in the upper sections of Fuyu reservoir. According to the analysis of reservoir profile and oil-bearing horizon distribution map, the overall distribution of oil-water in the longitudinal direction is characterized by the distribution of oil-water, and the oil-bearing horizon varies from the low part of the structure to the high part of the structure, and there is no unified oil-water interface in the whole area affected by faults and lithology changes. The oil layer is mainly

https://doi.org/10.1051/e3sconf/202233801027

distributed in the first group of Fuyu reservoir, and locally there are the oil-water layer and water layer. The second group of Fuyu reservoir and the lower formation are mainly composed of the oil-water layer and water layer, and the oil layer is locally developed. Plane reservoir is mainly distributed in the structural slope site, followed by the structural high part, affected by the dense fracture belt and sand body distribution, reservoir is mainly distributed in the dense fracture belt within and near in the sand body, and two fracture density distribution obviously different reservoir types, east fracture density in addition to the development of a small amount of lithologic reservoir, lithologic reservoir in fault is given priority to. Besides fault-lithologic reservoirs, fault blocks, fault-screened and lithologic reservoirs are also developed in the western fault dense zone.See Fig.1.

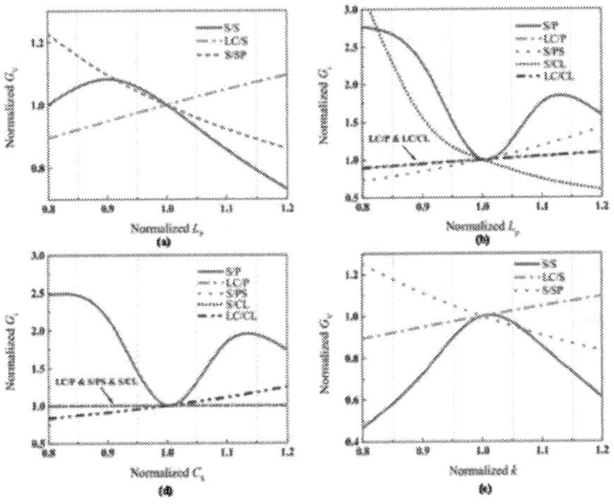

Fig.1 Reservoir type and oil distribution

4. Main controlling factors of oil accumulation

4.1 Hydrocarbon source conditions are the material basis for oil accumulation

The oil source correlation results which consider Sanzhao depression position relationship show that the oil in Fuyu reservoir from Qingl member in Sanzhao depression, the oil under the action of overpressure is generated through the source fracture into Fuyu reservoir by "backward" migration, then under the effect of buoyancy formed by fault and sand body with lateral conducting channel to study blocks, formed accumulation when meet effective traps, the oil distribution along the way. The oil of study blocks in Fuyu reservoir is mainly distributed in the migration of slopes, a few distribution in constructing the high place, the distribution results show that the oil source is insufficient, the closer distance from oil source, the more beneficial to oil accumulation, the more oil accumulation horizon. See Fig.2.

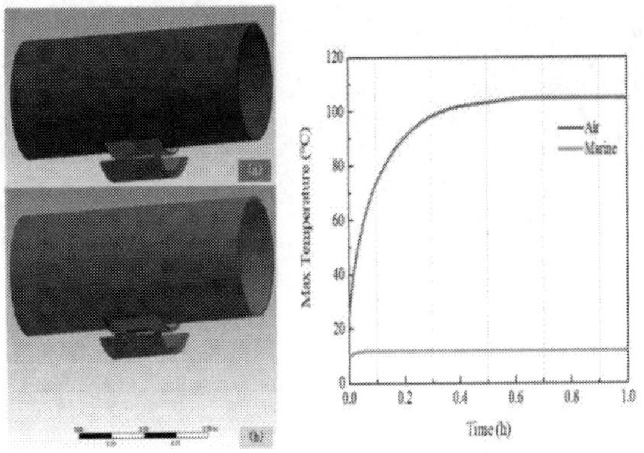

Fig.2 the material basis for oil accumulation

4.2 The transport system determines the migration path of oil

The faults in the study block mostly strike north-south, forming two fault concentrated belt, and presenting a "box-shaped" anticline combination on the profile. The internal faults of Fuyu reservoir were strongly active in the early deposition of Qingshankou Formation and the late deposition of Mingshui Formation, and the structure began to reverse in the late deposition of Nenjiang Formation, which is conducive to the formation of structural traps such as fault blocks and fault anticlines. Geo-office and Jason Integrated well and ground seismic exploration technology are used to predict the channel complex sand body, and the results show that the sand body is banded in the direction of SW to NE. Fault zone and channel sand body cooperate to form effective oil transport channel and oil trap. Oil migrates laterally along the transport channel and accumulates to form reservoirs. If the farther the transport channel extends, the farther the oil migrates laterally and accumulates in the area far from the oil source. And vice versa. In addition, oil accumulation is also affected by the distance from the oil source. For Wells far away from the oil source, although there are transport channels and traps, due to the lack of oil source, there may be no oil accumulation.See Fig.3.

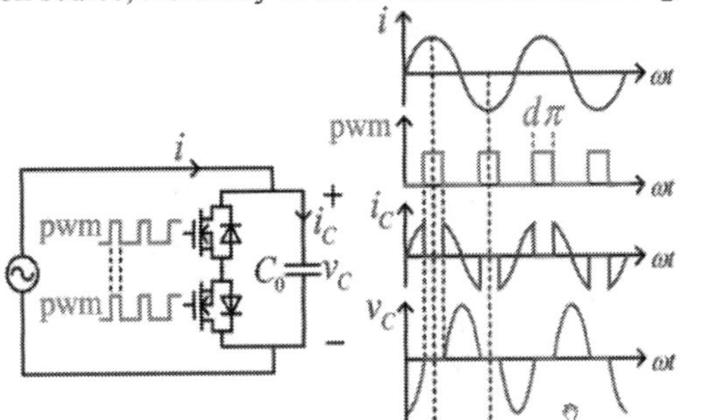

Fig.3 The transport system determines the migration path

 https://doi.org/10.1051/e3sconf/202233801027

4.3 High fault block trap is the main place for oil accumulation

Oil accumulation in this area is not only controlled by migration and transport channels, but also controlled by traps. If there are further traps connected by transport channels, oil accumulation can be formed. Fuyu reservoir in the study block has the largest number of oil Wells and the highest productivity in horst structure, followed by fault step structure, graben structure, and most of the Wells have low productivity. From the perspective of reservoir types, fault-lithologic traps and fault block traps have the largest amount of oil accumulation, while fault-screened and lithologic traps are relatively less.

Aiming at the problems of large starting current and bus voltage drop when three-phase asynchronous motor starts, a soft starting control system for heavy-load starting is designed. First of all, based on the motor control theory, the pulse generation module, three-phase voltage regulation module and PID closed loop are built, and the soft start control system is designed to control the terminal current and voltage of the asynchronous motor. Secondly, based on the Simulink software, according to the actual data of the feed water pump motor of a coal-fired unit in Heilongjiang Province, the soft start control model is built and simulated. Finally, the field test is carried out, and the test results are similar to the simulation results. The results show that the model can effectively limit the starting current of asynchronous motor and reduce the influence of feedwater pump motor start-up on other equipment on the busbar under the condition of heavy load starting. It provides a reference for the heavy-load start-up of the asynchronous motor.

5. Accumulation model

The period of hydrocarbon accumulation should be controlled by the period of hydrocarbon expulsion of source rocks, the period of fault activity and the period of trap formation. The hydrocarbon generation and expulsion history of source rocks in Qingl member of Sanzhao depression shows that hydrocarbon generation began at the end of Nenjiang Formation, and reached the peak at the end of Mingshui Formation, paleogene and Neogene. The study on the history of fault activity shows that the faults in Fuyu reservoir in this area began to be active at the end of Nenjiang Formation, Mingshui Formation and Paleogene deposition, and became the transport channel of oil migration. The study of structural trap to reservoir formation in this area shows that the time of structural inversion of Fuyu reservoir is at the end of Nenjiang Formation deposition, and is fixed at the end of Mingshui Formation deposition. Therefore, based on the above analysis, it can be concluded that the main period of oil accumulation of Fuyu reservoir in the study area should be at the end of Mingshui Formation deposition. See Fig.4 and Fig.5.

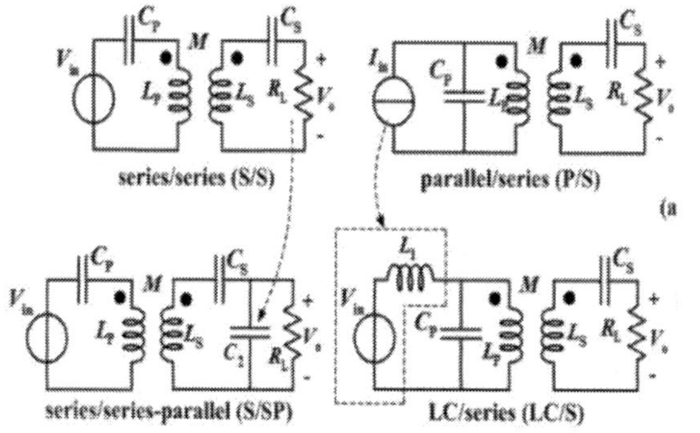

Fig.4 Accumulation model 1

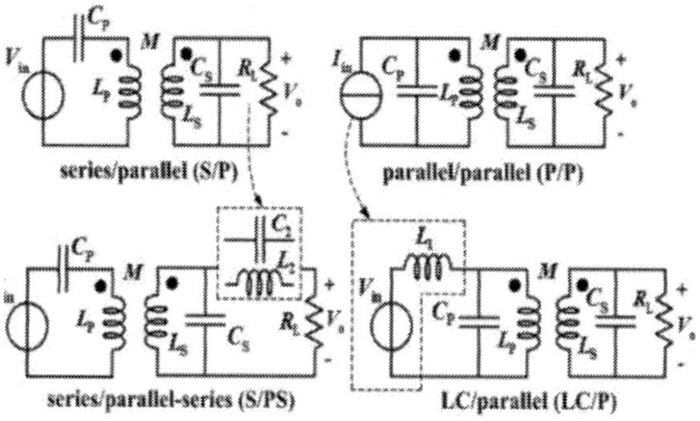

Fig.5 Accumulation model 2

Depending on the type of the reservoir and oil accumulation research on main controlling factors and accumulation period, patterns can be summarized: the oil goes downward and flow backward and transforms into Fuyu formation, which origins from the source rocks of Qingl member in Sanzhao depression, under the abnormal pressure through the source fault , and then the oil in the Fuyu formation of Sanzhao depression transforms to study block under the affect of floatage along the two fault concentrated belt which was linked up by the sand body , at the upstructure location lithology or fault aligns with lithology forms the trap which keeps together to oil reservation . See Fig.6.

https://doi.org/10.1051/e3sconf/202233801027

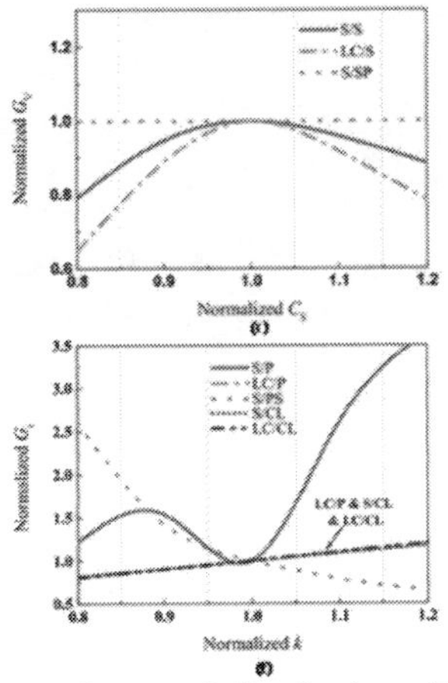

Fig.6 Reservoir type oil distribution of Sanzhao depression transforms to study block

Forming fault-lithologic, fault block, fault-screened and lithologic reservoir. Fault-lithologic and fault-block reservoirs are the most abundant, mainly distributed in horst blocks and fault terraces, and a small amount in graben blocks.

References

1. N. Yi, Q. Wang, L. Yan, et al., A multi-stage game model for the false data injection attack from attacker's perspective. Sustainable Energy Grids & Networks 28 (2021).
2. Xu Jianjun, Huang Lida, Yan Limei, Yi Na. Insulator Self-Explosion Defect Detection Based on Hierarchical Multi-Task Deep Learning[J]. Transactions of China Electrotechnical Society, 2021,36(07):1407-1415.
3. Limei,LIU Yongqiang,XU Jianjun,et al.Broken string diagnosis of composite insulator based on Grabcut segmentation and filler area discrimination[J].Power System Protection and Control,2021,49(22):114-119
4. Na Yi,Jianjun Xu,Limei Yan,Lin Huang. Task Optimization and Scheduling of Distributed Cyber-physical System Based on Improved Ant Colony Algorithm. Future Generation Computer Systems, 109(Aug. 2020),134-148.
5. Yang Zhao, Jianjun Xu, Jingchun Wu. A New Method for Bad Data Identification of Oilfield Power System Based on Enhanced Gravitational Search-Fuzzy C-Means Algorithm. IEEE Transactions on Industrial Informatics. VOL. 15, NO. 11, NOVEMBER 2019 5963-5970
6. Xu, J., Huang, L., Yin, S. et al. All-fiber self-mixing interferometer for displacement measurement based on the quadrature demodulation technique. Opt Rev. 2018,25(1):40-45.

A Brief Discussion on Environmental Impact Assessment Reporting System and Suggestions

Zhou Hang [1, 2, 3,4, 5, *], Wang Jian [1, 2, 3, 4, 5,]

[1] Shaanxi Provincial Land Engineering Construction Group Co., Ltd., Xi'an 710075 China
[2] Institute of Land Engineering and Technology, Shaanxi Provincial Land Engineering Construction Group Co., Ltd. Xi'an 710075 China
[3] Key Laboratory of Degraded and Unused Land Consolidation Engineering, Ministry of Natural Resources Xi'an 710075, China
[4] Shaanxi Provincial Land Consolidation Engineering Technology Research Center, Xi'an 710075, China
[5] Land Engineering Technology Innovation Center, Ministry of Natural Resources, Xi'an 710075 China

Abstract. Environmental impact assessment system has made great progress in recent years in China, but it still cannot meet the needs of practice, and there are still various problems in the compilation of environmental impact assessment report, but the existing environmental impact assessment system still needs to be improved. Therefore, in order to promote the normative and scientific development of the environmental impact assessment system, this paper constantly finds problems and draws experience from the development, improves the system, and provides improvement measures for the improvement of the environmental impact assessment(EIA) report in terms of content and form that adapt to the development of practice.

Key Words: Environmental Impact Assessment Report, Environmental Impact Assessment Law, System Improvement.

1. Basic Concepts of Environmental Impact Assessment System

The concept of environmental impact assessment was first proposed at an international environmental quality assessment academic conference held in Canada in 1964, and the environmental impact assessment system was first established in the United States in 1969.China first proposed the concept of environmental impact assessment in 1973. Article 6 of the Environmental Protection Law (for Trial Implementation) promulgated in 1979 clearly stated that "when new construction, reconstruction and expansion projects are carried out, a report on environmental impact must be submitted", formally established the environmental impact assessment system. China passed the "Environmental Impact Assessment Law" in 2002, establishing this system for the first time in the form of special legislation, and it was implemented on September 1, 2003. The implementation of this law marks that Chian's environmental legislation has entered a new era. The characteristics environmental impact assessment system in China are mainly reflected in: environmental protection laws are mandatory; planning and construction projects are included in the assessment; and environmental impact assessment is included in the capital construction procedure, which requires approval. The environmental impact assessment system combines law and science, and many of the laws and regulations are technical, and some scientific and technological means are used in the implementation of the system. It integrates a variety of disciplines, including environmental science, chemistry, biology, fluid mechanics, etc., and comprehensively analyzes the impact of various human activities on various environmental elements and the overall regional environment [1].

* Corresponding author: 260294988@qq.com

2. Problems in Environmental Impact Assessment Report System

Since the promulgation and implementation of the "Environmental Impact Assessment Law" in 2003, environmental management has formulated a large number of policies and regulations around environmental impact assessment in China. The evaluation is mainly carried out from the aspects of pollution prevention, technical standards and ecological protection, and at the same time, it also takes into account the relationship with economic development, and provides an institutional guarantee for environmental impact assessment. With the gradual improvement of the environmental impact assessment system, there are more and more environmental impact assessment problems in society, such as the confusion of EIA agencies, conflicts between environmental impact assessment standards, and the emergence of "intermediaries" in the environmental impact assessment technology market. Compared with some developed countries, there are still some problems.

2.1 The environmental impact assessment report lacks technicality and authority

Environmental protection related laws and regulations are gradually improving in China, but the environmental assessment mechanism still does not play its due role. One of the reasons is the lack of corresponding technicality and authority of environmental impact assessment report in China [2].

The EIA report is the conclusive document and the centralized presentation form of the environmental impact assessment, which plays a vital role. At present, China's "Environmental Impact Assessment Law" and "Construction Project Environmental Management Regulations" stipulate that major construction projects must first conduct an environmental impact assessment and pass an environmental impact assessment report, and be reviewed by a qualified EIA agency. However, the authenticity of the environmental impact assessment report has been questioned in practice, and it is believed that the EIA report can be concealed and falsified [3]. Even if the environmental impact assessment report is formulated in strict accordance with the law, it still cannot be implemented in practice, and it is just a piece of paper. Moreover, the environmental impact assessment report itself lacks corresponding technical support. The content of the environmental impact assessment report itself is too general and its authority is insufficient, which is also an important reason for questioning the validity and scientific nature [4].

2.2 Transition period is disorderly during environmental impact assessment work

The procedures of the environmental impact assessment system are imperfect, and the procedures for different objects are different. For example, there are obvious differences in the procedures followed between planning and construction projects, resulting in problems in the connection of the provisions of the environmental impact assessment system at different stages. From 2003 to 2018, a complete set of work system was gradually formed for the environmental impact assessment work. Each EIA agency is equipped with a corresponding number of professionals who have obtained the certificate of environmental impact assessment engineer, and employees who have obtained the employment certificate of environmental impact assessment, and are managed by industry category, reflecting the professionalism and pertinence of the environmental impact assessment work. In response to the policy guidelines, the "Environmental Impact Assessment Law of the People's Republic of China" has been revised to cancel the review and issuance of environmental impact assessment qualification certificates. The original environmental impact assessment system is abolished, and the new environmental impact assessment management system has not been fully established [5]. According to the latest draft of the Ministry of Ecology and Environment, the environmental impact assessment technical institution only needs to have professionals who have obtained the certificate of environmental impact assessment engineer to preside over the preparation. Since the environmental impact assessment work is quite professional, in the current transition period, some engineers ignore the technical nature of the environmental impact assessment documents for the sake of income and widen the business, do not pay attention to the quality of the environmental impact assessment documents, and do not systematically study the latest promulgated Relevant guidelines, standards, etc., disrupt the implementation of the environmental impact assessment system.

3. Analysis of the Causes of the Problems

3.1 Analysis from the perspective of Legal Positivism

In order to realize the system function and carry out effective environmental assessment, the environmental impact assessment report should be an analytical description with primary and secondary, rather than a comprehensive encyclopedia-style introduction. Important matters of environmental impact should be discussed and explained, rather than a brief description and explanation of the important matters. For example, if it is determined that a certain matter is not an important influencing factor, it is necessary to explain why the matter is not an important influencing factor, rather than ignoring or simply explaining the matter. In addition, the environmental impact assessment report should describe how the project's impact and alternative solutions are analyzed and demonstrated, and whether they comply with national standards, local standards or industry standards [6].

Article 17 of "Environmental Impact Assessment Law" stipulates the contents that should be listed in the environmental impact report of a construction project, mainly including: the general situation of the construction project, the current situation of the surrounding environment of the construction project, the analysis and prediction of the possible impact of the construction project on the environment and evaluation, environmental protection measures of construction projects and their technical and economic demonstrations, economic profit and loss analysis of construction projects' impact on the environment, recommendations for environmental monitoring of construction projects and conclusions of environmental impact assessment [7]. Judging from the specific content of the environmental impact report for construction projects in Article 17 of Environmental Impact Assessment Law, the report is mainly an explanation of the objective situation, lacking explanation and analysis of the objective situation, and the recommendations are mainly on the implementation situation, while lack of relevant analysis and explanation.

3.2 Analysis from the angle of ought to be

According to the analysis of my country's environmental assessment report, in order to achieve the institutional objectives of the "Environmental Impact Assessment Law", environmental impact assessment behavior should include the following contents in addition to the contents stipulated by laws, regulations and rules:

First, a proposal related to the environmental impact assessment reporting matter should be prepared in a timely manner. This suggestion is to prepare for the timely completion of the final explanatory report. The form of the suggestion can be flexible and diverse, it can be in the form of a separate document, or it can be an incidental explanation in a certain document of the formulation body. But recommendations must be presented at least in the form of normative documents in order to enhance the legal effect of the recommendations.

Second, the legal basis for the report must be clarified. In this sense, clarifying the legal basis is the legal obligation of the reporting body, because only the main responsible agency can write the environmental impact assessment report. The responsible agency shall be accountable to the entrusting agency.

Then, important behavior needs to be specified. The so-called important behavior refers to the behavior that may have important effects or the behavior that is potentially controlled and held by the government. This means that the analysis of specific behavior should be carried out in the society as a whole, in the affected area, in the affected interest, in the affected situation. For the description of important behaviors, it is necessary to describe both favorable and unfavorable situations, and more detailed descriptions of public health and safety impacts.

Finally, the possible effects must be stated. Effects include direct effects and indirect effects. Direct effects occur at the same time as the behavior, and indirect effects may appear within a certain period of time or within a certain distance, but are reasonably foreseeable results. Whether it is a direct or indirect effect, or even a cumulative effect, the possible benefits or harms must be reasonably met and fully explained and analyzed in the report.

4. Suggestions and Measures for Improving China's Environmental Impact Assessment Report

First, the environmental impact assessment report should state clear objectives and necessity. The environmental impact assessment report should briefly explain the alternatives proposed by the environmental protection agency, including the basic goals and necessity of the proposed behaviors [8].

Secondly, the matching of data and analysis with impact should be stated in the environmental impact assessment report, and important and unimportant materials and data should be classified, indexed and explained. The environmental impact assessment report should avoid citing a lot of useless content in it, and should describe the environment that may be affected in detail, and fully explain the measurement standard of environmental impact [9].

Finally, a list and index of the relevant participants should be included in order to identify tasks and hold them accountable. The environmental impact assessment report shall list the list of relevant participants, the qualifications of the relevant participants, and the list of persons who are mainly responsible for the personnel with important background qualifications in the environmental impact assessment report. Personnel should be substantially certified.

References

1. Wang KL. Research on Environmental Impact Assessment System and Its Improvement Strategy [J]. Resources Information and Engineering, 2019, 34(03): 116-117+119.
2. Wang JP, Zhang W. A review of research on strategic transformation of environmental management [J]. China Environmental Management, 2016, 2: 85-88.
3. Zhang H, Zuo L. Status and Development Trend of Environmental Impact Assessment Research [J]. Environment and Development, 2019, 31(02): 11+13.
4. Chen T. Deficiencies of Environmental Impact Assessment System in China and Its Improvement Suggestions [J]. China High-tech, 2018(24): 120-122.
5. Chen R. Brief Discussion on Planning Environmental Impact Assessment System in China and Its Improvement [J].Urban Planning, 2004(08):84-86.
6. T. Tietenberg. Emissions Trading: An Exercise in Reforming Pollution Policy [J]. Land Economics, 1986, 62(2): 214-216.

7. Chen Y. Environmental Impact Assessment System and Its Improvement in China [D]. China University of Political Science and Law, 2007.
8. Li SJ, Niu XJ. A Comparative Study of Public Participation in the Environmental Impact Assessment System of China and the United States [J]. Environmental Science and Management, 2007, 12:176-178.
9. Xiong J. The Shortcomings and Suggestions of China's Environmental Impact Assessment System [J]. Urban Geography, 2015 (6): 195.

E3S Web of Conferences **338**, 01029 (2022)
ESMA 2021
https://doi.org/10.1051/e3sconf/202233801029

A review of hyperspectral remote sensing of crops

Liheng Xia [1, 2, 3, 4, 5, *], Xueying Wu [1, 2, 3, 4, 5]

[1] Shaanxi Provincial Land Engineering Construction Group Co., Ltd. China
[2] Institute of Land Engineering and Technology, Shaanxi Provincial Land Engineering Construction Group Co., Ltd. China
[3] Key Laboratory of Degraded and Unused Land Consolidation Engineering, Ministry of Natural Resources China
[4] Shaanxi Provincial Land Consolidation Engineering Technology Research Center China
[5] Land Engineering Technology Innovation Center, Ministry of Natural Resources China

Abstract. With the development of space science and technology, various resource monitoring environmental satellites provide multi-platform, multi-spectral, multi-temporal and wide-range real-time information for the study of surface dynamic changes, and remote sensing technology has become a powerful technical means for human to study the earth's resources and environment, while high-resolution and hyperspectral remote sensing has become the main source for fruit tree growth monitoring and fruit quality detection acquisition. This paper has the following aspects to introduce the current situation of application of high-resolution and hyperspectral remote sensing data.

Key words: Hyperspectral Remote Sensing, Agricultural crops, Monitoring

1. Introduction

Remote sensing image classification is one of the most widely used methods for extracting spatial and temporal information of geological features. Remote sensing image classification plays a very important role in thematic mapping, classification of feature types and change monitoring. Remote sensing image classification is the process of classifying each image element into different feature types according to its spectral characteristics and spatial structure characteristics. It has developed from traditional unsupervised classification and parametric supervised classification to non-parametric supervised classification such as neural network classification, genetic algorithm, machine learning classification algorithm and the direction of multiple classifiers combined with integrated algorithms.

Hyperspectral remote sensing refers to the remote sensing technology that uses very narrow (λ/100) and continuous spectral channels for continuous measurement of features. Hyperspectral remote sensing technology is a new remote sensing technology that has been developed rapidly in recent decades, which is a comprehensive technology integrating detector technology, weak signal detection, precision optical machinery, information processing technology, and computer technology. Researchers have measured and analyzed the spectra of dried and mashed leaves of various plants in detail, and obtained about 42 absorption features corresponding to certain biochemical components in the spectral range of 0.4-2.4μm, which provides the possibility of estimating the biochemical components of leaves and even plants by remote sensing means. Therefore, hyperspectral remote sensing technology is widely used in agricultural crop growth monitoring[1]-[4].

In recent years, Unmannedaerialvehicle (UAV) technology has emerged as a bridge between surface measurement and satellite remote sensing. With its small size, light mass, low operating cost, high flexibility, real-time image transmission, and the ability to detect in special areas, it has played an important role in ecological environment monitoring, urban construction and planning, agricultural production, natural disaster monitoring during data It plays an irreplaceable role in real-time acquisition of data during ecological environment monitoring, urban construction and planning, agricultural production, natural disaster monitoring, etc. It is one of the important tools for high-resolution remote sensing data acquisition, and a useful supplement to ground observation (such as cameras) and high-altitude observation (such as remote sensing satellites). The application of UAV images in the field of agricultural remote sensing monitoring has great advantages and broad prospects. It has higher ground spatial resolution compared with satellite images and can bring additional remote sensing information such as fine texture of crops that satellite remote sensing does not have, and can be well applied in the field of fine agricultural remote sensing monitoring[5]-[8].

* Corresponding author: 576427877@qq.com

 https://doi.org/10.1051/e3sconf/202233801029

2. Research on hyperspectral remote sensing in agriculture

In agricultural production, hyperspectral remote sensing has been widely used in crop growth monitoring, yield estimation, quality monitoring, and pest and disease monitoring and prediction. At present, domestic and foreign research in remote sensing monitoring of crop diseases and pests mainly focuses on the spectral characteristics of crops subject to pest and disease stress and carries out feature extraction of pest and disease stress. Commonly used feature extraction methods include basic spectral operation and transformation methods, such as sensitive band extraction method, spectral vegetation index method, differential spectral analysis method, absorption valley (reflection peak and other spectral location parameters extraction method, etc.) and spectral data knowledge mining methods, such as principal component analysis, wavelet analysis, neural network method, support vector machine, partial least squares regression, etc. In order to carry out the research on the differentiation of different pests and diseases of crops, researchers have proposed novel spectral indices for disease identification. For example, by introducing RELIEF-F feature extraction algorithm, the spectral characteristics of wheat stripe rust, powdery mildew and aphids were elucidated, and new spectral indices (NSIs) for quantitative differentiation of specific diseases were constructed, including HI (Health-Index), PMI (PowderyMildew-Index), and YRI (YellowRust-Index). YRI (YellowRust-Index), and AI (Aphids-Index) [9], and these new vegetation indices were used for leaf and canopy-scale pest and disease differentiation with satisfactory results.

2.1 Research on rice based on hyperspectral remote sensing

2.1.1 Research method

In 2018, Yan Lin [10] obtained hyperspectral data spectral range of rice covering visible-near-infrared-short-wave infrared band, plants have unique absorption and reflection spectral characteristics in this range, and have different sensitivity to different vegetation on each band, so the correlation analysis between spectral data and crop physiological and biochemical parameters can be performed to find out the parameter in the effective range of spectral of the characteristic bands.

The correlation analysis of the spectral data with rice SPAD and leaf area index was carried out under MATLAB2014a environment using a self-programmed program, and the characteristic bands were selected according to the magnitude of the correlation coefficients. Statistical regression is the study of the relationship between the variation of a set of random variables Y relative to another set of random variables X. In hyperspectral remote sensing modeling, the physiological and biochemical parameters (e.g., leaf area index, chlorophyll content, leaf nitrogen content, water content, etc.) are usually taken as the dependent variables, and the hyperspectral data or their variation forms (e.g., original spectral reflectance and its derivative transformation, logarithmic transformation or spectral index) are taken as the independent variables, and the mathematical model based on the hyperspectral data is constructed by analyzing their variation patterns and mechanisms, and the physiological and biochemical parameters of vegetation are estimated theoretically. Theoretical estimation of vegetation physiological and biochemical parameters is carried out. In the modeling process, the total sample is usually divided into modeling samples and testing samples, which are used to support the construction of the model and the testing of the model accuracy, respectively.

2.1.2 Hyperspectral characteristics of rice

The structural and compositional information of different substances on the ground under the action of electromagnetic waves will form different absorption and reflection features in some specific bands within the electromagnetic spectrum, and such absorption and reflection features are usually referred to as the spectral features of the substances (Wang J. H. et al. 2008:1; Tong Q. H. et al. 2016:1) [11]-[12]. Such differences are precisely the important basis for remote sensing detection of the nature and shape of the features. In agricultural remote sensing, different vegetation or the same vegetation has different spectral characteristics at different growth and fertility stages, different production management measures, and different nutritional status, and the differences in the spectral characteristics of vegetation can accurately identify vegetation categories, monitor vegetation growth and development, estimate vegetation yield, and vegetation field management, which play an important role in the promotion of precision agriculture. In this chapter, the spectral characteristics of rice leaves and canopy will be discussed according to the factors affecting the spectral characteristics of rice, such as different nutritional status, different fertility stages, and different physiological and biochemical parameters.

2.1.3 Hyperspectral estimation of rice SPAD at different fertility stages

In 2018, Yan Lin et al. took rice at different fertility stages and firstly analyzed the changes of chlorophyll content of rice at different fertility stages, then calculated the correlation coefficients between the spectral reflectance and chlorophyll content of rice canopy at different fertility stages to establish a model for estimating chlorophyll content of rice based on spectral index and BP neural network, and used the coefficient of determination (R2), relative error (RE) and root mean square error (RMSE) to validate the model and lay the foundation for hyperspectral monitoring of chlorophyll content in rice.

2.1.4 Estimation of leaf area index of rice based on hyperspectral remote sensing

LeafAreaIndex (LAI), which refers to the total leaf area of vegetation per unit area, is an important functional evaluation parameter of vegetation canopy and plays a very important role in vegetation research, providing structured and quantitative information on the energy exchange between vegetation canopy and the environment (Huifengming et al. 2002; Fang Xiuqin et al. 2003; Li Kaili et al. 2005. Xie Qiaoyun et al. 2014) [13]-[16]. Leaf area index achieves control of physiological and biochemical processes such as photosynthesis, respiration, transpiration and charcoal cycling of vegetation by affecting vegetation light uptake, and can estimate vegetation net primary productivity more accurately, as well as effectively characterize vegetation growth and development and nutrient status and roughly estimate vegetation yield. The determination of leaf area index by traditional methods (area coefficient method, direct weighing method and square grid calculation method, etc.) has the shortcomings of large workload, time consuming and inability to perform large area measurement. The development of hyperspectral remote sensing technology has provided a reliable way for the non-destructive and rapid large-scale determination of vegetation leaf area index (LAI), and therefore the estimation of LAI using hyperspectral remote sensing has become an important area of research for scholars. When vegetation is photosynthesizing, chlorophyll strongly absorbs visible light and strongly reflects and scatters near-infrared light, so the reflectance of vegetation in visible and near-infrared bands contains a lot of information of canopy leaves. This unique spectral characteristic of vegetation is the basis for remote sensing quantitative analysis of leaf area index.

In 2018, Yan Lin et al. analyzed the variation of leaf area index of rice at different fertility periods as well as different fertilization levels to analyze the correlation between the spectral reflectance of rice canopy and leaf area index at each fertility period by selecting the spectral bands with the strongest correlation with leaf area index within each fertility period of rice, and constructed a model for estimating leaf area index at each fertility period of rice based on the characteristic bands by calculating the By calculating the correlation coefficients of six types of spectral indices and leaf area index in the range of 350-1000 nm, the BP neural network-based leaf area index estimation model for each fertility period was established by selecting the band combination with the highest correlation coefficient.

2.2 Research based on hyperspectral remote sensing of maize

2.2.1 Research Methods

In 2018, Wang Shuo [17] used two methods, traditional regression method and BP artificial neural network (BackPropagationNeuralNetwork, BPNN), to model the inversion of leaf chlorophyll content and leaf nitrogen content in maize canopy. The traditional regression methods mainly construct linear regression models and nonlinear regression models, and the nonlinear models include exponential models, polynomial models, logarithmic models, and power function models.

Artificial neural network is similar to the human brain nervous system, which is composed of many artificial neurons in parallel, so the amount of information that can be stored is huge, which makes artificial neural network can deal with problems with uncertainties and become a simple and effective means to deal with complex nonlinear problems. Artificial neural networks have high parallelism, fast processing speed and high fault tolerance; strong nonlinear mapping ability, capable of processing information by machine simulating human brain intelligence; strong self-learning and self-adaptive ability, as well as high fault tolerance, capable of solving problems that are difficult to be handled by mathematical models quickly and efficiently. In recent years, artificial neural networks are increasingly used in hyperspectral remote sensing research such as crop identification, monitoring crop growth, and crop biochemical parameter inversion with its above advantages (Luo Dan et al. 2016) [18].

To test the accuracy and reliability of the model, the coefficient of determination, root mean square error and relative error were selected as indicators for the modeling results, and the model estimates were fitted to the measured values by regression.

2.2.2 Model for monitoring maize SPAD values based on hyperspectral remote sensing

In 2018, Wang Shuo mainly studied canopy spectral reflectance and canopy leaf SPAD values, analyzed the changes of maize canopy leaf SPAD values at different fertility stages and the response characteristics of canopy spectral reflectance under different SPAD values, based on which, the spectra were first-order differential transformed, vegetation index and optimization index were constructed, and through correlation analysis, the SPAD values with greater correlation were selected Through the correlation analysis, we selected the original spectra, first-order differential spectra, vegetation indices and optimization indices, and constructed the SPAD estimation models based on the characteristic bands, vegetation indices, optimization indices and BP neural networks respectively, and verified the accuracy of each model, aiming to provide more accurate hyperspectral monitoring of the chlorophyll content of maize canopy in northwest China, and provide scientific basis for precision agriculture research and crop growth judgment.

2.2.3 Hyperspectral estimation model of maize leaf nitrogen content

Nitrogen transport is the most important management measure in crop production, and the right amount of nitrogen supply at the right time is the fundamental guarantee of high crop yield and quality, therefore, the production needs timely and reasonable nitrogen diagnosis and fertilization regulation based on timely grasp of crop growth and nitrogen status (Zhang et al. 2012) [19]. Leaf nitrogen content (LNC, %) is one of the main indicators to characterize the nitrogen status of crop leaves, so the analysis of leaf nitrogen content changes is important for crop growth monitoring. The usual method for monitoring plant leaf nitrogen is laboratory Kjeldahl nitrogen determination, which is a complex, time-consuming and inefficient operation process, and now, remote sensing monitoring using hyperspectral data has become the main choice for rapid, efficient and nondestructive monitoring of leaf nitrogen.

In 2018, Wang Shuo calculated the correlation between canopy spectra and maize leaf nitrogen content, and analyzed and compared the accuracy of models constructed based on characteristic bands, vegetation indices, optimized spectral indices, and BP neural networks, respectively, so as to provide a theoretical basis for nondestructive estimation of maize leaf nitrogen content and large-scale growth condition monitoring of maize.

2.3 Hyperspectral remote sensing based wheat research

2.3.1 Research methods

In 2017, Li Na [20] selected 72 sets of these sample spectral data for modeling. (1) Correlation analysis of the agronomic parameters with the original spectral reflectance and first-order derivative spectral data under different sowing and nitrogen levels was conducted to screen the sensitive spectral band range of the agronomic parameters; (2) Based on the previous research results, correlation studies were conducted on the existing spectral parameter numbers and agronomic indicators, with the spectral index, which is closely related to the agronomic indicators, as the independent variable and the agronomic parameters as the dependent variables, to establish simple linear (3) to correlate the canopy chla+b content with GPC, LAI and GY in each fertility period, so as to clarify the best fertility period for estimation, and interlink with the reflectance spectral data of the best fertility period to establish the GPC and GY estimation model of wheat based on spectral data. Independent samples of spectral data were selected to test the constructed models. Six indicators, correlation coefficient (r), precision (R2), root mean square error (RMSE), relative error (RE), mean absolute error (da) and ratio of the mean of the observed values (dap), were used for comprehensive evaluation, and a 1:1 relationship between the observed and predicted values was plotted. The smaller the RMSE, RE, da and dap, and the larger the r and R2, the greater the difference between the model-fitted values and the actual The smaller the difference between the measured values, the better the fitted model.

2.3.2 Wheat canopy reflectance spectral characteristics analysis

Wheat spectral reflectance characterizes the differences in the internal tissue structure and canopy layout of wheat. And the advancement of sowing amount, nitrogen application level and fertility period can significantly affect not only the canopy structure of wheat, but also the changes of the internal tissue structure of wheat (such as chlorophyll, etc.), which have important effects on the spectral characteristics. The experiments investigated the response characteristics of canopy spectral reflectance of Pu Bing 151 to seeding rate, nitrogen application and fertility period (Li Na 2017).

2.3.3 Wheat canopy chlorophyll content monitoring model

Chla+b content is one of the good parameters to respond to photosynthetic capacity, growth and development of vegetation as well as N nutrition status, and real-time rapid and non-destructive estimation of chla+b content is of great significance for wheat nutrition evaluation and N fertilization management. Jiang, H. L. et al. (2015b) [21] showed that spectral indices can reduce or even eliminate the noise caused by environmental backgrounds such as soil and water bodies, which is higher than that of single band. The spectral index mND(780,712) proposed by J. Yang et al. (2009b) [22] introduces the reflectance of 445 nm band, thus reducing the effect of reflectance differences on the leaf surface and making the constructed model more application-friendly. Seventeen known spectral parameters were selected as the basis of this experiment, and by analyzing the quantitative relationships between these spectral parameters and the amount of chla, chlb and chla+b containing chla+b, it was found that RVI(729,755) and GREEN-NDVI were most closely related to the chla+b content. To identify the reliability of the model, the better chlorophyll content monitoring model was tested separately using hyperspectral data from the remaining sample sites at the same location, and the fitting accuracy (R2) was used as the test index, and a 1:1 relationship plot was used to describe the test effect of this inverse model more intuitively, and it was concluded that the wheat canopy chlorophyll content monitoring model with GREEN-NDVI as the variable was better and more reliable.

2.3.4 Wheat leaf area index monitoring model

LAI is an important indicator of wheat growth status and population structure, so conducting LAI monitoring is an important part of crop growth monitoring and yield assessment. There have been some studies on the construction of wheat canopy leaf area index monitoring models based on hyperspectral remote sensing, Liang Liang et al. (2011b) [23] and others compared and analyzed the differences of 18 hyperspectral indices on LAI response and found that although the spectral index NDVI 705 is commonly used for vegetation survey and monitoring, it is disturbed by atmospheric conditions, soil components, and the presence of dead material in the plant canopy itself (Qietal. 1994), the spectral index OSAVI is relatively more sensitive to wheat LAI because it can overcome the influence of soil background and atmospheric conditions to a certain extent, and therefore can be used as the preferred index for wheat LAI inversion.

2.3.5 Wheat seed yield prediction model

Wheat is an important crop in China, and its yield is directly related to the food supply in China. The application of hyperspectral remote sensing technology in wheat yield prediction has received wide attention. Leaf area index (LAI) is one of the important indexes to characterize crop growth and development and predict yield, and a reasonable LAI is the basis for source reservoir coordination and balanced development of all parts of tissues and organs. Therefore, in this experiment, LAI was used as a linkage point to construct a prediction model based on canopy spectral data-LAI-seed yield of Pu Bing 151. Feng Wei (2008) [24] showed that the accumulation values of important spectral parameters in the pre-grazing period or characteristic spectral parameters from nodulation to maturity can be used to accurately and reliably predict the seed yield of different N applications and varieties in different years.

References

1. Zhao Chunjiang. Progress of agricultural remote sensing research and application[J]. Journal of Agricultural Machinery,2014,45(12):277-293.
2. Chen Zhongxin,Ren Jianqiang,Tang Huajun,et al. Progress and prospects of agricultural remote sensing research applications[J]. Journal of Remote Sensing,2016,20(5):748-767.
3. Shi Zhou,Liang Zongzheng,Yang Yuanyuan,et al. Current status and outlook of agricultural remote sensing research[J]. Journal of Agricultural Machinery,2015,46(2):247-260.
4. Xing Suli,Zhang Guanglu. Current situation and prospect of agricultural remote sensing application in China[J]. Journal of Agricultural Engineering,2003,19(6):174-178.
5. Wu BF, Zhang L, Li QZ, et al. Current status and prospects of agricultural and ecological remote sensing[J]. Journal of Remote Sensing,2009,13(s1):266-271.
6. Zhang Zengxiang, Wang Xiao, Wen Qingke, et al. Research progress of remote sensing application of land resources[J]. Journal of Remote Sensing,2016,20(5):1243-1258.
7. LIU Haiying,GAO Jixi,LI Zhenghai. Progress of remote sensing research on land cover and land use[J]. Remote Sensing of Land Resources, 2001(4):7-12.
8. Zhang Ruolin, Wan Li, Zhang Fawang, et al. Progress of land use remote sensing classification methods[J]. South-North Water Transfer and Water Conservancy Science and Technology,2006,4(2):39-42.
9. Tian M-L, Ban S-T, Chang Q-R, Ma W-J, Yin Z, Wang L. Inversion of chlorophyll content of cotton based on UAV imaging spectrometer data[J]. Journal of Agricultural Machinery,2016,47(11):285-293.
10. Yan Lin. Research on physiological and biochemical parameters of rice in Ningxia Yellow Irrigation Area based on hyperspectral remote sensing[D]. Northwest University of Agriculture and Forestry Science and Technology,2017.
11. Wang Ji-Hua,Huang Wen-Jiang,Laocai-Lian et al.2007.Inversion of nitrogen vertical distribution from wheat canopy reflectance spectra using PLS algorithm. Spectroscopy and Spectral Analysis,27(7):1319-1322.
12. Tong QX, Zhang B, Zhang LF. Frontier progress of hyperspectral remote sensing in China[J]. Journal of Remote Sensing,2016,20(05):689-707.
13. Fang Xiuqin,Zhang Wanchang.2003.A review of remote sensing quantitative methods for leaf area index (LAI). Remote Sensing of Land Resources,15(3):58-62.
14. Hui Fengming, Tian Qingjiu, Jin Zhenyu, et al. 2003. Study on the relationship between vegetation index and leaf area index and quantitative analysis. Remote Sensing Information,(2):10-13.
15. Li Kaili, Jiang JJ, Mao RZ, et al. 2005. Remote sensing monitoring model of vegetation leaf area index. Journal of Ecology,25(6):1491-1496.
16. Xie Qiaoyun. Study on the generalizability of leaf area index inversion method [Master's thesis]. Anhui University,2014.
17. Wang Shuo. Research on the estimation of maize agronomic parameters in Guanzhong area based on hyperspectral remote sensing [D]. Northwest University of Agriculture and Forestry Science and Technology,2018.
18. Li D,He J,Liu Guishan et al.2014.Nondestructive detection of cucumber moisture based on hyperspectral imaging technology. Infrared and Laser Engineering,43(7):2393-2397.
19. Zhang Xiaoyan,Wang Lili,Liu Feng et al.2012. Research on monitoring model of peanut leaf nitrogen accumulation based on hyperspectral remote sensing Shandong Agricultural Science,44(3):7-12,16.
20. Li Na. Construction of a model for monitoring agronomic parameters and seed protein content of wheat based on hyperspectral remote sensing[D]. Northwest University of Agriculture and Forestry Science and Technology,2017.
21. Jiang H L,Yang H,Chen S P,Wang Sh D,Li Xue Ke,Liu K,Cen Y. 2015.Research on the accuracy and stability of inversion of vegetation chlorophyll content using spectral indices. Spectroscopy and Spectral Analysis(04):975-981.
22. Yang J, Tian YC, Yao X, Cao Z, Zhang YS, Zhu Y. 2009a.Hyperspectral estimation model of chlorophyll

https://doi.org/10.1051/e3sconf/202233801029

content in upper leaves of rice. Journal of Ecology(12):6561-6571.

23. Liang L,Yang MH,Zhang LP,Lin H. 2011b.Hyperspectral inversion of leaf area index of wheat. Spectroscopy and Spectral Analysis.(06):1658-1662.
24. Feng W,Zhu Y,Tian YC,Yao X,Guo TC,Cao Z.2007.Research on wheat seed yield prediction model based on hyperspectral remote sensing. Journal of Wheat Crops (06):1076-1084.

A review of research methods for evaluation and analysis of suitability of well-facilitated farmland construction

Yutong Zhao [1, 2, 3, 4, 5, *], Shiqian Gao [1, 2, 3, 4, 5] and Bo Zhao [1, 2, 3, 4, 5]

[1] Institute of Land Engineering and Technology, Shaanxi Provincial Land Engineering Construction Group Co., Ltd. 710075, Xi'an, China
[2] Shaanxi Provincial Land Engineering Construction Group Co., Ltd. 710075, Xi'an, China
[3] Key Laboratory of Degraded and Unused Land Consolidation Engineering, the Ministry of Natural Resources, 710075, Xi'an, China
[4] Shaanxi Provincial Land Consolidation Engineering Technology Research Center.710075, Xi'an, China
[5] Land Engineering Quality Testing of Shaanxi Land Engineering Construction Group Co., Ltd. Shaanxi, China

Abstract. The setting direction of the evaluation indicators in the current research and the differences of the research methods in terms of principles, advantages and disadvantages and applicability are compared and analyzed. The results show that the current well-facilitated farmland construction has achieved remarkable results. In the suitability evaluation research before project construction, the setting of evaluation indicators focuses more on the natural endowment conditions of regional cultivated land; in the benefit evaluation research after project construction, from The early focus on economic benefit evaluation has gradually developed into an equal emphasis on economic, social and ecological benefit evaluation; in the analysis of influencing factors, the current research is still relatively weak, and there are still few explanations for the differences in the level of benefit improvement in different construction areas. Regarding research methods, future research should comprehensively consider the advantages, disadvantages and applicability of different methods. This study can provide a useful reference for scientifically promoting well-facilitated farmland construction.

Key words: Well-facilitated farmland; Method comparison.

1. Introduction

The arable land resources of China are extremely precious, The per capita arable land area is only 0.08 hm2, which is far below the global average[1-2]. Before 20th century, cultivated land resources have not been well protected. Since the reform and opening up, with the rapid social and economic development, the central government has gradually realized the serious food security problems caused by the reduction of cultivated land, and formulated and promulgated various policies to protect cultivated land. Since 1997, China has begun to vigorously summarize and promote the experience of land consolidation to improve the quality of cultivated land. In 2010, the Fifth Plenary Session of the Seventeenth Central Committee of the Communist Party of China proposed "large-scale construction of well-facilitated farmland for drought and flood protection".

Well-facilitated farmland refers to the land that is leveled, concentrated and contiguous, with complete facilities, agricultural power supply, fertile soil, good ecology, strong disaster resistance, and is compatible with modern agricultural production and management methods. It is designed as permanent basic farmland. Of arable land. Maintaining a certain amount of Well-facilitated farmland is of great significance for realizing the "equal emphasis on the quality" of farmland protection and meeting the rigid growth needs of major agricultural products such as grain. The construction of Well-facilitated farmland is an important part of China's land consolidation plan. Compared with traditional land reclamation, Well-facilitated farmland has been further improved and expanded in terms of construction content and construction requirements. It is an important strategic measure to increase the comprehensive production capacity of cultivated land, improve the agricultural production environment, ensure food security, and develop modern agriculture. . Well-facilitated farmland construction projects involve pre-evaluation of regional survey and planning site selection, follow-up and monitoring during the construction process, post-evaluation of comprehensive benefit evaluation and management, etc. Each stage is to ensure the long-term benefits of the project and guarantee the finances. An important link in the safe and efficient application of funds. Therefore, carry out the regional suitability evaluation before the construction of Well-facilitated farmland, the benefit evaluation research after the project

* Corresponding author: 285725361@qq.com

construction, and the analysis of the factors that affect the benefit of the project after the construction. Timely adjustment of management measures and other aspects have important theoretical and practical significance.

Since 2010, the central government clearly proposed the large-scale construction of well-facilitated farmland for droughts and floods, and the related research on the construction of well-facilitated farmland has yielded fruitful results. At present, there is still a lack of literature review on the suitability evaluation research before the construction of well-facilitated farmland projects, the benefit evaluation research after the construction, and the research progress of influencing factors. The research results produced by the setting direction of different evaluation indicators and the selection of research methods are often different. In view of this, in order to make up for the current research gaps, this research focuses on four parts: the background and current situation of well-facilitated farmland construction, the suitability evaluation study before construction, the benefit evaluation after construction, and the study of factors affecting the benefit of construction projects. It sorts out the selection of research methods and summarizes and summarizes the principles, advantages and disadvantages and scope of application of different research methods adopted by current scholars, aiming to provide a useful reference for scientifically and rationally promoting well-facilitated farmland construction work and research.

2. The current situation of Well-facilitated farmland construction

Land consolidation and well-facilitated farmland construction have promoted the protection of arable land resources and the improvement of comprehensive grain production capacity in China, with remarkable results. From 2001 to 2005, China has invested nearly 100 billion yuan in land consolidation funds and added 1.4267 million hectares of cultivated land, achieving a balance between land occupation and compensation. From 2006 to 2010, there were more than 150,000 land remediation projects in China's audit collection database, with a remediation scale of 8.29 million hectares and an increase of 2.7 million hectares of cultivated land. According to remote sensing monitoring, by 2010, China's high, medium, and low-yield fields accounted for 20.66%, 39.56%, and 39.78% of the country's arable land, respectively. According to the National Land Rehabilitation Plan, from 2011 to 2015, 530 million mu of agricultural land will be reorganized nationwide, and 26.7 million ha of well-facilitated farmland will be built.

Table 1. Index selection for suitability evaluation

Target	Criterion	index
Regional natural endowments	Site conditions	Altitude, slope
	Soil quality	Soil surface thickness
	Space Form	Field concentration
Infrastructure and Construction Conditions	location accessibility	Field road accessibility
	Irrigation and drainage conditions	Irrigation water quality
development stability	Socioeconomic conditions	Per capita agricultural output
	Acceptability	Public satisfaction

Through land consolidation and reclamation, a large amount of fragmented and scattered land has been appropriately merged, and the supporting construction of agricultural infrastructure has been clearly strengthened. After the improvement, the quality of cultivated land has increased by one grade on average, the yield per unit has increased by 10% to 20% on average, and the new grain production capacity will be 37.368 billion kg, which has improved the comprehensive production capacity of cultivated land. At present, the construction of well-facilitated farmland has achieved results nationwide, but there are still many problems. For example, in terms of the rationality of project layout, there is a lack of differentiated planning and layout; in terms of fund deployment and management and protection, departmental project construction funds are scattered, it is difficult to form a joint force to play the expected role, and the long-term management and protection mechanism after the construction project is still incomplete Wait. Faced with the new situation and new requirements, the National Land Rehabilitation Plan proposes that during the 13th Five-Year Plan period, it is necessary to ensure that the country will build 206.7 million hm2, and strive to achieve 40 million hm2 well-facilitated farmland, of which 1553 million to 200.7 million hm2 will be built through land improvement. The quality of the renovated basic farmland has increased by 1 grade on average.

3. Suitability evaluation of well-facilitated farmland before construction

The rational layout and scientific planning of well-facilitated farmland construction sites need to comprehensively consider the natural attributes of regional farmland and the suitability of social and economic construction [3]. The quality evaluation of regional arable land is not only a measure of arable land productivity, but also closely related to the natural quality, construction potential, agricultural infrastructure conditions, project capital investment and construction direction of the arable land itself. Scientifically delimiting well-facilitated farmland construction areas, and clarifying the degree of difficulty, construction potential, and construction direction of different types of areas are crucial for the orderly development of well-facilitated farmland construction. Therefore, the construction suitability evaluation research of regional cultivated land is often used as an important basis and basis for the delineation of key construction areas and construction timing.

The study found that in the setting of the target layer, the existing research mainly focuses on the regional natural endowment conditions, infrastructure and construction conditions, and the development stability after project construction. Some scholars further focus on policy planning [4], ecological security, etc. have been extended from other angles. In the setting of the criterion layer and the index layer, the natural endowment of the regional cultivated land is mostly concerned. The selection of indicators is mainly based on site conditions, natural quality of soil, spatial form of cultivated land, etc. [5]; in terms of infrastructure and construction conditions, emphasis is placed on location accessibility and the importance of farmland irrigation and drainage conditions; In terms of development stability after construction, it is mainly considered from the ex setting of the current construction suitability evaluation research involves the natural conditions, social and economic conditions of the construction area, etc. The proportion of the index selection based on the natural endowment condition of the regional cultivated land is relatively large, while the selection of the index considering the local human factors is relatively large. less. At the same time, the setting and evaluation of the index system

There are cross-cutting issues in content.

4. Research on the factors affecting the benefits after the construction of well-facilitated farmland

Well-facilitated farmland construction is a comprehensive adjustment and transformation of regional land use structure, layout and function. China has a vast territory, uneven distribution of resources, and large regional differences in agricultural resource conditions and social and economic development. According to existing research, the influencing factors of the benefits of well-facilitated farmland construction projects can be summarized into three aspects: natural factors, social and economic factors, and human factors in the construction area. In terms of natural factors, some researchers have discussed the influence of the topography, landform, slope, soil quality, climatic conditions, frequency of natural disasters, and water resources development and utilization conditions on the benefits of the construction area. In the existing layout, some areas have superior agricultural resources and good basic conditions for well-facilitated farmland construction. At the same time, there are also a certain number of well-facilitated farmland project areas where the construction area is low in arable land productivity, water resources shortage, groundwater over-exploitation and other constraints, which will have a certain impact on the benefits of the project after the completion of the project. In terms of socio-economic factors, some scholars have qualitatively analyzed the possible impacts of regional GDP, urbanization rate, labor conditions, and agricultural output. In terms of human factors, the artificial management and protection of agricultural infrastructure in the later stage, the construction and protection of road and forest network, and the application and promotion of water-saving irrigation technology have a certain impact on the benefits of well-facilitated farmland construction [6].

In the research on the influencing factors of the post-construction benefits of well-facilitated farmland projects, the relevant research methods mainly include factor analysis, multiple regression analysis, principal component analysis, path analysis, grey correlation analysis, and Logistic regression analysis. Among the multivariate statistical methods, principal component analysis (PCA) and factor analysis (FA) are widely used and are commonly used multivariate analysis methods. This kind of method can reduce the dimensionality of the proposed many influencing factors, synthesize the indicators in the evaluation system into several common factors with a small number, and retain as much original variable information as possible and are not related to each other, so as to achieve The purpose of reproducing the internal relationship between the original variables and factors is suitable for the study of the factors affecting the benefits after the construction of well-facilitated farmland.

However, the inability to ensure the full utilization of data is the main disadvantage of this type of analysis method. For this reason, some scholars use this type of analysis method as the basis for judging the validity of multiple regression, which can avoid the defect of discarding a large number of data while ensuring that the main explanatory common factors can be retained in the regression equation. Combined with the ridge regression analysis, it can effectively solve the multilinear problem of the data under the premise of ensuring the full use of the data. The advantage of gray correlation analysis (GCA) is that it can determine the degree of influence between systematic factors according to the degree of similarity or dissimilarity in the development trend between factors, that is, the "gray correlation degree", which affects the number of samples or samples. The same applies with or without rules. This method has a relatively small amount of calculation, and can sort the relative benefit levels of well-facilitated farmland construction projects in a certain area, and can explore the relevant indicators that affect the benefits. If you want to further explore the influence relationship between independent variables and dependent variables, the advantage of path analysis (PA) is that it can intuitively describe the direct and indirect influence between the respective variables and between the independent variable and the dependent variable degree. The method can decompose the correlation coefficient on the basis of multiple regression, and express the direct effect of an independent variable on the dependent variable, the indirect effect of other variables on the dependent variable, and the direct path, indirect path and total path coefficient respectively. combined effect. Logistic regression analysis is a widely used statistical model, which is a kind of generalized linear model. The generalized linear model is a generalization of the linear regression model, which can overcome the shortcomings of the linear regression model. In the field of geosciences, a large number of scholars use this model to predict and simulate and analyze the driving force of land use change. The independent variable input to the logistic regression model can be discrete or continuous, or it can be a categorical variable with multiple values. The contribution of the independent variable to the dependent variable is generally quantitatively explained by the odds ratio (OR) or marginal effect. This method is suitable for well-facilitated farmland benefit-influencing factors research and benefit-level prediction research, but the use of such methods can only clarify the dependence between dependent variables and independent variables, and the interpretation of causal relationships requires further use of relevant theories.

To sum up, among the multivariate statistical methods, regression analysis, principal component analysis, factor analysis and other methods are widely used, but at the same time there is collinearity, the quantitative relationship between independent variables and dependent variables cannot be clearly defined, and the lack of Further interpretation of the dependent variable and other issues. The advantage of the path analysis method is that it can use the path diagram to succinctly elucidate the relationship between the variables. Influence relationship between standard farmland benefits and influencing factors. The advantage of logistic regression analysis is that it is easy to deal with various types of data, can explain the occurrence probability of dependent variables, and helps researchers deal with influencing factors that are difficult to quantify. Prediction research has certain significance for the optimal layout of well-facilitated farmland.

5. Conclusion

In the research part of factors affecting the improvement of well-facilitated farmland benefits, both in terms of index selection and method research are still relatively weak, and there are still few explanations for the differences in benefit evaluation and benefit improvement levels after the construction of well-facilitated farmland projects. Principal component analysis, factor analysis and other methods can retain as much original variable information as possible, and cannot guarantee full utilization of data is the disadvantage of such methods. Combined with regression analysis, it can effectively solve the multi-linear problem of the data while ensuring the full use of the data; the path analysis method can intuitively describe the degree of direct and indirect influence between the respective variables and between the independent variable and the dependent variable ; Logistic regression analysis is suitable for well-facilitated farmland benefit factor research and benefit level prediction research, and researchers still need to rely on relevant theories to explain the causal relationship.

Acknowledgments

This work was financially supported by Innovation Capability Support Program of Shaanxi (Program No.2021PT-053) fund.

References

1. Qiang W L, Liu A, M, Cheng S K, et al. Agricultural trade and virtual land use: The case of China's crop trade[J].Land Use Policy, 2013,33(33):141-150.
2. Du X D, Zhang X K, Jin X B. Assessing the effectiveness of land consolidation for improving agricultural productivity in China[J]. Land Use Policy,2018,70:360-367.
3. Tian J S, Tian J J, Guo J C. Evaluation of comprehensive benefits of land consolidation based on AHP and Fuzzy[J].Asian Agricultural Research, 2013,1(1):17-20.
4. Abubakari Z, van der Molen P, Bennett R M, et al. Land consolidation, customary lands, and Ghana's Northern Savannah Ecological Zone: An evaluation of the possibilities and pitfalls[J]. Land Use Policy,2016,54:386-398.
5. Wang J, Lin Y F, Glendinning A, et al. Land-use changes and land policies evolution in China's urbanization processes[J].Land Use Policy,2018,75:375-387.
6. Minetos D, Polyzos S. Deforestation processes in Greece: A spatial analysis by using an ordinal regression model[J].Forest Policy & Economics,2010,12(6):457-472.

 https://doi.org/10.1051/e3sconf/202233801031

Research of Rotor Unmanned Aerial Vehicle (UAV) Production and GIS Integration Based on 3D Panorama

Jingsi Li [1,2,3,4,*], Jian Wang [1,2,3,4], Chenxi Yang [1,2,3,4]

[1] Institute of Land Engineering and Technology, Shaanxi Provincial Land Engineering Construction Group Co., Ltd., Xi'an Shaanxi
[2] Shaanxi Provincial Land Engineering Construction Group Co., Ltd., Xi'an Shaanxi
[3] Key Laboratory of Degraded and Unused Land Consolidation Engineering, the Ministry of Nature and Resources, Xi'an Shaanxi
[4] Shaanxi Provincial Land Consolidation Engineering Technology Research Center, Xi'an Shaanxi

Abstract. 3D panorama technology is a kind of virtual reality technology based on image creation, which is used real photos to show the scene to achieve the effect of immersive virtual roaming, and improve the interactivity between the network platform with the user. Panoramic images, UAV remote sensing and GIS technology is the application and development of new technology of surveying and mapping industry, but apply combination is rarely studied. In this paper, based on rotor unmanned aerial vehicle (UAV) fixed-point hover took photos of different angles using PTGui software to create panorama images stitching, optimization, software reuse Pano2VR making 3D roaming figure, and compared with Supermap GIS integration. Based on a downtown building community will be released on GIS 3D roaming figure, you can see, after the integration of 3 d panorama with two-dimensional GIS geospatial information, also can see the area the real scene. The surveying and mapping, tourism and other industries to provide a new technical method.

keywords: Panoramic image, 3D roaming figure, Rotor unmanned aerial vehicle, GIS integration

1. Introduction

Geographic Information System (GIS) is one of the fastest growing and most widely used technologies in various industries in recent years. The traditional thematic maps and vector maps generated based on GIS are two-dimensional images, which can only obtain geospatial information and can not reflect objective things. The emergence of 3D modeling makes up for this deficiency, but the 3D modeling process is cumbersome and time-consuming, which is not conducive to network transmission (LI,2013). The three-dimensional roaming map constructed by panorama can reflect the real scene, and can view things at any position and angle through mouse or keyboard (FENG,2013). Combining the three-dimensional roaming map with the electronic map database, the combination of GIS and virtual scene is realized through web embedded publishing (DENG,2014). In the past, the panorama was taken by fixing the digital camera or vehicle camera with a tripod, and the shooting range was small. The rapid development of UAV widens the way for panoramic shooting. The UAV has a series of advantages such as low cost, simple operation, fast image acquisition speed and high ground resolution. The multi rotor UAV is equipped with a high-definition SLR camera, hovering in the air at a fixed point to shoot multiple pictures at 360 degrees horizontally and nearly 120 degrees vertically, which is used to produce an all-round real map(ZHOU,2016).

Taking an urban area as the shooting base, this paper uses inspire1 Pro multi rotor UAV equipped with Zen X5 camera to hover at the height of 300m in the center of the shooting area, takes 57 photos by adjusting the camera angle, loads the photos into PtGui software, generates panoramic images through alignment optimization splicing, and uses Photoshop software to make up the sky for the panoramic images, Load a complete panorama after processing into pano2vr software to create 3D roaming map, and then integrate and publish it with GIS. The research aims to provide technical support for regional surveying and mapping, tourism publicity and other industries.

2. Panoramic shooting of multi rotor uav

UAV aerial photography technology takes the aircraft as the data acquisition platform and carries a high-resolution image acquisition system to obtain image data. It has the characteristics of low cost, high precision and flexible system acquisition(CHEN,2016). At present, UAVs can be divided into fixed wing and multi rotor. According to their advantages and disadvantages, it is concluded that fixed wing is suitable for patrol measurement of land and

* Corresponding author: 692302520@qq.com

https://doi.org/10.1051/e3sconf/202233801031

crops, while multi rotor is more suitable for fixed-point shooting.

Therefore, this shooting adopts "Wu" inspire1 Pro rotor type small UAV, with a maximum takeoff weight of 3500g, a maximum horizontal flight speed of 18m / s and a maximum flight altitude of 500m. The system is simple, convenient and flexible, and easy to popularize. The main parameters of the Zen X5 camera carried on the UAV are shown in Table 1.

Table.1 Camera Parameter Table

Essential Factor	Type
Camera model	ZenmuseX5
Focal length	30mm
Specifications	4/3 IN CMOS sensor
Pixel numbers	$1600*10^4$
Maximum resolution	4608×3456

According to the specific characteristics of the shooting area, the flight altitude is set to 300m, the shooting interval angle of each circle is less than 30 degrees, the rotation angle of each circle is less than 30 degrees, and 10-16 images are taken in each circle, so as to ensure sufficient image overlap and facilitate subsequent image splicing and processing. The shooting time of panoramic image can be completed within 10 minutes, and clear and complete images can be obtained.

3. Production of panorama and 3d roaming map

Panoramic images include cylindrical panorama, spherical panorama and cube panorama. The essence of the three models is to project the spliced and fused panoramic images onto different three-dimensional surfaces, and back project them according to the visual angle of the viewer, so as to obtain images of different visual fields(DONG,2015). According to the previous production experience, it is concluded that the spherical panorama is the closest to human vision, so this paper takes the production of spherical panorama as an example(GONG,2017).

3.1 PTGui Image Mosaic

PTGui is a widely used panorama making software, which is easy to operate and can also be used by non professionals. Firstly, the photos taken by the UAV are loaded into the software in order and aligned automatically(WU,2016). Due to the camera focusing problem and weather influence, some adjacent pictures cannot automatically identify the overlapping area, so it is necessary to add control points manually. Set the isometric spherical projection from the panorama editor and adjust the reference line to align the building seams(DIAO,2016). Then, the optimizer is used to repeatedly optimize the control points with large error until the accuracy requirements are met, as shown in Figure 1.

Figure 1. Image Splicing Adjust

3.2 Image Patching in Photoshop

When the UAV hovers in the air, the maximum elevation angle of the camera is 120 degrees, which can not illuminate the whole sky. Therefore, it is necessary to make up the sky on the ground, and then use Photoshop to splice and repair the sky picture and panorama, and color it(LIU,2012), as shown in Figure 2. Convert the panoramic picture and the sky picture into polar coordinates, integrate them into one picture, repair the seams, and use tools such as layer mask, gradient, imitation stamp and filling to achieve seamless combination.

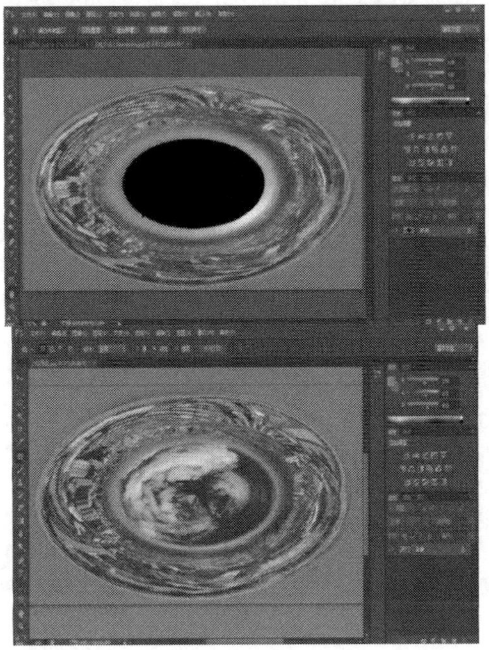

Figure 2. Under the Polar of Patch of the Sky

Then adjust the hue, saturation and contrast of the filled picture to make the picture clearer and the color more prominent. Finally, switch to the normal viewing angle and output the complete panoramic picture, as shown in Figure 3.

Figure 3. Complete Panorama

3.3 Production of 3D Roaming Map

Pano2vr is a panoramic image conversion application software based on flash animation technology. It can directly output animation files in Flash format by importing panoramic images in various formats and processing them(HUANG,2015).

Static panoramic pictures can not make people feel immersive, while 3D roaming pictures give people a new visual feeling and see wonderful images of different pictures from different angles(HUANG,2012). Load the panoramic image processed by PtGui and Photoshop software into pano2vr software, set image parameters, change image quality and playback frame number, turn on other functions as required, and output in the form of flash and HTML. Both of them have low requirements for players and can be played on any computer, as shown in Figure 4(YE,2012). At the same time, when the scene is not single, you can connect the scene by adding links or hotspots. The things to be annotated and navigation paths in the scene can be represented by specific symbols by adding hotspots(LIANG,2013).

Figure 4. Flash 3D Roaming Figure

4. Integration of 3d panoramic roaming and gis

The three-dimensional panoramic roaming map is published in the form of flash and HTML and embedded in various systems and web pages to show the real scene. However, you cannot view the geospatial and other attribute information of the image. GIS takes geospatial data as the core and realizes the interaction with users through professional interface. However, the image or map created based on GIS system itself is generally displayed in two-dimensional form. Even if the attribute data similar to DEM digital elevation map contains three-dimensional information, it can not be displayed well in the interface, and the three-dimensional modeling of GIS is very cumbersome. Therefore, the emergence of 3D panorama and GIS integration technology makes up for this defect. The 3D panorama is integrated with GIS to give spatial coordinates on the panorama and establish a unified database(GUO,2013).

Based on the vector electronic map on SuperMap GIS, this paper embeds the 3D panoramic roaming map. The position coordinates of the three-dimensional panorama are corresponding to the electronic map and an icon is added. Users can click the icon to enter the 3D panorama to realize scene roaming, as shown in Figure 5.

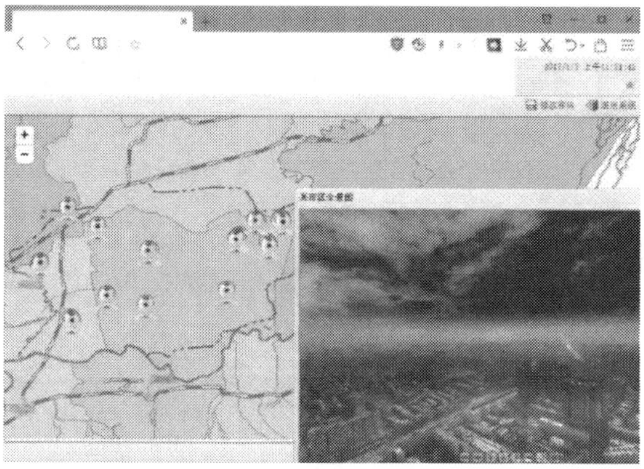

Figure 5. Panoramic Roaming and Gis Integration

5. Conclusion

The 3D panorama is processed by professional software PtGui and Photoshop to splice, fuse and repair the real image to generate a complete panorama. Then, the panoramic roaming map required by the user is generated through the parameter setting of pano2vr software. The rapid development of UAV provides a new and effective method for image data acquisition. Integrating 3D panoramic roaming map on GIS platform not only increases the geospatial information of 3D panorama, but also provides users with a better interactive platform. At the same time, the method discussed in this paper will be more widely used in surveying and mapping, tourism and other industries.

References

1. LI Shilei, DU Mingyi, LIU Yanwei, et al. The Research of the GIS Integration and Panorama Image[J]. Urban Geotechnical Investigation & Surveying. 2013(4).

2. FENG Jian, WU Lihua. Construction of the Tree-dimensional Panoramic Walk through Stem[J]. Computer & Digital Engineering. 2013(1):115.
3. DENG Feng, WAN Yuan, LEI Yu, et al. Online Roaming and GIS Integration Research and Development Based on Three-dimentional Panoramic[J]. Acta Scientiarum Naturalium Universitatis Nankaiensis. 2014(4):47.
4. ZHOU Zhiyong,DING Yulan. Research of Panoramic Maps Based on Multi-rotor UAV[J]. Urban Geotechnical Investigation & Surveying. 2016(2).
5. CHEN Wenlong, ZHANG Yu ,YE Song, et al. Application of UAV Panoramic Technology to Site Monitoring[J]. Journal of Yangtze River Scientific Research Institute. 2016(11):33.
6. DONG Xiaoyong. The Application and Research of Three-dimensional Panorama Technology in Modern Agriculture Extension[D].Northwest A&F University,2015.
7. GONG Qihui, WU Jianping, WANG Jiehua. The Research of the Production of 3D Real Scene and the GIS Integration Thereof Based on Panorama[J]. Geomatics & Spatial Information Technology. 2012(6):35.
8. WU Xiaodong, WEN Peng, GUI Lin. Application of 360 Panoama Technology in the Hydro Power Engineering[J]. Geospatial Information.2016(5):14.
9. DIAO Zhigang, Liu Zhinong, Wang Ningning.Use PT-Gui Software Product Panorama[J]. Information science.2016(7).
10. LIU Lang. The Usage of Photoshop CS5 Panoramic Photo[J]. Science Mosaic. 2012(11).
11. HUANG Guozheng. Research on Interactive Campus Roaming System Based on Pano2VR[J].Software Engineer.2015.(18):1.
12. HUANG Xianbing. The Design and Implement of Online Roaming Landscape Based on Panoramic Technology [D].Shanghai: Shanghai Jiao Tong University,2012.
13. YE Pingping， LUO Hong. Manufacture Methods and Application of Three –dimensional Panoramagram Based on PTGui Pro、Pano2VR[J]. Urban Geotechnical Investigation & Surveying. 2012(4).
14. LIANG Lijing, LIAO Chaowei. Realization of 360° Panoramic Roaming Animation Based on Static Images[J]. Journal of Ping Xiang University.2013(30):6.
15. GUO Lin-gang, ZHOU Jie, ZHANG Bing, YANG Jing, et al. Application of GIS Integrated 3D Panorama in Environmental Emergency[J]. Environmental Science Survey. 2013(32).

Effect of Organic Ecological Soilless Culture Substrate on Tomato Fruit

Yan Xu [1,2,3,4,*], Jian Wang[1,2,3,4], Hang Zhou[1,2,3,4]

[1] Insititute of Land Engineering and Technology, ShaanXi Provincial Land Engineering Construction Group, Xi'an 710075, China
[2] Key Laboratory of Degraded and Unused Land Consolidation Engineering, the Ministry of Natural Resources of China, Xi'an 710075; China
[3] ShaanXi Provincial Land Engineering Construction Group, Xi'an 710075, China
[4] Shaanxi Provincial Land Consolidation Engineering Technology Research Center, Xi'an 710075, China

Abstract: Based on agricultural biomass resources and utilization in Shaanxi province, this experiment used decomposing mushroom residues, pine needles, and peanut shells compounded with river sand as organic cultivation substrates, compared with garden soil, and carried out pot experiments to study the effect of different soilless cultivation substrates on tomato yield, size and number. The results show that compared with CK1 (garden soil) and CK2 (decomposed fungus residue: river sand = 1:1, volume ratio), the yield of greenhouse tomato of T5 (decomposed fungus residue: pine needles: peanut shells: river sand = 1:1:1:1, volume ratio) can be significantly improved; under the same amount of decomposed fungus residue and river sand, adding peanut shells has a better effect on tomato yield than adding pine needles; different treatments have little effect on the average height of tomato fruit, but have a greater effect on the cross diameter of the fruit.

Keywords: Soilless Culture Substrate; Organic Ecological; Tomato fruit

1. Introduction

Tomato is one of the main vegetables ultivated in facilities in China. It has the characteristics of high yield and efficiency, and is rich in nutrients such as vitamin C and lycopene [1-3]. In order to pursue high efficiency in agricultural production, farmers blindly invest excessive amounts of water and fertilizers, resulting in soil compaction, salinization, aggravation of soil-borne diseases, decline in yield and quality, and environmental pollution [4-6]. Organic ecological soilless culture technology not only has the characteristics of general soilless culture, such as improving crop yield and quality, reducing pesticide usage, product cleanliness, water saving, fertilizer saving and labor saving, etc.[7-8] Cultivated land to grow vegetables can effectively reduce production costs and reduce environmental pollution [9-12]. Based on the agricultural biomass resources and utilization foundation in Shaanxi, this experiment used decomposed mushroom residue, pine needles and peanut shells compounded with river sand as the organic cultivation substrate, and compared it with the garden soil to study the growth effect of tomato fruit, providing scientific basis and technical reference for the development of facility tomato cultivation in arable land and soil degradation areas and the full utilization of local agricultural waste resources.

2. Materials and methods

2.1 Test material

The organic matrix materials such as decomposed mushroom residues, pine needles, peanut shells, and river sand were purchased from natural nutrient soil supply stores; the pastoral soil and was used as the control group, which was collected from the Qinling Field Monitoring Center Station. Other test materials such as urea, superphosphate, potassium sulfate, and organic compound fertilizer were all collected from Yangling Agricultural Supply and Marketing Station. The tomato variety was selected from the potted cherry tomato variety, which was purchased from Yangling Agricultural Supply and Marketing Station.

* Corresponding author: 1213349323@qq.com

2.2 Test design

A total of 7 treatments were used in this experiment, and each treatment was repeated 3 times, as shown in Table 1. The experiment was set up in the solar greenhouse of Qinling Field Monitoring Center Station, and the flower pots of the same size were artificially filled according to the hierarchical structure of 10 cm gravel and 20 cm substrate with different ratios from the bottom to the surface. Urea (23.7g/m2), diammonium phosphate (26.7g/m2) and potassium sulfate (20.25g/m2) were applied as base fertilizers into different cultivation substrates. The trials were sown in early July 2020 and harvested in late November. The same number of tomato seeds are sown in each pot, and the seedlings are thinned according to the size and growth of the seedlings, and one seedling is fixed in each pot.

Table 1 Experiment design

Treatment	Materials (volume ratio)
CK1	pastoral soil
CK2	decomposed fungus residue: river sand=1:1
T1	decomposed fungus residue: pine needles: peanut shells: river sand =1:0:1:1
T2	decomposed fungus residue: pine needles: peanut shells: river sand =1:1:0:1
T3	decomposed fungus residue: pine needles: peanut shells: river sand =2:1:0:1
T4	decomposed fungus residue: pine needles: peanut shells: river sand =2:0:1:1
T5	decomposed fungus residue: pine needles: peanut shells: river sand =1:1:1:1

2.3 Sample determination and analysis

At harvest, the number and total yield of each tomato fruit were determined, and the cross diameter, fruit height and single fruit quality were determined. The experimental data were analyzed and plotted using Excel 2010 and SPSS 17.0.

3. Results and analysis

3.1 Differences in tomato number and yield in different treatments

Organic cultivation substrates provide certain nutrients and environment for tomato growth and development. Figure 1 shows that under the environmental conditions of this experiment, the number of fruits in different treatments from large to small is T4>T5>T1=CK1>T2>T3=CK2, the maximum number of T4 is 16, and the minimum of CK2 and T3 is 7. The total yield of fruit was T5>T1>CK1>T4>CK2>T2>T3 in descending order. The total yield of T5 tomato was 25.95g at most, and the minimum was 8.61g in T3. On the whole, compared with CK1 (pastoral soil treatment) and CK2 (decomposed fungus residue: river sand = 1:1), the T5 formula (decomposed fungus residue: pine needles: peanut shells: river sand = 1:1:1:1) can significantly improve the greenhouse tomato yield. Compared with CK2, under the same amount of decomposed fungus residue and river sand, adding peanut shells has a better effect on tomato yield than pine needles. Compared with T1 and T4, T2 and T3, the number and yield of tomatoes did not increase with the increasing volume proportion of decomposed mushroom residues, but decrease, indicating that the proportion of bacterial residue is not as high as possible.

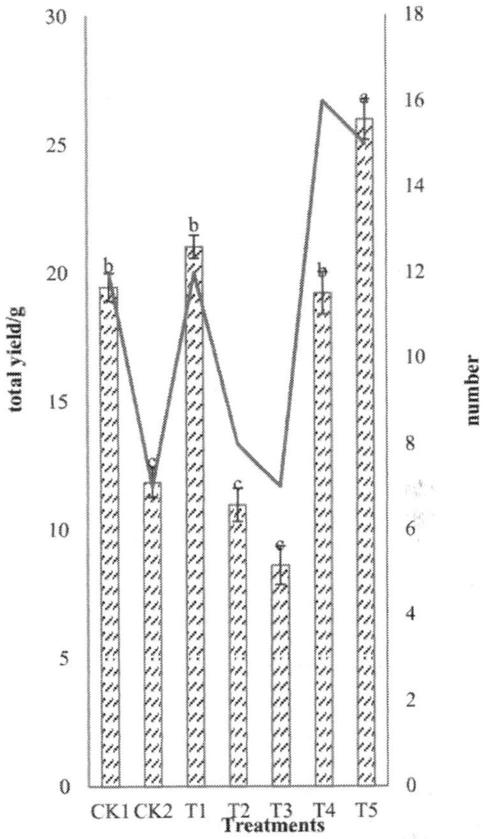

Figure 1 Total yield and number of tomato with different treatments

3.2 Differences in fruit size and single fruit quality among different treatments

Under the conditions of the solar greenhouse in this experiment, the average fruit transverse diameter of different treatments is T5>CK1=T1>T4=CK2>T2>T3 in descending order, the maximum tomato transverse diameter is 1.72cm, and the minimum is 1.29cm. The average height of tomato was T4>T5>CK1>T1>CK2>T2=T3 in descending order. The average height of tomato was 1.36 cm and the smallest was 1.22 cm. In addition, the average fruit weight of T1 treatment was the largest 1.75g, followed by T5 treatment was 1.73g, and the other treatments were all less than 1.70g. On the whole, compared with CK1 (pastoral soil treatment) and CK2 (decomposed fungus residue: river sand = 1:1), different treatments had little effect on the average height of tomato fruit, but had a greater effect on the transverse diameter of tomato. Except for the T5 formula (decomposed fungus residue: pine needle: peanut shell: river sand = 1:1:1:1), the transverse diameter of greenhouse tomato was greatly improved, and the other formulas had no significant effect on tomato size. This is different from the effect of each treatment on the total yield, indicating that each treatment has no significant effect on the fruit quality, and the total tomato yield is mainly affected by the increase of tomato number.

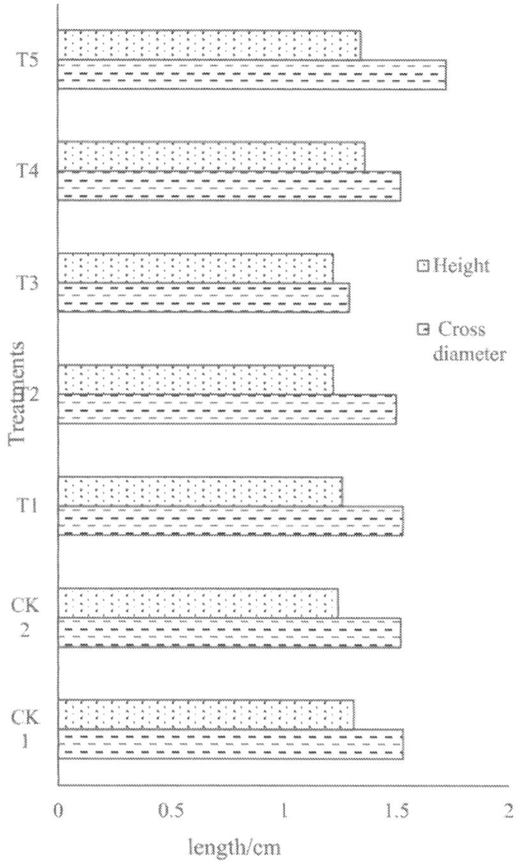

Figure 2 Variation of cross diameter and height of tomato in different treatments

4. Conclusion

Pot experiments show that, compared with loess, organic ecotype soilless culture medium can provide nutrients and environment for tomato growth and development. Under the test condition, compared with CK1 treatment and CK2 (decomposed fungus residue: river sand=1:1), the T5 formula (decomposed fungus residue: pine needle: peanut shell: river sand=1:1:1:1) can significantly improve the greenhouse tomato yield. Under the same amount of decomposed fungus residue and river sand, adding peanut shells had a better effect on tomato yield than adding pine. Different treatments had little effect on the average height of tomato fruit, but had a greater effect on the transverse diameter of the fruit.

Acknowledgements

Support Projects : Pre-research project of Insititute of Land Engineering and Technology, ShaanXi Provincial Land Engineering Construction Group (NBYY2020-15), the open fund of Land Engineering and Human Settlement and Civil Engineering Innovation Center (2021WHZ0093)

References

1. Li P P, Zhu Y L. Research progress in the development and application of plant cultivation substrates based on agricultural and forestry wastes [J]. Journal of Nanjing Forestry University (Natural Science Edition), 2015, 39(5):161-168.
2. Ji Y H, Zhao M L, Wu Z H, et al. Study on the suitable ratio of Jerusalem artichoke fermentation straw in tomato culture medium [J]. Journal of Horticulture, 2017, 44(8): 1599-1608.
3. Yu H X, Yang R, Wang S P, et al. Effects of organic matrix formulation on physiological characteristics and yield of pepper in greenhouse [J]. China Agricultural Science and Technology Herald, 2015, 17(3): 107-115.
4. Xu Y P, Zhu H G, Cheng X W, et al. Research on industrial evolution and multi-industry linkage of agricultural waste resource utilization[J]. Chinese Journal of Agricultural Machinery, 2018, 39(4): 90-94.
5. Zhang R F. Effects of matrix formula on the quality and yield of tomato seedlings in plastic greenhouses in spring [J]. Northern Horticulture, 2015, (14): 45-47.
6. Ma H Y, Jin L Z, Li X, et al. Effects of different substrate cultivation modes on the growth, yield and quality of greenhouse tomato [J]. Tianjin Agricultural Science, 2016, 22(11): 130-132.
7. Ren S Y, Ding L. Effects of Different Soilless Culture Media on Tomato Yield and Quality [J]. Changjiang Vegetables, 2018, 4: 62-64.
8. Li H Y. Research on formulation of organic soilless culture substrate and its effect on tomato growth [D]. Shandong: Shandong Agricultural University, 2012.
9. Wang H, Wei F, Chen Y W, et al. Effects of agricultural and forestry waste substrates based on grape branches on the growth and development of tomato [J]. China Agricultural Science and Technology Herald, 2019, 21(5): 1 41-151.
10. Liu Z L, Gao J J, Zhang Y Y, et al. Effects of different organic matrix formulations on yield and quality of facility tomato [J]. Journal of Shanghai Jiaotong University (Agricultural Science Edition)), 2019, 37(3): 34-38.
11. Song Z G. Study on the use of different crop straws as substrates for soilless cultivation of tomato [D]. Beijing: Chinese Academy of Agricultural Sciences, 2013.

12. Liu Z L, Zhang Y Y, Gu D Y, et al. Effects of returning agricultural waste to the field on tomato quality, yield and soil nitrogen, phosphorus and potassium[J]. Chinese Journal of Drainage and Irrigation Mechanical Engineering, 2018, 36(7): 639-644.

E3S Web of Conferences **338**, 01033 (2022) https://doi.org/10.1051/e3sconf/202233801033
ESMA 2021

Effects of different land consolidation methods on soil properties of cultivated land

Jianglong Shen[1,2*], Yilun Dai[1]

[1]Shaanxi Provincial Land Engineering Construction Group Co., Ltd. China
[2]Institute of Land Engineering and Technology, Shaanxi Provincial Land Engineering Construction Group Co., Ltd. China

Abstract. As an important reserve cultivated land resource in my country, its development and utilization are of great significance to ensure food security. Aiming at the problems of bare gravel leakage and shallow soil layer in the barren rock beach area, through community simulation experiments, different covering soil structures were set up on the basis of the underlying gravel, and the effects of different covering soil structures on soil physical and chemical properties and crop yield were monitored to obtain Find suitable soil structures. The results show that: when the covering thickness is 60cm, the content of total nitrogen and available phosphorus in the soil reaches the maximum; when the soil bulk density is set to 1.5 g/cm^3, the content of available phosphorus in the soil reaches the maximum. The content of available potassium increased with the increase of soil bulk density.

Key words: Barren rock beach, gravel,Soil physical and chemical properties, Soil bulk density.

1. Introduction

Cultivated land is the most precious resource in my country and the lifeblood of ensuring national food security[1-4]. At this stage, my country is facing a shortage of land resources[5,6] and the quality of cultivated land is declining. As an important reserve resource of cultivated land, barren rock beaches can significantly increase the area of cultivated land and have huge social and economic benefits[5,6]. However, in the process of remediation of barren rock beaches, there is the problem of extensive soil covering methods, and there is no basis for the thickness and bulk density of soil covering. How to construct a ploughing layer to meet crop growth is an urgent problem that needs to be solved[7-9]. By designing a community simulation experiment, in view of the serious leakage of soil water and nutrients and the unclear suitable soil structure in the land remediation of barren rock beach, different covering soil structures were set up on the basis of the underlying gravel, and the effect of different covering soil structures on the impact of different covering soil structures was monitored. The influence of soil physical and chemical properties and crop yield in order to obtain suitable soil structure.

2. Experimental program

2.1 Experimental area

The experimental area is located in Ducun Town, Fuping County, Shaanxi Province. The region has a semi-arid continental climate and is located in the transition zone between the Guanzhong Plain and the Northern Shaanxi Plateau. The rainy season is concentrated from July to September, accounting for 50% of the annual rainfall. The seasons are distinct, the spring is windy and less rainy, and the amount of water evaporation is large. The annual evaporation is 950-1290mm, which is 2-2.5 times of the rainfall. The frost-free period is 225 days, and the annual average temperature is 13.5 °C. The climatic conditions meet the growth needs of the main cash crops in the north such as wheat and corn.

*Corresponding author: jianglong_shen@163.com

https://doi.org/10.1051/e3sconf/202233801033

2.2 Experimental Design

A total of 12 test plots were designed in this experiment, each with an area of 2 m × 4 m = 8 m2. The test plot is divided into two treatment methods, one is treatment with different covering soil dimension, and the other is treatment with different covering soil bulk density. In the treatment of covering soil thickness, the dimension of the overlying soil sheet was 30 cm, 40 cm, 50 cm, 60 cm, 80 cm and 100 cm, respectively. In the control treatment, the bulk density of the whole body is $1.2g/cm^3$, and the other treatments are divided into upper, middle and lower layers, the upper layer is 20cm, the middle layer is 20cm, and the lower layer is 10cm, and the upper and middle layers are $1.2g/cm^3$ and $1.3g/cm^3$ remain unchanged, and the lower layer is set to $1.3g/cm^3$, $1.4 g/cm^3$, $1.5g/cm^3$, $1.6g/cm^3$ and $1.7g/cm^3$ according to the treatment method.

In the experiment, according to the recommended plan for wheat fertilization by the local agricultural department, the N, P_2O_5 and K_2O fertilization rates of the experimental fields were 255kg/hm2, 180kg/hm2 and 90kg/hm2, respectively. When sowing winter wheat, enrich according to the plot plan, and make the ground level by manual ploughing and deep loosening, and the fertilizer is fully mixed. All the experimental fields were artificially planted, and the phosphate fertilizer, nitrogen fertilizer, and potassium fertilizer were diammonium phosphate, potassium chloride, urea, etc. respectively. The sowing was artificially planted, and the field management measures during the experiment were the same as those in the local field.

2.3 Measurement items and methods

The soil index detection is stratified sampling detection. For soils with different depths and different covering soil thicknesses (covering soil bulk density), the soil mechanical composition is determined by the hydrometer method; the Kjeldahl method is used to determine the total soil nitrogen; the molybdenum antimony resistance colorimetric method is used. Determination of soil available phosphorus; using flame photometry to determine soil available potassium [10].

2.4 Data processing

R software was used for statistical analysis of the data, and Origin was used for plotting.

3. Results and Analysis

3.1 Analysis of soil pH in different treatments

Figure 1a shows the pH values of soils under different cover thickness treatments. It can be found that in the treatment with the covering thickness of 50, the highest reaches 8.4. Figure 1b depicts the pH value of soil under different bulk density treatments, and it can be found that with the increase of soil bulk density, soil pH value is also increasing. It was verified that different soil covering thickness and different soil bulk density have a significant effect on soil pH value.

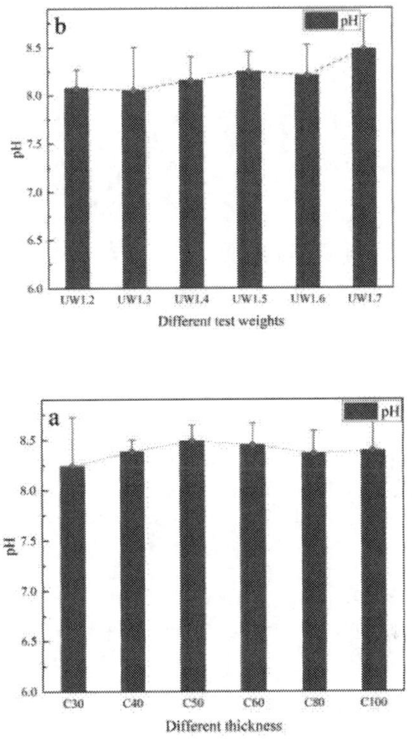

Figure. 1 Differences of soil pH in different treatments

3.2 Analysis of soil conductivity with different treatments

By measuring the conductivity of different treatments, the results are shown in Figure2. For different covering soil thickness treatments, the conductivity of C40 treatment is the largest. For different soil bulk density treatments, the treatment with bulk density of 1.7 g/cm3 has the highest conductivity, and the treatment with bulk density of 1.2 g/cm3 has the lowest conductivity.

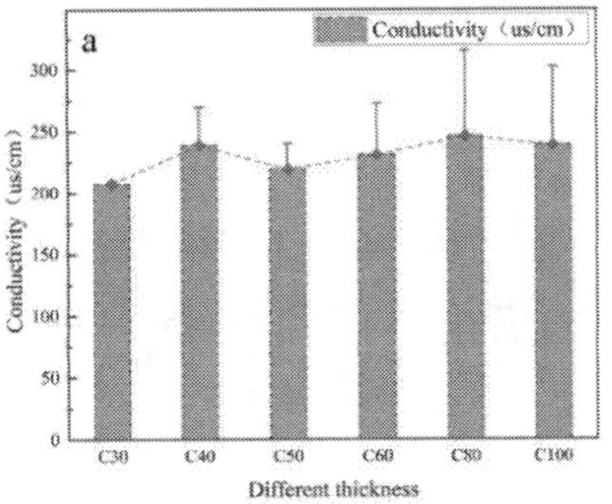

https://doi.org/10.1051/e3sconf/202233801033

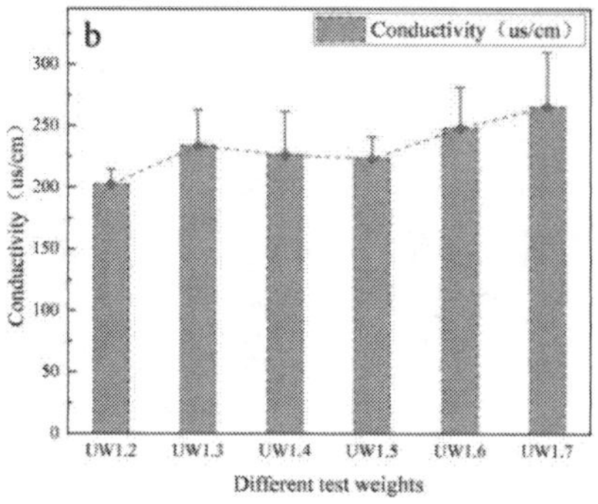

Figure 2 Differences in soil conductivity of different treatments

3.3 Analysis of Soil Available Phosphorus in Different Treatments

By testing the available phosphorus content of different treatments, it can be found that in different soil covering thickness treatments, the available potassium content is C60>C80>C100>C30>C50>C40; in different soil bulk density treatments, the available potassium content is UW1. 5>UW1.4>UW1.2>UW1.7>UW1.3. It shows that when the soil cover thickness is 60 cm, the bulk density of the soil tillage layer is set to 1.5 g/cm3, which is most conducive to the accumulation of soil available phosphorus.

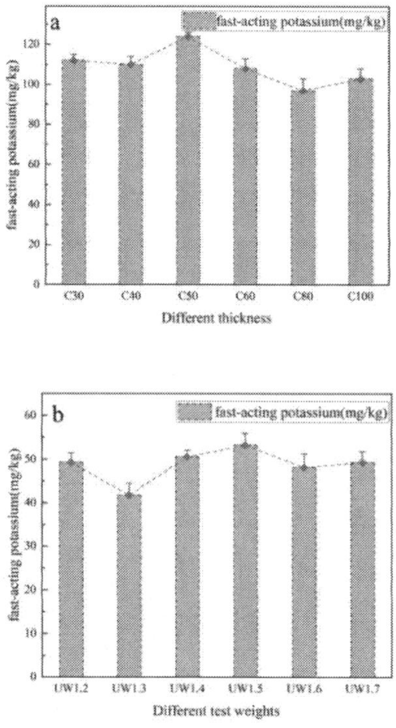

Figure 3 Differences of soil available potassium in different treatments

4. Conclusion

Different soil covering thickness had no significant effect on soil pH value. In different soil bulk density treatments, soil pH increased slightly with the increase of soil bulk density. When the covering soil thickness is 40cm, the conductivity of the soil is the largest. The treatment with a bulk density of 1.7 g/cm3 has the highest conductivity, and the treatment with a bulk density of 1.2 g/cm3 has the lowest conductivity.

The contents of total nitrogen, available phosphorus and available potassium in the soil did not show a simple linear relationship with the increase of the covering soil thickness. When the covering soil thickness was 60 cm, the total nitrogen and available phosphorus contents in the soil reached the highest. When the covering soil thickness was 50cm, the content of available potassium in the soil was the highest. The content of available potassium showed a linear growth trend with the increase of soil bulk density.

The research results of field experiments have confirmed that in the process of covering soil reconstruction of barren rocky beach, it is necessary to realize that it is not that the deeper the covering soil thickness is, the better the growth of crops, but that the covering soil thickness should be set at about 50cm, and the soil bulk density should reach 1.5g. /cm3, it can be well adapted to the growth of crops. It provides a reference for the reconstruction of barren rock beach soil.

References

1. Liang Han,Lin Wang,Xuanming Ding,Haijia Wen,Xingzhong Yuan,Wengang Zhang.Similarity quantification of soil parametric data and sites using confidence ellipses[J].Geoscience Frontiers,2022,13(01):223-235.
2. Zhang Puyang, Zhao Xing, Ding Hongyan et al. The wet-towing resistance of the composite bucket foundation for offshore wind turbines[J]Marine Structures, 2021, 80
3. Moises Jimenez-Martinez Fatigue of offshore structures: A review of statistical fatigue damage assessment for stochastic loadings[J]International Journal of Fatigue, 2020, 132(C)
4. E.U.Eyo,S.J.Abbey,T.T.Lawrence,F.K.Tetteh.Impro ved prediction of clay soil expansion using machine learning algorithms and meta-heuristic dichotomous ensemble classifiers[J].Geoscience Frontiers, 2022, 13(01):274-290.
5. LI Hanyu,KAUFMANN Hermann,XU Guochang. Modeling Spatio-temporal Drought Events Based on Multi-temporal,Multi-source Remote Sensing Data Calibrated by Soil Humidity[J]. Chinese Geographical Science, 2022, 32(01): 127-141.
6. ZHAO Fei-fei,HE Man-chao,WANG Yun-tao,TAO Zhi-gang, LI Chun.Eco-geological environment quality assessment based on multi-source data of the mining city in red soil hilly region, China[J].Journal of Mountain Science,2022,19(01):253-275.

7. Xu Xiaohui, Song Zhan, Li Zan et al. Establishment and characterization of a gill cell line from pearl gentian grouper (Epinephelus lanceolatus♂×Epinephelus fuscoguttatus♀) and its application in cadmium toxicology[J] Ecotoxicology and Environmental Safety, 2021, 208.
8. Zhou Yingjie,Tang Yanni,Hu Chengxiao,Zhan Ting,Zhang Simin,Cai Miaomiao,Zhao Xiaohu. Soil applied Ca, Mg and B altered phyllosphere and rhizosphere bacterial microbiome and reduced Huanglongbing incidence in Gannan Navel Orange[J]. Science of the Total Environment, 2021,791.
9. Orlando Patrick, Silvestri Sonia, Cirilli Ilenia et al. Involvement of different hemoprotein thiol groups of Oncorhynchus mykiss in cadmium toxicity[J] Journal of Trace Elements in Medicine and Biology, 2021, 66.

Investigation and Research on the Current Situation of Erosion Gully in Northeast Semi-arid Region

Shiqian Gao [2,3,4,5,*] and Yutong Zhao [1,2,3,4,5]

[1] Institute of Land Engineering and Technology, Shaanxi Provincial Land Engineering Construction Group Co., Ltd.. 710075, Xi'an, China
[2] Shaanxi Provincial Land Engineering Construction Group Co., Ltd. 710075, Xi'an, China
[3] Key Laboratory of Degraded and Unused Land Consolidation Engineering, the Ministry of Natural Resources, 710075, Xi'an, China
[4] Shaanxi Provincial Land Consolidation Engineering Technology Research Center.710075, Xi'an, China
[5] Land Engineering Quality Testing of Shaanxi Land Engineering Construction Group Co., Ltd. Shaanxi, China

Abstract: The occurrence and development of erosion gully will increase the area of soil erosion and continuously erode the cultivated land.The treatment of erosion gully is swing in the black soil region of Northeast China.However, they are all directed at the typical black soil area, while the soil erosion caused by the erosion gully in the semi-arid area of Northeast is less concerned.The study uses a combination of RS and census data.Exploring the number of erosion gully and the status of development,The survey results show that :the number of erosion gully is large, and most of them are developmental erosion gully.If the governance measures are not taken in time, the erosion ditch may continue to develop.

Keywords: semi-arid area in northeast, soil erosion, erosion gully

1. Foreword

Soil erosion is one of the most important ecological and environmental problems at present. Among them, trench erosion is the most destructive and has become one of the most serious indicators of land degradation. Gully erosion occurs on the earth except in the polar regions, and 85.7% occurs in agriculture and animal husbandry. On the ground, the quality of the land and the cultivability and area of the arable land are reduced, which seriously threatens the regional agriculture and ecological security. Therefore, trench erosion has always been the focus of research in domestic and foreign academic circles.With the increasingly serious environmental pollution and ecological degradation, the coordinated development of human, ecology and environment has become one of the most popular scientific and social issues in the 21st century. Dealing with this problem has become the goal of domestic and foreign scholars day and night.With the improvement of the soil erosion control project in the Loess Plateau of Northwest China, the problem of soil erosion in the Northeast has attracted people's attention. Channel erosion is the main form of soil erosion in Northeast China.With the launch of high-precision satellites and the development of high-tech such as UAV telemetry in recent years, the research content of erosion ditch in Northeast my country is also changing with each passing day. The research results show that nearly 90% of the erosion ditch in the Mangang area of Manchuan in the northeast are unstable erosion ditch, and the development intensity and distribution density of the erosion ditch in the north are significantly higher than those in the southern area. Some people also use high-resolution satellites and make full use of remote sensing technology to explore the identification method of erosion ditch, in order to provide technical means for follow-up research on the monitoring and management of erosion ditch.These studies are all from macroscopic considerations, studying the distribution and development characteristics of erosion ditch, and few people start from the microscopic soil physical properties.According to early research results: About 70% of the erosion trenches were formed around the 1960s[1],It has a long developmental process。After the founding of the People's Republic of China, in order to rapidly develop the economy, large-scale logging was used to make steel. The vegetation coverage on the ground was severely reduced, the ecological environment was severely damaged, and soil erosion was intensified[2,3].Ridge farming along the slope is one of the important reasons for the rapid development of eroded ditches in Northeast China.[4,5]. The concentrated rainstorm period from July to September each year is the high incidence period of farmland erosion gully[6-10]Erosion ditch is formed under the combined action of multiple external forces such as water flow and gravity. The occurrence and development of eroded gully will not only cause the gully head to advance, the gully bottom to be cut down, and the gully bank to collapse, increase the

* Corresponding author: 1129712869@qq.com

runoff intensity, and aggravate the soil erosion in the area[11-18]. It will also destroy the integrity of the land, destroy roads, block traffic, cause great inconvenience to people's lives, and reduce the arable area of crops, resulting in a significant drop in crop yields[19-21], restricting the economic income of residents, and erosion trenches can also fragment intact ecosystems

2. Overview of the study area

The semi-arid area of Northeast China mainly manifests in ecological and environmental problems such as low and concentrated annual rainfall, underdeveloped surface water system, thin and barren soil layer, poor vegetation growth environment, and poor site conditions for restoration and reconstruction. It is a typical soil erosion in Northeast my country. Ecologically fragile areas are highly sensitive to the occurrence and development of eroded gully.According to the typical study on the boundary definition of typical soil species and marginal soil species in black soil"People's Republic of China Industry Standard SL190-96 Soil Erosion Classification and Grading Standard"--the definition and description of the black soil area in Northeast China in the second-level division of the national soil erosion type division, as well as the national soil classification map soil types and the three northeastern provinces and four Inner Mongolia A spatial analysis of superimposed administrative boundaries of the Union,And refer to the distribution of vegetation types, precipitation contours, topography and other spatial distribution characteristics to identify the boundary of the sensitive area of the erosion ditch.The research area mainly includes the Fuxin Mongolian Autonomous Region in northwest Liaoning, Baicheng area in northwest Jilin, Chifeng area in Inner Mongolia and Tongliao area in Xing'an League

3. Research methods

The investigation on the current situation of eroded gully in semi-arid area is based on the 2013 water census, ArcGIS is used to superimpose the boundary data of key study districts and counties in the semi-arid region of Northeast China with it, and the distribution of erosion ditch and the degree of erosion in this area are obtained by cutting calculation.

4. Results and analysis

Data research and field investigation were conducted in the semi-arid area of Northeast China. The statistics of soil erosion area and erosion intensity classification in each region are shown in Table 1.The overall rainfall in this area is small, but the rainfall is concentrated, and the vegetation growth is restricted, resulting in widespread erosion of farmland and barren slopes. The development status and development characteristics of erosion ditch in this area are shown in Table 2. Among them, there are 41,019 erosion ditch over 100 meters in length, with a total length of 33,877,322 meters and a total area of 92,092.78 square hectares, with an average slope drop of 9.46%.

Table 1. Soil erosion and erosion intensity in ecological fragile area of black soil area

Location	Area (km^2)	Each Erosion Intensity Area (km^2)					
		Slight	Mild	Moderate	Strength	Extreme Strength	Severe
Xing'an League	20304	6693.59	6489.58	3565.55	2668.39	786.54	100.36
Tongliao	20313	6696.55	6492.46	3567.13	2669.57	786.88	100.40
Fuxin	4552	1500.65	1454.91	799.37	598.23	176.34	22.50
Total	45169	14890.7	14436.9	7932.05	5936.20	1749.76	223.26

Table 2. Characteristics of erosion gully in ecological fragile area of black soil area

Location	Quantity (n)	Length (m)	Area (hm2)	Mean slope (%)
Xing'an League	29352	24186503	67959.09	10.49
Tongliao	7815	7672509	20222.84	11.11
Fuxin	3852	2018310	3910.85	6.78
Total	41019	33877322	92092.78	9.46

The soil in the surveyed area of Xing'an League is complex. There are mainly brown coniferous forest soil and gray forest soil along the altitude gradient, and then gradually transition to dark brown soil and then chestnut soil at the bottom of the mountain;The soil texture in Tongliao City is mainly chestnut soil, and there are also aeolian sandy soil and gray meadow soil in some areas;The soil in Fuxin transitioned from brown soil to loess, mainly leaching cinnamon soil, juvenile forest brown soil, aeolian sandy soil, and meadow soil. Most of the region has a dry climate with poor soil and low soil moisture content.The management of erosion ditch should firstly be based on engineering and technical means, while effectively controlling soil and water loss, providing an environment for vegetation growth and laying a foundation for the subsequent ecological restoration of erosion ditch.

5. Conclusion

Erosion ditch is one of the main types of soil erosion in the Northeast semi-arid region. The research results show that the area of eroded ditch in Xing'an League is 67,959 hectares and the length is 29,352 meters, which is much higher than that in Tongliao and Fuxin.And most of them are primary erosion ditch with low erosion intensity. If it is not treated in time, it will inevitably lead to the continuous development of erosion ditch, increase the degree of soil erosion, further reduce the area of cultivated land, and affect the integrity of the land. Therefore, we should pay attention to the problems caused by soil erosion in this area, increase investment in a timely manner, strengthen remediation efforts, and control the further expansion of erosion ditch in this area.

6. Outlook

Erosion ditch governance is difficult. At present, the governance of erosion ditch is mainly based on engineering, which is divided into slope engineering and ditch engineering. Development ditch is generally chosen as the object of treatment, and there are some treatment measures for large, medium and small erosion ditch, but all of them are mainly gabion valleys.The protection measures at the head of the ditch are not implemented much, and the annular dam is mainly built with mortar and masonry, and no protection measures for falling water have been found,The slope measures are mainly to build horizontal grooves parallel to the contour lines, and plant water conservation plants to achieve the purpose of protecting the hillside from soil erosion.There are not many projects that specifically implement plant measures for ecological restoration of eroded channels.

However, the use of ecological restoration technology to control erosion ditch is the most reasonable model， It is also more difficult.Most of the trenches were built after the gabion valley, and the vegetation restoration relies on natural succession,but the effect is not outstanding at present.Mainly because the plant species is single, poplar trees are planted in places where the siltation at the bottom of the ditch reaches a certain level, and other plants are rarely used.Secondly, the vegetation coverage in these areas is low, and the grasses are not lush. The weeds that grow naturally in the erosion ditch become one of the places for cattle and sheep to graze. Therefore, cattle and sheep are frequently gnawed and trampled, and vegetation succession is slow. The effect is better after building a fence in a certain area. However, most of the eroded ditch in this area are steep and the wild plant seeds have no conditions for attachment. Even without disturbance, the vegetation restoration of the ditch slope is still difficult. Therefore, the ecological restoration of eroded ditch is more difficult.

References

1. Qin W,Zuo C D,Fan J R,et al.Countermeasures for erosion ditch control in Northeast black soil region[B]. Soil and Water Conservation,2014:37-41.
2. Li Z G,Wang Y S,Liu X C,et al.Census methods and results of erosion trenches in black soil region of Northeast my country[A].Soil and Water Conservation Science in China,2013,11(5):1672-3007.
3. E J P.Summary report of comprehensive scientific investigation on soil erosion and ecological security in China[J].Beijing: Soil and Water Conservation in China,2008.
4. Fan H M,Cai Q G,Cui M.Study on vertical zoning of soil erosion in black soil mangang area in Northeast China[J].Chinese Journal of Agricultural Engineering,2005,21(6):8-11.
5. ZHao Y M,Jiang H T,Wang S J.Study on relative soil and water conservation benefit of different topographic ridge slope in Northeast black soil region[J].Soil and Water Conservation Research,2015,21(5):28-34.
6. Yan B X,Yang Y H,Liu X T,et al.Status and evolution trend of soil erosion in black soil region of Northeast China[J].Soil and Water Conservation in China,2008(12):26-30.
7. Gu G H,Wang Y S,ZHong Y F,et al.Research on the development characteristics of erosion gulch in mangang area manchuan Northeast China[J].Soil and Water Conservation Research,2015,22(02):47-51+57.
8. Yu P X,ZHou X,Liu S H,et al.Feature extraction and identification of remote sensing images of erosion gully in black soil region of Northeast China[J].Acta Remote Sensing,2018,22(04):611-620.
9. Wang D A,Liu G,Wang X Y,et al.Difference analysis of the composition of eroded sediment particles measured by laser method and straw method in black soil area in Northeast China[J].Soil and Water Conservation Science in China,2016,14(01):114-122.
10. Castillo C,Gómez J A. A century of gully erosion research: Urgency, complexity and study approaches[J]. Earth-Science Reviews,2016:300-319.
11. Meng L Q,Research on gully erosion mechanism and control mode in black soil region of Northeast China[D].Chinese Academy of Agricultural Sciences,2009.
12. ZHao P,Peng S L,ZHang J W,Ecosystem fragility and degraded ecosystems[J].Journal of Tropical and Subtropical Botany,1998,6(3):179-186.
13. CHai Z P,Liang Z,Wang X M,et al.The effect of continuous cropping on soil physical properties of cotton fields[J].China Agricultural Science Bulletin,,2008(08):192-195.
14. Wang ZH M,Liu J X,Gao Y,et al.Classification of erosion trenches based on remote sensing and GIS[B].Northeast Water Conservancy and Hydropower,2016,5:40-43.
15. Wang Z P,Cai J P,ZHang Z K,et al.The dynamic changes of the status quo of soil and water loss in Liaoning Province and the countermeasures for its prevention and control[A].Soil and Water Conservation Science and Technology Information, 2002,5:32-36.
16. Bian F,ZHeng F L,Xu X M,et al.Comparison of slope erosion process between along-slope ridge farming and no-ridge farming in northeastern black soil region[J]. Soil and Water Conservation Bulletin,2016,36(1):10-17.
17. ZHang Y L,Wang Z M,Gao Y,et al.Investigation and research on the development trend of erosion gully in typical black soil area[J]. Soil and water conservation in China,2015,(10):63-69.
18. ZHong Y F,Benefit analysis of comprehensive management of soil and water conservation in small

watersheds in black soil region of Northeast China[D].Jilin University,2011.

19. ZHeng G X,Li X H,Ren L H,et al.Research and evaluation of soil and water conservation forest models in the rocky hilly area of western Liaoning[B].Soil and water conservation application technology,2007,5:7-9.
20. Lan J T,Fan H M,CHai Y,et al.Study on soil erosion characteristics of different land use types in low soil and rocky mountainous areas in western Liaoning[B].China Soil and Water Conservation SWCC, 2009, 8: 8-11.
21. Fan F,ZHang Y L,ZHu Z L,et al.Soil characteristics and remediation strategies of natural grassland in Tongliao City[A].Journal of Inner Mongolia University for Nationalities, 2002, 17(2): 130-135.

 https://doi.org/10.1051/e3sconf/202233801035

Literature Review on Farmland Landscape Pattern Change Analysis

Zhezhe Mu [1,2,3,*]

[1] Key Laboratory of Degraded and Unused Land Consolidation Engineering, Ministry of Natural Resources, xi'an 710021, China.
[2] Shaanxi Provincial Land Engineering Construction Group Co., Ltd., xi'an 710075, China.
[3] Institute of Land Engineering and Technology, Shaanxi Provincial Land Engineering Construction Group Co., Ltd., xi'an 710021, China.

Abstract. Farmland landscape pattern refers to the composition and spatial distribution of landscape elements in a certain spatial range. Farmland landscape pattern formation has natural, historical, cultural and other factors. Since the reform and opening up, China 's rapid socio-economic development, urbanization and a series of social development caused a large number of land occupation, farmland landscape pattern has undergone major changes. Domestic and foreign scholars based on natural geography, landscape ecology, combined with 3S technology, FRAGSTATES landscape index calculation method, from the aspects of landscape evolution process, landscape heterogeneity and diversity and landscape dynamics and driving factors correlation, analyzes the characteristics of regional landscape pattern change, and on this basis, analyzes the influence mechanism and correlation of landscape pattern succession. However, at present, most studies are based on the time axis, focusing on the changes of landscape patterns such as forests, wetland waters and towns. There are relatively few studies on the changes of farmland landscape patterns, and there are relatively few studies on the combination of time and space. Therefore, through the study and analysis of the characteristics of farmland landscape pattern change, the driving factors of landscape pattern change are known, and on this basis, the methods and ways of landscape pattern optimization are studied to provide scientific basis for constructing and optimizing farmland ecosystem, regional ecological network and protecting biodiversity.

Key words: Landscape; Landscape Pattern; Transfer Matrix; Landscape Index.

1. Introduction

Landscape is rich in connotation, including not only explicit content such as farmland, villages and ditches, but also implicit content such as farming culture, which is both a natural landscape and an artificial landscape. The formation of farmland landscape pattern is complicated due to historical, natural and cultural reasons. The scale, shape, structure and texture of farmland landscape are different, which is the result of the interaction of various complex natural and social conditions. Since the reform and opening up, with the rapid development of China ' s economy, the process of urbanization is accelerating, the population is constantly concentrated in urban areas, the contradiction between urban development and agricultural land is prominent, the development of' spread cake ' caused a lot of waste of land resources, high-quality farmland is occupied, so that the number of land for agricultural production is reduced and the quality of land is decreased, especially because the coordination and protection of resources and ecology are not fully considered in economic development, which makes the regional environment and ecological situation deteriorating. In addition, the implementation of household contract responsibility system has led to large-scale changes in farmland landscape pattern, the gradual disappearance of concentrated large-scale farmland landscape, the reduction of landscape diversity and the destruction of ecosystem. In the study of farmland landscape pattern in China, most scholars draw lessons from foreign farmland landscape theory and research results, too much emphasis on the impact and role of biological and natural processes on farmland landscape pattern, and weaken the impact of human social activities on farmland landscape pattern, attach importance to the application of foreign research theory and results, and ignore the social and cultural background of these theories. Studying the evolution of farmland landscape pattern can find the evolution law of farmland landscape pattern under the background of rapid social and economic development, and in-depth study of the mechanism of the evolution of farmland landscape pattern under this background, provide opinions and suggestions for the construction and optimization of farmland landscape

* Corresponding author: muzhezhe@126.com

https://doi.org/10.1051/e3sconf/202233801035

pattern, the construction and optimization of ecological network, the protection of ecological system and the management of agricultural production.

2. Research status

The introduction and development of landscape ecology in China are relatively late. Since the 1980s, landscape ecology has been introduced into China. Many scholars have actively studied and explored the content and theory of landscape ecology with landscape pattern as the main research content. From the perspective of time, Xiao Duning and Zhao Yi analyzed the changes of landscape pattern in the western suburbs of Shenyang in recent 30 years with landscape diversity index as the research index, which opened the precedent of research and application of landscape pattern in China. Tian Qifan, Yan Haiping selected landscape indicators (patch density, patch area, etc.) that can represent the characteristics of the study area to study the landscape pattern change of Xishan National Forest Park in Beijing and explore its influencing factors ; taking Liaohe wetland as the research object, Wang Xianli and Xiao Duning analyzed the changes of landscape pattern, and found that the main landscape pattern of Liaohe wetland was dense corridor system, which was greatly affected by human activities. Chen Xuebo analyzed and studied the advantages and disadvantages of landscape index from two aspects of landscape type level and overall landscape level. Guo Hongbin and Huang Yixiong, supported by 3S technology, used entropy method to analyze and evaluate different landscape patterns in Xiamen, and optimized its landscape structure and function. Ma Xiaofei selected remote sensing images of Ebinur Lake wetland in four periods to study and analyze the landscape pattern change of Ebinur Lake wetland and explore the relationship between landscape pattern change and ecological service value. Lin Junmin takes the landscape pattern change of Xiamen City as the research object, analyzes the change rule and provides suggestions for the landscape ecological construction of Xiamen City ; Supported by ArcGIS technology, Zhao Tingting studied and analyzed the change of farmland landscape pattern in Shunyi District of Beijing, and analyzed the influencing factors. Fu Meichen used historical literature analysis method to summarize the evolution law of general farmland landscape pattern.

In general, the research on landscape pattern in China is mainly from the perspective of natural geography and landscape ecology, and mainly focuses on the changes of landscape pattern such as forests, wetlands and cities. There are few studies on the changes of farmland landscape pattern. In terms of research scale, most of them are from the perspective of time, and summarize the evolution law of landscape pattern through the analysis of remote sensing images of a certain research area in the past 20 – 30 years.

3. Research method

Most of the researches on landscape pattern are based on the theory, knowledge and model of landscape ecology to construct landscape model and calculate landscape index to reflect the spatial and temporal characteristics of landscape pattern.

(1) Literature analysis. By reading and accumulating a large number of literature on landscape pattern changes, we learn the theoretical knowledge of landscape ecology, understand the meaning of landscape index, analyze the research progress on landscape pattern at home and abroad, and be familiar with the hot issues of current research to ensure the scientificity of this study.

(2) RS technology. RS (remote sensing) technology is a technology that detects and identifies targets from electromagnetic wave, visible light and infrared ray that is reflected or radiated by the target from a long distance. Modern remote sensing technology mainly includes information acquisition, transmission, storage and processing, and its core component is the remote sensor to obtain information.

(3) GIS technology. GIS (geographic information system) technology is a specific and very important spatial information system. It is a technical system for collecting, storing, managing, computing, analyzing, displaying and describing relevant geographic distribution data in the whole or part of the Earth 's surface (including the atmosphere) space with the support of computer hardware and software systems. For the processing of spatial data, most researchers use GIS as the support, which makes the complex traditional spatial tasks simple and easy, and can effectively analyze and explain the relationship between geographical features and spatial patterns.

(4) Selection and Calculation of Landscape Index. Landscape pattern index can quantitatively reflect the characteristics of landscape pattern. In the analysis of landscape spatial pattern, the selection and calculation of landscape index is a common method. Landscape index is usually calculated from three levels : plaque level, plaque type level and landscape level. Many scholars choose the landscape index which can represent the characteristics of the study area, calculate the landscape index on different scales, analyze the change, summarize the law, and combine the meaning expressed by the landscape index to obtain the characteristics of landscape pattern change. Because the analysis of patch level and type level often belong to a landscape type, the landscape pattern index of the two has corresponding repeatability. Therefore, in practical applications, scholars often merge patch level and type level into one class, which is simplified as landscape type level characteristics and landscape overall level.

(5) Transfer probability matrix. The transition probability matrix was proposed by Markov, a Russian mathematician, who discovered in the early 20th century that in the transition of some factors in a system, the nth result is only affected by the n-1 result, that is, only related to the current state, but not to the past state. Each element of the matrix is nonnegative, and the sum of the elements of each row is equal to 1. Each element is expressed by

probability and is transferred to each other under certain conditions, so it is called transfer probability matrix.

In the analysis of landscape pattern index, many researchers used this method to study the transformation characteristics, relationships and transformation ratios between various landscape types through the transfer matrix method.

4. Research progress

4.1 Research on related concepts

(1) Landscape. The term landscape is widely used, but there are also different understandings. Speaking of landscape, we usually understand it as natural existence, artificial construction, as well as urban, forest and farmland landscape, but most of them reflect the topography, geomorphology, scenery or comprehensive terrain characteristics of a geographical area. Landscape understanding can be from a narrow and broad perspective. Landscape in a narrow sense is what we usually call a landscape in a general sense, which is limited to a mesoscale range (tens of kilometers to hundreds of kilometers). Based on human sensory cognition, it reflects human subjective will, such as woodland, grassland, farmland and residence. The landscape in a broad sense is centered on organisms and has a wide range, which can be small to a single pond or large to a global scale. The most prominent feature is that it reflects the multi-scale and hierarchical structure of the ecological system. The landscape in this study is defined in a broad sense as a mosaic composed of heterogeneous landscape components (patches, corridors, and matrices).

(2) Landscape pattern. Landscape pattern generally refers to the composition and spatial distribution of landscape. With the deepening of landscape ecology research, Fu Bojie defined landscape pattern as the spatial distribution and combination characteristics of landscape components, that is, the size, shape and distribution of patches, which only contain spatial characteristics. Bi Junliang defines the landscape pattern as : the structural characteristics of landscape space, as the comprehensive embodiment of landscape diversity and heterogeneity in the study space, the mosaic of different landscape types. Yang Zhuo takes the landscape elements as the breakthrough point, and defines the landscape pattern as : the distribution of landscape elements dispersed or aggregated in space, which is the performance of the spatial distribution and combination characteristics of landscape components. Zhao Zhongjian believes that landscape pattern is the result of interaction between biological natural process and human disturbance, which is reflected by landscape elements such as patch shape, corridor composition and road network distribution. In this study, the landscape pattern is defined as : within a certain spatial range, the composition of the landscape elements and spatial distribution characteristics.

(3) Plaques. Patches, also known as patch or patch, are scale-dependent, different from the surrounding environment in nature or appearance, showing obvious boundaries, and have certain internal homogeneity of spatial entities. In a broad sense, patches can be alive, such as flora and fauna, forests, grasslands, etc. Can also be lifeless, such as residential areas, geological landforms. In the narrow sense, patches only indicate plant communities. The study of patches in landscape ecology is of great significance. The size of patches not only affects the survival of species, but also affects the necessary energy and nutrients for species survival. Generally, the larger the patch area is, the higher the species diversity is. The change of the number of patches reflects the existence and absence of animal and plant habitats. The decrease of the number of patches means the decrease of biological habitats. In this study, the concept of plaque reference Zhang Na and other scholars point of view, defined as : refers to the surrounding environment in appearance or nature is different, but also has a certain internal homogeneity of the space part.

(4) Corridor. Corridors refer to narrow areas that are distinct from both sides of the matrix, such as forest belts, rivers, riparian vegetation, highways, etc. Corridor can be regarded as a special form of plaque, and it is also a bridge and link connecting the plate. It is generally believed that the patches with length-width ratio at least 10-20, and the landscape components that are segmented and connected by patches can be considered as corridors. Corridor affects the connectivity between patches to a large extent, and also affects the exchange of nutrients and energy between patches, which plays an important role in the protection of biodiversity. In this study, corridors are defined as linear or zonal landscape elements with channel or barrier functions, which are important bridges and links to connect patches. It is different from both sides of the matrix, can be seen as a linear or banded plaque.

(5) Matrix. Substrate is also known as the background, basement, etc., is the widest range, the largest distribution area, the best connectivity, dominant landscape components. Matrix may be a single landscape component, or heterogeneous mixture, to a large extent determines the nature of the landscape, by affecting energy, species and species flow, leading landscape dynamics and functions. The concept of matrix in this study is : the background of landscape is the landscape elements with the best area connectivity and the strongest landscape control.

4.2 Research content

The research on landscape pattern mainly analyzes and describes the process of landscape evolution, landscape heterogeneity and diversity, and the correlation between landscape dynamics and driving factors. Pattern problem, heterogeneity problem and scale effect problem are several key areas of landscape structure research.

Pattern research includes landscape diversity analysis, fragmentation analysis, adjacency analysis and heterogeneity analysis. Although many people are trying to construct a new landscape pattern index, they all belong to the correction and improvement of the existing index, and there is no new description idea. For landscape pattern research from the perspective of time and space more. Through remote sensing images of different periods, with ENVI, ArcGIS and other software as technical support, the evolution law and influence mechanism of landscape pattern were studied and analyzed. From the perspective of space, the focus is on the statistical analysis of landscape spatial distribution changes and the calculation and analysis of landscape pattern index to understand the distribution characteristics of landscape pattern in space. Bi Junliang, Zhao Tingting, Zhang Guokun combined time and space to analyze the landscape pattern changes in the study area, and in-depth study of the driving forces leading to this change. However, the research on the driving factors of landscape pattern change is mainly qualitative or simple quantitative analysis of landscape pattern change in a single study area. There are few studies on different spatial scales and time scales. It is one of the main aspects to study the formation and evolution of agricultural landscape pattern from the perspectives of human geography, landscape ecology and aesthetics. In addition, some studies have begun to focus on the relationship between agricultural landscape and landscape architecture, or analyze the composition of agricultural landscape. Through the calculation of landscape index in landscape ecology, combined with the meaning expressed by landscape index, it reflects the change of landscape pattern in the study area, and discusses the mechanism of causing this change. At the same time, through the establishment of landscape model and ecological network model, it aims to provide reference for the optimization of landscape pattern and the construction of farmland ecosystem network.

5. Summarize

Studying the change of farmland landscape pattern plays an important role in constructing and optimizing farmland ecosystem. Chinese scholars mainly study the formation and evolution of landscape pattern from the perspectives of human geography, landscape ecology and aesthetics. It can be seen that the changes of landscape pattern, landscape heterogeneity and scale effect are the key issues in the study of landscape structure. The research contents of landscape pattern include landscape diversity analysis, fragmentation analysis, adjacency analysis and heterogeneity analysis. Most researchers from the perspective of time, through the selection and calculation of landscape index, analyze the transfer changes between the landscape elements, and analyze the mechanism of these changes. On this basis, combined with the background of social development, the purpose is to understand the change law of landscape pattern through research, in order to provide scientific reference for the construction and optimization of farmland landscape pattern, agricultural ecosystem and ecological network.

Acknowledgments

Project Fund : 2021WHZ0093 - Urban Landscape Ecological Effect Research and Demonstration Application.
DJNY2021-34- Internal Research Project of Shaanxi Land Engineering Construction Group.

Author Information : Mu Zhezhe (1994-), male, Qingyang, Gansu, master, assistant engineer, mainly engaged in land resources management, land economics, land engineering research.

References

1. Z L He. *Investigation of agricultural landscape in northeast area*. Beijing Jiaotong University. 2013,6 : 9-10.
2. M C Fu, Z Q Hu, G G Wu. *Analysis of farmland landscape pattern evolution*. Journal of Agricultural Engineering. 2005,6 (6) : 2-4.
3. Z J Zhao. *Study on land transfer way of farmland landscape spatial pattern evolution*. Anhui Agricultural Science. 2013, 41 (4) : 1795-1798.
4. D N Xiao, Y Zhao, Z W Sun, etc. *Study on landscape pattern change in west suburb of Shenyang*. Applied Ecology. 1990, 1 (1) : 75-84.
5. Q F Tian, H P Yan, Y Liu, etc. *Preliminary study on landscape pattern of Xishan National Forest Park in Beijing*. Journal of Beijing Forestry University. 1994, 03 : 8-16.
6. X L Xiao, D N Xiao, R C Bu, etc. *Landscape pattern analysis of Liaohe delta wetland. Journal of Ecology*. 1997, 03 : 317-323.
7. W B Chen, D N Xiao. *Landscape index classification, application and construction. Applied Ecology*. 2002, 13 (1) : 121 – 125.
8. H B Guo, Y X Huang, G F Ye, etc. *Evaluation and optimization of urban ecological function network in Xiamen*. Journal of Natural Resources. 2010, 01 : 71-79.
9. X F Ma. *Study on the relationship between landscape pattern change and ecological service value of Ebinur Lake wetland*. Xinjiang Normal University. 2017, 5 : 19-21.
10. Z M Lin. *Study on landscape dynamic change and ecological environment effect in Xiamen*. Fujian Normal University. 2007, 4 : 87-89.
11. T T Zhao, F R Zhang, Z G Niu, etc. *Study on farmland landscape pattern change in Shunyi District of Beijing*. Regional research and development. 2009,6 (3) : 2-6.
12. K L Chen. *Study on the evolution and optimization strategy of urban ecological landscape pattern in karst area - - Anshun as an example*. Huazhong University of Science and Technology. 2016.5 : 12-13.
13. B j Fu, L D Chen, K M Ma, etc. *Landscape ecology principles and applications* (Science Press, Beijing, 2001) .
14. J G Wu. *Landscape ecology-pattern, process, scale and grade (second edition)* (Higher Education Press, Beijing, 2007) .

15. N Zhang. *Landscape ecology* (Science Press, Beijing, 2014) .
16. J L Bi. *Analysis of forest landscape pattern changes and driving factors in the Yangtze River Basin from 1992 to 2012*. Huazhong Agricultural University. June 2014 : 13-14.
17. Z Yang. *Land use and landscape pattern change in typical agro-pastoral ecotone in Northeast China*. Beijing Forestry University. 20144 : 8 – 9.
18. Y Zhao, Y H Li. *Practical landscape ecology* (Science Press, Beijing, 2001) .
19. G K Zhang, J H Lu, K S Song, etc. *Landscape pattern changes in Zhenlai County of Jilin Province in recent 10 years*. Journal of Ecology 2012,32 (12) : 3958-3965.

https://doi.org/10.1051/e3sconf/202233801036

Population characteristics and influencing factors of terrestrial earthworms in Qinling Mountains

Jian Wang [1, 2*], Chenxi Yang [1, 2], Jingsi Li [1, 2]

[1] Institute of Land Engineering and Technology, Shaanxi Provincial Land Engineering Construction Group Co., Ltd., Xi'an Shaanxi China
[2] Key Laboratory of Degraded and Unused Land Consolidation Engineering, the Ministry of Nature and Resources, Xi'an Shaanxi China

Abstract: Earthworms can have an important effect on a variety of processes that determine soil fertility and play a very important role in natural ecosystems. The biomass and density of earthworms in 4 different land utilize types in the Qinling mountains were investigated using the wet funnel method. The relationship between the characteristics of earthworm populations characteristics and environmental factors were analysed, and the significant differences in soil earthworm density ($P < 0.05$) and fresh weight ($P < 0.05$) were discovered under different land utilize types, and all showed the highest value in orchard land, followed by woodland and grassland, in addition, the lowest was discovered in cultivated land. In addition, Pearson correlation analysis indicate that soil earthworm population characteristics was strongly negatively correlated with soil ammonium nitrogen (NH_4^+-N), and strongly positively correlated with fine root biomass. The clarified relationship between earthworm population characteristics and soil physical and chemical properties will help qualitatively predict and evaluate the ecological functions of terrestrial earthworms in Qinling mountains.

Keywords: Terrestrial Earthworms, Land Utilize Types, Soil Physical and Chemical Properties, Qinling Mountains

1. Introduction

As one of the most active soil animal groups in the formation of soil biological fertility, soil animals are not only the objects of protection but also important biological resources that can be used in the process of land use. Earthworms, as large animals in soil, belong to Annelida, Oligochaaeta, and Opithopora [1]. They play an extremely important role in organic matter decomposition, nutrient cycling and soil formation. They regulate soil material circulation and energy conversion processes through activities such as feeding, digestion, excretion, secretion, and burrowing, and are called "ecosystem engineers" [2]. Changes in land use patterns often lead to changes in the community structure of earthworms, and even lead to the invasion of alien species and the disappearance of native species of earthworms [3]. It can cause changes in microbial biomass and activity [4], change soil physical and chemical properties [5], and even cause plant community degradation [6].

Qinling Mountains is an important forest distribution area in my country. The forest area accounts for 75.2% of its total area. It is an important water conservation area in central my country and has extremely important functions in soil conservation and water conservation. However, since the 1970s and 1980s, due to intense human activities, the natural vegetation has been severely damaged, the landscape fragmentation degree is high, and the natural forest has been replaced by farmland, grassland and shrubs [7]. At present, the research on the characteristics of earthworm populations and their relationship with soil environment under different land use patterns in this area is still blank, and the influencing factors are still unclear. Based on this, this study selected four common land use types in the Qinling Mountains, namely cultivated land, garden land, forest land, and abandoned land. Using a combination of field investigation and biostatistical analysis, the study focused on the characteristics of earthworm populations under different land use types and their relationship with soil environmental factors. The purpose is to provide a theoretical basis for the utilization of soil animal resources and ecological environment protection in this area.

2. Materials and methods

2.1 Overview of the study area

The survey site is located in Huyi District, Xi'an City, Shaanxi Province, in the southwest of Xi'an City, Shaanxi Province, with Qinling Mountains in the south and Weihe River in the north. The area belongs to the warm tropical

* Corresponding author: 574435401@qq.com

semi-humid continental monsoon climate zone in North China, with four distinct seasons of cold, warm, dry and wet. The annual average frost-free period is 219 days, the average precipitation is 879 mm, and the annual average temperature is 13 °C. Light, heat, and water resources are abundant, showing the alternation of wet and dry seasons. In Huafeng Village, Huyi District, Xi'an City, Shaanxi Province, which is close to the Guanzhong Ring Road, the sample plots were selected according to the actual situation of local land use patterns. There are 4 land use types including cultivated land (corn land), garden land (pear orchard), forest land (secondary forest land) and abandoned land, and 4 plots are selected for each type, with a total of 16 plots .

2.2 Sampling and measurement

Using the quadrat combined with freehand separation method, and in August 2020, three representative quadrats were selected from the 16 plots of the above four different types of land use types, and the size of the quadrat was 50 cm × 50 cm × 20 cm (length × width × depth), remove the ground cover, dig with a shovel, carefully break the clods and place them on a white plastic sheet, pick the earthworms by hand, count the body length and fresh weight of the earthworms, and calculate the population density period Adult ratio.

Soil moisture content was determined by drying method; soil pH was determined by pH meter (Mi150); soil organic matter was determined by concentrated sulfuric acid-potassium dichromate external heating oxidation method; total nitrogen was determined by concentrated sulfuric acid digestion-semi-trace Kjeldahl method Determination; available phosphorus was determined by sodium bicarbonate extraction molybdenum antimony anti-colorimetric method; available potassium was determined by ammonia acetate extraction-flame photometer method; soil fine root biomass and soil bulk density were determined by drying method

2.3 Data analysis

One-way ANOVA and Duncan's multiple comparison method were used to analyze the influence of habitat on earthworm characteristics. When the significance level was greater than 0.05, it was considered to pass the significance test. The correlation analysis method was used to calculate the Pearson correlation coefficients between earthworm characteristics and soil pH, organic matter content, total nitrogen content, available potassium content, and available phosphorus content. The R language software was used for statistical processing and graphing of data.

3. Results and analysis

3.1 Differences in soil environmental factors under different land use types in qinling mountains

It can be seen from FIGURE 1 that under different land types, soil ammonium nitrogen ($F = 7.372$, $P = 0.0168$) and fine root biomass ($F = 201.1$, $P < 0.001$) were significantly different, while other soil physicochemical properties were not significantly different difference (all $P > 0.05$). Soil ammonium nitrogen was the smallest in situ and the largest in cultivated land. On the contrary, soil fine root biomass was the smallest in cultivated land and the largest in garden land.

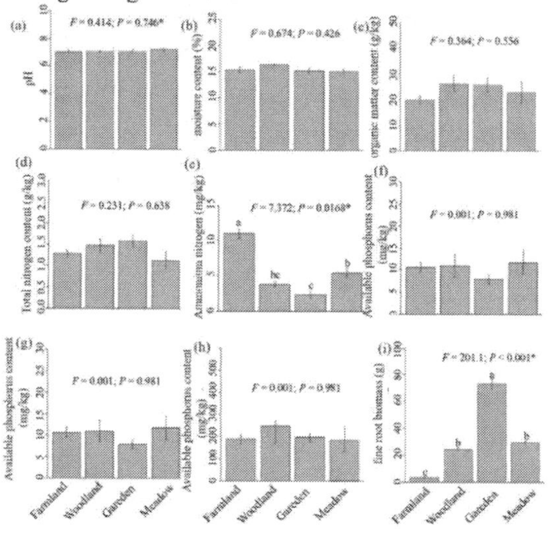

Figure 1. Analysis on the difference of soil environmental factors under different land use types

3.2 Differences in soil earthworm population characteristics under different land use types in qinling mountains

It can be seen from FIGURE 2 that there were significant differences in soil earthworm density ($F = 1.17$, $P = 0.03$) and fresh weight ($F = 4.651$, $P = 0.048$) under different land types. The density of soil earthworms was in the order of garden > woodland & grassland > cultivated land, and the fresh weight of soil earthworms also showed the order of garden > woodland & grassland > cultivated land.

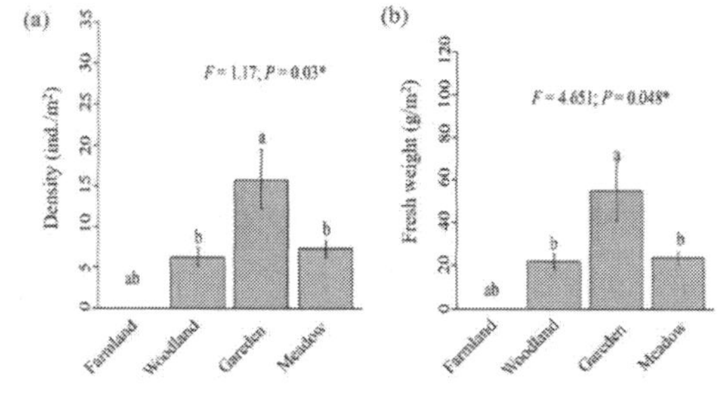

Figure 2. Analysis on the difference of soil earthworm population characteristics under different land use types

3.3 Correlation analysis between soil earthworm population characteristics and soil environmental factors

As shown in FIGURE 3, there was a strong positive correlation between soil earthworm population density and earthworm fresh weight; soil earthworm population characteristics were strongly negatively correlated with soil ammonium nitrogen, and strongly positively correlated with fine root biomass. In addition, fine root biomass was strongly negatively correlated with soil ammonium nitrogen.

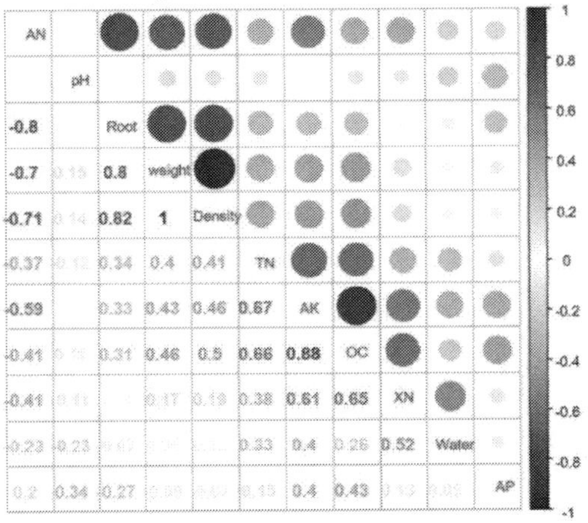

Figure 3. Correlation analysis of earthworm population characteristics and soil environmental factors

4. Discussion and conclusions

The soil environment can also affect the diversity of earthworm communities. Previous studies have found that differences in environmental elements will affect the physical and chemical environment of the soil, resulting in changes in the relationship between earthworms and microorganisms and other symbiotic and symbiotic organisms [8,9], which in turn lead to changes in earthworm population density, distribution and other characteristics [10]. Among them, land use, vegetation type and structure are the most important influencing factors. The research on the correlation between earthworm diversity and soil environment mainly focuses on the significant correlation between soil type, texture, farmland crops and earthworm density and biomass. sex. The present study also found significant differences in earthworm population density and fresh weight under different land types, confirming previous studies.

14 native species of earthworms were recorded in Tabasco, Mexico. The individual density and biomass of earthworms were only significantly affected by soil type, but had no significant correlation with other soil factors [11]. In the Palouse prairie wetland in the United States, there is a significant positive correlation between clay content and earthworm density and biomass, and the increase of sand content will significantly reduce the density and biomass of earthworms [12]. In some areas of my country, such as Qianjiang, Hubei, researches on earthworms and soil environment were carried out earlier [13], and then preliminary discussions were also carried out in Handan and Quzhou [14], Liaodong and Jiaodong [15]. There was a very significant positive correlation between earthworm density and soil productivity, organic carbon, total nitrogen, available phosphorus and porosity [16]. A total of 3 earthworm species were recorded in the butterfly-shaped depression of the Sanjiang Plain of Heilongjiang Province, namely the Aisensis chinensis, Norden Aisensis and Harbin Aisensis. The density of earthworms decreased in sequence in island forest, shrub and swamp meadow. The flooding water level and soil moisture content are the key factors affecting the distribution of earthworms in the dish-shaped depression. Meanwhile, the distribution of earthworms is significantly positively correlated with the soil total organic carbon content, pH and total nitrogen content [17]. These findings reflect the significant effects of dryland soil pH, organic matter, total nitrogen, available phosphorus content and wetland moisture content on earthworm diversity. However, in this study, it was found that soil earthworm population characteristics were only significantly correlated with soil available nitrogen and fine root biomass, but had nothing to do with other soil environmental factors.

In summary, the study found that there were significant differences in soil earthworm density and fresh weight under different land types. All are presented as Garden Land > Woodland & Grassland > Cultivated Land. There was a strong positive correlation between soil earthworm population density and earthworm fresh weight; soil earthworm population characteristics had a strong negative correlation with soil ammonium nitrogen, and a strong positive correlation with fine root biomass.

Acknowledgments

This work was financially supported by Shaanxi Provincial Land Engineering Construction Group internal research project (DJNY2021-22) fund.

References

1. Xu Qin, Xiao Nengwen. China's terrestrial earthworm [M]. Beijing: China Agricultural Press, 2011.
2. Zhang Weixin, Chen Dima, Zhao Cancan. The role of earthworms in ecosystems [J]. Biodiversity Biodiversity, 2007(2): 38-49.
3. Lavelle, P. (1988). Earthworm activities and the soil system. Biology and fertility of soils, 6(3), 237-251.
4. McLean, MA, Migge-Kleian, S. and Parkinson, D. (2006) Earthworm Invasions of Ecosystems Devoid of Earthworms: Effects on Soil Microbes. Biological Invasions, 8, 1257-1273.
5. Lavelle, P. (1983). The structure of earthworm communities. In Earthworm ecology (pp. 449-466). Springer, Dordrecht.
6. Frelich, L. E., Hale, C. M., Reich, P. B., Holdsworth, A. R., Scheu, S., Heneghan, L., & Bohlen, P. J. (2006). Earthworm invasion into previously earthworm-free temperate and boreal forests. In Biological invasions belowground: earthworms as invasive species (pp. 35-45). Springer, Dordrecht.
7. Kang Yan. Spatial distribution pattern and ecological conservation strategy of vegetation water conservation function in Qinling Mountains [D]: [Master's Thesis]. Xi'an: Northwest University, 2005.

8. Bini, D., Santos, CAD, Carmo, KBD, et al. (2013) Effects of Land Use on Soil Organic Carbon and Microbial Pro-cesses Associated with Soil Health in Southern Brazil. European Journal of Soil Biology, 55 , 117-123.
9. Li Wei, Cui Lijuan, Zhao Xinsheng, et al. The structure and diversity of soil animal community in Taihu Lake riparian wetlands [J]. Chinese Journal of Ecology, 2013, 35(4): 944-955.
10. Raw, F. (1959). Estimating earthworm populations by using formalin. Nature, 184(4699), 1661-1662.
11. Spurgeon, D. J., Weeks, J. M., & Van Gestel, C. A. (2003). A summary of eleven years progress in earthworm ecotoxicology: The 7th international symposium on earthworm ecology Cardiff· Wales· 2002. Pedobiologia, 47(5-6), 588-606..
12. Fragoso, C., & Lavelle, P. (1992). Earthworm communities of tropical rain forests. Soil Biology and Biochemistry, 24(12), 1397-1408.
13. Bouché, M. B. (1983). The establishment of earthworm communities. In Earthworm ecology (pp. 431-448). Springer, Dordrecht.
14. Zhang Ning, Liao Yan, Sun Fulai, et al. Characteristics of earthworm populations under different land use patterns and their relationship with soil biological fertility [J]. Soil Journal, 2012(2): 162-170.
15. Zhang Yufeng, Wu Yupeng, Sun Qian, et al. Research on earthworm biodiversity in Shandong Peninsula and Liaodong Peninsula [J]. Journal of China Agricultural University, 2014, 19(4): 67-73.
16. Tang Zheng, Li Jiguang, Li Hui, et al. Changes of earthworms and soil fertility under water and fertilizer management mode in facility vegetable fields [J]. Journal of Ecology, 2015(8): 136-140.
17. Cao Siping, Tan Can, Wang Huan, et al. Distribution and influencing factors of terrestrial earthworms in Nanniwan wetlands [J]. Resources and Environment in Arid Regions, 2018, 32(4): 80-84.

Research on Monitoring Information Management of Deep Foundation Pit Engineering Based on BIM Technology

Peng Wang [1,2,3,4,*], Yan Li [1,2,3,4] and Na Wang [1,2,3,4]

[1] Shaanxi Provincial Land Engineering Construction Group Co., Ltd., Xi'an, China.
[2] Institute of Land Engineering and Technology, Shaanxi Provincial Land Engineering Construction Group Co., Ltd., Xi'an, China.
[3] Key Laboratory of Degraded and Unused Land Consolidation Engineering, the Ministry of Natural Resources, China.
[4] Shaanxi Provincial Land Consolidation Engineering Technology Research Center, China.

Abstract. With the rapid development of construction industry, there are more and more deep and large foundation pit projects with complex architectural environment and geological conditions. Deformation monitoring in deep foundation pit as a basic element of engineering quality assurance is becoming more and more important. At present, the management and expression form of monitoring data in deep foundation pit still stays in the stage of two-dimensional form and curve expression, and it can not reflect the deformation of deep foundation pit in real, fast and effective way.Take the 3#, 4# high-rise residential and underground garage project of a college in Xi'an as an example. Based on Revit software, taking BIM technology and Revit API as the theoretical basis, and taking Microsoft Visual Studio 2012 and Autodesk Revit 2014 as the development platform, we use C# programming language to carry out the two development of information management module for deep foundation pit engineering monitoring. Combining BIM technology with monitoring data management of deep foundation pit, the information management mode of monitoring data of deep foundation pit is improved, which makes express expression of deep foundation pit construction monitoring more rapid and effective, and has guiding significance for safety construction of deep foundation pit engineering.

Key words: BIM; deep foundation pit engineering; monitoring management; Revit API; secondary development.

1. Project overview

With the rapid economic development, the construction scale of cities is getting bigger and bigger, and the number of super large-scale cities is also increasing. With the rapid growth of the urban population, in order to meet people's requirements for the living environment, the basements of high-rise and super high-rise buildings are getting deeper and bigger. According to the regulations, the excavation depth of more than 5 meters or the basement of three floors or more is called a deep foundation pit project, and its construction safety and construction quality must be strictly guaranteed.

Through the summary, analysis and research of many deep foundation pit projects, we can know that the combination of deep foundation pit engineering theory, construction experience and deformation monitoring during construction is the way to correctly guide the design and construction of deep foundation pit engineering. For large and medium-sized deep foundation pit projects with relatively complicated geological conditions or deep foundation pit projects with strict requirements on the environmental impact of surrounding buildings, it is often difficult to draw lessons from the same or similar deep foundation pit engineering construction experience, and it is also difficult to be theoretically accurate Quantitative analysis and prediction of the deformation of deep foundation pits. If the construction plan of a deep foundation pit project is designed and determined only based on the survey report before construction and the laboratory's geotechnical test parameters, there are too many uncertain factors. Through the summary and analysis of a large number of deep foundation pit engineering accidents, it can be seen that some units always believe that the foundation pit project as a temporary project does not need to invest too much capital and manpower, and ignores the importance of deformation monitoring during the construction of deep foundation pit projects. In the end, serious engineering accidents were caused. Common accidents such as the instability of foundation pit supporting structure, uneven settlement of surrounding buildings and roads, destruction of underground pipelines and facilities, and even casualties. Therefore, the deformation monitoring of the soil properties, the supporting structure of the foundation pit, and the surrounding building road environment during the construction process has obviously become an indispensable part of the construction process of the deep foundation pit engineering, and the deformation monitoring of the deep foundation pit engineering is regarded as An information technology is a necessary measure to ensure the quality of construction while avoiding accidents. Carrying out rigorous deformation monitoring for deep foundation pit projects is also accumulating valuable experience for the design and construction of more complex deep foundation pit projects.

It is proposed to build 3#, 4# high-rise residential buildings and underground garages of a college in Xi'an, which are located in the urban area of Xi'an, Shaanxi

* Corresponding author: 694298560@qq.com

https://doi.org/10.1051/e3sconf/202233801037

Province, adjacent to the secondary main road of the city to the south. The terrain of the proposed site is relatively flat, the geomorphic unit is Huangtuliangwa, and the project ±0.00 corresponds to an absolute elevation of 419.90m. The plane size of the foundation pit: 67.275m at the widest point from east to west and 57.06m at the widest point from north to south. The perimeter of the bottom line of the foundation pit is 248.67.0m, the actual side slope height of the foundation pit is about 7.0m, the garage is about 12.12m, and the local area is about 14.12m. The elevation of the excavation base of the foundation pit is -7.37m for the main building and -13.27m for the garage. It is planned to build 3# and 4# high-rise residential buildings with 33 floors and 1 basement.

2. Engineering model creation

Establish a BIM model based on the CAD drawings provided by the construction party, and import the CAD drawings into the Revit software to assist in modeling before creating the model. There are two ways for Revit software to import CAD drawings: The first way is to directly import the selected CAD drawings into Revit as the base drawing of the created model through the "Import CAD" command. This command is suitable for situations where you are not sure whether the CAD drawings are modified; The second is to import CAD drawings into Revit through the "Link CAD" command. This command is suitable for CAD design changes. If the source file is changed, the linked CAD drawing will also be changed accordingly. Once the source file is deleted or its location If there is a change, the corresponding CAD base drawing in Revit will be lost.

Step 1: CAD construction plan processing and import. This project uses the "Import CAD" command to import drawings as a base map for creating a deep foundation pit model. Since general CAD drawings are the basis for construction, component annotations, text descriptions, etc. are more detailed and complicated. In the Revit modeling process, these complex instructions will increase the burden on computer hardware, and the software will freeze or even crash, which will seriously affect Modeling efficiency. Therefore, before importing CAD drawings, delete unnecessary text, lines, and blocks, leaving only the axis and key nodes, and perform efficient modeling by automatically capturing the axis and key points. Use the "Import CAD" command in Revit to import the processed CAD construction plan. The import unit is uniformly selected in millimeters to facilitate project management.

Step 2: Positioning and creation of the deep foundation pit model. The ground surface is established through site options. The geological model is created using the floor slab in the Revit model. Five types of floor slabs with different thicknesses are created according to the engineering survey report, and different material attributes are assigned to replace the five different soil qualities within the excavation range of the foundation pit. Use the imported CAD drawings to locate the excavation boundary of the foundation pit, and use the building floor option to set the elevation to negative to create the excavated foundation pit model.

Use the "Pit Family Library Plug-in" to quickly load specific foundation pit engineering supporting structure families such as slope protection piles, plain soil compaction piles, and anchor rods. Here is how to display a pop-up window from which to select and apply the AIP Proceedings template paragraph styles.

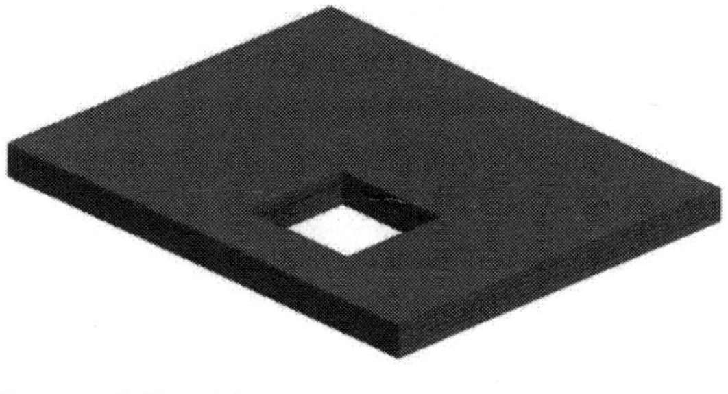

Figure 1. Soil model

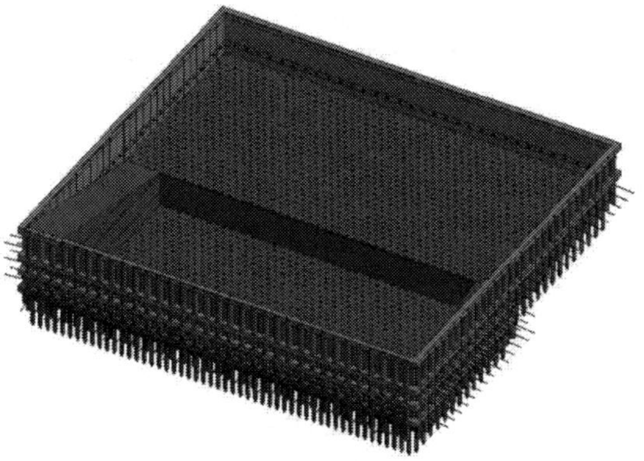

Figure 2. Foundation pit support structure

Step 3: Create a model of the surrounding environment of the foundation pit project. After the foundation pit model is created, according to the positioning of the surrounding buildings in the construction plan, follow the model creation steps to create the surrounding environment model of the deep foundation pit project.

Step 4: Arrangement of deformation monitoring points. According to the regulations, the horizontal displacement monitoring points on the top of the foundation pit slope are arranged. The horizontal displacement monitoring points on the top of the foundation pit slope are arranged on the crown beam of the foundation pit slope support structure, and are arranged along the periphery of the foundation pit. Monitoring points should be arranged at the sunny corners, the horizontal and vertical spacing of monitoring points should not be greater than 20m, and the number of monitoring points on each side should not be less than 3. According to the above requirements, a total of 16 foundation pit horizontal displacement monitoring points (JKJC1-JKJC16) are arranged in the foundation pit engineering model created above. The actual monitoring point layout should be appropriately adjusted according to the site conditions, and the layout should be made as far as possible when the requirements of the specification are

https://doi.org/10.1051/e3sconf/202233801037

met. The monitoring points are convenient for deformation observation.

Figure 3. Monitoring point layout

Step 5: Parameterized setting of deformation monitoring points. After the layout of the deformation monitoring points of the foundation pit is completed, the location of the monitoring points shall be numbered according to the different monitoring items of the foundation pit engineering, and the early warning value and alarm value shall be set.

3. Create a monitoring information management plug-in

To realize the information management of deep foundation pit monitoring, the created plug-in program needs to realize the following functions: 1. The plug-in can identify and extract the point number of the deformation monitoring point in the three-dimensional deep foundation pit model; The deformation monitoring data of the deep foundation pit is imported into the deep foundation pit model, and the monitoring date and monitoring data in the Excel file can be recognized; 3. The plug-in contains an algorithm for processing the deformation monitoring data of the deep foundation pit, and the deformation of the deep foundation pit is calculated by the algorithm 4. If the deformation of the monitoring point exceeds the specified value, the deformation of the monitoring point will be displayed in the form of a dialog box and an alarm interface will pop up; 5. Using the visual advantages of BIM technology, deep The color of the excessively deformed point in the foundation pit model changes in the real view mode. Perform programming design on the secondary development platform. The specific steps are as follows:

Step 1: Create a new class library project with the help of Visual Studio 2012 environment, and rename the project as "Monitoring Management". After creating the project, you need to reference the interface group files Revit API.dll and Revit APIUI.dll in Revit. After the reference is successful, change the "copy local" in the reference properties of these two files to flase, otherwise a large number of .dll files will be copied Go to the run directory. The purpose of citing these two interface group files is to extract the interface for access to the Revit API.

Step 2: Add the reference to the namespace needed to write the plug-in program. The namespace is actually a specific memory area named by the developer. According to the specific needs of the user's secondary development, some named space domains are specified, and the global entities of the monitoring and management plug-in programming are placed in each namespace to prevent Confused with other global entities.

The namespace cited in this article mainly includes Revit API, Windows Forms controls, and input and output streams. The programming statements are as follows:

```
using System;
using System.Collections.Generic;
using System.Linq;
using System.Text;
using System.Threading.Tasks;
using Autodesk.Revit.DB;
using Autodesk.Revit.UI;
using Autodesk.Revit.UI.Selection;
using Autodesk.Revit.ApplicationServices;
using Autodesk.Revit.DB.Structure;
using System.Windows.Forms;
......
```

Step 3: Add command attributes to the main program, set the update mode and transaction mode of the control command before writing the main program of each function. The programming statement is as follows:

```
[Autodesk.Revit.Attributes.Transaction(Autodesk.Revit.
Attributes.TransactionMode.Manual)]
[Autodesk.Revit.Attributes.regeneration(Autodesk.Revit.
Attributes.regenerationOption.Manual)]
```

The main part of this program is an external command, which is implemented by creating a new class derived from the IEternal Command interface and reloading the IExteral Command. execute() method.

Step 4: Write the main program that realizes each function. After the plug-in is running, it needs to be able to identify the point number of the deformation monitoring point in the deep foundation pit engineering model.

Step 5: After the completion of the main behavior program, the Visual Studio 2012 platform is required to compile the source code. If the source code fails to compile, return to the program to modify the problem code; if the compile succeeds, the software automatically generates the plug-in program and test results.

Step 6: After the compilation is successful, load the plug-in into the Revit software. The program is successfully compiled, VS2012 will automatically generate test results and plug-in programs, start the Revit software to open the deep foundation pit model containing complete model information, use Revit's add-on module function to load the generated plug-in file into the software, and load and run on the model Plug-in program.

This is the paragraph spacing that occurs when you use the [ENTER] key.

4. Application of monitoring management module

The horizontal displacement monitoring data of the foundation pit of this project is measured by a total station. All the monitoring data in txt format will be exported through the computer, and the monitoring data will be extracted and exported to an Excel table. The application plug-in is loaded in the following order: "Add-on module" →"External tools"→"Add-In Manage (Manual) "→

" Loaded commands " 、 " Loaded Application " → "Monitoring management.dll。

Click on "Run" Button The displacement monitoring dialog box pops up, select "Data", click the "Import xl" button to import the monitoring data into the plug-in; select "Control value" to input the deformation control value of the deep foundation pit project's horizontal displacement of 15mm, speed 2mm, The warning value is 10mm. After all the data and control values are loaded, click the "Apply" button. If the deformation monitoring data is normal and the deformation of each monitoring point does not exceed the deformation control value, no dialog box will pop up to prompt; if the data of the monitoring point exceeds the deformation Control value, a warning dialog box will pop up, and the cumulative displacement of the monitoring point and the deformation rate at the two monitoring time points will be displayed at the same time.

Close the warning dialog box and return to the 3D view mode of the foundation pit model. According to the setting of the module program, when the deformation of the monitoring point exceeds the warning value, the color of the monitoring point changes to yellow. At this time, the monitoring points in the deep foundation pit model that exceed the warning value change from normal color to yellow as a warning. According to regulations, the entrusting unit shall be notified immediately, and the entrusting unit shall report to relevant departments such as design and construction and assist in analyzing the cause, and encrypt it at the same time. Monitoring to prevent accidents.

5. Conclusion

In this paper, the entry point is to improve the management expression of traditional foundation pit monitoring information, based on the secondary development process of Revit software, and based on Revit API technology, combining traditional foundation pit engineering monitoring data management with BIM technology. The information management of foundation pit engineering monitoring based on Revit software has been realized, and the conclusions obtained are as follows:

(1) Create a BIM model to facilitate the construction personnel to understand the complex site conditions. Based on the specifications, fully consider the convenience and feasibility of the deformation monitoring process, reasonably arrange the deformation monitoring points, select the optimal monitoring route, and reduce the human error of the monitoring process .

(2) Through the analysis and research of RevitAPI, VS2012 and RevitSDK are used as secondary development tools, and Revit2014 is used as the platform to realize the rapid loading of parameterized families in deep foundation pit engineering; create a "monitoring management" plug-in to realize deep foundation pit Import, calculation and result display of engineering monitoring data in BIM model.

(3) Apply the foundation pit monitoring information management module to the actual project, use BIM technology to change the monitoring data management method of the deep foundation pit project, change the two-dimensional table and curve representation form of the monitoring report, and display the monitoring in a three-dimensional manner in the BIM model As a result, the information management of foundation pit engineering monitoring was realized, and the project feasibility of the foundation pit monitoring information management module based on BIM technology was verified.

References

1. Wilkins R, Bastin G, Chrzanowski A, et al. A FULLY AUTOMATED SYSTEM FOR MONITORING PIT WALL DISPLACEMENTS[J]. Mining Engineering, 2003.
2. Hashash Y M A, Liu L Y, Ghaboussi J, et al. New Technologies for Tracking Urban Excavation Progress and Estimating Deformations[C]//Geoshanghai International Conference. 2006:336-341.
3. Matveenko V P, Fedorova V A, Shardakov I N. Theoretical justification of the possibility of constructing a fiber-optic earth surface deformation monitoring system[J]. Mechanics of Solids, 2013, 48(5):520-524.
4. Vaziri A, Moore L, Ali H. Monitoring systems for warning impending failures in slopes and open pit mines[J]. Natural Hazards, 2010, 55(2):501-512.
5. Eastman, Charles|And Others. An Outline of the Building Description System. Research Report No. 50.[J]. Architectural Drafting, 1974:23.
6. Monteiro A, Martins J P. A survey on modeling guidelines for quantity takeoff-oriented BIM-based design[J]. Automation in Construction, 2013, 35(11):238-253.
7. Nederveen G A V, Tolman F P. Modelling multiple views on buildings ☆[J]. Automation in Construction, 1992, 1(3):215-224.
8. Malherek E, Laing G. Finer Points of Building Information Modeling[J]. Heating/piping/air Conditioning Engineering, 2011.
9. Smith D K, Tardiff M. Building Information Modeling: A Strategic Implementation Guide for Architects, Engineers, Constructors, and Real Estate Asset Managers[M]. Wiley, 2009.

Research status of different improvement measures for saline-alkali land

Jian Li [1,2,3,*]

[1] Key Laboratory of Degraded and Unused Land Consolidation Engineering, Ministry of Natural Resources, xi'an 710021, China.
[2] Shaanxi Provincial Land Engineering Construction Group Co., Ltd., xi'an 710075, China.
[3] Institute of Land Engineering and Technology, Shaanxi Provincial Land Engineering Construction Group Co., Ltd., xi'an 710021, China.

Abstract: Cultivated land is the fundamental guarantee of food security, and saline-alkali land affects the quality of cultivated land to varying degrees. It is of great significance to study saline-alkali land improvement measures to solve the problem of saline-alkali land utilization, promote the healthy development of agriculture and animal husbandry, and improve the quality of cultivated land. The author has sorted out the relevant literature and reports on the improvement methods and technologies of saline-alkali land at home and abroad in recent years, and introduced the status and effects of different improvement measures for saline-alkali land from four types: chemical improvement measures, physical improvement measures, water conservancy improvement technology and biological improvement measures. It provides a theoretical basis for the study of governance and saline-alkali land improvement measures.

Key words: Saline-alkali land; improvement measures; research status.

1. Introduction

Saline-alkali land is a general term for saline soil and alkaline soil. Its low organic matter content and poor soil fertility will seriously affect the survival and growth of plants, which has become a worldwide problem. In China, with population growth and the advancement of urbanization, arable land has become a precious and limited resource, and the existence of saline-alkali land has led to a decline in the quality of a large amount of arable land. At present, more than 20% of China's arable land is exposed to varying degrees of salinity. The influence of alkalization, with its large area and wide distribution, further stimulates the problem of contradiction between man and land. Therefore, it is an urgent problem to take effective measures to improve the salinized soil and make it can be effectively used.

In order to develop and utilize saline-alkali land, it is first necessary to find an effective method for controlling saline-alkali land. For a long time, how to reduce the degree of soil salinization, improve soil fertility, and use effective improvement measures to create a suitable soil ecological environment has been the focus of many experts and scholars [1]. The improved measures and mechanism research have achieved remarkable results, and some measures have achieved good results in practical applications and have been promoted [2]. Among them, the method of comprehensive management is the most effective, mainly as follows: prevention first and equal emphasis on prevention and control; comprehensive management and water conservancy first; unified planning and measures according to local conditions; In recent years, in addition to using traditional methods to transform soil, many experts and scholars have also begun to extend and transfer to the direction of cultivating salt-tolerant plants [3], and develop new crops and new technologies to improve the management of saline-alkali soils [4]. At present, the traditional improvement measures can be roughly divided into four major aspects: physics, chemistry, water conservancy and biology.

2. Chemical Improvement Measures

Chemical improvement measures have a wide range of applications, mainly using chemical reagents in saline-alkali land to promote salt leaching, thereby improving soil structure. The main types of soil conditioners for saline-alkali land improvement include peat, organic fertilizer, perlite, vermiculite, humic acid, compound fertilizer, water retention agent, soil thickener, trace elements, bacteria, etc. The main types of saline-alkali land improvement solutions are Malay Acid anhydride, wood acetic acid, amino acid, humic acid, black diamond, trace elements, etc. According to the research results, the application of phosphogypsum can effectively improve the soil structure, and the application of polymerized

* Corresponding author: 601515179@qq.com

aluminum ferric sulfate, phosphogypsum, and desulfurized gypsum in saline-alkali soil can reduce soil pH and total alkalinity, eliminate soda salt, accelerate the desalination rate of saline-alkali soil, and reduce the generation of exchange of sodium and alkalinity, thereby improving the physical shape of the soil. However, heavy metal elements in amendments often enter the soil along with beneficial components. These metal elements are not easy to migrate, remain for a long time, have strong concealment, and are highly toxic [5]. On the one hand, they may be absorbed by plants, affecting the normal growth and development of plants. development, and they may enter the food chain, threatening the health of humans and the reproduction of other animals. On the other hand, they may enter groundwater with surface runoff, posing a threat to environmental safety and causing irreversible pollution. Therefore, in the process of applying chemical modifiers, it is necessary to ensure an appropriate amount.

3. Physical Improvement Measures

The physical measures of saline-alkali land improvement mainly adjust the interaction between water and salt in the soil by changing the physical structure of the soil, and finally achieve the purpose of inhibiting soil evaporation and improving the effect of salt leaching and infiltration. It mainly includes improvement methods such as leveling the land, deep plowing, raising the terrain, irrigation and drainage system flushing and desalination, and sand pressing. Salt washing is to dissolve the salt in the soil through irrigation, and use the water infiltration process to discharge the soluble salt on the soil surface to the lower soil layer, and finally discharge the salt in combination with the drainage system [6]. Cutting the bottom and leveling the land can make the water irrigated to the surface and the surface water generated by rainfall infiltrate evenly, reducing the damage of salinity and alkali . In deep ploughing, the soil with more surface salt is turned to the lower layer, and the soil with less salt in the lower layer is turned to the surface again [7]. Deep plowing and drying can cut off soil capillaries, reduce soil water evaporation, improve soil activity and fertility, and enhance soil permeability, thereby effectively controlling soil salt return. With the research and development of materials science, the method of using zeolite and ground cover to improve saline-alkali land has appeared. Zeolite has a wide range of sources, low cost, non-toxic and harmless, and has strong adsorption capacity and ion exchange capacity [8]. Adding zeolite to soil can not only play a role in maintaining fertilizer and supplying fertilizer, but also reduce soil alkalization. and salinity, and buffers the pH of the soil. The advantage of the physical improvement method is that it can effectively reduce the salt content in the soil, with high speed and high efficiency.

The intelligent transmission and data management control system of the Internet of Things is gradually applied in the management and construction of saline-alkali land management and utilization. Use information technology to scientifically manage and control project cost control, construction, and maintenance of demonstration bases, connect the Internet of Things through testing equipment, use professional software and more advanced methods to process the collected data, and realize the information management of saline-alkali land sorting and utilization. Coverage is an important quantitative index to measure the structure of plant community. The traditional measure of grassland vegetation coverage adopts the grid method, and now the digital image method is being promoted. It has the advantages of small error, high accuracy and simple operation, and can be applied Based on quadratic measurements of grassland vegetation coverage. For large-area vegetation coverage measurement, remote sensing images or high-altitude digital aerial photography can be used to estimate grassland vegetation coverage more accurately and conveniently. Therefore, the digital image method is expected to become the main method of grassland vegetation coverage measurement in the future.

4. Water Conservancy Improvement Technology

The water conservancy improvement technology mainly adopts the drainage method, which discharges the salt in the soil from the farmland, reduces the soil salt content, and provides a good water and salt environment for the growth of crops. At present, the main forms of farmland drainage include underground pipes, shafts, and open ditch drainage, etc., and underground underground pipes are mostly used to drain salt. According to the principle of "salt comes with water, salt goes with water; salt comes with water, water disperses salt and stays", it makes the salt in the soil drain away with water, and controls the groundwater level below the critical depth to achieve soil desalination and The purpose of preventing secondary salinization is to improve the physical environment of the topsoil. Concealed pipe drainage has the advantage of occupying less cultivated land, reducing bridges and culverts and facilitating mechanized farming [9]. Han Jichang et al. summarized the practice and skillfully used the scientific mechanism of water-salt balance. By laying out the water storage ditch system, adjusting the water level change of the storage ditch to accelerate the convective and dispersing effect of salt, and developed a "storage" as the core. "The technology of water storage and salt pressure in saline-alkali land realizes the dynamic circulation between water and soil to press salt [10].

5. Biological Improvement Measures

Among the various technologies of saline-alkali land treatment, biological measures are generally considered to be the most effective improvement methods, mainly by planting salt-tolerant plants in saline-alkali land, leaching soil salt to the lower soil through irrigation, and controlling the salt below the plant root system Soil layer, improve the soil structure of the plough layer, increase soil fertility, and gradually improve soil physical and chemical properties. The development of salt-tolerant plants can not only improve soil productivity and reduce the cost of using high-quality irrigation water, but also contribute to a virtuous cycle of agroecology and environmental improvement in saline environments [11]. Since the 1930s, scholars in many countries have begun to pay attention to the study of salt tolerance of plants. Since the 1980s, my country has also carried out research and screening on the salt tolerance of plants, and has achieved certain results. Many scholars have successfully planted salt-tolerant crops such as Casuarina, Populus euphratica, Seabuckthorn, Zhumei Begonia, Sand jujube and other salt-tolerant tree species, as well as Suaeda salsa and Salvia chinensis in saline-alkali land. While planting salt-tolerant crops in saline-alkali land, screening of halophytes was also carried out [12], such as the cultivation of salt-tolerant rice, potato, wheat, sorghum, tomato and other varieties. There are also studies on the improvement of different saline-alkali wastelands using Xingxingcao and D. koreanica, and the benefits of soil improvement are also very significant. These studies have greatly contributed to biological measures for saline-alkali land improvement. At the same time, combining planting and aquaculture to improve saline-alkali land with biological cycle as a mechanism has good economic benefits [13].

Microorganisms are the most active components in soil and play an important role in soil occurrence, development and development. Some studies have shown that the microbial fertilizer can change the physical and chemical properties and biological species of the soil, the application of microbial inoculants can promote the number and species of soil heavy microorganisms, and the organic acids generated in the metabolic activities of microorganisms can affect the alkalinity of saline-alkali soils. Neutralization, a variety of enzymes produced by the activities of microorganisms can promote the decomposition and synthesis of soil organic matter, and reduce the fixation of phosphorus and potassium in the soil, which is conducive to the transformation of insoluble phosphorus and potassium. Some studies have used microbial fertilizers to replace traditional chemical fertilizers, and carried out afforestation tests on soda saline-alkali land. The results show that the plant survival rate and preservation rate of microbial fertilizers have been improved, and microbial fertilizers have effectively improved saline-alkali land and showed long-term effectiveness[14].

6. Conclusion

Most of the technical measures for the improvement of saline-alkali land are to reduce the soluble salt content in the soil through desalination and salt removal. Methods such as water conservancy engineering measures, agricultural farming measures, halophytes, and chemical modifiers have been widely used. Although chemical improvement measures can quickly change soil structure, they may also bring about secondary pollution; agricultural measures require a lot of manpower, material and financial resources; biological improvement measures are slow to take effect and have a long cycle. Due to the different regional distribution of saline-alkali lands, different geological conditions, climate differences and other factors resulting in different saline-alkali geography characteristics, for the saline-alkali lands of different soil qualities and different regions, it is necessary to take the improvement measures of "adjusting measures to local conditions and comprehensive prevention and control". As an important land reserve resource, saline-alkali land has been paid more and more attention. The effective use of saline-alkali land will play an important role in ensuring food security, promoting rural revitalization, and promoting the construction of ecological civilization[15]. However, there are still some problems in the key technologies of saline-alkali land management that need to be solved. How to turn saline-alkali land into a usable land resource is the main ecological and environmental problem facing agriculture in arid and semi-arid areas, and it is also an effective way to ease the tension of land resources.

Acknowledgments

Project Fund: DJNY2021-26 Internal Research Project of Shaanxi Land Engineering Construction Group.

References

1. Uzoma K C, “Inoue M,Andry H,et al.Effect of cow manure biochar on maize productivity under sandy soil condition”.Soil Use and Management,2011,27(2):205-212.
2. Yang L Q.“Xinjiang Saline-Alkaline Soil Resources and Comprehensive Management”.Chinese Journal of Soil Science,1993(s1):15-17.
3. Bai X, Wu F F, Lin F M, et al.“Establishment of Soybean Salt Tolerance Identification System”. Journal of Northeast Agricultural University,2013, 44(4):8-13.
4. Liu C H,Zhang W S“Study on Salt Tolerance of Sixty-nine Alfalfa Varieties and Two Physiological Indicators of Salt Tolerance”.Pratacultural Science,1993(6):1-6.
5. Lu J“Remediation mechanism and application study of improver in heavy metal contaminated soil”China Energy and Environmental Protection,2018, 40(6):103-107.
6. Wang S J, Chen Q, Li Y, et al.“Experimental Investigation on Distribution Profiles of Heavy Metals in the Desulfurization Gypsum Amended Saline and Sodic Soils”.Ecology and Environmental Sciences, 2013, 22(5): 851-856.
7. Wang J C,Yin L“Technical measures for improving saline-alkali land”Modern Agricultural Science and Technology,2011(12):282-282 .
8. Ma C,Ma L Y,Liu T X,et al.“Research progress on improvement and utilization technology of saline-alkali land”.World Forestry Research,2010,23(2):28-32.
9. Wang H J,Li C,Zhong X M,et al.“Research progress of saline-alkali land improvement

https://doi.org/10.1051/e3sconf/202233801038

technology".Agricultural Engineering,2014,4(s1):44-47.

10. Han J C,Xie J C,Zhu J W,et al."Study on Comprehensive Management Model of Saline-Alkali Land in Lubotan, Shaanxi ".Journal of Hydraulic Engineering,2009,40(03):372-377.
11. Niu D L,Wang Q J."Research progress of saline-alkali land management ".Chinese Journal of Soil Science,2002,33(6):449-455.
12. Lv Z S,Wang R Y."Preliminary Study on Fuzzy Comprehensive Evaluation of Effects of Different Biological Measures on Soda Salt Soil Improvement".Chinese Journal of Soil Science,1989,20(5):200-205.
13. Jin J Y,Zhang N,Liang M Z,et al."Application of systematic research method of soil nutrient status in soil fertility research and soil testing and fertilization "Journal of Plant Nutrition and Fertilizers,1996(1):8-15.
14. Tian X L."Micro-organisms fertilizer and its effectiveness evaluation improvement saline-alkali soil in Daqing"Northeast Forestry University,2010.
15. Zhang H O,Shi C D."Brief Analysis of Saline-Alkali Land Treatment Technology ".Rural Economy and Science-Technology,2021,32(13):7-9.

Review and Analysis on Trajectory Big Data

Xueying Wu [1, 2, 3, 4, 5, *], Liheng Xia [1, 2, 3, 4, 5]

[1] Shaanxi Provincial Land Engineering Construction Group Co., Ltd. China
[2] Institute of Land Engineering and Technology, Shaanxi Provincial Land Engineering Construction Group Co., Ltd. China
[3] Key Laboratory of Degraded and Unused Land Consolidation Engineering, Ministry of Natural Resources China
[4] Shaanxi Provincial Land Consolidation Engineering Technology Research Center China
[5] Land Engineering Technology Innovation Center, Ministry of Natural Resources China

Abstract: A trajectory can be seen as the imprint left in space by a moving object over time. In recent years, with the widespread use of civil GPS and other positioning devices on mobile terminals and the development and popularity of location-based services and mobile social networks, a large amount of trajectory data is increasingly accumulated in daily life and served by different types of applications. A large amount of trajectory data is generated in the fields of traffic, weather, ecology and mobile services. The effective understanding and utilization of these data requires not only automatic and efficient analysis methods, but also intuitive and vivid visualization, and this paper summarizes the application of trajectory data in cities.

Key words: Trajectory big data, visualization, urban planning.

1. The overview of the trajectory data

Nowadays, with the rapid development of satellite positioning technology, LBS (Location Based Service) technology and mobile Internet, trajectory data is generated anytime and anywhere in our daily life. Briefly, trajectory data is the data information formed by sampling the position, time, direction and speed of one or more moving objects by means of GPS locator, mobile phone service, radio frequency identification, etc. [1]. It is a kind of spatial big data, which conforms to the characteristics of volume, velocity and variety.

1.1 The features of trajectory data

Trajectory data contains rich spatiotemporal and behavioral information of moving objects. In addition to the typical "3V" (volume, velocity, variety) feature of big data, trajectory data has the following characteristics due to the disuse of equipment, frequency and storage mode.
Space-time sequence. As mentioned before, the trajectory data is to collect the information of the object in the spatiotemporal environment, the trajectory point contains the space-time dynamics of the object, the sequence is also the unit of data operation.
Heterofrequency sampling. Because of the randomness of object activity trace and the difference of sampling equipment, the interval difference of trajectory data is obvious. The trajectories are not only measured in seconds and minutes, such as vehicle GPS, but also collected in hours and days on social media. This discrepancy also increases the difficulty of data processing and analysis.
Road network correlation and Poor data quality. In the traffic data, the running state of the trajectory is limited by the actual traffic network, the data is closely related to the road network, so the spatio-temporal topology information of the road network is often used to optimize the data processing. When the sampling interval reaches more than minutes, the track data of continuously moving objects present a discrete state, if the position accuracy is affected by the equipment at the same time, the data quality may not be guaranteed.

1.2 The types of trajectory data

Generally, the trajectory data include human activity trajectory, traffic activity trajectory, animal activity trajectory and natural activity trajectory. Human activities trajectory data includes both active and passive. Active recording refers to the trajectory data obtained by people in the daily social process through the exchange of photos, emails or outdoor sports enthusiasts using GPS devices to record their itinerary, while passive means that users inadvertently turn on the GPS location (e.g. bus card, credit card consumption) to converge into trajectory data. Traffic activity trajectory is mainly the movement data recorded by car GPS in the city, which can be used to analyze the demands of cars, Shared car parking, charging and so on. The activity track data of animals are mainly acquired through sensors, while the activity track of natural phenomena is studied by collecting the activity track of typhoon and ocean events.

* Corresponding author: 243681563@qq.com

According to the sampling method and driving factors, all the above trajectory data are generally divided into the following three categories, Trajectory data based on time sampling, based on position sampling and based on event-triggered sampling. The two types of trajectory data we talk about currently are GPS and cell phone signaling.

GPS is sampled according to time, and this time-based data is the information recorded at the same time interval, such as vehicle GPS, animal migration, or the data obtained by global reverse deduction, such as hurricane data [2]. vehicle GPS, for instance, these devices at a fixed frequency send their geographic coordinates to the center. Although it can cover all activities, the representativeness of the data is not strong, there may be many useless data or data omissions, for example, when the vehicle is not moving, the onboard GPS will still collect data and the data loss caused by the sensor signal loss is inevitable in the transmission process.

As for cell phone signaling data, cell is the smallest unit in the GSM system that is an area where a user can communicate with the antenna. A location region consisting of a sequence of cells can be used to locate the user when communication occurs. Mobile service providers can track down the base stations that are communicating with the phones. Therefore, when the mobile phone is used such as turned on, turned off, phone calls and connected to the Internet, the GSM system would record the user's information.

2. Visual analysis of trajectory data

Visual analysis combines visualization, human-computer interaction, and automated analysis. Although the technology of machine automated analysis has been relatively mature, it is necessary for human beings to define analysis tasks and patterns in data analysis. In a typical visual analysis, users can evaluate the visual results of automatic analysis of the system, modify the analysis model, and obtain new automatic analysis results.

2.1 The Methods of visual analysis

2.1.1 Direct visualization

Direct visualization is the most basic visual analysis method to depict and display the trajectory data one by one. There is no further modeling in this method, so that it accurately has kept the information and display the dynamic changes more clearly. Furthermore, direct visualization can be divided into position animation(e.g. the location of the personnel to participate in the meeting), path visualization(e.g. the path of the ship), space-time cube visualization(e.g. the spatiotemporal trajectory of personal movement), time axis visualization(e.g. changes in vehicle speed) and parallel coordinates(e.g. Parallel visualization of traffic trajectories at intersections). However, when there are too many trajectories, the manual task is heavy, visual result trajectories will block each other.

2.1.2 Cluster visualization

If the data is large, cluster visualization could be considered. This method firstly preserves the important track data, removes the duplicate data, and then makes statistics on each dimension according to the requirements. According to the different dimensions, it can be divided into space-time and attribute clustering, points-destination clustering and path clustering.

The first one can not only act on a single dimension (space, time, attributes), but also combine them, such as ship track density, the number of times a taxi takes a passenger, the activity intensity distribution of different regions and time, etc. As for points-destination clustering, in the data pre-processing stage, the trajectory data will be converted into OD data (origin - destination data). It does not record the specific movement data, and generally USES the flow chart to visually display the result, such as the flow chart of the population migration in the United States. These "flows" in chart have different properties and can change over time. Path clustering is to specify the appropriate similarity function in advance, obtain the trajectory of different paths according to the density, segmentation and other algorithms, and then display the path of each class [3].

In practice, due to the complexity of problems, the researchers also developed interactive clustering methods. The progressive system allows users to manually select trajectories and specify them as one or more classes. Semi-supervised clustering system users can also specify parameters before clustering starts, monitor in real time and manually modify the results after completion. Summary, cluster visualization can analyze a large amount of trajectory data with the help of computer, but it is difficult to study the interaction and relative motion between trajectories, and extra programming is also needed.

2.1.3 Feature visualization

If the characteristics of the data can be determined and calculated directly, in visualization, the characteristics (e.g. events, behaviors, locations) could be extracted firstly, and then plotted. It can directly reflect the characteristics which the user's most concerned about, making the automatic search more system more efficient. At the same time, it may also lose a lot of information that seems irrelevant to features. This information, on the one hand, can explain the features more clearly, on the other hand, this data processing method in feature visualization is not applicable to exploratory tasks.

2.2 Data processing techniques in visualization

Regardless of the method of visual analysis chosen, it is usually necessary to preprocess the trajectory data before visual analysis, including cleaning, segmentation, compression, and storage.

2.2.1 Hadoop distribution processing based on MapReduce model

MapReduce is a programming model that can process data sets, consisting of job tracker for assignment and task tracker module for executing user-defined tasks, and it performs calculations on Hadoop composed of thousands of servers. MapReduce divides the data into each node, the results of each node are returned to the control center regularly to update the global state, and in the continuous development, the quadtree search method is applied to the model to speed up the calculation. Hadoop platform optimized the k-means algorithm to process lots of trajectory data, in Hadoop, the square error is used to evaluate the quality, improving the efficiency and accuracy of the algorithm [4].

2.2.2 Spark and Storm platforms

Spark is a kind of computing framework similar to Hadoop MapReduce. Its memory distribution data set can better process trajectory data that with high requirements for iterative computing power. Storm platform has a fault-tolerant real-time system, which solves the processing needs of data that have high real-time requirements and cannot be stored in advance, such as intelligent traffic and LBSN (Location-based Social Network) location recommendation.

3. Application areas of trajectory data

Trajectory data can help researchers mine human movement patterns and activity patterns, and help cities develop into smart cities.

3.1 Urban life

The trajectory data can mine the user's interests, activity patterns, etc. For example, at a given time, the weather and the previous passenger drop-off point, predicting the location of the next passenger, or predicting the time required by the taxi at a specific time and place, etc. This not only brings convenience to the taxi industry, but also helps passengers to shorten the waiting time or arrange their travel according to the predicted waiting time. In addition, through the analysis of similar trajectory data, when residents travel, they can receive more accurate push to the location and landscape in line with their interests and hobbies, arrange their schedule more efficiently.

3.2 Urban planning

In terms of urban traffic, real-time monitoring of urban traffic can be conducted according to the trajectory data of vehicle GPS. Through the analysis of these data, we can clearly see the situation of urban traffic, such as the degree of congestion and the main time of congestion. Then researchers combine it with route navigation to intelligently plan the most suitable route according to users' needs. In addition, the trajectory data can also predict the demand for parking and riding, and planners can make targeted adjustments in urban renewal.

In urban development, using the trajectory data analysis of the urban population of travel purpose, methods and paths, the evolution regularity of the residents' activity and urban geography can be revealed. This can provide auxiliary decision-making for urban public space layout, land use, infrastructure and other planning. For example, the hot areas of residents' activities should be equipped with corresponding infrastructure to increase the comfort level, and the population density and prosperity of the area that will be analyzed will be used as a reference for advertising and commercial location selection.

3.3 Urban public health

The interaction among people and the movement of people are often one of the important factors that determine the spread of epidemic diseases. As early as 2012, Pindolia used mobile phone call data and malaria transmission map to show the impact of population movement on malaria transmission, and proposed the prevention and control mechanism [5].And just this year, when the Novel Coronavirus (COVID-19) outbreak broke out, China also used the trajectory data of mobile phone signals to monitor and find some people who passed through the epidemic area or who might be in contact with the suspected people, notify these people as soon as possible and quarantine themselves for observation at home. To a certain extent, secondary transmission is avoided. Not only that, combined with Internet technology, everyone can see the confirmed cases around on the mobile phone during the epidemic, increasing the transparency of information and raising the awareness of the people to prevent and control the epidemic. These measures have greatly reduced the impact of the new coronavirus on the national epidemic.

Although the analysis and application of trajectory data have begun to change our lives, it is still in the development stage, which requires more reasonable algorithms to improve the efficiency of data analysis, and can produce more intuitive, dynamic and real-time updated visual effects. In addition, as mobile phones and GPS have become an indispensable part of daily life, the collection and analysis of trajectory data have the problem of user privacy leakage. How to obtain more useful data while protecting privacy is also a problem worthy of attention.

https://doi.org/10.1051/e3sconf/202233801039

References

1. Li X, Han J, Kim S, et al. (2007). "Roam: Rule-and motif-based anomaly detection in massive moving object data sets", Proceedings of the seventh siam international conference on data mining. Philadelphia, PA: Siam: 273-284.
2. Nanni M. (2002). "Clustering methods for spatio-temporal data". University of Pisa.
3. Pelekis N, Andrienko G, Andrienko N, et al. (2012) "Visually exploring movement data via similaritybased analysis". Journal of In-telligent Information Systems, 38(2), 343–391.
4. Tom White. (2012) "Hadoop: The Definitive Guide, 3rd ed". O'Reilly Media, Inc. Sebastopol, Calif, USA, 2012.
5. Pindolia D K, Garcia A J, Wesolowski A, et al. (2012) "Humanmovement data for malaria control and elimination strate-gic planning". Malaria Journal, 11(1),205.

Study on the Single Toxicity of Five Azole Fungicides for Green Algae

Yilun Dai [1, 2, 3, 4, 5, *], Jianglong Shen [1, 2, 3, 4, 5], Yutong Sun [1,2,3,4,5] and Yanan Li [1, 2, 3, 4, 5]

[1] Shaanxi Provincial Land Engineering Construction Group Co., Ltd. China
[2] Institute of Land Engineering and Technology, Shaanxi Provincial Land Engineering Construction Group Co., Ltd. China
[3] Key Laboratory of Degraded and Unused Land Consolidation Engineering, Ministry of Natural Resources China
[4] Shaanxi Provincial Land Consolidation Engineering Technology Research Center China
[5] Land Engineering Technology Innovation Center, Ministry of Natural Resources China

Abstract. Azole fungicides are widely used to control diseases and insect pests of vegetables, fruits and flowers because of their good antibacterial effect and regulating plant growth. However, their extensive use inevitably enters the water environment with rainfall and surface runoff, which leads to potential harm to aquatic organisms. At present, the research on the biological toxicity of azole fungicides mainly focuses on single azole compounds, such as Paclobutrazol, hexaconazole, propiconazole and Difenoconazole. However, the systematic study on the toxic effects of multi-component mixtures of azole fungicides is still very lacking, and it is unable to accurately assess the ecological risk. Therefore, in this paper, five common azole fungicides (imidazole, tebuconazole, triadimefon, tricyclazole and hymexazol) in the environment were taken as target pollutants. Scenedesmus obliquus was used as the toxicity indicator. The mixture system was designed by the equal effect concentration ratio method and linear average ray method. Study the 96h toxicity and interaction of Scenedesmus obliquus under combined stress of azole fungicides. The main research results are as follows:The 96 h toxicity test of five typical azole fungicides to Scenedesmus obliquus was determined by microplate toxicity analysis method. Fitting with Weibull function and taking EC50 as the criterion,the results show that the single toxicity order of the five tested fungicides was:tebuconazole > Triadimefon > oxacillin > Tricyclazole > imidazole.

Key words: azole fungicides, Scenedesmus obliquus, toxicity.

1. Introduction

Fungicides usually refer to chemical preparations that can effectively control or kill microorganisms such as bacteria, fungi and algae in the water system environment [1], and generally in the international arena, can be used as agents for the control of various pathogenic microorganisms, known as as a fungicide. The early fungicides were mainly inorganic fungicides, such as Bordeaux mixture, the world's earliest inorganic fungicides. In 1914, Germany took the lead in using organic mercury compounds to control wheat smut [2,3], which marked the beginning of the development of organic fungicides [4]. In 1944, Woolley successfully synthesized the first azole fungicide, benzimidazole. During this period, after more than 70 years of development [5], azole fungicides have gradually become the protagonist of the sterilization market, and are widely used in agricultural production and personal skin care products. and medical drugs. In agriculture, the production of a large number of food crops is reduced every year due to fungal infection, and sometimes even threatens human health. For example, Fusarium can produce mycotoxins when plants grow. The use of azole fungicides can not only prevent the infection of crops, but also can prevent the infection of crops. Infected crops can be effectively treated [6-11]. By 2017, more than 60 azole pesticides have been sold worldwide, accounting for 25% of the global application of fungicides [12]. In terms of personal skin care products, azole fungicides are widely used in household products such as shampoos, skin care products, soaps, toothpastes and shower gels due to their low toxicity, broad spectrum and high efficiency [13], such as ketoconazole It is often used in anti-dandruff hair care formulations [14]. Cribazole is not only used as an anti-dandruff active ingredient, but also as an anti-fungal preservative and anti-aging agent, and its content is up to 2% in washing products. The highest in washing products is 0.5%, and the highest in cosmetic products is 0.5% [14]; the annual sales volume in my country exceeds 3,800 tons [15]. In medical terms, of the 2 million fungi known to date, about 600 are known as human fungal pathogens, of which 3% to 4% can cause invasive fungal infections [16]. Over the past 30 years, annual Invasive fungal infections kill between 1 and 2

* Corresponding author: 373289543@qq.com

 https://doi.org/10.1051/e3sconf/202233801040

million people, and the mortality rate far exceeds that of malaria and tuberculosis [17]. Among the more than 40 brands of antifungal drugs clinically used on the market, azole fungicides are considered to be the most It has the best curative effect and the most widely used fungicides [18-21].

Chemical pollutants in the actual natural environment often do not exist alone, but in the form of mixtures. With the vigorous development of industry, agriculture, and manufacturing, the types of pollutant mixtures are increasing, and new types of pollutants are increasing. The ecological and environmental problems caused by them are not optimistic. Therefore, in the past half century, the research on the combined toxicity of mixtures has become more and more Having attention. For example, on the issue of industrial sewage treatment, the possibility that there are still unclean pollutants in the treated industrial sewage cannot be excluded. Various new types of pollutants are increasing day by day, and their toxicity is rare, and their detection cannot be analyzed and expressed by a single physical and chemical index. On the other hand, biological monitoring can more vividly reflect the pollution and toxicity of pollutants in different situations in a certain area.

In order to reveal the ecotoxicity of azole fungicides exposed in the natural environment, this study took five azole fungicides as target pollutants, and investigated the effects of azole fungicides at different concentrations on the growth of the toxicity indicator organism, Scenedesmus obliquus. To clarify the single toxicity of these five typical azole fungicides to Scenedesmus obliquus, and to provide basic toxicity data for the risk assessment of mixed pollutants in the water environment.

2. Matrials and methods

2.1 Experimental Materials

2.1.1 Experimental Reagents

Five typical azole fungicides were selected in this paper as the research target pollutants. The specific physical and chemical properties are shown in Table 1, and the chemical structure is shown in Figure 1.

Table 1 Physicochemical properties of 5 target pollutants

Serial Number	Compound	Short Name	CAS	Relative molecular mass	Purity (%)	Source
1	Imidazole	IDZ	288-32-4	68.08	99.50	Accustandard
2	Tebuconazole	CDT	80443-41-0	307.82	98.70	Dr. Ehrenstorfer GmbH
3	Triadimefon	TDF	43121-43-3	293.75	99.60	Accustandard
4	Tricyclazole	TCL	41814-78-2	189.24	99.50	Accustandard
5	Oxymetholone	MHZ	10004-44-1	99.09	99.00	Dr. Ehrenstorfer GmbH

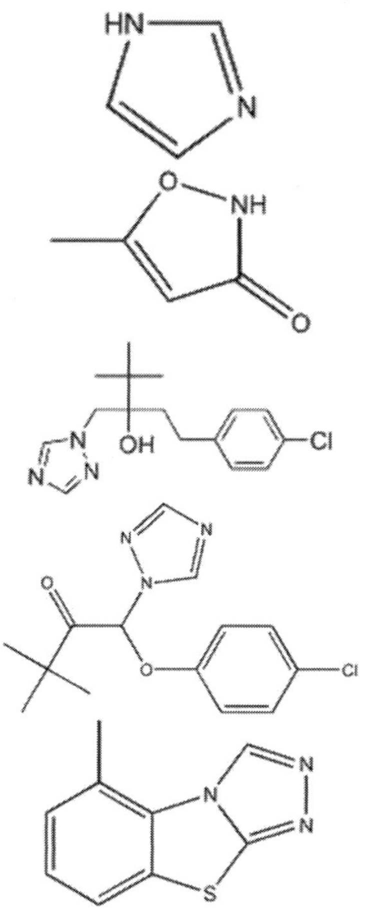

Figure 1. Chemical Structures of Five Azole Fungicides

2.1.2 Algae Species

Scenedesmusobliquus were purchased from the Freshwater Algae Seed Bank (FACHB) of the Type Culture Collection Committee of the Chinese Academy of Sciences, and the serial numbers were FACHB-12. After receiving the algae seed, transfer the algae seed to the prepared medium for cultivation in the clean bench.

2.1.3 Cultivation of Algae

The BG11 medium was used to culture Scenedesmus obliquus, and the medium was sterilized in a sterilizing pot at 121 °C and 101 KPa for 20 min. After cooling, green algae were aseptically inoculated in the ultra-clean workbench, and then placed in an artificial constant temperature light incubator for cultivation. The set temperature was 22°C, the illuminance was about 2000lux, and the light-dark cycle was 12h:12h. Expand the culture every 5-7d, that is, dilute the transfer algae at a ratio of 1:2, so that the algae can fully enter the logarithmic growth phase. The most vigorous period of algal cell metabolism is at 8-10 am, so it is the best time for algal species transfer [66]. The algae should be cultivated in a sterile environment throughout the process. Before the toxicological test, the algal seeds in the logarithmic growth phase were transferred to fresh medium for cultivation, and the experiment was carried out after culturing for 2 days until the initial light absorption value of the algal seeds was 0.22-0.25. In order to avoid the experimental error caused by the volatilization of the drug, a transparent cover plate should be added during the experimental exposure period.

2.2 Toxicity Experiment

2.2.1 Green Algae Acute Microplate Experiment

The algal microplate toxicity test uses a standard transparent 96-well microplate, and the microplate sample loading design method is as follows.

First, add 200 μL of ultrapure water to the four sides of the 96-well microplate (36 wells in total) to prevent edge effects; 100 μL of ultrapure water was added to the 24 wells in columns 2, 6, 7 and 11 respectively as blank control; A total of 6 wells in the 3rd column and 6 wells in the 8th column were respectively added with different concentrations of pesticide pollutants designed according to the dilution factor (see Equation 2.1, and supplemented with ultrapure water to make the volume 100 μL; The parallel trials for column 3 are columns 4 and 5, and the parallel trials for column 8 are columns 9 and 10; Finally, 100 μL of algae liquid with an optical density value of about 0.15 was added to the middle 60 wells, so that the total volume of each well was 200 μL; After adding samples to the microplate, cover with a transparent cover, and place it in a biochemical incubator with a temperature of 22 °C, an illuminance of 2000 lux, and a light-dark ratio of 12h: 12h. At 96h, the microplate was placed in a spectrophotometer to measure the optical density (OD) at a wavelength of 681 nm. The microplate was repeated at least 3 times.

$$F = \left(\frac{C_L}{C_H}\right)^{\frac{1}{n-1}}, \quad n=1,2..... \tag{1}$$

Among them, CH and CL are the highest and lowest concentrations of the experiment, respectively, and n represents the number of concentration gradients in the range of CH and CL. Then the twelve concentration points are Cn=C0*Fn, n=1,2... Among them, C0 is the concentration of the stock solution, and Cn is the set concentration. In this paper, the growth inhibition rate (I) of pollutants to Scenedesmus obliquus is used as the toxicity index of the microplate test, and the calculation formula of I is as follows: I=(ODt,i-ODt,0)/(OD0,i-OD0,0), where ODti is the OD value of the pollutant experimental group at the i-th time, and the OD value of the OD0i blank control group.

2.2.2 Data Processing

The experimental toxicity data were processed by the MATLAB program written by Qin Litang, and the graph of the fitted curve was drawn by the Origin software. To derive effect sizes and effect concentrations for individual compounds and mixtures, a nonlinear fit to the observed concentration-response data must be performed. For classical S-type CRC, Logit or Weibull nonlinear function is generally used for fitting. The function expression is shown in Table 2., where I represents the effect, c represents the concentration of a single compound or mixture, α is the position parameter, and β is the slope parameter [23]. The Logit function and the Weibull function are classical two-parameter functions. The Logit function is based on the integral statistics of logistic distribution and takes half effect (50%) as the center symmetry, so it is suitable for fitting a symmetrical curve. The Weibull function, originally proposed by Gompertz, is based on extreme value distribution integral statistics and is suitable for most asymmetric concentration-effect curves. The MTA method used in this study has only 12 concentration gradients, and the two-parameter Logit and Weibull functions should be used for nonlinear fitting [24].

Table 2. Two Common S-Type Concentration-Effect Curve Fitting Models

Function type	Analysing way
Logit	$I=1/\left(1+\exp(-\alpha-\beta \lg c)\right)$
Weibull	$I=1-\exp\left(-\exp(\alpha+\beta \lg c)\right)$

3. Results

Table 3. Concentration-effect fitting curve parameters of five azole fungicides on Scenedesmus obliquus

Compound	Fitfunction	α	β	R2	RMSE	EC50 /(mol·L-1)
IDZ	Weibull	5.706	2.200	0.987	0.0393	2.20E-03
CDT	Weibull	6.446	1.509	0.991	0.0242	3.22E-05
TDF	Weibull	4.966	1.331	0.975	0.0339	9.81E-05
TCL	Weibull	3.174	1.175	0.977	0.0287	8.86E-04
HMZ	Weibull	5.827	1.708	0.992	0.0299	2.55E-04

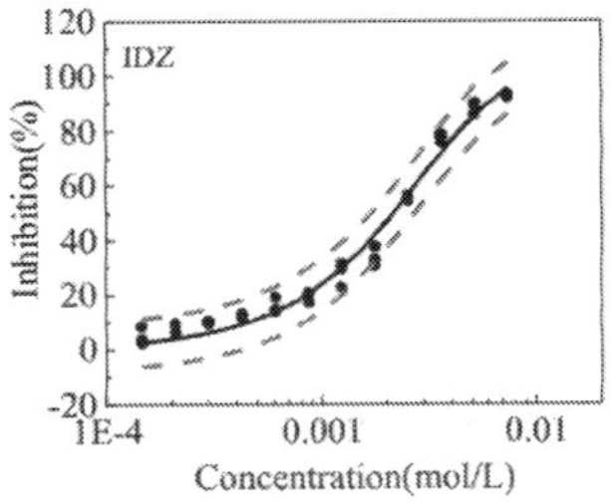

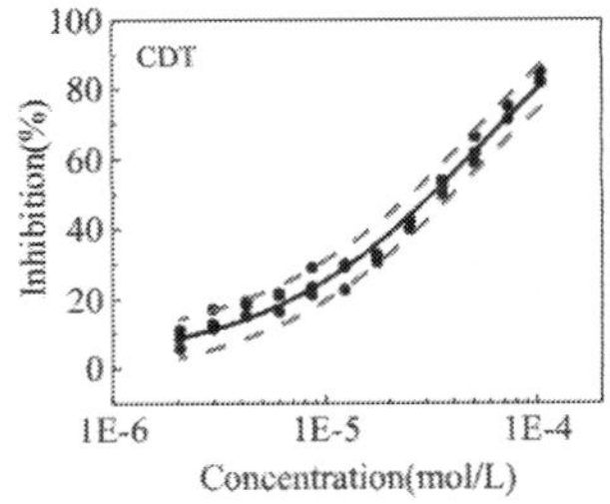

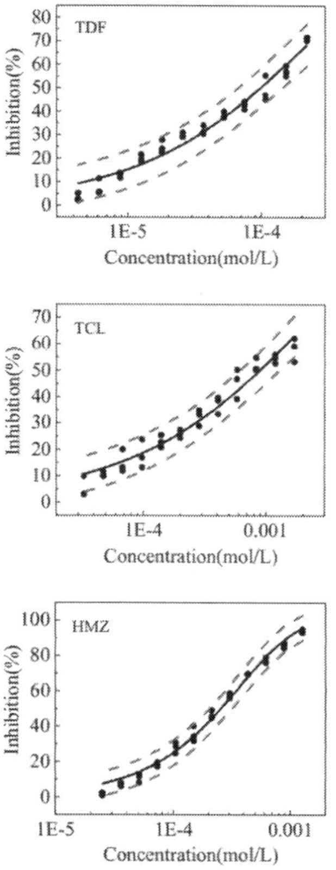

Figure 2 Concentration-response curves (CRC) of five azole fungicides on Scenedesmus obliquus

The biological toxicity of azole fungicides was tested with Scenedesmus obliquus as the indicator organism, and the toxicity of azole fungicides was expressed by the inhibition rate of Scenedesmus obliquus at 96 hours. The concentration-effect data of the five azole fungicides on Scenedesmus obliquus can be fitted by the Weibull function or the Logit function. The fitting model parameters (regression parameters α and β values, statistical parameters R2 and RMSE) are shown in Table 2. The R2 values of the five azole fungicides on the toxicity data of Scenedesmus obliquus were between 0.975 and 0.992, all greater than 0.95; The RMSE values of the fitted curves ranged from 0.024 to 0.0339, all less than 0.028, which indicated that the fitting results of the Weibull model were accurate and reliable. Figure 2. shows the concentration-response number fitted curves (CRCs) of the five azole fungicides, all showing a classic S shape. From Table 3, the toxicity under 50% effect can be obtained as: tebuconazole > Triadimefon > oxacillin > Tricyclazole > imidazole.

References

1. Liuchen Zhao. Bactericidal properties of bisdecyl dimethyl ammonium formate and its composite system[D]. China Daily Chemical Industry Research Institute,2017.
2. Large, E. C. Control of Potato Blight (Phytophthora infestans) by Spraying with Suspensions of Metallic Copper[J]. Nature, 1943, 151(3820): 195-206.
3. Melnikov N N, Gunther F A, Gunther J D. Chemistry of pesticides[M]. Residue Reviews, 1971, 36(1).
4. Klittich C J. Milestones in Fungicide Discovery: Chemistry that Changed Agriculture[J]. Plant Health Progress, 2008, 9(1):1-8.
5. Woolley D W, Pringle A. Relationship of chemical structure to antibacterial activity among analogues of dimethyldiaminobenzene[J]. Journal of Biological Chemistry, 1952, 194(2): 729-746.
6. Janna H, Scrimshaw M D, Williams R J, et al. From Dishwasher to Tap Xenobiotic Substances Benzotriazole and Tolyltriazole in the Environment[J]. Environmental ence & Technology, 2011, 45(9): 3858-3864.
7. H., Dooley, M., et al. Effect of azole fungicide mixtures, alternations and dose on azole sensitivity in the wheat pathogenZymoseptoria tritici[J]. Plant Pathology, 2015.65(1):124-136.
8. Giavini E, Menegola E. Are azole fungicides a teratogenic risk for human conceptus[J].Toxicology Letters, 2010, 198(2): 106-111.
9. Brauer V S, Rezende C P, Pessoni A M, et al. Antifungal Agents in Agriculture: Friends and Foes of Public Health[J]. Biomolecules, 2019, 9(10): 521-534.
10. Escher B I, Baumgartner R, Koller M, et al. Environmental toxicology and risk assessment of pharmaceuticals from hospital wastewater[J]. Water Research, 2011, 45(1): 75-92.
11. Thomas K V, Hilton M J. The occurrence of selected human pharmaceutical compounds in UK estuaries[J]. Marine Pollution Bulletin, 2004, 49(5/6): 436-444.
12. Hof H. Critical Annotations to the Use of Azole Antifungals for Plant Protection[J]. Antimicrobial Agents & Chemotherapy, 2001, 45(11): 87-90.
13. David, Allen, Dustin, et al. Azole antifungals: 35 years of invasive fungal infection management: Expert Review of Anti-infective Therapy: Vol 13, No 6[J]. Expert Review of Anti Infective Therapy, 2015.13(6):787-798.
14. Wishart D S, Knox C, Guo A C, et al. DrugBank: a knowledgebase for drugs, drug actions and drug targets[J]. Nucleic Acids Research, 2007, 36(Database): D901-D906.
15. Autrup H. SCCP (Scientific Committee on Consumer Products) / SCHER (Scientific Committee on Health& Environment Risks) / SCENIHR (Scientific Committee on Emerging and Newly-Identified Health Risks) opinion on:Risk assessment methodologies and approaches for genotoxic and carcinogenic substances[J].Radiographics A Review Publication of the Radiological Society of North America Inc, 2009, 22(2): e4.
16. Gouin T, Egmond R V, Price O R, et al. Prioritising chemicals used in personal care products in China for

https://doi.org/10.1051/e3sconf/202233801040

environmental risk assessment: Application of the RAIDAR model[J]. Environmental Pollution, 2012, 165(Jun.): 208-214.

17. Kathiravan M K, Salake A B, Chothe A S, et al. The biology and chemistry of antifungal agents: a review[J]. Bioorg Med Chem, 2012, 20(19): 5678-5698.
18. Roemer T, Krysan D J. Antifungal Drug Development: Challenges, Unmet Clinical Needs, and New Approaches[J]. Cold Spring Harbor Perspectives in Medicine, 2014, 4(5): a019703-a019703.
19. Perlroth J, Choi B, Spellberg B. Nosocomial fungal infections: epidemiology, diagnosis, and treatment[J]. Medical Mycology, 2007, 45(4): 321-346.
20. Wróbel T M, Kosikowska U, Kaczor A A, et al. Synthesis, Structural Studies and Molecular Modelling of a Novel Imidazoline Derivative with Antifungal Activity[J]. Molecules, 2015, 20(8): 61-76.
21. Shafiei M, Peyton L, Hashemzadeh M, et al. History of the development of Antifungal azoles: A review on structures, SAR, and mechanism of action[J]. Bioorganic Chemistry, 2020: 104-240.
22. Jingxiang Zhou, Tao Yun, Quan Huang,et al. Comparative study on digestive enzyme activities of common carp, yellow croaker, mulberry and walleye[J]. Journal of Jilin Agricultural University, 2001, 23(1): 94-96.
23. Zhjiqiang Bian, Jin Zhang, Tao Wang, et al. Characteristics and mechanism of combined toxicity of carbamate pesticides to Chlorella pyrenoidosa [J]. Acta Ecotoxicology, 2019, 14(4): 150-162.
24. Renlong Cheng. Two-stage model predicts time-dependent mixed toxicity of antibiotics to Chlorella pyrenoidea [D]. Anhui University of Architecture,2016.

Research Progress of the Salt Barrier in Saline Alkali Land

Xiaomei Sun [1,2,3,4], Jian Wang[1,2,3,4], Dongwen Hua[1,2,3,4, *]

[1] Key Laboratory of Degraded and Unused Land Consolidation Engineering, the Ministry of Natural Resources of China, Xi'an 710075 China
[2] Shaanxi Provincial Land Engineering Construction Group, Xi'an 710075, China
[3] Insititute of Land Engineering and Technology, Shaanxi Provincial Land Engineering Construction Group, Xi'an 710075, China
[4] Shaanxi Provincial Land Consolidation Engineering Technology Research Center, Xi'an 710075, China

Abstract. As an important land resource, the poor physical and chemical properties of soil in saline alkali land are the biggest obstacle to plant growth and development in saline alkali land. Carrying out targeted research on saline alkali land improvement is of great significance to ensure food security and protect the ecological environment. In recent years, it is urgent to fully tap the potential of such areas in agricultural production and ecological greening through economic and effective original soil improvement measures. The existing research and engineering projects of saline alkali land treatment at home and abroad are mostly realized through water conservancy, physics, chemistry, biology and other measures, and tend to form a comprehensive treatment system integrating engineering, plant, microorganism and other technologies. Among them, salt separation layer + concealed pipe drainage is a more effective and commonly used engineering measure in saline alkali land treatment. Through the research and development of supporting new materials and processes, constantly improving the technical system can greatly promote saline alkali land treatment. This paper discusses the improvement of salt barrier in saline alkali soil

Key words: Salt barrier; Saline alkali land; Biochar.

1. Introduction

Soil salinization is a serious problem facing agriculture in the world [1-4]. The accumulation of salt in soil and groundwater threatens agricultural production and its sustainable development [5-6]. The increase of soil salt content and salinization area lead to the salinization of fertile land, the sharp decrease of crop yield, the change of land planting adaptability, and even fallow and fallow in the region [7-9].

The core problem of saline alkali land treatment is the problem of water. Less water is early and more waterlogging is more. The level of saline alkali and groundwater level is directly related to climate change. The key to comprehensive treatment is to control water. Without water control, it is impossible to improve soil. However, we can't just drain water, and drainage will also bring a series of problems. Therefore, we must change the water and soil distribution, then change the regional salt distribution, reduce human intervention, and emphasize dynamic adaptive adjustment and balance. The law of soil water and salt movement is to study the characteristics and change law of water and soil soluble salt in different periods with environmental conditions in a certain ecological environment. Soil texture, structure, fertility, salt content of soil and groundwater, high and low water level all have a great impact on water and salt movement. In addition, climate and vegetation all have an impact on water and salt movement. Correctly understanding the law and relationship of water and salt movement is the key to regulating soil salinity and alkalinity.

In recent years, it is urgent to fully tap the potential of such areas in agricultural production and ecological greening through economic and effective original soil improvement measures. The existing research and engineering projects of saline alkali land treatment at home and abroad are mostly realized through water conservancy, physics, chemistry, biology and other measures, and tend to form a comprehensive treatment system integrating engineering, plant, microorganism and other technologies. Among them, salt separation layer + concealed pipe drainage is a more effective and commonly used engineering measure in saline alkali land treatment. Through the research and development of supporting new materials and processes, constantly improving the technical system can greatly promote saline alkali land treatment.

* Corresponding author: 739972229@qq.com

2. Research status

In nature, due to the effects of meteorological, hydrological, geological and biological processes, soil is not a simple homogeneous material, but mostly presents a staggered layered structure. Miller and Gardner (1962) [10], in 1962, conducted infiltration tests of sand covered and sand covered layered soil respectively, which proved that when the texture and hydraulic conductivity of the subsoil are different from that of the topsoil, its role will be to reduce the infiltration rate, regardless of whether the subsoil is coarser or finer than the topsoil. And although the infiltration on the surface did not stop, the wetting front stopped moving forward for a period of time. Hill and parlange (1972) [11] found that when the wetting front passes through the fine and coarse sand interface, the wetting front becomes "fingers flow", and the water is retained at the fine and coarse sand interface. Hillel and Baker (1988) [12] analyzed the formation mechanism of "finger flow" phenomenon from the viewpoint of energy conservation, and believed that soil stratification would lead to the instability of wetting front, that is, in the early stage of ponding infiltration, the wetting front was located in the upper fine soil with low hydraulic conductivity, and the soil suction at the wetting front was large, so that the water can not directly enter the coarse sand layer with high hydraulic conductivity after reaching the interface, the wetting front pauses at the interface, while the upper water continues to infiltrate under the water potential gradient, and the water suction gradually decreases until the water can enter the smallest pore connected with the lower layer, and then reduce to the surrounding macropores.

The groundwater level in saline alkali areas is generally high and contains a certain amount of salt. Therefore, the rising height of capillary water and water conveyance speed have a great impact on soil salt accumulation. WillisW. O. (1960) [13] and Miller D E. (1962) [10] found in the test of layered soil that when the capillary water rises through the interface of layered soil composed of clayey sand, there is a stagnation phenomenon, and the stagnation time increases with the increase of interlayer level and the difference between soil and sand particle size. Luo Huanyan (1965) [14] of China also discussed this phenomenon. Shi Wenjuan (2004) [15] systematically demonstrated the influence of sand layer on the rise of soil capillary water through indoor test, and proposed that sand layer will affect the height and speed of capillary water rise.

The effect of soil interlayer on evaporation is mainly clay interlayer soil. There are mainly two views on the influence of clay layer on evaporation. One view is that the closer the clay layer is to the groundwater level, the more difficult it is for the surface to return salt [16,17]; Another view is that the inhibition of clay layer on salt is strengthened with the increase of its horizon [18-20]. Most views believe that the salt inhibition is stronger with the increase of clay interlayer thickness [18,19,21]. Shi Wenjuan (2004) [15] is the most systematic research on the influence of sand layer soil on soil salt accumulation during evaporation. She puts forward that the influence of sand layer on phreatic evaporation intensity, soil surface return salt and salt solution concentration is basically the same as that of sand layer on capillary water rising speed. At the same time, salt is retained at the upper and lower interfaces of soil and sand, and the higher the sand layer or the larger the effective particle size, the greater the retention. And the inhibition rate of sand layer to salt is greater than that to water. In addition, the sand layer has different effects on the movement of different ions, among which Na+ and Cl- are most affected by the sand layer.

Salt barrier technology is mainly realized by the change of water and salt movement caused by the change of soil layer. According to the principle of soil water energy, when water infiltrates into layered soil, regardless of whether the texture of the interlayer soil is thicker or finer than that of the surface soil, the soil interlayer will block the water flow, increase the water storage capacity of the upper soil, and then reduce the infiltration [22]. The research on saline alkali soil barrier [23-25] shows that the soil barrier causes uneven pore distribution at the junction of soil barrier, affects the soil moisture content, hydraulic gradient and conductivity, changes the movement track of soil moisture at the junction of soil barrier, and then affects the law of soil water and salt movement in saline alkali soil and the leaching and improvement of saline alkali soil. Biochar is a solid product of organic materials after pyrolysis under high temperature and hypoxia [26], which has the characteristics of high carbon content, high porosity, strong adsorption and high stability [27]. Biochar materials have been widely and deeply studied in the fields of soil improvement, fertilization, soil pollution remediation, water pollution remediation and coping with greenhouse effect at home and abroad. Biochar materials are generally alkaline, but subject to the influence of raw materials, some are also acidic, such as the preparation of biochar from furfural residue [28]. Biochar generally contains high calcium content [29], which helps to exchange Na+ in saline alkali soil and promote the formation of soil agglomeration structure; The porosity of biochar material is conducive to improve soil structure and form hydraulic conductivity; The low apparent density makes its transportation and construction more convenient. In addition, due to the structural stability of biochar itself, it can maintain a long-term effect. Biochar materials have certain application potential in saline alkali land improvement. The existing research on biochar in saline alkali land improvement [30] mainly adopts the mixing method, paying attention to soil physical and chemical properties, plant growth and soil respiration.

3. Conclusion

The research on the law of soil water and salt transport is not only an important aspect of soil physics and farmland irrigation, but also the core problem of preventing and improving saline soil. In the previous research on soil salt barrier, it is mainly Sandy and clay salt barrier. In addition, in recent years, straw has been used as a salt barrier and its water and salt movement law has been studied. In terms of construction, granular biochar is similar to the traditional gravel and stone chip salt separation layer.

There are no obstacles in the construction technology. Due to the lightweight characteristics of its materials, its construction is more flexible and convenient. Mechanical construction can be carried out in a large range and manual construction can also be used in a small range. In terms of material cost alone, the price of biochar is higher than that of the traditional gravel salt barrier, but the preparation of biochar takes agricultural and forestry wastes as raw materials, which is an effective way for the resource utilization of agricultural and forestry wastes, and can play a huge ecological benefit in reducing carbon emissions.

The selection of salt barrier has a great impact on the effectiveness of saline alkali land treatment. In view of the problems such as easy decomposition and decay of straw, inconvenient transportation and construction of sand and gravel materials, the porous structure (enhanced drainage), light material (convenient for construction), high stability (long-term effect), strong adsorption and other properties of biochar materials can be fully utilized, This paper explores its leaching and salt suppression effect as a salt barrier of saline alkali soil, and discusses the positive role of salt barrier materials in the construction of saline alkali soil, so as to provide scientific basis and theoretical support for the improvement and restoration of saline alkali soil.

Acknowledgments

This work was financially supported by the Fund Project of Shaanxi Key Laboratory of Land Consolidation (2019-JC08) and the Fund Project of Shaanxi Provincial Land Engineering Construction Group Internal Research Project (DJNY2021-25). Sincere gratitude is extended to the editor and anonymous reviewers for their professional comments and corrections.

References

1. Han Jichang. Study on comprehensive management model and mechanism of saline alkali land in halobotan, Shaanxi. Xi'an University of technology, 2009.
2. Zhang Yuwen Improvement of physical properties of coastal saline alkali cotton field by straw returning. Tai'an: Shandong Agricultural University, 2016.
3. Ye Xiaofei Study on salt transport law between water body of storage ditch and adjacent soil under water storage condition. Xi'an: Xi'an University of technology, 2010.
4. Li Bin, Wang Zhichun, sun Zhigao, et al. Study on saline alkali land resources and sustainable utilization in China. Agricultural research in arid areas, 2005,23 (2): 154-158.
5. SCHOUPS G, HOPMANS J W, YONG C A, et al . Sustainability of irrigated agriculture in the San Joaquin Valley, California. PNAS, 2005, 102(43):15352-15356 .
6. Sun Zhaojun Study on improvement model of saline alkali wasteland in Yinchuan Plain. Beijing: Beijing Forestry University, 2011.
7. R OZEMA J, FLOWE R S T . Crops for a salinized world. Science, 2008, 322 (5907) :1478-1480 .
8. Zhou Zaiming Study on spatial variability and influence mechanism of soil salinity in low plain around Bohai Sea.Beijing: Chinese Academy of Geological Sciences, 2012.
9. Wang Xianghui Research on environmental change and agricultural sustainable development in Northwest China. Yang Ling: Northwest University of agriculture and forestry science and technology, 2012.
10. Miller D E, Gander W H. Water infiltrate into the stratified soil. Soil Sci Soc Amer Proc, 1962,26:115-118.
11. Hillel D E, Parlange J Y. Wetting front instability in layered soil. Science Society American Proceeding, 1972,36(5):697-702.
12. Hillel D, Baker R S A. descriptive theory off fingering during infiltration into layered soils. Soil Science,1988,146(1):51-55.
13. Willis W O. Evaporation from layered soils in the presence of a water table. Soil Sci Soc AmJ. 1960,24(4):239-242.
14. Luo Huanyan, Xie Juhua Experimental study on capillary water rise in layered soil. Journal of soil, 1965,13 (3): 312-324.
15. Shi Wenjuan, Wang Zhirong, Shen Bing, et al Experimental study on capillary water rise of soil configuration in sand intercalated layer [J] Journal of soil, 2004,18 (6): 167-170.
16. Yuan Jianfang, Zhou Yuehua Influence of clay interlayer on groundwater ascending operation. Journal of soil, 1980,17 (1): 94-99.
17. Liu Fuhan, Wang zunqin Soil water and salt movement in different soil profiles under phreatic evaporation. Journal of soil, 1993.30 (2): 173-180.
18. Liu Siyi, Liang Guoqing, Xing Wengang, et al Experimental study on water and salt movement in clay interlayer soil structure. Journal of soil, 1992, 29 (1): 109-112.
19. Liu Siyi, Wei Youqing Study on several factors affecting soil salinization in Majia River Basin. Journal of soil, 1988.25 (2): 110-118.
20. Wang Jinping Numerical simulation of layered soil water movement under evaporation. Journal of water conservancy, 1989.5:49-54.
21. Liu Youchang Discussion on critical depth of groundwater in Lubei Plain. Soil bulletin, 1962, 24:13-22.
22. Shao Ming'an, Wang Quanjiu, Huang mingbin, soil physics [M] Beijing: Higher Education Press, 2006:23-36.
23. Yin Xiaolin, Ding Guodong, Zhang Weicheng. Effects of rainfall and salt barrier on water and salt

movement in coastal saline alkali land Chinese Journal of soil and water conservation, 2011,9 (3): 40-44.

24. Zhang Jianfeng, Wang Wenyan, Wang Zhirong, et al. "Calculation of soil infiltration with sandy interlayer"[J]. Journal of agricultural engineering, 2004,20 (2): 27-30.
25. Shi Wenjuan, Shen Bing, Wang Zhirong, et al Study on soil water and salt transport characteristics of shallow groundwater with sand layer under evaporation. Journal of agricultural engineering, 2005,21 (9): 23-26.
26. Bridgwater A V D. Meier D. Radlein. An overview offast pyrolysis of biomass. Organic Geochemistry1999,30:1479-1493.
27. Didem O. Aysegul E M. Characterization of biocharand bio-oil samples obtained from carbonization of various biomass materials. Renewable Energy, 2010.351319-1324.
28. Sun Junna, Dong Lukang, Xu Gang, et al Comparative study on the effects of furfural residue and its biochar on the physical and chemical properties of saline soil. Journal of Agricultural Environmental Sciences, 2014.33 (3): 532-538.
29. Gerardo O. Stefania M. Anna A. et al. Are soil-waterfunctions affected by biochar application?. Geoder-ma, 2015.249/250:1-11.
30. Vijayasatya N C. David M C. Evaluating the relativecontribution of physiochemical and biological factors inameliorating a saline-sodic soil amended with composts and biochar and leached with reclaimed water. Geo-derma,2015,259/260:45-55.

E3S Web of Conferences **338**, 01042 (2022) https://doi.org/10.1051/e3sconf/202233801042
ESMA 2021

The Significance of Soil Micromorphology Research in Land Reclamation

Tingting Cao [1,2,3,4,*], Jian Wang[1,2,3,4], Haiou Zhang[1,2,3,4]

[1] Shaanxi Land Engineering Construction Group Co., Ltd. Xi'an 710075, China;
[2] Institute of Land Engineering and Technology, Shaaxi Land Engineering Construction Group Co., Ltd. Xi'an 710075, China;
[3] Key Laboratory of Degraded and Unused Land Consolidation Engineering, the Ministry of Natural Resources, Xi'an 710075, China
[4] Shaanxi Land Consolidation Engineering Technology Research Center, Xi'an 710075, China

Abstract. Soil micromorphology is an emerging branch of soil science that aims to study the formation and structure of soils at a microscopic level. The study of soil micromorphology can be used for the analysis of soil genesis and evolution, the development of land remediation techniques, the analysis of the causes of geological hazards, the mechanisms of soil quality degradation, the process of soil formation and material changes in "anthropogenic soils" and many other aspects. With the gradual development of instrumentation, scanning electron microscopy, light microscopy and scanning CT have been widely used in the study of soil micromorphology. This paper presents a detailed analysis of the current state of development of soil micromorphology techniques and the possible problems that may exist in the future.

Key words: Soil micromorphology; Micro structure; Land reclamation

1. introduction

With economic development, the intensity and breadth of exploitation of land resources is becoming more and more obvious, and the conflict between man and land is becoming more and more prominent. Remediation of difficult-to-use land and degraded land to make it meet the real needs of resource exploitation, increase the area of arable land, improve food production and ensure food output is a scientific problem that needs to be solved urgently in land engineering nowadays. Shaanxi Province, for example, is high in the north and south and low in the centre, with the Shaanxi-North Plateau in the north, the Guanzhong Plain in the centre and the Qinba Mountains in the south. According to the classification of landforms, Shaanxi Province can be divided into six landform type regions: the Wind and Sand Transition Region, the Loess Plateau Region, the Guanzhong Plain Region, the Qinling Mountain Region, the Han River Basin Region and the Daba Mountain Region. In different landscape environments, soil properties are inevitably different and the problems that need to be solved differ, but the objective of remediation of degraded and difficult-to-use land is the same, i.e. to turn these difficult-to-use and unused lands into usable, high-standard and high-yielding agricultural land through scientific land engineering remediation methods.

Land degradation is a major scientific problem that limits agricultural production, affects ecological security, and threatens the natural environment with the development and utilization of land resources at a certain stage of social development. In response to this scientific problem, domestic and foreign scholars and associations have carried out relevant research, paid sufficient attention to the obvious degradation of soil, and carried out fruitful scientific research on various obvious degradation problems, and achieved remarkable results. However, up to now, enough attention has not been paid to the recessive degradation of soil, and there is a lack of knowledge about its occurrence mechanism and its harmfulness, and the occurrence mechanism has not yet been proved.

In Shaanxi Province, for example, the soil quality in the Guanzhong region of Shaanxi is excellent, and most of the unused land in this region needs to be remediated using techniques such as land restoration, raw soil ripening and concentrated patchwork. In southern Shaanxi, the remediation of unused land requires techniques such as soil and water conservation, viscosity reduction and soil loosening. The northern Shaanxi windsand region is a key area of concern because it has a vast land area and is one of the most promising areas for the development of arable land resources in Shaanxi Province, but due to the impact of local ecological problems such as wind and sand erosion and soil erosion, the land is infertile and food production is not high. The sandy land leaks water and fertiliser severely, making it difficult for vegetation to attach and grow. However, the arsenic sandstone, which is widely distributed in Yulin, is as hard as stone without water and as soft as mud with water, and is easily eroded by water and wind. Both are important sources of local

* Corresponding author: 956874403@qq.com

https://doi.org/10.1051/e3sconf/202233801042

ecological problems. One study has made full use of the characteristics of their soil properties to mix them in optimal proportions, i.e. to compensate for the poor soil structure of sandy soils and to make full use of the local arsenic sandstone colloidal material. The result is a soil with a good structure for crop growth, which can be improved in other ways using organic soil reconstruction techniques, resulting in a new land remediation technology that can be used for large-scale conversion.

The development of this land remediation technology is based on the full use of soil micromorphology research, i.e. the development of a new land remediation engineering technology, and also reveals the scientific mechanism of this land remediation technology from a microscopic point of view, making up the basic theory of the new land remediation technology and laying a solid scientific foundation for the positive development of the effects of land remediation. The research results are important for enhancing the social benefits of land remediation technology. The ecological and economic benefits also have important strategic significance.

2. The current state of development of soilmicromorphology techniques

Soil micromorphology is an emerging branch of soil science that aims to study soil formations and formation structures at the microscopic level, mainly by using high magnification instruments and equipment to observe the original microscopic morphology of the soil, and at present, the widely used equipment mainly includes scanning electron microscopy, optical microscopy, scanning CT and other instruments. The main objective is to observe the morphology of soil skeletal particles, fine-grained material, soil basal structures and soil formations, as well as the configuration, structure and spatial distribution of the components of each type of particle, and to study the occurrence and formation mechanisms of soil micromorphology. This research tool is now widely used in land remediation techniques, analysis of the causes of geological disasters, mechanisms of soil quality degradation, soil formation processes and material changes in "anthropogenic soils".

In the analysis of soil micromorphological elements, the skeletal particles of soil micromorphology are classified as skeletal particles if they are larger than 2 microns. It is difficult to change the composition of the soil within a short period of time.

Soil fine-grained material consists mainly of soil mucilage components and humus. The fine-grained material of the soil consists almost exclusively of clay minerals, which aggregate to form the soil matrix. The structure of the soil matrix refers to the relevant distribution of each of the skeletal particles in the soil, as well as the size distribution of the skeletal particles and the state of existence of the fine-grained material in terms of shape and size as a form of organisation. There are various types of soil formations, including soil property-related formations, depletion formations, crystalline formations, amorphous and cryptocrystalline formations, basal formations and excretion formations. The first four formation types are related to the soil parent rock and its developmental processes and are not significantly influenced by roots under short-term plant growth.

This shows that soil microstructure plays a key role in determining soil quality, with different soil structures directly affecting the amount of water stored in the soil, the amount of gas held and the nutrient storage. Different soil microstructure characteristics also have a direct impact on the penetration capacity of the root system, which in turn affects the contact surface of the plant with the subsoil and the efficiency of the use of nutrients in the soil. The study of soil microstructure can therefore contribute to a deeper understanding of soil formation processes and their changes, and provide an important basis for the development of land use, management and improvement measures. There are many methods for studying soil microstructure, which can be broadly divided into direct and indirect methods depending on the nature of the indicators used to characterise the microform of the soil, and depending on the equipment used and the method of study, the information used to characterise soil microstructure varies. One of the most common devices used to observe soil micromorphology is the scanning electron microscope, which, at different magnifications, can be used to obtain soil micromorphology at different scales and provide a more intuitive view of the morphological information of the soil structure.

For a good soil configuration, the cementing material is the key to soil formation and the key material for the formation of soil agglomerates. This agglomeration force refers to the bonding of soil particles to each other through cohesion. The formation of this force can lead to an increase in the forces between the soil particles, so that the soil has sufficient resistance to external forces, of which the longest interparticle forces are mainly Van der Waals forces, Coulomb forces and surface tension. Because of the key role of colloidal forces in the soil formation process, the components of colloids, in their distributed form, are crucial for the development of soil succession. Soils are developed and stabilised by a combination of subtle forces within the soil. The research results on soil colloidal substances and microstructure are gradually being enriched in China. With the continuous improvement of research methods, the state of the soil basement is studied on a microscopic scale with the aid of scanning electron microscopy, light and electron microscopy, the mode of action of colloidal substances is analysed, and the composition of organic carbon functional groups is analysed semi-quantitatively by means of synchrotron radiation. In addition, soil structure has been studied using computed tomography, nuclear magnetic resonance and corresponding image processing techniques to investigate soil agglomerates, the relationship between cementing substances and soil structure and function, etc. However, due to the complexity of soil types and soil-forming environments, there is no universal theory of agglomerate formation processes and mechanisms.

Raman spectroscopy is a type of scattering spectroscopy and has been used in recent years in the field of soil science to study land engineering techniques. When a sample is examined, the sample is irradiated by a laser and the scattered laser light is generated by the interaction between the rotation of the sample molecules and the laser, which mainly includes Rayleigh scattering, Torx scattering and anti-Stokes scattering. Raman spectroscopy instruments can detect mainly the anti-Stokes scattering. Different substances have their own unique Raman spectral lines. The information on the position of the characteristic peaks, the full width of the half-peaks and the intensity of the peaks in the spectrum can be used for the analysis of the structure, state and special properties of the soil. Raman spectroscopy has a wide range of applications and plays an important role in the fields of materials, biology, environmental protection and geology. The analysis of soil samples using Raman spectroscopy enables a more in-depth and detailed study of soil structure and properties at the microscopic level.

3. Conclusion

With the increasing importance of basic research, the study of soil micromorphology from a microscopic perspective plays a vital role in improving the basic theory of soil science and aiding scientific and technological research and development in the field of land remediation techniques. Research in this area is becoming an important branch of the discipline. The study of soil microstructure provides a visual representation of soil conditions on a microscopic scale, and the results can be used to analyse soil genesis and evolution, as well as for land remediation techniques, analysis of the causes of geological hazards, mechanisms of soil quality degradation, soil formation processes and material changes in "man-made soils", depending on the purpose of the research. Research. Due to the instrumentation and sample preparation requirements for the observation of soil microstructure, only a small number of samples are required to observe the microform of the soil, so the representativeness of the sampling needs to be further explored, and a comprehensive description of the overall soil profile based on the results of a spot scan of a small number of samples requires a large number of observations to be compared to obtain a scientific and objective result. As the micromorphological properties of soils require the observer to compare the results of the images based on what has been observed, combined with specialist knowledge, to obtain specific results on soil micromorphology, the observer's control of specialist knowledge, and image recognition techniques are also essential for qualitative conclusions on soil micromorphology.

Acknowledgments

This study is financially supported by the Natural Science Basic Research Program of Shaanxi (2021JZ-57)；Shaanxi Province Innovative Talents Program-Youth Science and Technology Rising Star Project (2021KJXX-88)

References

1. Cao Mingjie, Hao Zhe, Yang Jingshuai, Xiang Tingting, Ni Junkang, Xu Ying, Kaibi. Effects of different improvement measures on soil micromorphology in drainage sites[J]. Nonferrous Metal Engineering,2020,10(05):96-102.
2. Zhang Baohua,Tao Baoxian,Cao Jianrong,Liu Ziting. Pore micromorphological characteristics of tidal soils in the lower Yellow River alluvial plain[J]. Geography of Arid Regions,2020,43(03):687-693.
3. Yang Jianjun,Wang Yihao,Wang Jian,Hu Yongfeng.Progress and prospects of microscale heavy metal soil chemistry research[J]. Journal of Soil Science,2020,57(03):530-539.
4. Charles S, Wu KN, Liang SY, Zhuang DC. Advances in the study of paleoanthropogenic activities based on site soil analysis[J]. Soil Bulletin,2019,50(04):958-964.
5. Zhang Baohua,Tao Baoxian,Liu Ziting,CaoJianrong. Micromorphological characteristics of different textured tidal soils in the lower Yellow River alluvial plain[J]. Shandong Agricultural Science,2019,51(07):67-71.
6. Li Zhenzhen,Wang Shu,Zhang Hongfei,Mao shuailei,REN Naou. Micromorphological study on the effect of clay on sandy soil improvement in the horqin sandy area of Inner Mongolia[J]. Journal of China Agricultural University,2018,23(11):115-123.
7. Ye Xiqiong. Study on the removal characteristics of petroleum hydrocarbons by microbial remediation and environmental changes of soil microbiology[D]. Xi'an University of Architecture and Technology,2018.
8. Hu Hui. Comparative study on the micromorphology of loess-paleosols in the north and south of the Qinling Mountains[D]. Shaanxi Normal University,2018.
9. Hu Hui,Pang Jiangli,Huang Chunchang,Zha Xiaochun,Zhou Yali,Mao Peini. Comparison of micromorphological characteristics of loess-paleosols in the north and south of the Qinling Mountains[J]. Soil Bulletin,2018,49(02):275-282.
10. Liu Ying, Wang Shu, Zhang Fengrong, Lv Yizhong, Li Zhenzhen, Mao shuailei,REN Naou. Micromorphological evaluation of fertility of sandy soils under different improvement measures: the case of horqin sandy land in Inner Mongolia[J]. Soil,2017,49(05):1023-1031.
11. Bai Yang, Chen Yiqian, Zhang Xiaohui. Study on the microstructure and mechanical properties of paleosols from landslides in freeze-thaw cycles [J]. People's Yangtze River, 2021, 52(07): 192-197+203. DOI: 10.16232/j.cnki .1001-4179.2021.07.032.
12. Luo Xilian, Wang Yike, Han Jichang, Gu Zhaolin. The effect of experimental period on the microstructure of arsenic sandstone-improved aeolian soil [J]. Journal of Xi'an Jiaotong University, 2021, 55(12): 172-179.

13. Wu Jiangpeng. Study on the influence of temperature and salt solution on the microstructure of clay based on nuclear magnetic resonance [D]. Guilin University of Technology, 2021.
14. Zhao Tianxiang. Study on the effect of grass ash on improving the mechanical stability of sandy subgrade slopes [D]. Inner Mongolia Agricultural University, 2021. DOI: 10.27229/d.cnki.gnmnu.2021.000429.
15. Huang Jianjia. Effects of free iron oxide on shear and consolidation strength of granite residual soil [D]. Huazhong Agricultural University, 2021.
16. Wang Huaixing. Experimental study on microbial solidification and erosion resistance of loess [D]. University of Chinese Academy of Sciences (Research Center for Soil and Water Conservation and Ecological Environment, Ministry of Education, Chinese Academy of Sciences), 2021.DOI:10.27558/d.cnki.gsthc.2021.000036.
17. Dong Shaowen, Ma Shuhua, Chu Mo, Wang Xiaohui, Wang Yuejiao, Liu Chenxu, Han Fenglan. Changes in the microstructure of saline-alkali soil under the action of fly ash-based soil conditioners [J]. Chinese Journal of Process Engineering: 1-9[2022- 01-12].
18. Guo Lina, Zhang Yongbo, Duan Qing, Shi Hong, Wu Aijing. A review of the research on the mechanical properties of soil modified by nanomaterials [J]. Water-Saving Irrigation, 2021(03):79-84.
19. Bai Linjie, Yin Song, Wang Jin, Li Xinming, Li Li. Experimental study on microstructural properties of silt under freeze-thaw cycles [J]. Journal of Zhongyuan University of Technology, 2021,32(01):55-59+73.

Treatment of Waterborne Coating Wastewater by Coagulation Sedimentation Fenton Oxidation Process

Chenxi Yang [1, 2, 3, 4, *], Jian Wang [1, 2, 3, 4]

[1] Institute of Land Engineering and Technology, Shaanxi Provincial Land Engineering Construction Group Co., Ltd., Xi'an 710075, China
[2] ShaanXi Provincial Land Engineering Construction Group Co., Ltd., Xi'an 710075, China
[3] Key Laboratory of Degraded and Unused Land Consolidation Engineering, the Ministry of Land and Resources, Xi'an 710075, China
[4] Shaanxi Provincial Land Consolidation Engineering Technology Research Center, Xi'an 710075, China

Abstract: waterborne coatings have become the development trend of the coating industry because of their less use of organic solvents and good environmental protection performance. However, the wastewater produced in the production process of waterborne coatings has become a difficult pollution source. Based on this, this paper uses coagulation sedimentation method and Fenton oxidation method to treat waterborne coating wastewater. Taking the COD of treated wastewater as the research index, this paper studies various factors affecting the treatment effect of coagulation sedimentation and Fenton oxidation. Through single factor analysis, the results show that the best dosage of PFS and PAM is PFS: 8 g/L and PAM: 0.8 g/L; In Fenton oxidation, the dosage of H2O2 is 9.98mL/L, the dosage of FeSO4 · 7H2O is n (Fe2+): n (H2O2) = 1:6, pH is 2, and the dosage times are 2.

Key words: coagulation sedimentation, Fenton oxidation, waterborne coating wastewater

1. Introduction

The water-based coating takes water as the dispersion medium. During the construction and subsequent drying process, the water volatilizes and returns to nature in a gas state, which will not harm the human body and the environment. Therefore, with the enhancement of people's awareness of environmental protection and the government's efforts to improve environmental protection, the water-based coating has become more and more popular [1,2]. However, in the production process, water-based coatings will produce a large amount of wastewater with high chroma, turbidity and COD content [3,4]. Therefore, how to treat water-based coating wastewater in an economical and simple way to make it meet the national discharge standard has become a major problem in water pollution control.

The main components of waterborne coatings include waterborne acrylic resin (film-forming material), deionized water, film-forming additives, wetting agent, defoamer, leveling agent, pH regulator, preservative, thickener, filler, pigment, etc [5]. The main sources of wastewater are batching tank washing liquid and cleaning wastewater. In principle, the washing solution of batching tank is the wastewater after the dilution of the original coating sample solution, so its chroma, turbidity and COD content are large. At present, aiming at the basically known pollution sources and types of water-based coating wastewater, the methods for treating this kind of organic wastewater at home and abroad mainly include incineration method, coagulation sedimentation method, chemical oxidation method, electrolysis method, biological method and combined method [6].

Taking the waterborne coating wastewater produced by a waterborne coating production company in Guangdong as the research object, this paper discusses the treatment conditions of waterborne coating wastewater by coagulation sedimentation method and Fenton oxidation method. Taking the COD removal rate as the screening index, various factors were compared and analyzed and the optimization conditions were studied.

2. Experiment

2.1 Materials and instruments

The reflux condenser, 250 mL conical flask, heating jacket, acid burette and thermometer are all purchased from the local chemical glass station. Silver sulfate (Ag2SO4, AR), mercury sulfate (HgSO4, AR), sulfuric acid (H2SO4, AR), phenanthroline (AR), potassium hydrogen phthalate (AR), polymeric ferric sulfate (PFS, AR), polypropylamide (PAM, AR), H2O2 (30%), ferric sulfate heptahydrate (FeSO4·7H2O, AR) and sodium hydroxide (NaOH, AR) were purchased from Sinopharm group.

* Corresponding author: 1098002212@qq.com

 https://doi.org/10.1051/e3sconf/202233801043

2.2 Coagulation sedimentation method

PFS is selected as coagulant and PAM as coagulant aid. Take several 100 mLwater samples into the beaker, add 8 g/L PFS and 0.6 g/L PAM respectively for coagulation test, and conduct the experiment by selecting the stirring strategy of fast stirring for 1 min and slow stirring for 1.5 min, and then set the sedimentation time as 1h.

2.3 Fenton oxidation method

H_2O_2 dosage, $FeSO_4 \cdot 7H_2O$ dosage, pH value and dosing times are selected as the control conditions. According to the literature, the ratio of n (Fe^{2+}): n (H_2O_2) is 1:5 ~ 8. Therefore, the amount of $FeSO_4 \cdot 7H_2O$ is calculated by calculating the amount of H_2O_2. The single factor test is carried out by controlling the variable method, so as to determine the optimal conditions of H_2O_2 dosage, $FeSO_4 \cdot 7H_2O$ dosage, pH value and dosing times.

3. Result Analysis

3.1 Treatment effect of coagulation sedimentation

Coagulation sedimentation can make the colloids and suspended solids in wastewater agglomerate into flocs through coagulation through the addition of coagulant, so as to precipitate and separate pollutants through sedimentation. The dosage of coagulant PFS and coagulant aid PAM determines the treatment efficiency of coagulation sedimentation. In the test, different amounts of PFS and PAM are added to treat coating wastewater, and the COD content of effluent is shown in Figure 1. With the increase of PFS dosage, the effluent COD decreases sharply. When the dosage increases to 8 g/L, the effluent COD removal rate reaches the peak. If the dosage of PFS continues to increase, the effluent COD decreases. The addition of PFS will hydrolyze and polymerize to form a variety of colloidal complex ions, which will promote the suspended solids and other pollutants in the coating to gather into flocs, so that the pollution can precipitate in the form of coagulation and sedimentation. However, when PFS is excessive, the opposite charges in the colloid will attract each other to form a new stable system, which reduces the coagulation and precipitation effect. Therefore, the optimal mass concentration of PFS is 8 g/L.

When the amount of PFS is controlled to be 8g / L, the effect of different coagulant aid dosage on COD removal rate is shown in Fig. 2 (b). The COD content of effluent decreased with the increase of PAM dosage, and reached the highest value at 0.8 g/L. When the dosage of PAM continues to increase, the COD of effluent will increase. This is because too many polymers will cover the surface of colloidal particles, and the polymers will repel each other due to the same charge, so that the colloidal particles cannot gather. Moreover, because PAM is a high molecular organic matter, when the dosage of PAM is excessive, only one part will precipitate through bridging adsorption, and the other part will remain in the supernatant to increase the cod, The removal rate becomes smaller. Therefore, the best mass concentration of PAM is 0.8 g/L.

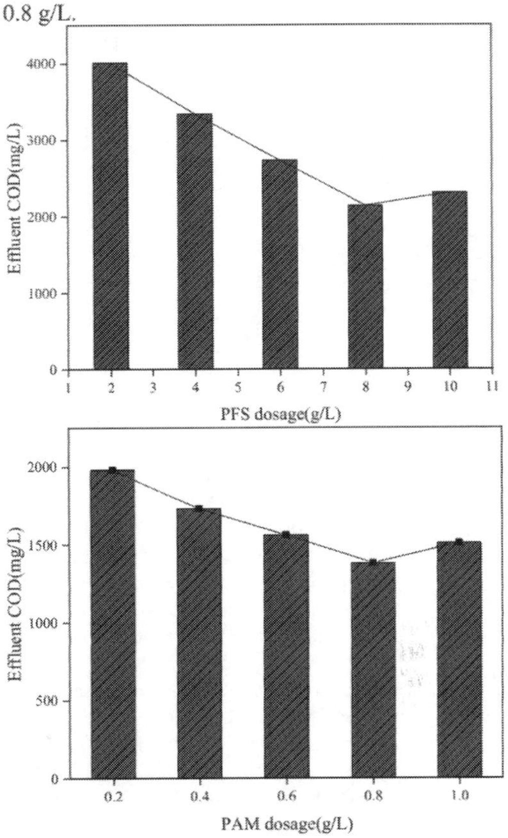

Figure 1. (a) effect of PFS dosage on effluent COD; (b) Effect of PAM dosage on effluent COD.

3.2 Treatment of coating wastewater by Fenton oxidation

2.2.1 Influence of H2O2 Dosage on Treatment Effect

Fenton process refers to the reaction between H_2O_2 and Fe^{2+} to produce · oh. This hydroxyl radical can oxidize the organic matter in coating wastewater, so as to shorten the molecular chain segment of organic matter or mineralize it into CO_2 and H_2O. The ·OH produced by H_2O_2 is the core of chemical oxidation method. Therefore, firstly, the effect of H_2O_2 dosage on Fenton reaction is studied. Experimental conditions: the wastewater used in Fenton oxidation treatment is the wastewater treated under the best conditions of coagulation and sedimentation. At this time, the COD is 1380 mg / L. the effect of H_2O_2 on Fenton reaction is determined by fixing the dosage of $FeSO_4 \cdot 7H_2O$ as n (Fe2 +): n (H_2O_2) = 1:6 And pH 2.

The amount of H_2O_2 added is 1.66 mL/L, 3.33 mL/L, 6.65 mL/L, 9.98 mL/L, 13.30 mL/L and 16.63 mL/L respectively. After adjusting the pH to 2, detect the CODcr concentration and turbidity. The results are shown in Figure 2.

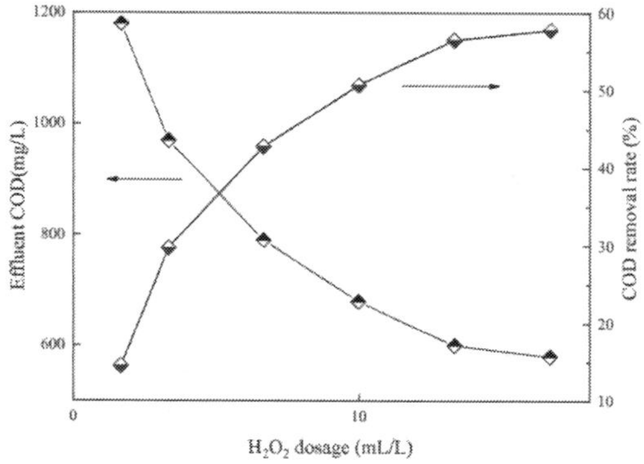

Figure 2. Effect of H_2O_2 dosage on COD removal effect

It can be seen from Figure 2 that the dosage of H_2O_2 will affect the treatment effect of wastewater. When the dosage was less than 9.98 mL/L, the CODcr removal rate increased significantly with the increase of H_2O_2 dosage; After 9.98 mL/L, the change of CODcr removal rate tends to be gentle. This is because when the H_2O_2 dosage is low, with the increase of H_2O_2 dosage, H_2O_2 will produce more · OH, so as to oxidize organic matter, reduce COD and increase COD removal rate. When the dosage of H_2O_2 is greater than 9.98ml/l, even adding more H_2O_2 will not reduce the COD of wastewater, because adding more H_2O_2will only produce ineffective decomposition and cannot increase the COD removal rate. Therefore, it can be seen from the above data that the optimal H_2O_2 dosage for wastewater treatment is 9.98 mL/L.

2.2.2 Effect of pH on Treatment Effect

According to the wastewater treatment mechanism of Fenton oxidation reaction, pH value will affect the direction of reaction. From the reaction formula Fe^{2+} + $H_2O_2 \rightarrow Fe^{3+}$ + OH + · OH, it can be seen that Oh will be continuously consumed under acidic conditions, which promotes the reaction to the right. When the pH is low, it will inhibit the progress of the above reaction and reduce the production of · OH. In order to explore the optimal pH value of oxidation treatment of waterborne coating wastewater, the optimal pH value of Fenton reaction in waterborne coating wastewater was studied by controlling single factor experiment. Experimental conditions: the experimental raw water is the wastewater treated under the best conditions of coagulation and sedimentation. The COD is 1380 mg/L, the dosage of H_2O_2 is 9.98mL/L, and the dosage of $FeSO_4 \cdot 7H_2O$ is 3.03g/L calculated according to n (Fe^{2+}): n (H_2O_2) = 1:6. The effect of pH on Fenton reaction was studied by changing pH, and the results are shown in Fig. 3.

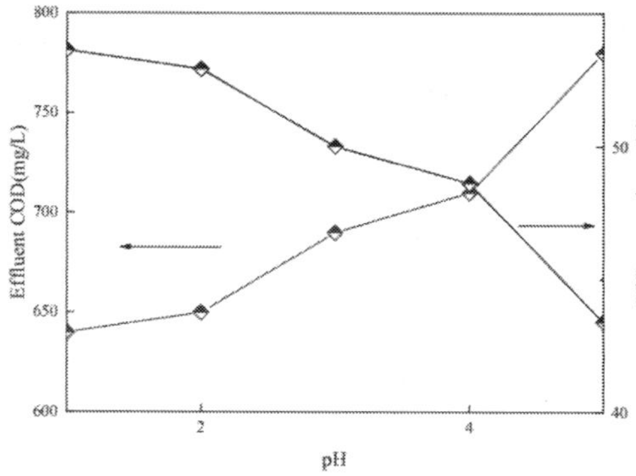

Figure 3. Effect of pH Dosage on COD Removal Effect

As shown in Figure 3, pH will affect the effect of Fenton oxidation treatment of wastewater. The COD of water-based coating wastewater after Fenton oxidation treatment decreases with the decrease of pH, and the COD removal rate increases. When the pH is 2, the effluent COD reaches the peak value of this single factor test treatment. When the pH continues to decrease to 1, the COD of the treated wastewater basically does not change. It shows that the Fenton reaction has reached the best acidic condition of Fenton oxidation reaction when the pH is 2. Further reducing the pH can not continue to improve the oxidation treatment effect. Therefore, when the pH is 2, it can be used as the best pH for Fenton oxidation treatment of waterborne coating wastewater. [7]

4. Conclusion

The optimal treatment conditions were explored by coagulation sedimentation and Fenton oxidation. The following conclusions are drawn through the single factor test method:

(1) The effect of PFS and PAM dosage on effluent COD in coagulation sedimentation method is discussed through single factor experiment. The optimal conditions are PFS: 8 g/L and PAM: 0.8 g/L.

(2) According to the experimental results of Fenton oxidation reaction, the optimal reaction conditions for COD removal rate are determined: the dosage of H2O2 is 9.98mL/L; The dosage of $FeSO_4 \cdot 7H_2O$ is: n (Fe^{2+}): n (H_2O_2) = 1:6; PH 2; The number of dosing is 2.

Acknowledgments

This work was financially supported by Shaanxi Provincial Land Engineering Construction Group internal research project (DJNY2021-22) fund.

Reference

1. Chen Xiuning, Xu Ning, he Chenglin, Yang Jinsong, Xu Yuhua, Xu Yujun, Lin Jianxin. Current situation and Prospect of waterborne coatings [J]. Coating technology and abstracts, 2016,37 (03): 41-45

2. Wang Xiaoming. Research on waterborne acrylic resin coatings [D]. Nanjing University of Aeronautics and Astronautics, 2012
3. Tang Hongxia. Analysis on hazardous characteristics of sludge from water-based building coating wastewater treatment [J]. Environmental protection science, 2019,45 (04): 45-49
4. Zhang Zhonghua. Emulsion wastewater treatment during waterborne coatings production [J]. China building waterproofing, 2018 (21): 34-36.
5. Tang Benhui. Study on compatibility of waterborne wood coating additives [D]. South China University of technology, 2013
6. Xing Yao, Cheng Aihua. Study on the treatment of camouflage coating wastewater by coagulation Fenton oxidation [J]. Industrial water treatment, 2016, 36 (07): 48-51
7. Song Xiaozhi. Wastewater treatment technology for coating additive production [J]. Water purification technology, 2014, 33 (S1): 64-67

https://doi.org/10.1051/e3sconf/202233801044

Preparation of supercapacitors based on sludge utilization

Qingying Ye *

School of environment, North China Electric Power University, Baoding, China

Abstract. The acceleration of urbanization has made environmental problems increasingly prominent. With the continuous increase in the volume of urban sewage discharged annually, the problem of urban sludge pollution has gradually become an environmental problem in our country. At the same time, the expansion of grid-connected new energy has also continuously raised new challenges to low-cost and high-efficiency energy storage technology. This paper uses municipal sludge to prepare low-cost supercapacitors, that is, using municipal sludge as a raw material, through a series of physical and chemical processes such as drying, doping, impregnation, and activation, to prepare carbon-based porous electrode materials that can be used for supercapacitors. On the one hand, it solves the problem of sludge disposal. On the other hand, it greatly reduces the cost of supercapacitors and provides a new idea for preparing supercapacitors.

1. Introduction

With the acceleration of China's urbanization process, the discharge of urban sewage and sludge is increasing year by year. The sludge contains a lot of heavy metals, viruses, pathogens and other harmful substances. If improperly disposed of, it will cause serious secondary environmental pollution [1,2]. How to effectively treat urban sludge is a new issue that China faces after air and water pollution control. The main disposal methods of foreign sludge include sludge landfill, incineration and reclamation. European and American countries mainly use landfill and farmland. Japan's sludge from sea reclamation accounts for more than 70%. At present, there are many domestic research methods for sludge treatment in China, including sanitary landfill, incineration, ocean dumping, anaerobic digestion, supercritical gasification, and hydrothermal treatment.

Supercapacitors are widely used in the new power industry due to their super fast charge and discharge capabilities and reliability. At present, China has not independently mastered the super capacitor technology, while foreign super capacitors are expensive and costly. There have been many studies on the preparation of activated carbon from sludge and the preparation of supercapacitors by using activated carbon, but there are few studies on the preparation of supercapacitors by directly using sludge. The reason is that the purity of the sludge carbon source is not high and ordinary activated carbon is difficult to meet the requirements of supercapacitors. Based on this background, this paper uses sludge as a raw material to prepare super electrode materials. The aim is to improve the purity of activated carbon from sludge through carbon source (straw) method, and use template method to realize porous carbon-based materials, and use modification methods to improve the specific energy density of the electrode of super electrode materials.

2. Preparation process

The entire preparation process roughly includes: after the collected municipal sludge is initially refined and purified, cellulose carbon sources such as straws are added for template design, and then the performance of the prepared electrode material is characterized. Under the diaphragm, the supercapacitor monolithic package is completed.

2.1 Refining

This part intends to use the activated carbonization method to prepare porous carbon-based materials. After drying, the municipal sewage sludge is crushed and screened (with straw blending), and then soaked in phosphoric acid solution for a certain period of time. The acidified sludge is subjected to shaking, pyrolysis, and carbonization treatment, and the phosphoric acid is recycled and reused. The processed sample is fully immersed in hot water and phosphoric acid is recovered at the same time. Finally, the carbon-based product is dried and milled, the whole process as shown in Figure 1.

Fig. 1 Sludge scouring and purification process

* Corresponding author: 1265439827@qq.com

Improved on the basis of traditional sludge purification activated carbon technology, taking into account the pseudocapacitance needs of supercapacitors, the treated sludge should maintain a certain amount of metal-containing impurities (as composite or doping), which greatly reduces the traditional technical requirements .At the same time, it is also conducive to the subsequent doping modification process of electrode materials. The carbon-based material obtained through preliminary refining and purification has the characteristics of being fluffy, doped to a certain degree, and porous. However, it is not suitable for electrode materials of supercapacitors, and further chemical design and electrical performance improvement are required.

2.2 Chemical design

With the help of MS software, a variety of possible topologies can be designed. In this step, the research focuses from the macroscopic sludge to the microscopic single-molecule structure design. Using the template method, adding highly fibrous straw and waste paper for mixed treatment, so that the organic carbon molecules in the sludge grow along the highly fibrous carbon skeleton, and then gradually remove its hydrogen and oxygen during the subsequent activation carbonization process. Retaining carbon skeleton, its porous lattice structure and good thermal stability make the activated carbon at this stage have certain electrochemical properties.

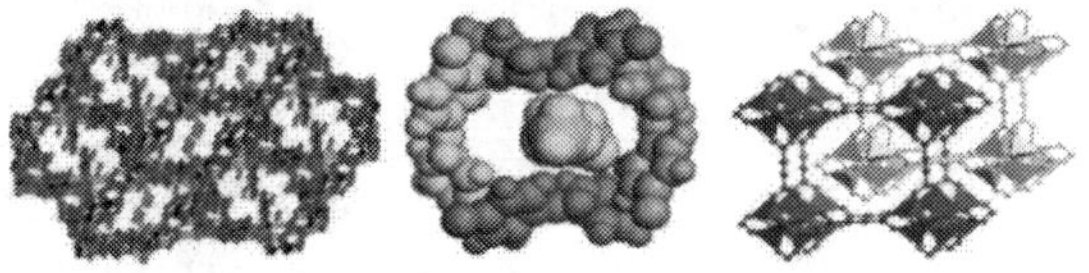

Fig 2. Micro-molecular structure design of sludge

Figure 3 shows the comparison of carbon-based materials before and after the molecular structure design of sludge under the electron microscope. The sludge sample designed by the template method is more dispersed and porous under the electron microscope, and has a larger specific surface area than before. Its ultra-microstructure enables it to have a complex ion channel unique to the super electrode material, which can hold more electrons. However, macroscopically, the battery performance is not yet known, and further measurement and characterization work is still needed.

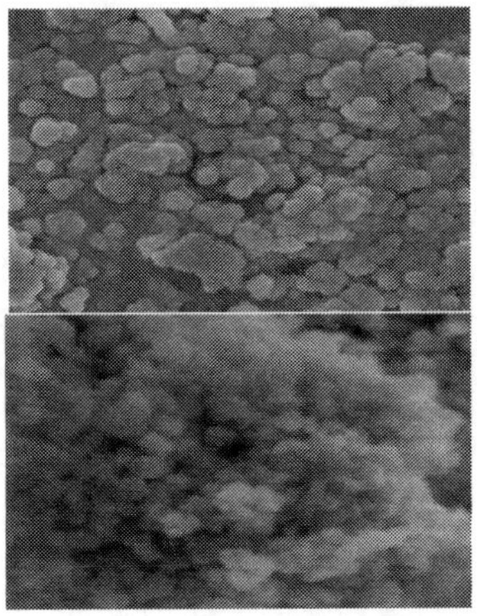

Figure 3. Comparison of carbon-based materials before and after sludge molecular structure design under electron microscope

2.3 Research on the characteristics of supercapacitors

At this stage, the development of high-energy-density electrodes must be realized. The carbon-based samples prepared above are combined with faraday pseudocapacitance materials, such as MnO2, Ni(OH)2, etc[4].to prepare composite electrodes to obtain better specific capacitance characteristics. The electrode material after the composite pseudocapacitance material tends to have a higher porosity, and has a preliminary fibrous template, which indicates that the electrode material produced has preliminary requirements in terms of physical and chemical structure. However, further research on its electrochemical performance is still needed through electrochemical experiments.

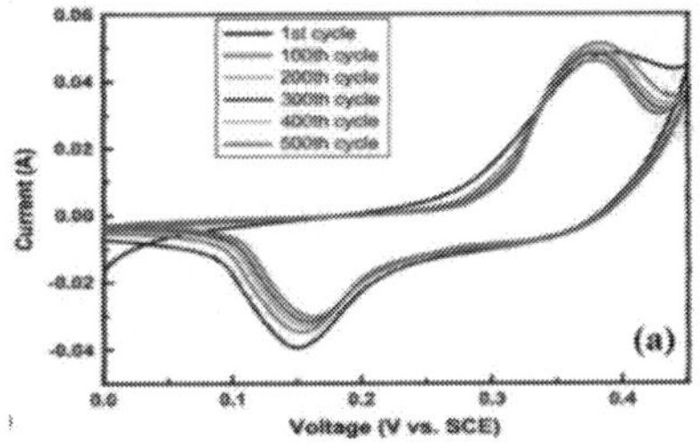

Fig 4. Cyclic Voltammetric Test of Capacitor Material

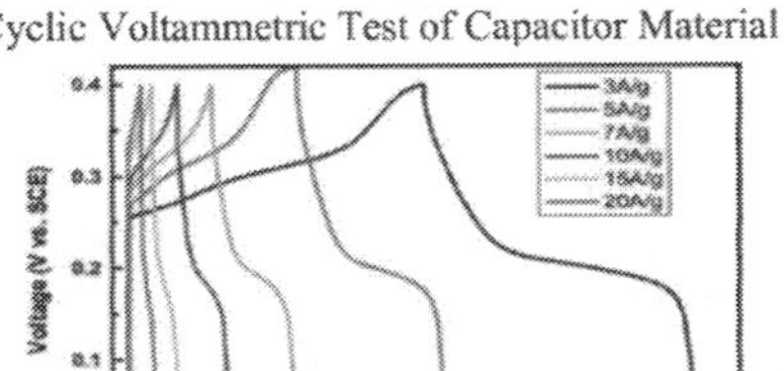

Fig.5 The relationship between the highest capacitance ratio and time under different electrolyte concentrations

In order to verify the electrochemical characteristics of the fabricated electrode materials, electrochemical tests are required. From Figure 4, we can clearly see the uniform and symmetrical redox window, which proves the high reversibility of the charge and discharge of the material. Figure 5 shows that under different electrolyte adaptations, the highest specific capacitance can reach 265.6F/g. This result can even be compared with some graphene parameters (200~300F/g) on the market.
At this time, the sludge electrode material we have developed has the characteristics of a super electrode. The next step is to focus on the adaptation of the electrolyte, so that the performance of the material can be thoroughly demonstrated and improved.

2.4 Screening of electrolyte and diaphragm

Study the coupling of organic electrolyte and sludge carbon-based materials and the selection of membrane materials, and carry out screening experiments on high-separation membrane materials with selective permeability to obtain membranes suitable for sludge carbon-based super electrodes. After hundreds of adaptation processes at this stage, we finally screened out the electrolyte and selective diaphragm that are supported by the sludge composite material, and its capacitance performance can be adequately guaranteed.

2.5 Package molding

After completing the synthesis of the electrode material, the capacitor needs to be encapsulated. Mix the electrode material, conductive additives and binder according to the proportions, and evenly coat them on a current collector such as foamed nickel. Use a tablet press to press the current collector sheet to a thickness of about 0.3 mm, and wind it with a winding machine. In the vacuum glove box, the prepared electrode sheets are assembled into the super capacitor shell, electrolyte is injected, the diaphragm is added, and the aluminum shell is sealed with a sealing machine.

2.6 Field test

After completing the packaging of the capacitor monomer, in order to further study its energy storage performance and application prospects, with the cooperation of the Shanghai Electric Power Research Institute, the developed sludge supercapacitor was connected to the test bypass of its high-voltage main building for on-site assembly and test. The test results show that the operating temperature distribution is stable and the temperature rise is not obvious under normal operating conditions and long-term overload conditions, which is in line with the temperature rise of normal batteries. It shows that the capacitor meets the preliminary requirements of the power grid and has certain application value.
The power grid's requirements for the energy density of supercapacitors are not as high as those in the field of electric vehicles, so the use of sludge carbon-based materials to prepare supercapacitors can fully meet the performance requirements. At the same time, because the cost of supercapacitors is mainly concentrated in the synthesis and preparation of electrode materials, the use of sludge activated carbon can greatly save the expense of electrode materials. When the initial investment is the same, the supercapacitors made of this material will get better than traditional electrochemical supercapacitors. Large energy storage power and energy storage capacity, that is, higher cost performance.

Figure 6. Field test and operation

3. Conclusion

In this paper, sludge is used as a raw material, through refining and purification, molecular design, electrochemical testing, electrolyte adaptation and encapsulation, and finally a supercapacitor material with higher specific energy density and higher cycle times is obtained. After on-site testing, it shows that it basically meets the requirements of the power grid.
After the super capacitor energy storage technology is applied to wind power and photovoltaic power generation, it can smooth the short-term power output fluctuations of the power station caused by unstable natural conditions such as wind and light. Due to the shortcomings of volatility, intermittentness, and unpredictability of renewable energy power generation, as well as traditional energy storage power sources used as wind power pitch power sources, power distribution network backup power sources have high maintenance costs and limited service life [5]. These all lead to long response time of physical energy storage and substandard power density of battery energy storage when compensating the pulse load of the grid. The output power density of the low-cost supercapacitor developed in this paper is as high as several kW/kg, and the cycle life can reach hundreds of thousands or even millions of times. It has reached the microgrid requirements in terms of cycle times, charging time, and safety, and has strong application value for the large-scale grid connection of new energy in the future.

References

1. Zhou Xuhong, Carbon nanotube-nickel hydroxide composite electrode electrochemical capacitor [J]. Electronic Components and Materials, 2015, 04: 16-18+21.
2. Qian Jueshi, Xie Congbo, Xie Xiaoli, et al. Utilization status and research progress of urban

https://doi.org/10.1051/e3sconf/202233801044

sewage sludge as building materials. Journal of Building Materials, 2014, 17(5): 830~835.

3. Wang Dazhi, Preparation of nickel oxide/carbon nanotube supercapacitors from sludge[J]. Chinese Journal of Inorganic Chemistry, 2013, 02:137-141.
4. Wang Xiaofeng, Electrochemical behavior of deposited nickel oxide and its supercapacitors[J]. Journal of Inorganic Materials, 2013, 02:331-336.
5. Chen Yingfang, Li Yuanyuan, Deng Meigen. The principle and application of supercapacitors[J]. Electronic Components and Materials, 2015, 04: 6-9.

https://doi.org/10.1051/e3sconf/202233801045

Study on advanced treatment of wastewater by advanced oxidation based on sulfate radical

Qingying Ye*

School of environment, North China Electric Power University, Baoding, China

Abstract. At present, the use of water in each country increases sharply, which also brings increasingly prominent environmental pollution problems. A large amount of wastewater is discharged into the water body, which seriously pollutes the water environment. Wastewater treatment has become the focus of global environmental protection workers. Among them, advanced oxidation technology based on sulfate radical is used to treat refractory organic pollutants. The technology has good cleaning efficiency and oxidation stability. In order to improve the universality of research and application and in-depth decontamination, this free radical advanced oxidation method was applied to the advanced treatment of wastewater. However, divalent iron ions react with Na2S2O3 very quickly, resulting in the reaction stopping soon. Therefore, zero valent iron (ZVI) is used to activate sodium persulfate to produce sulfate radical instead of divalent Fe ion. ZVI activation is applied to wastewater treatment.

1. Introduction

At present, the use of water in every country in the world increases sharply, which also brings increasingly prominent environmental pollution problems [1]. Although some measures have been taken to recover, treat and recycle the wastewater in the production process, a large amount of wastewater is still discharged into the water body, causing serious pollution to the water environment. Wastewater treatment has become the focus of global environmental protection workers. There are many components in sewage that directly affect the environment, such as colloidal substances, sulfonates, sugars, ketones, calcium, magnesium salts and residual sulfites. Then there is the sewage condensate. The main pollutants include methanol, ethanol, acetone, butanone, furfural and mushroom olefins. The pollutants in sewage are various, toxic and difficult to treat, so they pose a great threat to human health development. There is an urgent need for relevant research, which can not only effectively remove pollution in depth, but also realize the effect of green economy.

Advanced oxidation method is an effective method for advanced sewage treatment. Advanced oxidation is a new wastewater treatment method rising in the last century. Under this treatment method, the relevant organic pollutants in the sewage are transformed into CO_2, H_2O, etc., or some substances that are easy to explain [2]. This method has the advantages of high processing efficiency, simple equipment requirements and high green. Advanced oxidation method is subdivided into ozone oxidation method, O/H_2O_2 oxidation method, $UV/O_3/H_2O_2$, etc. Among them, advanced oxidation technology based on sulfate radical is used to treat refractory organic pollutants. The technology has the advantages of good cleaning efficiency, good oxidation stability, strong popularization, good oxidant stability and little influence by pH value [3].

In detail, sodium persulfate is one of them. Of course, it also has many of the above advantages, such as strong oxidation, good water solubility and low price. It has received extensive attention from researchers in the research of advanced oxidation technology. However, it is difficult to achieve the ideal effect of degradation and decontamination by sodium persulfate oxidation alone. At present, the methods of stimulating sodium persulfate to produce sulfate radical mainly include thermal activation method, illumination method, ultrasonic activation method [4], microwave activation method, transition metal activation method and so on. Divalent iron ions are widely used in advanced oxidation technology. Many previous studies have confirmed that the sulfate radical produced by sodium persulfate activated by divalent iron ion can effectively degrade aromatic organic pollutants. Therefore, in order to improve the universality and in-depth decontamination of research and application, this free radical advanced oxidation method is applied to the advanced treatment of wastewater in this experiment. In order to make up for the defects of Fenton oxidation in practical application, and explore the process conditions, so as to lay a foundation for the optimization of the process in the future. However, divalent iron ions react with $Na_2S_2O_3$ very quickly, and the reaction can be completed in an instant, resulting in the rapid stop of the reaction [5]. In order to control the concentration of divalent Fe ions, zero valent iron (ZVI) was used to activate sodium persulfate instead of divalent Fe ions to

* Corresponding author: 1265439827@qq.com

 https://doi.org/10.1051/e3sconf/202233801045

produce sulfate free radical. ZVI activation was applied to wastewater treatment.

2. Experimental design and concentration determination

In this paper, ZVI activation is applied to wastewater treatment in order to achieve better treatment effect, and the process conditions are preliminarily explored. Zero valent iron (ZVI) replaces divalent Fe ion to activate sodium persulfate to produce sulfate radical. Its principle is shown in formulas (1) and (2). The principle is to use ZVI as the source of divalent Fe ions, continuously release divalent Fe ions to activate sodium persulfate, and continuously produce SO_4 negative ions to oxidize and degrade organic pollutants.

$$Fe^0 + S_2O_8^- \rightarrow Fe^{2+} + 2SO_4^{2-} \quad (1)$$

$$Fe^{2+} + S_2O_8^- \rightarrow Fe^{3+} + SO_4^- + SO_4^{2-} \quad (2)$$

Take 100ml waste water sample into 250ml sample, adjust the pH value to 2.8~3.1 with 12% dilute sulfuric acid, add quantitative reduced iron powder, and then quickly add oxidant ($Na_2S_2O_8$) for rapid mixing. Set the mixing time as 20min. After that, take out a certain amount of water sample and add NaOH solution to adjust the pH to 9~9.5 to terminate the reaction. Then centrifuge for 26min under the working condition of 3250r/min, and take the supernatant for detection. The experimental temperature was 26℃ and the reaction time was 3 hours. 2~3 parallel experiments were performed in each group.

This part mainly gives the concentration determination method of divalent iron ion and $Na_2S_2O_8$. The concentration of divalent iron ion is determined by o-phenanthroline spectrophotometry, and the determination steps are as follows. First, prepare iron standard stock, weigh 0.6985g ammonium ferrous sulfate, completely dissolve it with 48ml sulfuric acid, and bottle it for standby. Then, prepare iron standard solution. Accurately measure 24ml of prepared iron standard stock solution with a pipette, add distilled water, shake well, and leave for use. Each ml contains 24.8 micrograms of iron.

Draw the standard curve below, measure 0, 2, 4, 6, 8 and 10ml of iron standard solution successively with a pipette, transfer it into a 150ml conical flask, add about 50 ml of distilled water, slowly transfer it into a conical flask, add 10ml of 10% hydroxylamine hydrochloride, heat it, put 1~2 glass beads into it, vibrate and boil it, stop heating when 15ml of solution is left, and place it to cool to room temperature, Transfer the remaining solution to a 50 ml stoppered colorimetric tube. Add a small piece of Congo red test paper into the colorimetric tube, and drop saturated sodium acetate solution into the colorimetric tube. The end point of titration is as soon as the test paper turns red. Then transfer 5 ml buffer solution and 2ml 0.5% o-phenanthroline solution into the colorimetric tube, add distilled water to the mark, shake well and develop color for 15 min. Then, the absorbance value was measured with an ultraviolet spectrophotometer at 510nm with water as the reference. Figure 1 shows the obtained standard curve. Finally, the concentration of ferrous ion in the reaction is determined: according to the above method, the absorbance of ferrous ion in each reaction solution is measured by ultraviolet spectrophotometer at 510 nm, and it is converted into the concentration value through the standard curve.

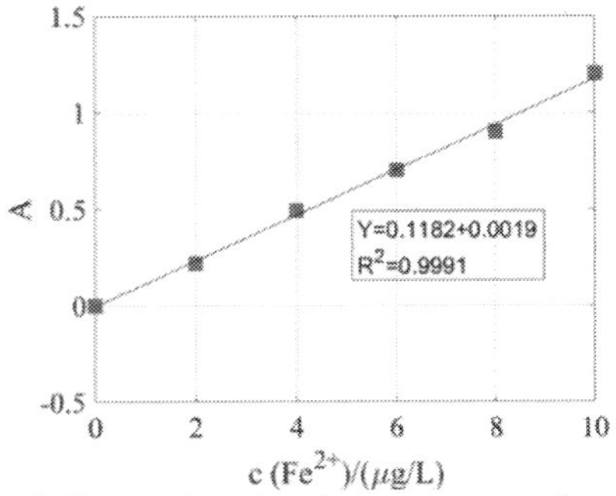

Figure 1. Ferrous ion absorbance concentration standard curve.

The determination steps of $Na_2S_2O_3$ concentration are as follows. First, prepare $Na_2S_2O_3$ storage solution. Weigh 0.0476g $Na_2S_2O_3$ powder and dissolve it in 100ml deionized water. After it is completely dissolved, slowly transfer it into a 1000ml volumetric flask, add distilled water to dilute it to the scale mark, shake it evenly and leave it for use. The solution concentration is 0.20mmol/l.

The absorbance concentration standard curve of $Na_2S_2O_3$ is drawn below. Take 0, 2, 4, 6, 8 and 10ml $Na_2S_2O_3$ stock solution successively with a pipette into a 50ml colorimetric tube and dilute with distilled water; Then add 0.2g $NaHCO_3$ and 4G ki into the colorimetric tube in turn and fully dissolve them. Dilute them with deionized water to the scale line, shake them evenly to fully mix them. After standing for color development for 15min, use unicuv-2100 UV-Vis spectrophotometer to measure their absorbance value with water as reference at the maximum absorption wavelength of 352nm. Figure 2 shows the standard curve drawn with $Na_2S_2O_3$ concentration as the abscissa and absorbance value as the ordinate. The concentration of $Na_2S_2O_3$ in the reaction was determined. Determine the absorbance of $Na_2S_2O_3$ in the solution to be tested in sequence according to the above steps, and convert it into the concentration value by using the standard curve.

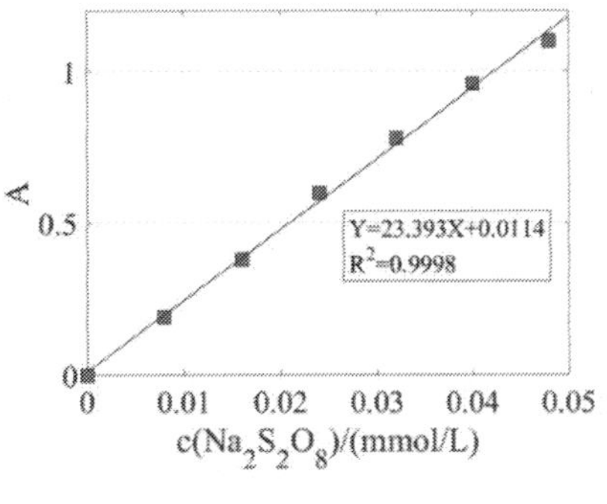

Figure 2. $Na_2S_2O_8$ absorbance concentration standard curve.

https://doi.org/10.1051/e3sconf/202233801045

3. Results and analysis

Figure 3 shows the effect of pH value on CODcr degradation rate and chroma removal rate of biochemical effluent from papermaking wastewater by ZVI activated $Na_2S_2O_3$ oxidation degradation. It can be seen that the CODcr degradation rate and chroma removal rate of biochemical effluent of papermaking wastewater by oxidation and degradation of $Na_2S_2O_3$ activated by ZVI decreased with the increase of pH value. When the initial pH value was 3, the degradation effect was the best, and the CODcr degradation rate and chroma removal rate reached 41.4% and 83.5% respectively; As the pH value increased gradually, the degradation effect began to deteriorate, and the downward trend suddenly increased when the initial pH>7; When the initial pH was adjusted from 7 to 10, the degradation rate of CODCr decreased from 39.3% to 27.3%. At this time, the reduction of chroma removal rate was more obvious, from 83% at initial pH=7 to 18.5% at pH=10. This shows that the suitable initial pH range for the oxidative degradation of organic matter by sulfate radical produced by ZVI activated sodium persulfate is acidic to neutral, and strong acidic conditions are more conducive to the formation of sulfate radical. The experiment shows that under the weak alkaline condition of papermaking wastewater without adjusting the initial pH value, the sulfate radical produced by ZVI activated sodium persulfate can still reduce the CODcr and chromaticity of papermaking wastewater, which is of great significance for the application of advanced oxidation method in papermaking wastewater engineering.

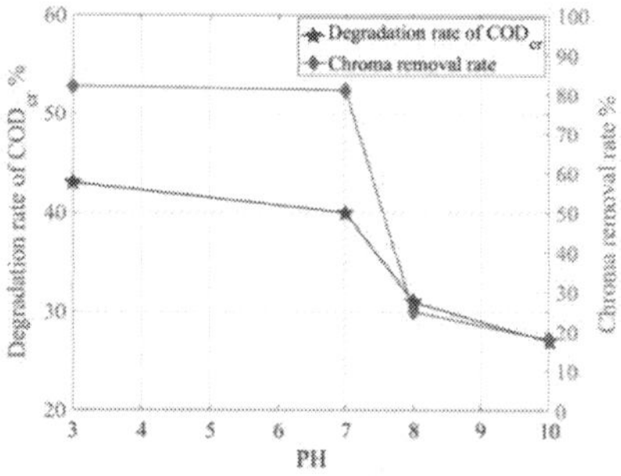

Figure 3. Effect of pH value on CODcr degradation rate and chroma removal rate.

The following is about the changes of pollutants in the secondary effluent of wastewater before and after advanced oxidation treatment, as shown in Table 1. Here, only 10 types are listed.It can be seen from table 1 that the refractory organics in the secondary biochemical effluent of papermaking wastewater are mostly aromatic substances with benzene ring and long-chain alkanes. After the oxidation and degradation of sulfate radical, the benzene substances in the wastewater have been degraded to a certain extent, the relative content has changed to a certain extent, and the types have basically not changed. This may be due to the competitive consumption of sulfate radical by various organic pollutants. The type and content of alkanes increased significantly, indicating that the pollutants were further oxidized and degraded.

Table 1. Changes of pollutants in wastewater before and after advanced oxidation treatment.

Numble	retention time/ min	Compound name	Chemical formula	Relative content%	Confidence%
1	4.729	N-octane	C8H18	1.312	24
2	6.413	ethylbenzene	C8H10	5.015	92
3	6.692	P-xylene	C8H10	14.014	98
4	7.376	O-diphenyl	C8H10	6.875	98
5	7.697	n-Nonane	C9H20	0.985	97
6	9.350	Cumene	C9H12	1.514	92
7	9.601	3-ethyltoluene	C9H12	7.068	96
8	9.698	O-ethyl toluene	C9H12	3.224	96
9	9.874	Mesitylene	C9H12	3.254	97
10	10.136	Trimethylene	C9H12	3.401	97

4. Conclusion

Sulfate radical can effectively degrade organic pollutants in secondary biochemical effluent of papermaking wastewater under acidic to neutral conditions. The increase of pH range of advanced oxidation method based on sulfate radical is of great significance in the practical engineering application of advanced oxidation technology. PH value has an important effect on CODcr degradation rate and chromaticity removal rate of secondary biochemical effluent of advanced treatment of papermaking wastewater by sulfate radical The effects are as follows: pH3.0⩾pH7.0>pH10.0.

The changes of substances before and after the oxidative degradation of sulfate radical show that sulfate radical can effectively degrade the refractory organic pollutants in the secondary biochemical effluent of papermaking wastewater. The decrease of the relative content of benzene substances and the obvious increase of alkanes indicate that the pollutants have been effectively oxidized and degraded.

References

1. P. Qiao, J. Wu, H. Li, et al. Plasmon Ag Promoted Solar-Thermal Conversion on Floating Carbon Cloth for Seawater Desalination and Sewage Disposal.Acs Applied Materials & Interfaces, 2019.
2. K. Koop, P. Hutchings.Disposal of sewage to the ocean – Still a sustainable solution?. Marine Pollution Bulletin, 2019, 145.

https://doi.org/10.1051/e3sconf/202233801045

3. A. Ding, R. Zhang, H. H. Ngo, et al. Life cycle assessment of sewage sludge treatment and disposal based on nutrient and energy recovery: A review. Science of The Total Environment, 2021, 769:144451.
4. B. S. Choudri, Y. Charabi. Health effects associated with wastewater treatment, reuse, and disposal. Water Environment Research, 2019, 91(10).G.R. Mettam, How to prepare an electronic version of your article, in: B.S. Jones, R.Z. Smith (Eds.), Introduction to the Electronic Age, E-Publishing Inc., New York, 1999, pp. 281-304.
5. Chen N, Tao S, Xiao K, et al. A one-step acidification strategy for sewage sludge dewatering with oxalic acid. Chemosphere, 2020, 238(Jan.):124598.1-124598.11.P.G. Clem, M. Rodriguez, J.A. Voigt and C.S. Ashley, U.S. Patent 6,231,666. (2001).

Application of adjacent heating technology in thermal power unit

Yongqiang Che [1, 2, *], Yanfei Zhang [3] and Haizhen Lv [4]

[1] Shandong Electric Power Research Institute, Jinan, China
[2] State Grid Shandong Electric Power Research Institute, Jinan, China
[3] National Energy Group Shenhua Guohua Shouguang Power Generation Co., Ltd, Shouguang, China
[4] Shandong Zhongshiyitong Group Co., Ltd, Jinan, China

Abstract. There are many problems in the start-up stage of thermal power unit, which seriously affect the safe and economic operation of the unit. Therefore, it is of great significance to study the energy-saving technology of thermal power unit in the start-up stage. The adjacent heating technology is put forward to solve these problems in the boiler start-up stage. Thermal power unit USES the adjacent machine heating technology, improve the conditions of the boiler ignition and steady combustion conditions, improve the safety of the boiler start-up, saves the costs of fuel oil, coal, electricity, strengthened the flushing efficiency, shorten the flush time, improve the economic benefit of the adjacent machine, and prevent the scale caused by dramatic change wall temperature fall off, It can also ensure the safe operation of desulfurization, denitration and dust removal devices, and reduce the emission of pollutants, so it has a broad application prospect.

1. Introduction

As the goal requirements of "carbon peak, carbon neutralization" and "building a new power system with new energy as the main body" are put forward one after another, the position of thermal power units in the power supply structure is changing from electric power to regulatory power, and the frequency and depth of thermal power units' participation in the peak and frequency regulation of the power grid is increasing day by day. In this new situation, thermal power units should not only meet the demand of peak and frequency modulation of power network, but also ensure the safety and economy of unit operation. However, in the start-up stage of thermal power units, problems such as high energy consumption, stable combustion difference, and excessive emissions have always existed, which seriously affect the safe and economic operation of thermal power units [1]. Therefore, it is of great significance to study the energy-saving technology of thermal power units in the start-up stage. The adjacent heating technology is put forward to solve these problems in the boiler start-up stage.

This paper mainly studies the application of the adjacent heating technology in thermal power units. After fully investigating the situation of the power plant that adopts the adjacent heating technology, the adjacent heating technology is summarized from the aspects of the technical scheme, operation measures, considerations for switching off, economic benefits, safety benefits, environmental benefits and so on. Other types of adjacent heating schemes are also briefly described.

2. Problems existing in boiler start-up stage

Once-through boiler of supercritical unit and above for soda quality request is higher, when the boiler is in a state of cold start, the need for boiler body heat exchange surface and tube first, such as water supply pipeline, economizer, water wall, such as water separator for cold washing and hot washing [2-3], the purpose is to remove sediment in the water pipe and heat surface of impurities such as scale, Ensure the surface of boiler heat exchange surface is clean.

In cold flushing, the furnace side should be flushed through the feed water flow rate of about 25%-30%BMCR. When the water quality Fe ion concentration at the inlet of the separator or the outlet of the storage tank passes the test, the cold flushing is finished. According to the requirements of the manufacturer, in order to effectively prevent the generation and peeling of steam side oxide skin on the heating surface, it is necessary to control the temperature rise rate of the heating surface wall and the pressure rise rate of steam side pressure. When the temperature of the outlet of the water wall of the boiler or the inlet of the separator rises to 190℃-280℃, hot flushing shall be started. Until the water quality Fe ion concentration at the inlet of the separator or the outlet of the storage tank passes the test, the hot flushing is finished. Boiler hot flushing has certain requirements on water temperature, so before boiler hot flushing, it is necessary to start the boiler to heat the water supply.

* Corresponding author: cheyongqiang163@SEPRI.com

https://doi.org/10.1051/e3sconf/202233801046

2.1 Large energy consumption and stable combustion difference

Startup boiler in the cold, ignition directly, because the temperature is low, pulverized coal injection into the boiler furnace cannot quickly caught fire, the flames of the risk of fluctuating even flameout in order to ensure the stable combustion, need with lard gun firing or micro oil ignition or plasma ignition combustion mode, it will bring a certain amount of oil, coal, electricity cost, startup boiler efficiency is low, economical efficiency. And the start-up stage of pulverized coal combustion rate is low, fly ash, ash and other combustible content is high, low temperature corrosion and secondary combustion risk exists in the tail flue, seriously affecting the safe operation of boiler tail flue equipment.

2.2 Overtemperature of superheater and reheater

The flame in the starting stage of the dc boiler has strong rigidity, and the long and high temperature flame directly scour the convection heat exchange surface. Before the water supply in the water wall is heated from liquid to vapor state, the superheater and reheater are always in the dry burning state, and the tube wall is easy to overtemperature. If there is water in the U-shaped arrangement of the heat exchange tube, the steam flow is small at the start stage, which is not enough to discharge the water, and the heating surface will still be in a local dry burning state. In addition, the oxide scale accumulated at the bottom of the heat exchange tube or the elbow will also make the steam flow in the tube smaller, resulting in poor cooling effect of the tube wall and tube wall overtemperature, which will affect the safe operation of the boiler.

2.3 Scale generation and shedding

Before boiler ignition, the tube of superheater and reheater is filled with air with high oxygen concentration. After boiler ignition, the wall temperature of superheater and reheater rises, the tube is in a state of oxygen rich and there is a certain amount of water vapor, and the inner wall is easy to produce oxide skin. At the initial stage of startup, the low temperature wet saturated steam enters the superheater and reheater, which has high convective heat transfer coefficient and strong heat absorption capacity, good cooling effect on the tube wall, and fast wall temperature drop. Due to the different linear expansion coefficient of the tube wall material and the oxide skin on its surface, the oxide skin falls off.

If the peeling oxide skin can not be taken away by steam, but accumulated at the bottom or elbow of the heat exchange tube, it is easy to cause overtemperature and lead to tube explosion. If it is taken away by steam and broken into small particles, it will enter the cylinder in the process of starting and turning of steam turbine, which will easily cause erosion damage to the dynamic and static blades of the flow part of steam turbine, leading to a significant decrease in the efficiency of steam turbine.

2.4 Emission levels

SCR inlet flue gas temperature at the start stage generally needs to reach 290℃ or higher, denitration system can be put into operation, for SCR denitration system, due to the unburned soot or soot adhesion of the boiler, catalyst surface temperature is lower than the wall acid dew point, prone to low temperature condensation, ash blocking, catalyst poisoning and even secondary combustion, etc., Nitrogen oxide emissions in the start-up stage exceeded the standard.

In addition, the risk of low temperature corrosion and secondary combustion caused by high combustible ash and low smoke temperature is also the same. In order to ensure the safety and efficient operation of electrostatic dust removal device, the power plant generally puts into operation electrostatic dust removal device late, which also causes the flue gas dust in the start-up stage to exceed the standard. In the start-up stage, due to poor dust removal effect, flue gas including unburned oil, coal powder and dust enters the desulfurization system, affecting the activity of absorbent, leading to the decrease of desulfurization efficiency, resulting in sulfur dioxide exceeding the standard.

3. Adjacent heating technology

In order to solve the above problems in the boiler start-up stage, some power plants in Shandong province have implemented or configured adjacent heating technology. The general idea is to use adjacent steam to replace fuel oil and coal to heat the water supply, the specific approach is to connect the adjacent steam to the high-pressure heater to heat the local water supply, improve the temperature of the local water supply. Heat the water through the economizer of boiler, steam separator, water wall, etc., to the whole preheating of boiler body, when the boiler ignition is in "hot, hot stove, hot environment" the favorable condition, to avoid the partial combustion for pulverized coal furnace caused by low temperature caused by the tail flue of the boiler and air preheater secondary combustion, Greatly improve the boiler ignition conditions and stable combustion conditions, improve the boiler start safety. In addition, in the hot flushing stage, the boiler does not need ignition, thus reducing the consumption of fuel oil or coal at the initial stage of the boiler start-up, and also reducing the power consumption of the boiler's main auxiliary machine, reducing the emission of pollutants.

It is worth noting that the adjacent heating mentioned in this paper is different from the adjacent heating. The latter is mostly used in the subcritical steam drum furnace. The steam source comes from the adjacent steam drum or auxiliary steam system, and is connected to the water wall descending pipe or water wall lower collecting box of the boiler.

In the hot flushing stage of boiler, the boiler feed water is heated to the temperature required by hot flushing as soon as possible through the adjacent heating system, which improves the hot flushing effect and shorts the hot flushing time. In the stage of boiler temperature rise and pressure boost, the temperature of boiler feed water is

 https://doi.org/10.1051/e3sconf/202233801046

further raised through the adjacent heating system, and the steam production of boiler is increased, so as to shorten the time of boiler temperature rise and pressure boost, so that the main steam pressure can meet the requirements of blanking conditions as soon as possible.

3.1 Steam access machine high add scheme

Configuration between the two sets of machine heating system, need to first select extraction steam source, in order to heat the boiler feed water from 80 ℃ to 190 ℃ to 280 ℃ , adjacent machine for high pressure steam extraction steam source, a smoke generally comes from the high pressure cylinder body, three smoke generally comes from the middle pressure cylinder body, restricted by the existing pipe diameter and pipe flow, the extraction steam quantity is limited, So it's out of the question. And two pumping (generally from high pressure cylinder exhaust steam) or cold again, pumping steam volume is large and sufficient, so choose this way pumping steam source. Combined with the direction and space of the on-site pipeline of secondary pumping or cold reheating and the convenience of transformation, the available steam extraction positions generally include secondary pumping, cold reheating, cold reheating to auxiliary steam [4] and cold reheating to small machine. For the ultra-supercritical secondary reheat unit, the third pumping is the high exhaust, so the selected extraction position is the third pumping. The #2 high heater of the machine is matched with the steam source of the temporary machine extraction steam. The #2 high heater has the strongest heat exchange capacity and the largest water side temperature rise in the high heater.

Taking a unit as an example, the adjacent unit heating system is shown in Figure 1. The steam contact mother pipe is set between the second section of the extraction pipe of the two units, and the steam is supplied to the #2 high of the two units respectively. An electric gate valve and a pneumatic regulating valve are set between the mother pipe and the #2 high steam adding pipe, respectively, to adjust the high amount of steam added into the starting unit #2, so as to control the temperature rise rate and temperature of the water supply. If the hydrophobic artefact flows through the normal hydrophobic pipe of #2 high heater to #3 high heater, the input of #3 high heater will be affected. Part of heat will be lost if it is discharged to the condenser through the #2 high-add accident drain pipe. Therefore, a #2 high-add drain pipe to the deaerator is added in front of the #2 high-add normal drain electric door, which is connected to the standby interface of the deaerator to recover the #2 high-add drain [5] during the heating of the neighboring machine.

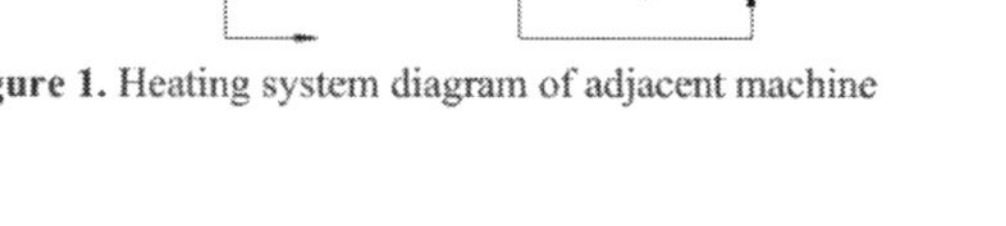

Figure 1. Heating system diagram of adjacent machine

3.2 Heating in and out of adjacent machine

Adjacent machine normal operation, the machine starts up, using auxiliary steam to deaerator heating water to the boiler water after the required temperature, feed water pump to start cold rinse boiler, in the process of driving the auxiliary steam to adjust the door deaerator admission, slowly lift deaerator water temperature, and adjacent machine two smoke to the machine # 2 high pipeline warming pipe, preheating. After the cold flushing, slowly open the adjacent machine to heat the steam supply regulating valve, and increase the volume of steam added by #2. When the water temperature at the outlet of #2 high heating reaches the temperature required for hot flushing, hot flushing is performed on the boiler. After the hot state flushing is completed, the boiler is ignited and started. The boiler enters the stage of pressure boost and temperature rise, and continues to slowly open the adjacent unit to heat the steam supply regulating valve to improve the water supply temperature. During the process of pressure boost and temperature rise, the change rate of high water supply temperature is strictly controlled to not exceed the prescribed limit. After the turbine is turned on or the generator is juxtaposed, input #3 high heater and #1 high heater in turn. With the increase of unit load, gradually close the heating inlet adjustment door of #2 high heater, switch the steam source of #2 high heater from the adjacent machine to the machine, and switch the hydrophobic self-flow operation mode of #2 hydrophobic self-flow to exit the heating system of the adjacent machine.

3.3 Precautions for heating operation of adjacent machine

1) The pipes of adjacent heating and connecting two machines are generally longer, and the temperature and pressure of adjacent heating and steam supply are higher, so it is necessary to carry out adequate heating pipe and drainage before putting into adjacent heating to prevent the impact of soda water and the severe vibration of the pipe and damage the equipment. When heating pipe of adjacent machine, it is necessary to strengthen the monitoring of wall temperature change of adjacent machine heating pipe and check the vibration of pipe locally.

2) In order to prevent the steam turbine from entering water, it should be confirmed that the steam trap pipe and crisis trap pipe of #2 high feeder can be put into operation normally, and the protection of #2 high feeder water level can also be put into operation normally before the adjacent unit is put into operation. When steam heating of #2 high heating machine is put into operation, the temperature rise rate of heater should be controlled, and the feed water flow should be kept stable to prevent #2 high heating leakage caused by the excess of #2 high heating temperature rise. At the same time, attention should also be paid to the #2 high water level, control the difference between the #2 high water level and the lower end of the #2 high water level, to prevent the steam liquid two-phase flow in the hydrophobic cooling section from causing the vibration of the hydrophobic pipeline or the #2 high water level leakage.

3) During the heating of the adjacent machine, the steam is taken from the cold reheater of the adjacent machine, which leads to the reduction of the steam intake of the reheater of the adjacent machine, which may lead to the overtemperature of the wall of the reheater [6], and may also lead to the change of the axial thrust of the adjacent machine. Therefore, the wall temperature of the reheater of the adjacent machine should be monitored during the heating of the adjacent machine, the inlet steam regulating valve of the adjacent machine should be opened slowly, and the combustion of the adjacent machine can be properly adjusted in advance. The axial displacement and thrust bearing temperature of the adjacent machine should also be monitored. At the same time, attention should also be paid to monitor the pressure of the first and second monitoring sections of the neighboring machine to prevent overload of the last stage blade of the high-pressure cylinder of the neighboring machine.

4) After the heating of the adjacent machine is put into operation, attention should be paid to the temperature difference between the upper and lower cylinders of the high-pressure cylinder and the turning speed of the machine, so as to prevent the heating steam of the adjacent machine from flowing back into the high-pressure cylinder of the machine due to the loose check valve and electric valve of the cold reheating pipe.

5) When the adjacent machine is heated out, the feed water temperature should be well controlled to prevent the boiler feed water temperature change rate from increasing due to the rapid drop of the feed water temperature, resulting in the increase of the stress on the supertemperature heating surface of the pipe wall. After the heating and exit of the adjacent machine, the steam supply regulating valve and gate valve of the adjacent machine should be strictly closed to prevent the steam leakage between the units caused by the loose valve.

4. Benefit analysis of adopting adjacent heating technology

4.1 Economic benefits

For the machine, the cost of steam heating water supply is far lower than the cost of fuel oil or coal heating water supply, saving the fuel oil and coal cost in the start-up stage, and in the process of steam heating water supply, the furnace side of the three fans and the coal mill did not start, saving the auxiliary boiler power. In the hot state flushing stage of boiler, the effect of state flushing is strengthened and the time of state flushing is shortened. In the stage of boiler temperature rise and pressure boost, the temperature of boiler feed water is further increased by the adjacent machine heating, and the rate of boiler temperature rise and pressure boost is accelerated.

For the neighboring machine, because the heating steam from the neighboring machine has been sent to the exhaust steam, equivalent to the combined heat and power supply, according to the current calculation method of heat and power unit economic indicators, the thermal efficiency of this part of the steam is 100%, improve the economy of the neighboring machine.

4.2 Security benefits

After adopting the steam heating technology of adjacent machine, the boiler is in the favorable state of "hot air, hot furnace and hot environment" when ignition and starting, and the boiler starts from the cold state to the hot state, which improves the ignition condition and stable combustion condition of the boiler and improves the safety of boiler starting. As a result of raising the furnace temperature, improve the initial combustion environment of boiler ignition, improve the combustion efficiency and burnout rate of pulverized coal, fuel oil, avoid incomplete combustion of oil smoke caused by boiler tail flue equipment, electric dust removal equipment harm. It also improves the exhaust temperature at the start-up stage, greatly reduces the probability of condensation and ash blocking of SCR denitration device and air preheater, and reduces the adhesion of unburned ash.

After heating technology adopted adjacent machine, the boot process, the boiler water wall temperature rise rate is more gentle, avoid the superheater and reheater shall be under dry and then steam into after quenching, which can effectively prevent scale caused by dramatic change wall temperature fall off, also reduced the solids flow part of steam turbine dynamic and static blade erosion damage, The safety and reliability of unit operation are improved.

4.3 Environmental benefits

In the stage of boiler hot flushing and the stage of temperature rise and pressure boost, it is put into the heating system of adjacent machine, which reduces pollutant discharge and can obtain good environmental protection benefit. When the boiler hot flushing is over and the boiler ignition is started, the SCR denitration device can be put into operation normally, ensuring that the NOx in the exhaust does not exceed the standard. The electric dust removal device can also be put in early to ensure that the dust in the smoke exhaust does not exceed the standard. At the same time, due to the good dust removal effect, prevent the flue gas of unburned oil, coal powder and dust from entering the desulfurization system to affect the activity of absorbent, ensure the desulfurization efficiency, reduce the content of sulfur dioxide in the flue gas.

5. Other types of adjacent heating

As mentioned above, adjacent steam is used to heat water supply during the boiler start-up stage, which is a common technical scheme. There are also some other adjacent steam heating schemes in the actual application of power plants.

5.1 The steam of adjacent machine realizes the start of medium pressure cylinder

For the unit with no high pressure bypass and low pressure low side bypass and only one large bypass, the steam engine can only use the high pressure cylinder starting mode. Single start-up mode, and after the unit is flushed, the high discharge temperature is low, and the cold reheat and reheat pipeline is long, making the reheat temperature into the medium pressure cylinder low, easy to cause the vibration of the bearings at both ends of the medium pressure cylinder, resulting in prolonged startup time, increasing the start-up cost.

This problem can be effectively avoided by using adjacent steam to start the medium pressure cylinder [10]. The cold and reheated steam from the adjacent machine is introduced into the cold and reheated pipe of the machine, and after pre-heating the high pressure cylinder of the machine, it enters the reheater of the machine. After the boiler is ignited, it enters the medium pressure cylinder of the machine through the hot reheated pipe to start the medium pressure cylinder of the machine.

5.2 Steam trial operation of adjacent machine in commissioning stage

During commissioning of a new unit, a series of test items should be carried out when it is running at no load and low load. This requires boiler ignition to maintain low load combustion, and these test projects are difficult to succeed at a time, with the exposure and elimination of defects, the unit repeatedly start and stop, which brings high energy consumption, pollution problems. In order to solve this problem, some units adopt the adjacent steam scheme during commissioning. The specific method is to direct the main steam of the adjacent cooling regenerator or the high side of the adjacent cooling regenerator after temperature reduction and pressure reduction to the cooling regenerator pipe of the machine, and then through the reheater and heat regenerator pipe of the machine to the main door of the machine to complete the turbine turning and carry out corresponding test projects [11].

6. Conclusion

Thermal power unit adopts adjacent heating technology, which improves the ignition conditions and stable combustion conditions of the boiler, and enhances the start-up safety of the boiler. Both saving the cost of the fuel oil, coal, electricity, strengthened the flushing efficiency, shorten the flush time, improve the economic benefit of the adjacent machine, and prevent the oxide skin peeling caused by dramatic change wall temperature, also can guarantee the safe operation of desulphurization and denitration, dust removal equipment, reduce the pollutant emissions, therefore has wide application prospect.

References

1. CAO Yan. Research on steam Heating start-up technology of large ultra (ultra) critical direct current boiler. Shanghai University of Electric Power, 2014.
2. Xiao Feng. Research and application of economic start-up of 1000MW unit. Guangdong electric power, 2011, 24(02): 37-40+96.
3. Cui Min, Zhao Hongwei. Design of adjacent Steam Heating system for 2×1000MW Unit Expansion Project of Anqing Power Plant Phase II. Energy conservation, 2015, (12): 34 to 37.
4. Li Yanmin. Application of adjacent heating technology for 1000MW ultra-supercritical unit. Electric power safety measurement, 2016, 18(01):10-12.
5. Liu Linqiang. Application of Adjacent Steam Heating for 600MW Unit. Chinese Energy Society. China Energy Society: Beijing Zhongneng Lianchuang Information Consulting Co., LTD, 2015:6.
6. Niu Liquan. Application of adjacent heating system in supercritical unit. Huadian technology, 2015, 37(08): 56-58+78.
7. Xu Jiaye, Zhu Xiaolei, Li Jianning, et al. Application and analysis of full load denitrification technology. Journal of power engineering, 2020, 40(07): 580-585+604.
8. Xia Jing. Adjacent heating startup technology of 600 MW supercritical unit. Electric power safety technology, 2014, 16(07): 15-16.
9. Jia Lifeng. Application of adjacent Heating technology in 1000 MW ultra-supercritical unit. Huadian technology, 2019, 41(04): 66-67+73.
10. Liu Bin, Shao Changnuan. Application of adjacent Heating start-up technology in 1000 MW ultra-supercritical unit. Huadian technology, 2019, 41(01): 74-76.
11. Bu Junfeng. Trial operation scheme of supercritical unit using adjacent steam. Shandong electric power technology, 2020, 47(03): 70-73.

https://doi.org/10.1051/e3sconf/202233801047

Technical study on the treatment of PCB production waste liquid and copper extraction

Chen Ru*

College of Information Engineering, Shaanxi Institute of International Trade &Commerce, Xi'an 712046, Shaanxi, China

Abstract. The increase in the use of electronic products has increased the production of printed circuit boards, in the production of circuit boards in the etching, micro-etching process, will produce a large number of high concentration of copper-containing etching waste liquid, these waste liquid, if directly discharged, will not only cause serious pollution to the human living environment, but also a large number of copper resources will be wasted. Therefore, this paper adopts a closed circulation system to treat the etching mother liquor discharged from the production line, extracting copper ions from the high concentration copper-containing etching liquid, and then returning the low concentration copper-containing etching liquid to the production line, which can not only effectively recover copper resources, but also make the pollution emission of etching waste liquid zero and not produce secondary pollution, so as to realize the harmony between human and nature by increasing production without increasing pollution. Development.

1. Introduction

PCB (printed circuit board) is an electronic component that uses electronic printing to etch on the surface of an insulated and heat-insulated copper-clad board that is not easily bent, leaving a mesh of tiny lines to connect various electronic components to form a predetermined circuit [1] and to achieve the role of relay transmission between electronic components, from smartphones to the small appliances we use every day, the core component of every electronic product is Circuit board. With the development of China's economy, the introduction of intelligent products, more accelerated the application of PCB.

At present, the development of the world's printed circuit board industry towards the high-end field of rapid progress. With the rapid development of HDI, flexible boards and high-grade IC carrier boards, a huge industry chain has been formed in the world, and has a relatively stable circuit board production base [2]. With the continuous emergence of electronic products, the use of circuit boards is also increasing dramatically, which in turn will lead to an increase in the amount of waste liquid discharged from the production of circuit boards, which contains a large number of metal substances, if directly discharged, will cause environmental pollution and a great waste of resources. Therefore, it is important to recycle and dispose of the waste liquid discharged during the production of circuit boards. This wasted resource is recycled [3], and the copper contained in it is extracted and turned into a treasure to achieve the maximum use of resources.

The laminate industry is an industry with a large capital requirement and relatively high concentration. Is the manufacture of printed circuit boards the most important material, in the printed circuit board production cost of copper clad board accounts for about 20% to 40% proportion. According to information, in recent years, China's copper laminate production capacity and output are steadily increasing, communications and computers are still when the main application areas of printed circuit boards, followed by automotive electronics, industrial electronics and other fields. Relatively speaking, the proportion is relatively low.The industry chain of the printed circuit board industry is shown in Figure 1.The application segment share of printed circuit boards in 2019 is shown in Figure 2.

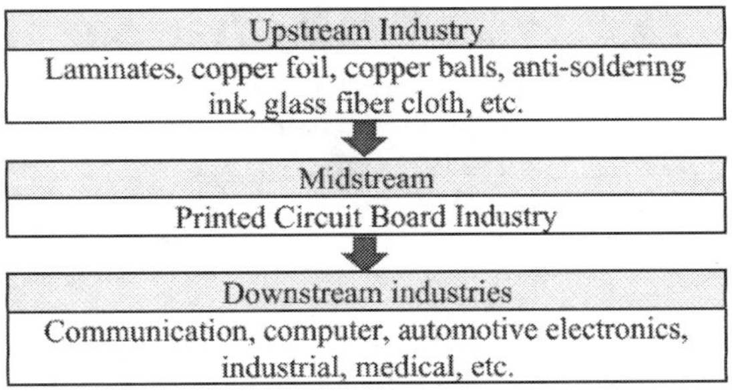

Figure 1 Printed Circuit Board Industry Chain

* Corresponding author: 24131266@qq.com

https://doi.org/10.1051/e3sconf/202233801047

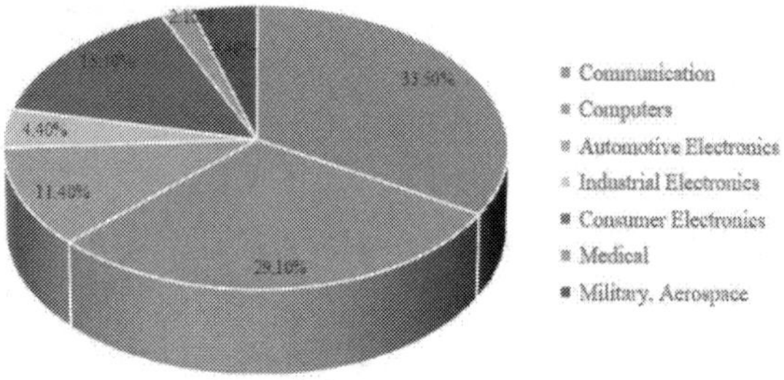

Figure 2 Printed Circuit Board Application Segment Share 2019

2. PCB production waste liquid and the source of heavy metals

In the production of PCBs will produce a large number of waste streams, and these waste streams are mainly generated in the wet processing process, the quality of the waste streams are different, and the copper content is different.

Table 1 Sources of wastewater and copper content

Wastewater type	Primary Sources	Copper content
Abrasive plate cleaning brush water	Steel plate grinding and brushing line; surface treatment; ceramic grinding plate line, etc.	Copper-containing powder
General cleaning water	Inner and outer layer pre-treatment line. Inner and outer DES lines; sinking copper lines; solder resist treatment lines; OSP and floor cleaning, etc.	Contains ionic copper
Organic wastewater	Cleaning water for DES line development, de-filming, wet film development, wet film rinsing, etc.; browning line; pre-treatment line and solder resist development;	Contains ionic copper
Wastewater complexation	Immersion copper/plating/MCP vertical plating line; mainly chemical immersion copper and its cleaning water, alkaline etching cleaning water, browning after water washing;	Copper-containing complexes
Copper plating cleaning water	Cleaning water for copper plating section	Contains CuSO4

The analysis shows that different types of wastewater contain different copper elements, which should be recovered with corresponding technology and reused after treatment.

3. Treatment of waste liquid and extraction of copper

In fact, the printed circuit board (PCB) uses a closed loop system for waste liquid treatment, and the etching master batch discharged from the production line is treated with this system to extract copper ions from the high concentration of copper-containing etchant, and then the low concentration of copper-containing etchant is returned to the production line. In the etching process of circuit boards, the concentration of copper ions in the etchant will continuously increase thus weakening the etching capacity. If you want to make the etchant achieve the best etching capacity, you must keep the copper ions, chloride ions and PH value in the etchant within a reasonable and stable range. To maintain the optimum concentration of various components in the etchant, it is necessary to continuously add sub-fluid to the etchant to replace the waste etchant that has lost its etching ability. Adding a small amount of supplement to the waste etchant that needs to be discharged to compensate for the part lost due to the etching process will allow the waste solution to be returned to the production line as a new sub-fluid, i.e., regenerated etchant. The etchant can be recycled, and the ammonia wash water can be recycled.

Firstly, starting from finding the factors affecting the copper content after waste liquid treatment, combined with the actual production of enterprises, according to the volume of mother liquor storage tank and the volume of electrolytic tank, a high and low level device is set in the mother liquor storage tank. If the volume of liquid in the mother liquor storage tank is less than the volume of electrolytic tank, the system detects that the mother liquor is insufficient and will stop automatically after the discharge of this mother liquor into the regeneration liquid storage tank after electrolysis, waiting for enterprises to discharge the mother liquor. If there is enough mother liquor in the mother liquor storage tank, the etching liquid after electrolysis will be discharged into the regeneration liquid tank after the electrolysis of the electrolytic tank is completed, and then the mother liquor to be electrolyzed in the mother liquor storage tank will be pumped into the electrolytic tank, and the pumping will be stopped automatically when the electrolytic tank is full, and the automatic electrolysis will start. The cycle continues. The anode plate used in the electrolysis tank is very important. In this project, graphite plate with good corrosion resistance, stable chemical properties, high temperature resistance, corrosion resistance and good electrical conductivity is used as the anode. The cathode uses inexpensive national standard 304 stainless steel plate (or copper plate of the same size), and copper is plated on the stainless steel plate after electrolysis, which can be torn off to form copper foil after a few days.The process of direct electrolysis regeneration cycle is shown in Figure 3.

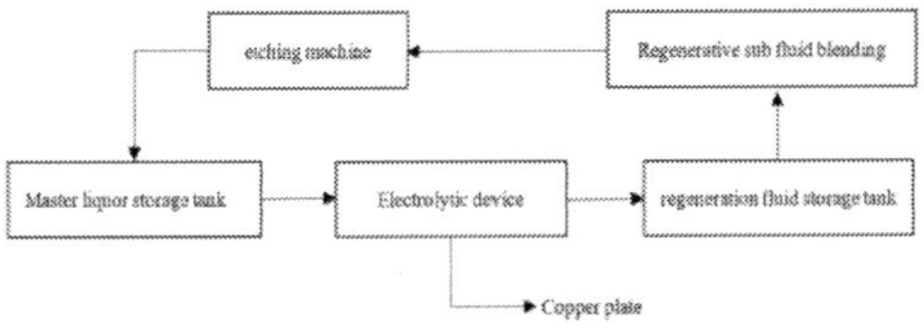

Figure 3 Direct electrolytic regeneration cycle process

The anode plate used in the electrolysis of the electrolyzer is crucial, and the graphite plate with stable chemical properties, good high temperature resistance, corrosion resistance and good electrical conductivity is used as the anode in the experiment. The cathode uses inexpensive national standard 304 stainless steel plate (or copper plate of the same size), high concentration of copper-containing waste solution after electrolysis will be copper plated on the stainless steel plate, copper can be torn off from the stainless steel plate after reaching a certain thickness to form a copper foil, as shown in Figure 4, the regenerative recycling of etching waste solution and copper extraction.

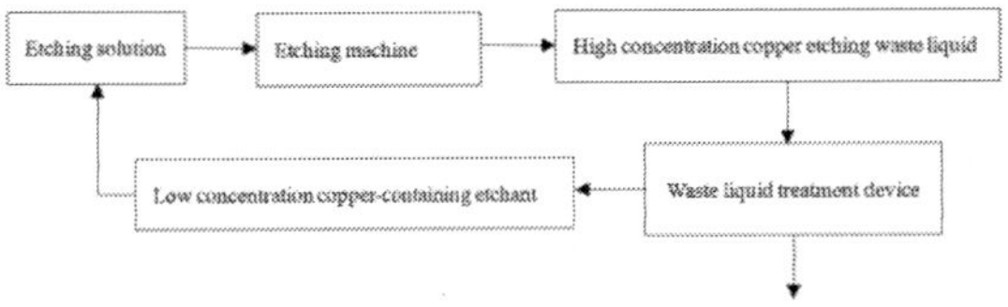

Figure 4 Regenerative recycling of etching waste solution and copper extraction

The reduction of divalent copper ions in solution to copper through the gain and loss of electrons at the cathode, the specific chemical electronic formula is:

The reaction of the cathode is:

$$Cu^{2+} + 2e \rightarrow Cu \quad Cu^{+} + e \rightarrow Cu$$

The reaction of the anode is:

$$2OH^{-} - 2e \rightarrow O_2 \uparrow + H_2 \uparrow$$

Electrolysis tank: tank body, circulation tank, exhaust gas tower and cooling tower, the upper part of the tank body is provided with an exhaust gas tower, the tank body is connected to the circulation tank by a circulation pump and a pipe, the bottom of the tank body is provided with a pipe, the tank body includes a shell, a steel plate and a graphite plate, the cooling pipe is evenly distributed inside the circulation tank, the graphite plate and the steel plate are vertically located inside the tank body, and the graphite plate is connected to the anode of the electrolysis power supply, and the steel plate is connected to the cathode of the electrolysis power supply. The electrolytic power supply is located at the top of the tank, and the diagram of the electrolytic tank is shown in Figure 5 below.

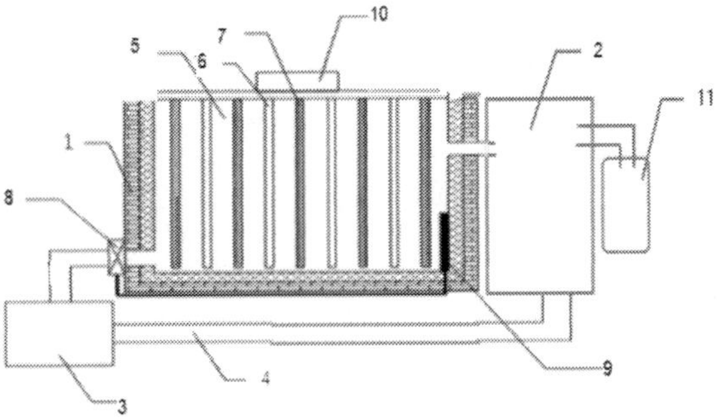

Figure 5 Electrolytic tank

Where: 1-Tank, 2-Circulation tank, 3-Circulation pump, 4-Pipe, 5-Electrolyte, 6-Graphite plate, 7-Steel plate, 8-Valve, 9-Electrolyte concentration sensor, 10-Waste gas tower, 11-Cooling tower.

The upper part of the tank 1 is equipped with a waste gas tower, and the tank 1 is connected to the waste gas tower 10 through a pipe, and the bottom of the tank 1 is equipped with a pipe 4, and the tank 1 is connected to the circulation tank 2 through a circulation pump 3 and the pipe 4, using the circulation flow of electrolyte 5 in the electrolytic tank and the circulation tank, which can effectively improve the electrolysis capacity inside the tank 1 and increase the copper precipitation rate and copper grade. The electrolytic treatment tank 6 is also used to treat the discharged electrolyte 5, which flows into the electrolytic tank after treatment, so that the waste liquid can be recycled, and the density of electrolyte 5 is intelligently controlled by the electrolyte density sensor 9, which achieves an intelligent effect and at the same time reduces costs and increases resource utilization.

The electrolytic tank and circulation tank are used to keep the circulation flow of electrolyte inside the tank, which can effectively improve the electrolytic capacity inside the tank and increase the copper precipitation rate and copper grade, while the electrolytic treatment tank is used to treat the discharged electrolyte, which flows into the circulation tank after treatment, so that the waste liquid can be recycled. To avoid the vaporization of electrolyte, a sealed shell is used to ensure that the air is not polluted and to protect the environment. The graphite plate is used as the anode, which is not easily consumed, and the purity of the copper electrolyzed is very high, basically reaching 99.95% or more.

Conclusion

In summary, this paper conducts an in-depth study on the treatment of circuit board production waste liquid and copper recovery technology, first analyzing which water quality contains copper in the wastewater discharged from the production line, and then using a closed loop system to treat the etching master batch discharged from the production line using this system, extracting copper ions from the high concentration of copper-containing etchant, and then returning the low concentration of copper-containing etchant to the production line for recycling. The low concentration copper etchant is then returned to the production line for recycling. This method avoids the pollution to the environment and human beings caused by the waste liquid discharge, and also achieves the maximum utilization of resources.

https://doi.org/10.1051/e3sconf/202233801047

Acknowledgements

This paper is supported by Xi'an Science and technology plan project (2020KJRC0150); Key R & D plan project of Shaanxi Province (2019GY-038); Shaanxi Province Natural Science Basic Research Program (2021JM-539); Scientific and technological innovation team of computer vision and image processing technology.

References

1. Liu Houchuan, Qi Jianjian, Lu Zhaohui, Tang Zhengtao, Yu Shaoming. Research progress of printed circuit board etching and copper-containing etching waste liquid treatment technology[J]. Contemporary Chemical Research,2019(15):109-110.
2. Zeng Yifeng. Research on the application of double film process in the treatment technology of Meizhou printed circuit board wastewater[D]. Guangdong University of Technology,2018.
3. Chen Ru. Technical research on copper recovery from printed circuit board etching solution and microetching solution[J]. Automation and Instrumentation,2016(01):11-12.DOI:10.14016.
4. Yang L.H. Technical solutions and engineering application research of PCB wastewater treatment and reuse [J]. Building Materials and Decoration,2017(40):108-109.
5. Luo G, Wu S G, Zheng W Z, Peng Y, Zhang Y. Exploration of wastewater classification treatment process in PCB industrial park [J]. Technology and Innovation,2019(03):110-111.

An Economic-technical Method of Calculating Power Grid Reliability Improvement Scheme

Jiefu Lia*, Peng Xin, Zhongfeng Kan, Zhenxin Li, Donglin Li, Bo Jiang, Xuerui Zheng

State Grid Jilin Electric Power Co., Ltd. Jilin Power Supply Company, Jilin 132000, China

Abstract. A program to enhance the economic & technical grid reliability is proposed in the light of improving grid reliability, The economic model of power grid upgrade program is built up. The solutions to optimize efficiency are presented step by step based on the estimated investment program & minimum portfolio optimization program. Taking the real data of certain power supply company as example, the proposed method is proved to have certain practical value.

Keywords: power; grid reliability; economic benefits; investment estimate.

1. Introduction

In order to reduce the losses caused to users by distribution network failures, many researchers are actively expanding research in various aspects. The literature[1] puts forward a statistical index system of power supply reliability for users of low-voltage power distribution systems in our country, defines the meanings and calculation formulas of each index, determines the statistical boundary conditions, and proposes a low-voltage power distribution system reliability prediction method based on artificial neural network algorithms, using the past results of the reliability statistics of power supply users and the basic data of the power grid as the training samples of the neural network to predict the future reliability of the system[2]. The distribution transformer monitoring system given in the literature [3] can accurately record the start and stop time, cumulative time and number of power outages, count the voltage qualification rate, line loss rate and power supply reliability rate, provide necessary data for comprehensive assessment of power supply quality. This distribution monitoring system can realize the calculation and comprehensive management of the reliability index of the distribution network. It improves the management level of the reliability of the power supply system, and provides a scientific basis for the decision-making of the management.

Many studies have laid a solid foundation for the improvement of power supply reliability of the distribution network and provided a theoretical basis for management decision-making. But while the reliability of power supply is improving, there are few practical economic and technical methods. Therefore, based on recent years of experience in distribution network management, this paper constructs a model of the technical and economic improvement plan, and discusses the technical and economic efficiency of the improvement plan in three parts, which can provide a theoretical basis for improving the reliability of urban distribution network power supply and future work. Fully meet the power supply needs of users, and provide users with a more abundant, continuous, safe and reliable power supply.

2. Constructing the Economic Model of the Power Grid Promotion Scheme

The economic model of the power grid upgrading plan is mainly composed of three parts: input volume, data analysis, and benefit and investment optimization. The flowchart is shown in Figure 1.

Fig.1 Economic model of power grid upgrading scheme

* Corresponding author: 13051381788@163.com

2.1 Determination of the initial plan

In actual operation, various factors such as the structure of the distribution network's grid structure, equipment configuration, equipment technology and management level may reduce the reliability and affect the power consumption of users [4][5]. In terms of distribution network construction, maintenance, operation and management, the main consideration is to adopt five methods to improve the reliability of power supply by equipment transformation, grid optimization, management improvement, introduction of new technologies, and improvement of power supply capacity [6][7].

2.2 Scheme optimization based on benefit and investment estimation

Comprehensive consideration of benefits and investment, with the goal of improving reliability, so that business decisions can be optimally solved [8]. According to the actual situation of the distribution network operation and operating company, based on the preliminary plan, construct the mathematical model of investment calculation and benefit analysis, as follows.

The general unit investment benefit mathematical model of each scheme :

$$r = SH / C_T$$
$$C_T = Z_J L_{\text{exposed}}$$

Where: SH is the number of households per year can be reduced by replacing old equipment; C_T is the total investment; r is the unit investment effect.

2.3 Optimized strategy for power grid improvement plan

In order to select the optimal solution, under the established target reliability requirements, the investment amount of the solution portfolio is minimized, that is, in the case of the target reliability improvement T , the smallest investment portfolio $P_{\min}$ is sought, and the reliability improvement program portfolio at this time It is the best solution. Its mathematical expression is:

$$T = F_a P_a + F_b P_b + F_c P_c + 5$$
$$P = P_a + P_b + P_c + 5$$

Where: T is the number of households that need to be reduced to meet reliability requirements; P series is investment; F is the number of households when unit investment reliability is improved.

The analysis strategy of the reliability improvement optimization plan is:

(1) Find the value of QF the unit investment effect of each reliability improvement plan (Q is the weight of the reliability improvement plan determined by the company's current business strategy, which is discussed by relevant experts), and rank it from high to low. The higher the QF , the better the investment effect of the reliability program under consideration of the current company's business strategy.

(2) Calculate the optimal scheme combination for reliability improvement under the condition that the target T is satisfied. If the upper limit of the number of households that can be reduced is $T_{\max 1} > T$, then plan (1) is the optimal plan; if $T_{\max 1} + T_{\max 2} > T$, plan (1) + plan (2) is the optimal plan; plan (1) + plan (2) + Plan N, if $T_{\max 1} + T_{\max 2} + T_{\max N} > T$, plan (1) + plan (2) is the optimal plan.

(3) The investment required to calculate the optimal combination plan is $P = P_a + P_b + ...$

In this way, the optimal plan for the company's business decision-making can be obtained.

Linking the model with the company's actual database and combining with local actual conditions can quickly determine the optimal power supply reliability plan and improve the work efficiency of relevant personnel. The model can be applied to the operation and management of various regions.

3. Case Analysis

The reliability of power supply in a power supply area in Jilin province in 2019 was 99.941 6%, the average annual outage time for users was about 0.1169 h/household, and the average annual scheduled outage time was 4.999 1 h/household. Investigate and count specific user reliability indicators, as shown in Table 1.

In Table 1, the power supply can consider RS-1 as the proportion of the total non-outage time statistics; the power supply reliability rate RS-2 is the statistical non-outage time proportions without external influence; the electricity reliability rate RS-3 is the statistical non-outage time proportions Percentage of non-outage time; the average user outage time (AIHC-1) is the average number of outage hours of the user during the statistical period; the average user outage time (AIHC-2) is the average outage time of the user during the statistical period if external influences are not taken into account The number of hours; the average user outage time (AIHC-3) is the average number of outage hours of the user during the statistical period if the system is insufficiently powered and the power is restricted; the average outage time of the user outage ICATI-1 is the average outage of the user during the statistical period Hours; Average number of power outages for users (AITC-1) is the average number of power outages for users during the statistical period; Average number of power outages for users (ICAIT-1) is the average number of power outages for users during the statistical period; Average number of power outages for users during the statistical period. The number of times (AFTC) is the average number of outages of the user during the statistical period.

Table 1. Statistics Table of Reliability Indexes of Power Supply by Users.

Reliability index	Statistical data
Power supply reliability rate (RS-1)/%	99.9416
Power supply reliability rate (RS-2)/%	99.9419
Power supply reliability rate (RS-3)/%	99.9416
Average user outage time (AIHC-1) / (h·household^{-1})	5.116
Average user outage time (AIHC-2) / (h·household^{-1})	5.0925
Average user outage time (AIHC-3) / (h·household^{-1})	5.116
Average power outage time of outage users (ICATI-1) / (h·household^{-1})	7.7234
Average number of power outages by users (AITC-1) / (times·household^{-1})	1.0523
Average number of power outages for outage users (ICAIT-1) / (times·household^{-1})	1.5886
Average number of power failures for users (AFTC-1) / (times·household^{-1})	0.062

Applying the economic model of the power grid improvement scheme, calling the mathematical model of benefit and investment estimation, the calculation can obtain the technical and economic indicators of each reliability improvement scheme, as shown in Table 2. According to the strategy weight assigned by experts, analyse and calculate the optimal plan.

Table 2. Optimized investment plan investment amount and effect.

Plan code	Unit investment effect (h·household /10,000 yuan)	Business strategy weight	Unit investment effect considering the strategy (h·household /10,000 yuan)	Lower limit of the number of h·household (h·household)	Increased reliability (h·household)	Investment amount (10,000 yuan)
E	98.37	0.05	4.92	1967	1967	20
H	40.27	0.05	2.01	805	805	20
C	7.49	0.2	1.50	7907	7907	1056
F	18.40	0.05	0.92	920	920	50
J	4.07	0.05	0.20	1980	1980	486
G	2.68	0.05	0.13	4878	2557	954
I	0.47	0.05	0.02	684	0	0
D	0.05	0.2	0.01	114	0	0
A	0.002	0.2	0.0003	102	0	0
B	0.00	0.1	0.00	0	0	0

The scale and effect of each program are:

Plan E: Optimize the power outage plan, invest about 200,000 yuan, and reduce the total number of households during power outage by 5%.

Plan H: Strengthen the management of power transfer, invest about 200,000 yuan, and increase the proportion of power transfer by 2%.

Plan C: The overhead line adds section and branch switches, and 264 pole-mounted circuit breakers are added. The investment is about 10.56 million yuan, and the average number of households per section is reduced to 6 households/section.

Plan F: Strengthen maintenance and inspection work, invest about 500,000 yuan, and reduce the number of households caused by power failure by 5%.

Plan J: Provide temporary power supply for generator vehicles, and increase the investment of generator vehicles by about 4.86 million yuan.

Plan G: Strengthen users' live connection operation, invest about 9.54 million yuan, and increase the target live operation rate to 47%.

The analysis draws the following conclusions:

(1) Calculate the reliability improvement target. The reliability target of a power supply company in the State Grid Corporation of China is 99.965%. In order to achieve the reliability target, compared with the current reliability level, the number of households that needs to be reduced is 16 136 (h · households)/a.

(2) Optimized combination plan for reliability improvement. The total upper limit value that can be improved for the 10 schemes is 28 000 (h · households)/a. After sorting according to the reliability improvement effect considering the operating weight, 6 reliability improvement schemes are selected.

The optimized combination plan can reduce the number of households per hour by 16 136 h/household. At this time, the investment amount is 25.86 million yuan (plan E + plan H + plan c + plan F + plan J + plan G), and the reliability index is 99.965% equal to the target The value is 99.965%, reaching the reliability target.

4. Conclusion

Based on the experience of the distribution network, an economic model of the power grid upgrading scheme was constructed. This model completes the economic and technical calculation of the reliability improvement plan of the entire power grid from the input of basic data, benefit analysis, and determination of the minimum investment optimal combination plan. Considering the actual operation of the distribution network, the scheme type and scheme name are given, and the preliminary scheme of the reliability of the distribution network is determined based on this. According to the mathematical model of investment benefit and investment estimation, the preliminary plan is analyzed for benefit and investment, and comprehensive consideration is combined with the reliability improvement target. In the case of reliability improvement goals, the smallest investment portfolio is the goal to optimize the final improvement plan. According to the actual data of a certain company, calculation and analysis, the model makes the reliability reach the target value, and the plan is optimized, indicating that the model has certain practical value.

https://doi.org/10.1051/e3sconf/202233801048

Acknowledgments

This work was supported by State Grid Jilin Electric Power Co., Ltd 2021-10.

References

1. Cheng F. M. (2007) Research on Power Supply Reliability Calculation and Online Monitoring of Distribution Network.: Zhengzhou University.
2. Li P. Wu J. W., Zhang Z. H., Liu S. M. & Shi H. W. (2015) Design of static synchronous compensator for distribution network based on dual DSP structure. High Voltage Apparatus, 51, 28-33.
3. Wei R. 2013. Evaluation and prediction of power supply reliability for users of low-voltage power distribution system.: Shanghai Jiaotong University.
4. He Y. Q, Liu D. G, Zeng C & Wen M. (2011) Distribution network reconfiguration model and its staged algorithm considering reliability. Automation of Electric Power Systems, 35, 56-60.
5. Wei J., Lu L., Wei Z. B., Liu Y. B., Gong Hui & Cui Wei (2013) Distribution network multi-objective reconfiguration algorithm considering reliability factors. Power System Protection and Control, 41, 71-75
6. Wu S. M., Cai X. W. & Wang H. L. (2014) Distribution network planning method and practical application for power supply reliability. Journal of Electric Power System and Automation, 26, 70-75.
7. Zhou J. Q., Wang Z. D., Zhang D. H., Sun F. & Feng S. (2012) Practical method of distribution network planning based on key measures to improve reliability. Power Supply, 29, 34-38+43.
8. Wang S. F., Zhang Y. J., Ren Q. & Zhang Y. 2008. A review of quantitative analysis of distribution network reliability. Relay, 79-83.

https://doi.org/10.1051/e3sconf/202233801049

Construction of a new levelled cost model for energy storage based on LCOE and learning curve

Zhe Chai [1], Xing Chen [1], Shuo Yin [1], Man Jin [1], Xin Wang [2], Xingwu Guo [1], Yao Lu [1]

[1] State Grid Henan Electric Power Company Economic and Technical Research Institute Zhengzhou, China
[2] Henan University of Economics and Law Zhengzhou, China

Abstract. New energy storage is essential to the realization of the "dual carbon" goal and the new power system with new energy as the main body, but its cost is relatively high and the economy is poor at present. This paper studies the levelized cost of new energy storage based on the whole life cycle perspective. Based on LCOE and learning curve methods, a new levelled cost estimation model and prediction model for energy storage are constructed. Based on the latest development status of electrochemical new energy storage, the levelized cost of energy of lithium-ion batteries, flow-aluminum batteries, and flow-zinc batteries were measured, the cost composition and proportion of various types of energy storage are analyzed, and on this basis, the levelized cost of lithium-ion batteries was predicted. Comparative analysis shows that the levelized cost per kilowatt-hour of lithium-ion batteries is the lowest. This article provides a certain reference for the construction and layout of energy storage on three sides of the source network and load.

Keywords: New energy storage; levelized cost model; cost forecast model; LCOE; learning curve.

1. Introduction

In recent years, energy shortages and pollution problems have become increasingly obvious. The development and utilization of new energy sources such as wind and light, improvement of energy structure and reduction of pollutant emissions have become urgent problems to be solved by countries all over the world [1]. New energy power generation such as wind power and photovoltaic power generation has strong randomness and volatility. After large-scale access to the grid, it will lead to a large demand for system regulation resources, and the large-scale and long-period power balance of the system will be significantly more difficult, posing a serious threat to grid security[2]. Energy storage plays a key role in promoting the implementation of China's "emission peak and carbon neutrality" goals and ensuring the smooth construction of new power systems with new energy as the main body. It is an important support for ensuring the large-scale development of new energy and China's energy security[3] . New types of energy storage, such as electrochemistry, have the advantages of fast response speed, short construction period, and small development scale due to resource constraints. They will play an important role in the construction of new power systems. However, its current cost is relatively high, it cannot make up for investment and operating costs, its self-financing capability is poor, and its business model is unclear, which has a certain negative impact on the application and development of new types of energy storage such as electrochemistry[4-6]. Therefore, it is necessary to analyze and predict the technical and economic costs of new types of energy storage such as electrochemistry, so as to study and judge the future cost changes and provide decision-making references for relevant stakeholders of the power system.

2. Analysis of the cost composition of new energy storage

The cost of new energy storage mainly includes investment and construction costs, operation and maintenance costs, financial costs, residual value, etc. The specific connotations and characteristics are as follows.

2.1 Investment and construction costs of new energy storage

The system construction cost of a new energy storage power station, also known as construction cost, refers to the cost of an energy storage system per unit capacity. The cost of energy storage projects varies greatly, mainly due to the power-to-energy ratio, project scale, project complexity, configuration redundancy, and local regulations. The construction cost of the energy storage system accounts for about 83% of the total cost[7-9].

The construction cost of an energy storage power station, also known as the system cost, refers to the cost of the energy storage system per unit capacity. It is mainly composed of equipment installation cost (including

https://doi.org/10.1051/e3sconf/202233801049

battery cost) and construction cost (not counted and land cost). Energy storage equipment includes energy storage batteries, battery management systems, energy storage inverters and power distribution systems, etc. The purchase cost of these equipment constitutes the equipment installation cost[10]. Construction costs mainly include construction engineering fees, installation engineering fees, and equipment and facility design and commissioning expenses.

2.2 Operation and maintenance costs of new energy storage

Operation and maintenance costs refer to the funds that are dynamically invested to ensure the normal operation of the energy storage system during the life cycle[11]. The operation and maintenance costs of energy storage power stations mainly include the labor costs, maintenance costs and the replacement cost of some energy storage devices. Operation and maintenance costs account for about 5% of the total cost. The survey shows that the ratio of operation and maintenance costs to the cost of the energy storage system is 5.5%[12]. After conversion, it accounts for about 5% of the total cost.

The operation and maintenance cost of the energy storage power station is the cost required to maintain the energy storage power station in a good standby state. Operation and maintenance costs include photovoltaic panel cleaning costs, power station management, and maintenance costs[13]. No matter how much storage is used, the fixed maintenance costs are the same. Variable maintenance costs are directly proportional to the frequency and duration of storage usage. The operation and maintenance cost is generally obtained by multiplying the initial investment by the transportation inspection rate[14]. Considering that the energy storage system (ESS) has a limited service life, certain losses will occur during the operation of the system, resulting in system life loss costs. Therefore, when calculating the operation and maintenance costs of energy storage power stations, it is necessary to comprehensively consider parameters such as the total construction cost reduction ratio, operation and maintenance rate, unit energy construction cost, and energy storage capacity[15].

2.3 Financial costs of new energy storage

Financial cost refers to the financing expenses incurred by an enterprise to raise funds in the process of production and operation. Financial costs generally include interest generated by bank loans, bond issuance and other financing measures. The financial cost of this study mainly considers the interest generated by long-term bank loans. The ratio of the financial cost of the energy storage system to the cost of the energy storage system reaches 15%. After conversion, it accounts for about 12% of the total cost [16].

2.4 Residual value of energy storage

When the life of each part of the energy storage system is exhausted, it needs to be treated in a harmless manner, and the capital invested is the disposal cost. The cost is mainly divided into two aspects: recovery expenditure and equipment residual value[17]. The residual value of energy storage power station is between 3% and 40%, and the specific value is related to the type of technology.

Ideally, the disassembled battery and its chemical substances can be recycled, which can offset the loss caused by partial disassembly and disposal of hazardous materials, but the final disposal-related costs should be included in the total cost of the energy storage power station among. In the foreseeable future, the impact of recycling value on the economics of battery energy storage will become greater and greater due to the establishment and improvement of energy storage battery recycling mechanisms[18]. However, this mechanism has not yet been fully established, and the recycling of waste lithium batteries is facing many problems because of its complex recycling technology. The residual value of the power station is the residual value after the end of service of the energy storage power station, excluding the disposal cost. The metal materials and some devices in the energy storage power station have the value of recycling and reuse. At present, the recycling value of lead-acid batteries and all vanadium flow battery is relatively high, about 20% to 40%[19]. Because the electrode material contains noble metal elements such as cobalt and nickel, the recycling value of ternary lithium batteries is about 10% to 18%, while the recycling value of lithium iron phosphate batteries is low. In addition, the power conversion components of the electrochemical energy storage power station at the end of its life are still of use value. Therefore, the residual value of energy storage power station is between 3% and 40%, and the specific value is related to the type of technology.

The cost composition ratio of each part of the new energy storage is shown in Figure 2-1.

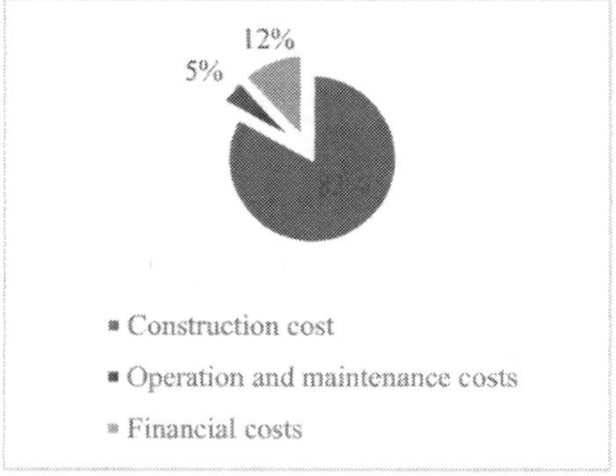

Figure 1. The cost proportion of each part of the energy storage system(data sources: Bloomberg NEF)

3. New-type energy storage levelling cost estimation and forecasting model construction

3.1 New type of energy storage levelling cost estimation model

The levelization of the cost of new energy storage, that is, the levelization of costs, requires consideration of the life cycle costs of the new energy storage, including

https://doi.org/10.1051/e3sconf/202233801049

investment costs, operating costs and maintenance costs, and sometimes the effect of project residual value needs to be considered. Considering the life cycle refers to considering the time value of energy storage in different periods. This evaluation method relatively effectively avoids the problem of NPV and other methods that are difficult to compare between different technologies, and achieves comparability among various energy storage technologies and even power generation technologies. Energy storage projects need to consider the level of total power consumption from the perspective of life cycle costs. The National Renewable Energy Laboratory originally issued the LCOE formula, as shown in equation (1), by calculating project operations Life cycle cost and power generation during operation cycle, and discount the cost and power generation of the whole operation cycle according to a fixed discount rate to obtain the calculation formula of the levelized electricity cost.

$$\mathrm{LCOE}=\frac{\left[I_0+\sum_{n=1}^{N} O\&M_n\right]}{\sum_{n=1}^{N} G_n} \quad (1)$$

In the formula: I0 represents the initial investment of the energy storage project, including construction costs and equipment-related purchase costs. O&Mn represents the operation and maintenance costs of the nth year, this value includes common personnel costs, insurance costs, etc. during the project period. Gn is the amount of energy storage and discharge in the nth year. N is the service life of energy storage.

The above-mentioned LCOE calculation model has not yet considered the time value of money. In response to this problem, this article comprehensively considers its technical characteristics and service life from the perspective of the full life cycle of energy storage projects, and introduces the discount rate of funds to consider the time value of money, as shown in formula (2) .

$$\mathrm{LCOE}=\frac{\left[I_0+\sum_{n=1}^{N}\frac{O\&M_n}{(1+i)^n}\right]}{\sum_{n=1}^{N}\frac{G_n}{(1+i)^n}} \quad (2)$$

In the formula: V represents the residual value of the project, and i represents the discount rate of funds.

In formula (2), the electricity generation needs to be discounted is actually not a discount to the electricity generation itself but a discount to a conceptual electricity revenue. Specifically, the discounted value of electricity in the denominator can be moved to the left end of the equation and multiplied, which shows the essence of the levelized cost, that is, the discounted electricity revenue measured by the levelized cost needs to be equal to the discount of each year's expenditure. Therefore, the discount rate of the denominator is necessary.

3.2 New energy storage levelling cost prediction model

The learning curve theory used to measure the progress of energy technology is currently a widely used method in the world. The learning curve is a graphical representation of the learning rate of a certain activity or tool, also known as the proficiency curve, which is a dynamic production function. The learning curve theory originated from the study of aircraft manufacturing in the 1930s, and was developed and applied to other fields in the following decades. Since the 1990s, due to the need for energy technology policy analysis, the learning curve theory has been widely used to estimate changes in the cost of energy technology [20].

The basic logic of the learning curve is: the current unit output cost of new energy technology is higher than that of conventional energy technology; however, with the development of new energy technology and the accumulation of production experience, its unit cost is showing a gradual decline.

The original model of the learning curve can be expressed by the following formula:

$$Y = aX^b \quad (3)$$

In the formula: Y is the unit cost of the product; a is the unit cost of the first product; X is the cumulative output of the product; b is the learning rate index, $0 \le b \le 1$.

Taking the logarithm of both sides of the learning curve equation can be converted into a straight line form. Therefore, it is usually necessary to linearly fit the logarithmic form of the learning curve during calculation. Specific steps are as follows:

(1) Data collection. Collect the output and cost of each time period according to a specific time period (using output as the standard).

(2) Data processing. Calculate the unit cost under different cumulative production levels and take the logarithm.

(3) Regression analysis. Perform regression analysis on the dependent variable and independent variable to get the regression equation.

(4) Goodness of fit test. Use the learning curve equation for cost forecasting, compare it with the actual situation, and make necessary corrections to the original equation.

At present, there are three forms of energy technology learning curve: single factor learning curve model, which describes the unit cost of an energy technology as a function of its cumulative total output. With the deepening of energy technology research, some scholars believe that the single-factor learning curve has certain limitations on the description of the development of energy technology, and then developed a two-factor learning curve model, by integrating R&D's promotion of energy technology progress separating and considering the growth of output independently is, to a certain extent, a refinement and beneficial exploration of the learning curve theory. On the basis of the two-factor learning curve model, some scholars have further considered the energy technology learning curve model from the perspective of the Cobb-Douglas-like production function, and obtained a number of factors including cumulative output, cumulative knowledge, scale effect, and input factor price factors. Factor energy technology learning curve model.

Considering the availability of data, this project constructs a two-factor learning curve model for energy storage cost. The cost learning curve of energy storage mainly considers the development scale of energy storage and the impact of R&D investment on the initial investment cost of energy storage. In view of the availability of data, this project selects the sum of the R&D investment of several typical listed companies in the energy storage industry as a substitute variable for the overall R&D investment. This project builds a cost learning curve for energy storage and predicts the future trend of energy storage cost changes. The cost learning curve can be expressed as the following form:

$$C(x_t,y_t)=C(x_0,y_0)\left(\frac{x_t}{x_0}\right)^{-\alpha}\left(\frac{y_t}{y_0}\right)^{-\beta} \quad (4)$$

In the formula: C(xt,yt) is the unit cost of energy storage technology in year t; C(x0,y0) is the initial unit cost of the technology in the base year; xt is the cumulative development scale of energy storage technology in year t; x0 is the cumulative development scale of the technology in the base year; α is the cumulative output elasticity coefficient; yt is the cumulative R&D investment of energy storage technology in year t; y0 is the cumulative R&D investment of the technology in the base year; β is the cumulative R&D investment elasticity.

4. Conclusion

The proposal of the "Double carbon" goal and the construction of a new power system with new energy as the main body will play a rapid role in promoting the development of China's wind, solar and other renewable energy. As a flexible energy storage method, new energy storage plays a key role in solving the impact of large-scale grid connection of renewable energy on the safety and stability of the power system, but the cost is still high, which has an adverse impact on its promotion and application. From the perspective of the entire life cycle, this paper uses LCOE and learning curve methods to construct a levelized cost calculation and prediction model for new energy storage. Based on the latest development status of new energy storage, the levelized cost per kilowatt-hour of the three new electrochemical energy storage batteries of the flow-zinc battery has been calculated, and the results show that the levelized cost per kilowatt-hour of lithium-ion batteries is the lowest. At the same time, this article uses lithium-ion storage as an example to predict its cost. The results show that the levelized cost of lithium-ion electrochemical storage will drop to 0.55 yuan/Wh and 0.32 yuan/Wh by 2025 and 2030, its application in the new power system will have a certain economic efficiency.

References

1. Su Jian, Liang Yingbo, Ding Lin, Zhang Guosheng, Liu He. Discussion on China's energy development strategy under the goal of carbon neutrality[J]. Bulletin of the Chinese Academy of Sciences, 2021, 36(09): 1001-1009.
2. Li Zheng, Chen Siyuan, Dong Wenjuan, Liu Pei, Du Ershun, Ma Linwei, He Jiankun. Research on the low-carbon transition path of the power industry under carbon constraints[J]. Proceedings of the Chinese Society of Electrical Engineering, 2021, 41(12): 3987- 4001.
3. Yao Liangzhong, Deng Zhanfeng, Li Jianlin, Zhang Caiping. Progress in large-scale energy storage technology and its application in high-proportion renewable energy and power electronic equipment power systems [J]. Global Energy Internet, 2021, 4(05): 425-426.
4. Zhu Liuzhu, Ye Bin, Ren Xijun, Wang Bao. Research on the cost recovery mechanism of energy storage on the grid side: taking electrochemical energy storage as an example[J]. Price Theory and Practice, 2020(11): 76-80.
5. Wang Bing, Wang Nan, Li Na, Zhao Jin, Zhou Xichao. Research on the industrial policy of electrochemical energy storage for large-scale new energy grid connection[J]. Electrical Appliances and Energy Efficiency Management Technology, 2021(04):1-5+23 .
6. J. Oberschmidt, M. Klobasa, F. Genoese. Techno-economic analysis of electricity storage systems[M]. Electricity Transmission, Distribution and Storage Systems, 2013:281-308.
7. Mostafa H. Mostafa, Shady H.E. Abdel Aleem, Samia G. Ali, Ziad M. Ali, Almoataz Y. Abdelaziz. Techno-economic assessment of energy storage systems using annualized life cycle cost of storage (LCCOS) and levelized cost of energy (LCOE) metrics[J]. Journal of Energy Storage, 2020, 29:101345-101369.
8. Manasseh Obi, S.M.Jensen, Jennifer B. Ferris, Robert B. Bass. Calculation of levelized costs of electricity for various electrical energy storage systems[J]. Renewable and Sustainable Energy Reviews, 2017, 67:908-920.
9. Asmae Berrada, Khalid Loudiyi, Izeddine Zorkani.System design and economic performance of gravity energy storage[J]. Journal of Cleaner Production, 2017, 156:317-326.
10. Chun Sing Lai, Giorgio Locatellic, Andrew Pimmc, Xuecong Lic, Loi Lei Laic. Levelized cost of electricity considering electrochemical energy storage cycle-life degradations[J]. Energy Procedia, 2019, 158:3308-3313.
11. Jaephil Cho, Sookyung Jeong, Youngsik Kim.Commercial and research battery technologies for electrical energy storage applications[J]. Progress in Energy and Combustion Science, 2015, 48:84-101.
12. Liu Dahe, Han Xiaojuan, Li Jianlin. Economic analysis of cascade battery energy storage based on photovoltaic power station scenarios[J]. Electric Power Engineering Technology, 2017, 36(06): 27-31+77.
13. Yang Yusheng, Cheng Jie, Cao Gaoping. Criteria for economic benefits of large-scale energy storage devices[J]. Battery, 2011, 41(01): 19-21.
14. Zhao Shuqi, Wu Mengjie, Liao Qiangqiang, Liu Yu, Zhi Yuqing, Zhou Guoding, Ge Honghua. Technical

https://doi.org/10.1051/e3sconf/202233801049

and economic analysis of battery energy storage based on grid-connected wind farms[J]. Electric Power Construction, 2015, 36(05): 131- 135.

15. Xue Jinhua, Ye Jilei, Tao Qiong, Wang Deshun, Sang Bingyu, Yang Bo. Economic feasibility study of user-side battery energy storage using life cycle cost model[J]. Power System Technology, 2016, 40(08): 2471 2476.
16. Xiu Xiaoqing, Li Jianlin, Huidong. Capacity configuration and economic evaluation of energy storage system used for grid peak shaving and valley filling[J]. Electric Power Construction, 2013, 34(02): 1-5.
17. Shen Hanming, Yu Xiahuan. Economic analysis of user-side distributed electrochemical energy storage[J]. Zhejiang Electric Power, 2019, 38(05): 50-54.
18. Xing Jie, Cao Zhe, Zhang Yi, Sun Qiang. Technical and economic analysis of energy storage system applied to the user side[J]. Electrical Application, 2017, 36(01): 26-30.
19. Huang Jiyuan, Liu Bo, Li Xinran, Chang Min, Yang Jun, Cui Xiwen. Economic analysis of energy storage batteries participating in rapid frequency regulation of power grids[J]. Electrical Appliances and Energy Efficiency Management Technology, 2017(23): 65-70.
20. Chi Chunjie, Ma Yifan. Wind power industry learning rate estimation based on improved learning curve theory[J]. Economics and Management Research, 2018, 39(05): 69-77.

https://doi.org/10.1051/e3sconf/202233801050

Research on thermal power new energy integration transaction model based on power reform system

Xingwu Guo[1,*], Shuo Yin [1], Xing Chen [1], Shiqian Wang [1], Man Jin [1], Jiabin Feng [2]

[1] State Grid Henan Electric Power Company Economic and Technical Research Institute, Zhengzhou, Henan, 450052, China
[2] School of Electrical Engineering, Zhengzhou University, Zhengzhou, Henan, 450000, China

Abstract: Thermal power is the main power supply in China, but it brings serious environmental pollution; The introduction of renewable energy consumption responsibility weight system means that users need to increase the consumption of green power, which has a significant impact on the competitive strategy model of power producers. This paper also uses game model and cooperative game model to analyse the impact of thermal power new energy integration transaction model and market equilibrium point. The results show that the profit of generator under cooperative game is greater than that under competition.

1. Introduction

In order to reduce my country's traditional fossil energy consumption and promote the rapid development of the renewable clean energy industry, the Chinese government has formulated a series of policy tools such as fixed electricity price subsidies and renewable energy quotas. The quota policy urges traditional power producers to pay for their external environmental pollution, and they can also subscribe for green certificates to compensate for the cost of green power producers and reflect environmental values to guide green consumption. In a specific market environment, it is indispensable to consider the gaming role of power generators with different market power in the interactive decision-making of green certificate transactions and power production.

At present, some scholars' research on the green certificate system is focused on the macro policy of the green certificate, and they have not conducted in-depth research on the strategic behavior of power generators in the electricity market and the green certificate market regarding the change of assessment subjects. Therefore, on the basis of analyzing the competition factors of power companies, this article summarizes and analyzes the possible strategic behaviors of thermal power companies and green power companies, and uses Stackelberg game model and cooperative game model to explore the power companies' strategies and market equilibrium point change factors. Influence.

2. The quota system and the evolutionary mechanism of the strategic behavior of power generation companies

The implementation of the quota system requires a complementary system, namely the green certificate trading system. The implementation carrier of the green certificate trading system is the green certificate market. Generally, green certificates have a validity period and the changes in installed capacity of power plants have time lag. Therefore, the price of green certificates is determined by the short-term market supply and demand relationship. Therefore, a necessary condition for the success of the quota system is that a sufficient number of power generation companies believe that other manufacturers will abide by this rule, and it is more advantageous for them to also abide by the rules given that other manufacturers abide by the rules. The key to the success of the quota system is that the government has the ability to enforce its appropriate rules. Therefore, the government, as the supplier of the system, should make a scientific design to achieve the goal of the system and the goal of economic actors, and thus make it the common belief of all economic actors to achieve the long-term stability of the system. As far as power generation manufacturers are concerned, the quota system determines the feasible space for the green power manufacturers and thermal power manufacturers as participants (trade or not trade green certificates). If choosing to trade green certificates can achieve the goal of maximizing profits, then trading green certificates becomes a strategic equilibrium for manufacturers. If all manufacturers abide by the rules of trading green

* Corresponding author: guoxingwu@outlook.com

certificates, the quota system becomes the common belief of all manufacturers.

3. Analysis of the strategic behavior of power companies under the weight of renewable energy consumption responsibility

In recent years, the weight of responsibility for the consumption of renewable energy and the green certificate system have received widespread attention. The green certificate is the only certificate for the consumption of green electricity, and users can complete the assessment of the weight of consumption responsibility by purchasing the green certificate.

(1) Competitive factors analysis of power generation companies under the weight of consuming responsibility There are two main types of demand subjects for green certificates: one is power grid companies and power sales companies; the other is direct purchase users and companies with self-use power plants. The main body of green certificate supply is non-water renewable energy generators, and the two trade in the green certificate market. With the implementation of the consumption responsibility weight, emerging green certificate transaction entities represented by load aggregators and virtual power plants will also participate Green certificate trading is coming.

(2) Analysis of thermal power suppliers' strategic behavior under the weight of absorbing responsibility Thermal power has a certain price advantage for green power. The strategic focus of thermal power companies should be on competition for user quota power. Thermal power companies have the following options: First, through new green power plants or mergers and acquisitions The existing green power plants have completed their own strategic transformation and competed with other green electricity suppliers for quota electricity; second, thermal electricity suppliers do not participate in the competition of quota electricity; third, thermal electricity suppliers cooperate with green electricity suppliers to combine thermal power with Green electricity is sold in bundles according to a certain proportion; fourth, thermal power companies transfer part of the power generation rights to green electricity companies to obtain the proceeds from the transfer of power generation rights.

(3) Analysis of the strategic behavior of green e-commerce under the weight of consumption responsibility. The revenue of green e-commerce mainly comes from green electricity sales and green certificate sales. In green power sales, the cost of green power generation is the key, and the lower the power generation cost, the stronger the competitiveness. Green electricity sales revenue also depends on the expansion of business models. The rate of abandoning wind and light in some areas in China is still high, and green e-commerce can develop new business models. Electricity sales companies and large electric power users who did not complete the assessment indicators during the assessment of the weight of consumption responsibility can avoid deviation penalties by purchasing green certificates. The strategic actions of green e-commerce mainly include: reducing the cost of renewable energy power generation, opening up sales channels for abandoning wind and light, and increasing the trading volume of green certificates.

4. Game analysis of power companies' strategic behaviors under the weight of renewable energy consumption responsibility

4.1 Description of game problem

Assume that there are only thermal power suppliers and green power suppliers in the power market, and power generation companies compete for output. With reference to the strategic behaviors of thermal power companies mentioned above, considering that new green power plants and mergers and acquisitions are long-term investment, and trading green certificates is the original intention of the government to implement RPS, this article makes two assumptions. One is that thermal power companies and green power companies are competing for competition. Users, each adopting profit maximization strategies, can be analyzed by non-cooperative game equilibrium. This non-cooperative game equilibrium is analyzed from the perspective of Nash game and Stackelberg game. The second is that thermal power providers and green power providers cooperate to make joint decisions for the purpose of maximizing overall benefits, which can be analyzed by cooperation games.

Non-cooperative game equilibrium analysis

Assuming that there are only thermal power suppliers and green power suppliers in the power market, thermal power companies and green power companies jointly meet the electricity demand of the power market. In the Stackelberg model, green e-commerce and thermal e-commerce constitute the "leader-follower" Stackelberg model. This article considers a game analysis of a duopoly market consisting of a thermal electricity supplier and a green electricity supplier. In the Stackelberg model, green e-commerce is the leader and thermal e-commerce is the follower. The output response function of thermal e-commerce is changed with the response of green e-commerce.

When the weight of the consumption responsibility is fixed, the green certificate price, feed-in tariff, thermal power output and thermal power profit will all decrease with the increase of the marginal cost of thermal power; the number of green certificates Qr, green power output, and market electricity will increase with the increase of thermal power cost . This shows that the increase in the cost of thermal power will enable more green power to be successfully cleared in the electricity market, and the number of green certificates in the market will increase, and the price of green certificates will fall. Under this circumstance, a large number of green power can be successfully cleared out of the market, the output of green power has increased, and the amount of electricity on the grid has increased, realizing the substitution effect of green power for thermal power. Green certificate prices

and on-grid electricity prices will increase as the marginal cost of green electricity increases, and other variables will decrease as the marginal cost of green electricity increases. This shows that the increase in the cost of green power will reduce the amount of green power bids, reduce the output and profit of green power, and then reduce the number of on-grid electricity and green certificates, and raise the price of green certificates; when the green power quotation increases, the price is higher. Green electricity suppliers have become marginal generators, and the on-grid electricity prices have therefore increased. Therefore, thermal and green e-commerce companies have an incentive to reduce their power generation costs.
It would have been more profitable. By comparing the position of the equilibrium point of the Nash model and the Stackelberg model, it can be found that the partial monopoly caused by the merger of thermal power companies will increase the bargaining power of thermal power companies in the electricity market, thereby affecting the bidding of renewable energy in the electricity market.

4.2 Equilibrium analysis of cooperative game

In the scenario of thermal power supplier and green power supplier cooperation, thermal power supplier and green power supplier form an interest group to make decisions with the goal of maximizing collective interests.
In the cooperative game, the total revenue of thermal power and green power is greater than the total revenue of both parties in the non-cooperative game. The increased profits of the cooperation will help thermal power companies to get rid of their loss dilemma, and it can also help new energy power generation companies gain a foothold under the trend of "de-subsidy".
With the gradual increase of the quota ratio, the total power supply has a tendency to decrease. Through analysis, it can be seen that when the user side assumes more quota, only relying on the thermal power supplier to purchase the green certificate for the user cannot meet the user's quota assessment requirements, and the user will pass Other ways to complete the assessment, thermal power is less attractive to users, and the existence of a supply-demand balance mechanism leads to a reduction in thermal power output, which in turn leads to a reduction in the total power supply. The reduction in thermal power output also directly leads to a reduction in the profits of thermal power companies. Reasonable manufacturers will increase the declared price of electricity, which will lead to an increase in the feed-in tariff.
Since the profit of cooperative games is greater than that of non-cooperative games, manufacturers will spontaneously seek cooperation. (2) The cooperation between manufacturers will increase the profits of power generators, help thermal power companies to get rid of the dilemma of losses, and also help new energy power generation companies to gain a foothold under the trend of "de-subsidy". (3) Cooperation between manufacturers will raise the price of on-grid electricity and reduce the amount of electricity cleared from the market. The government should issue relevant policies to appropriately restrict cooperation between manufacturers.

5. Suggestions

By combining the renewable energy consumption guarantee mechanism with the power spot, the traceability and uniqueness of the green power certificate is used to ensure that the renewable energy consumption guarantee mechanism is implemented, and the scale of subsidies is reduced by stimulating the green certificate market.
In order to protect the enthusiasm of green power demand, the participation of the whole society, and the return and reflection of green value, it is recommended that renewable energy companies and users conduct bilateral direct green power transactions at the initial stage of the market; promote project progress at the government level and strengthen the relationship with the power grid. In order to promote the realization of green electricity trading, and as a powerful supplement to the quota system to be implemented, it will release the vitality of the market as the consumption of renewable energy is gradually improving.
The quota system assesses the electricity sales side, which increases the market's demand for electricity from renewable energy generation, thereby promoting the transformation of the country's energy structure. As traditional power sources such as thermal power bear the increased demand for ancillary services from renewable energy access, the prices of the electric energy market and the ancillary service market cannot truly reflect the actual value under the above-mentioned circumstances. It is recommended to add a flexible power supply layout to improve the peak and frequency modulation capabilities in the system.

Ackonwledgments

The authors gratefully acknowledgments the financial support from the State Grid Henan Electric Power Company Science and Technology Project in 2021 (5217L021000F)

References

1. Shang Bo, Huang Taozhen. Research on green production decision-making of heterogeneous power generators under renewable energy quota system[J]. Operations Research and Management, 2021, 30(11): 6-13.
2. Xu Jiang, Gao Yuan, Liu Kangping, Wang Meng, Ma Baoming, Li Duo, Wen Yadong, Liu Dunnan. Research on the impact of thermal power and green power competition strategy on market equilibrium and bargaining power——Based on the weight of renewable energy consumption responsibility Game Analysis of Market Behavior of Power Generation Companies[J]. Price Theory and Practice, 2020(12): 139-143.DOI:10.19851/j.cnki.cn11-1010/f.2020.12.527.
3. Li Ming, Lin Tingkang, Kuang Shifang, He Xinying, Zhang Kailin, Zeng Ming. Research on Market Transaction Decisions Considering the Weight of

https://doi.org/10.1051/e3sconf/202233801050

Renewable Energy Power Consumption[J]. Power Demand Side Management, 2021, 23(06): 21-25 +36.

4. Zhao Xingang, Ren Lingzhi, Wan Guan. Renewable energy quota system, the strategic behavior and evolution of power generation companies[J]. Chinese Management Science, 2019, 27(03): 168-179. DOI: 10.16381/j. cnki. issn1003-207x.2019.03.017.

E3S Web of Conferences **338**, 01051 (2022)
ESMA 2021
https://doi.org/10.1051/e3sconf/202233801051

Research on the regeneration technology of etching waste solution

Chen Ru*

College of Information Engineering, Shaanxi Institute of International Trade & Commerce, Xi'an 712046, Shaanxi, China

Abstract: With the increase in the use of electronic products, the consumption of circuit boards also increased sharply, the amount of waste liquid discharged in the process of producing circuit boards will follow the increase, and these waste liquids, if discharged directly, not only cause a great waste of resources, but also cause serious water pollution, soil pollution, and thus with the food chain into the body of people and animals, seriously endangering human health, so we need to Therefore, we need to recycle and utilize this resource. In this paper, we adopt the recycling treatment system to transport the waste solution from the production line to the electrolyzer, and the overflow tank stores the electrolyte discharged from the production line. We adopt the waste electrolyte after treating the micro-etching waste solution for waste solution recycling treatment, and electrolyze the micro-etching waste solution again after treatment, and use it repeatedly to improve the utilization rate of electrolyte.

1. Introduction

PCB (printed circuit board) in the electronic information industry chain plays a vital role in the top and bottom, that is, integrated circuits can not be separated from the printed circuit board, military and civilian, high-tech electronic products can not do without the printed circuit board [1], in the next few years, in the automotive, smart grid, medical equipment, aerospace and military and other applications to increase the circuit board. Printed circuit board is the key electronic interconnections of electronic products, "the mother of electronic products," said.

With the increase in demand for electronic products, the need for PCB circuit boards is also increasing year by year. Printed circuit board industry upstream raw materials including copper laminates, copper balls, copper foil, semi-curing sheet, gold salt, ink and dry film; PCB in the downstream field of application of the breadth of electronic products irreplaceable and the need to decide. For the current application areas, the global field of large-scale application of PCB mainly in the field of computers, communications, consumer electronics, in these three areas of application scale accounted for 70% of the overall PCB application scale [2]. The PCB industry chain is shown in the following figure:

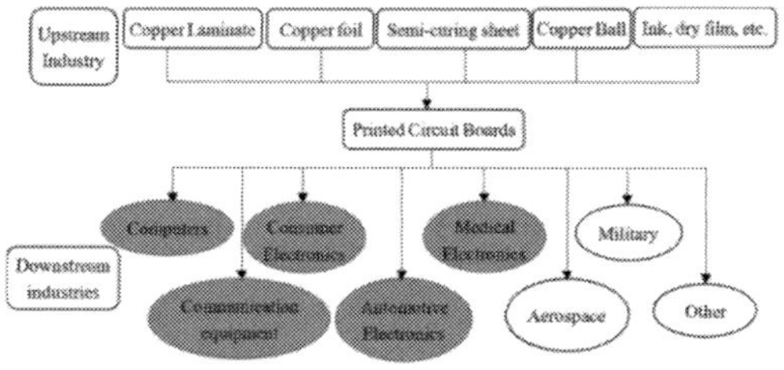

Figure 1 PCB industry chain

The laminate industry is an industry with a large capital requirement and relatively high concentration.In 2015, the global total output value of rigid copper laminates (including semi-curable sheets) was $9,299 million, and the total output value in Asia was $8,699 million, including $6,043 million in mainland China, $509 million in Japan, and $2,217 million in other Asian countries. Similar to the PCB industry, the production of copper laminates is mainly concentrated in the Asian region, the global rigid copper laminates in 2015 by production statistics of 517.5 million square meters, Asia 502 million square meters, accounting for 97.00% of the world, including 361.9 million square meters in mainland China, China Taiwan 56.2 million square meters, South Korea 32.3 million square meters, Japan 0.192 million square meters. According to the China Printed Circuit Association (CPCA) report, China's printed circuit board manufacturers have about 1,000 about the total output value of about 100 billion yuan, has surpassed Japan to rank first in the world. The development of China's PCB upstream industry is mature, well supported and well supplied, providing a good environment for the development of the PCB industry[5].

* Corresponding author: 24131266@qq.com

The production of PCB is a leading industry in our province, with the expanding scale of industrial industries in our province and the increasing popularity of printed board production, the number of electronic equipment factories is increasing[6]. The treatment of waste liquids is an important part of the production that must be handled. The random discharge of waste liquid will cause a great waste of resources, so this wasted resource can be recycled and reused. And if the waste liquid is discharged arbitrarily without treatment, it will cause serious water pollution and soil pollution, and thus enter the body of human and animals with the food chain, seriously endangering human health.

PCB production to consume a large number of copper clad board, the annual consumption of copper accounted for 30% of the total national consumption, and in the production process of etching, micro-etching, more than 50% to 60% of its substrate copper clad board to be etched into waste etching solution, resulting in a large amount of high concentration of copper wastewater, waste liquid out, seriously polluting the environment [3], a great danger to human health, The amount of copper in the waste stream is shown in Figure 2.

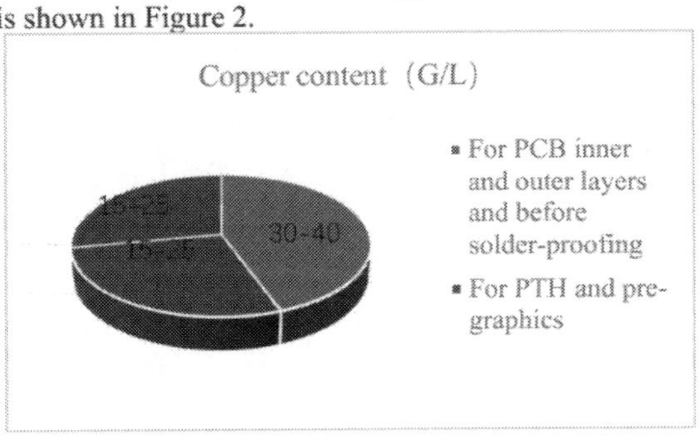

Figure 2 Copper content in waste liquid

2. Technical route

Combined with the actual production of the enterprise, the waste liquid generated in the production line is firstly recycled to the overflow tank, and this equipment adopts non-toxic, sanitary, high temperature resistant and recyclable PP pipe. Then the waste liquid in the overflow tank is transferred to the storage barrel, because when the waste liquid is processed, the waste liquid has to be transferred to the electrolytic tank continuously, and this transfer process is extracted by pump, so the waste liquid in the production line flows to the overflow tank first, and then the waste liquid in the overflow tank is extracted to the storage barrel by pump (to prevent the overflow tank from being empty when there is no waste liquid in the production line, which burns out the pump and stores the waste liquid in advance). If the liquid level reaches the highest point, the pump between the overflow tank and the storage tank will stop working; if the liquid level reaches the lowest point, the pump between the storage tank and the electrolysis tank will stop working. The waste liquid in the storage barrel is extracted to the electrolytic tank through the pump. The anode plate used in the electrolysis of the electrolytic tank is crucial, and titanium with good corrosion resistance, stable chemical properties, good resistance to high temperature, low temperature, strong acid and strong alkali is used in this project, and the surface coating of the titanium plate is a precious metal of iridium-tantalum alloy as the anode, and this plate is relatively expensive but stable in performance. Cathode using inexpensive stainless steel plate, electrolysis will be copper plated on the stainless steel plate, a few days later it can be torn off to form a copper foil.

When the electrolyte is not enough, the electrolyte can be directly extracted from the inside of the storage barrel, which can prevent the pump from being damaged due to the electrolyte being pumped out. After treatment, the electrolysis of micro-etching waste solution is carried out again, which can be used repeatedly to improve the utilization rate of electrolyte, and the fan is used to ventilate the inside of the electrolysis tank, and the copper is taken off after drying quickly. The hydrogen is discharged to the standard, and the electrolyte is circulated in the whole device to minimize the contact with the outside environment and reduce pollution. The schematic diagram of the system structure is shown in Figure 3.

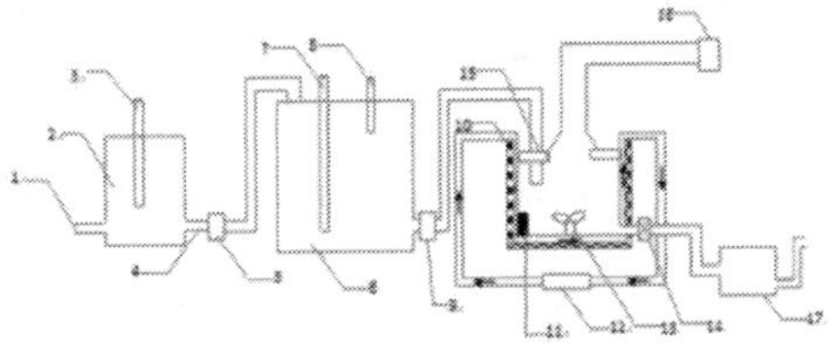

Figure 3 The schematic diagram of the system structure
Among them, 1 - Production line discharge pipe, 2 - Overflow tank, 3 - Infrared level detector,
4 - Pipeline, 5-Pump, 6-Storage drum, 7-Low level detector, 8-High level detector,
9-Pump,10-Electrolysis tank, 11-Concentration monitoring probe, 12-Pump,
13-Mixer, 14-Solenoid valve,15-Sealing cover, 16-Fan, 17-Waste liquid mediation box

Figure 3 System structure schematic

(1) Working principle.

The waste liquid from the production line is injected into the overflow tank 2 through the discharge pipe 1 of the production line for centralized collection, and when the overflow tank reaches a certain liquid level, the infrared liquid level detector 3 transmits the signal to the control box to automatically start the pump 5 to inject the waste liquid into the storage barrel 6, and the amount of waste liquid in the storage barrel 6 is detected by the infrared liquid level detector 7 and infrared liquid level detector 8 to prevent the pump 9 from dry pumping when the waste liquid in the storage barrel 6 is insufficient. The waste liquid flows into the electrolytic tank 10 for electrolysis driven by pump 9. When the liquid level of the storage barrel is not enough to pump the whole electrolytic tank, pump 9 is automatically turned off, and then the infrared level detector checks whether there is waste liquid in the overflow tank 1, and if the liquid level is checked, then pump 5 is automatically turned on, and after injecting a

certain amount pump 9 is automatically turned on to continue to inject waste liquid into the electrolytic tank to make it reach a full tank of waste liquid, and then turn on electrolysis, the concentration of electrolyte is detected by concentration detection probe 11, and the electrolyte is circulated in electrolytic tank 10 by pump 12, and when chemical reaction occurs (chemical equation is as follows:)
The reaction of the cathode is:

$$Cu^{2+} + 2e \rightarrow Cu \quad Cu^{+} + e \rightarrow Cu$$

The reaction of the anode is:

$$2OH^{-} - 2e \rightarrow O_2 \uparrow + H_2 \uparrow$$

The copper ions around the titanium plate are reduced, so the concentration of the electrolyte in the electrolytic cell 10 is made the same by using the mixer 13 to stir.

After the electrolysis is completed, the solenoid valve 14 opens to flow the waste liquid after electrolysis into the waste liquid mediation box and then discharges it. After all the electrolyte inside the electrolytic tank 10 flows out, the fan 16 blows wind to the inside of the electrolytic tank 10 to dry the copper monolith quickly, and after the copper monolith is blown dry, the sealed cover 15 is opened to take out the copper monolith.

(2) Electrolysis tank: tank, liquid supply tank, electrolysis power supply and liquid discharge tank, the upper part of the tank is provided with liquid supply pipe, the tank is connected to the liquid supply tank through the liquid supply pipe, the bottom of the tank is provided with liquid discharge pipe, the tank is connected to the liquid discharge tank through the liquid discharge pipe, the liquid discharge tank is connected to the electrolysis treatment tank in the middle of the liquid supply tank and connected to the tank through the pipe, the tank includes a shell, a heating pipe, a steel plate and a titanium plate, the heating pipe is evenly distributed in the interior of the shell, and The heating tubes are evenly distributed inside the shell, and the two ends of the heating tubes are connected to the heat source, the titanium plate and the steel plate are vertically located inside the tank, and the titanium plate is connected to the anode of the electrolysis power supply, and the steel plate is connected to the cathode of the electrolysis power supply, and the electrolysis power supply is located on the top of the tank. The diagram of the electrolysis tank is shown in Figure 4 below.

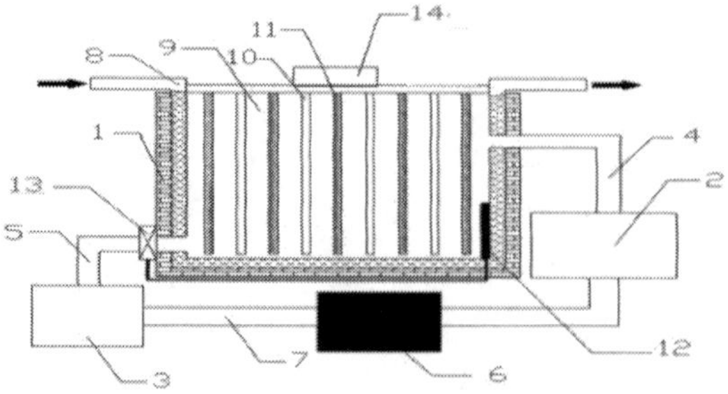

Figure 4 Electrolysis tank

Where: 1-Tank, 2-Supply tank, 3-Discharge tank, 4-Supply pipe, 5-Discharge pipe, 6-Electrolytic treatment tank, 7-Pipe, 8-Heating pipe, 9-Electrolyte, 10-Titanium plate, 11-Steel plate, 12-Exhaust pipe, 12-Electrolyte density sensor, 13-Valve, 14-Power supply, 15-Anode, 16-Cathode.

The upper part of the tank 1 is equipped with a liquid supply pipe 4, and the tank 1 is connected to the liquid supply tank 2 through the liquid supply pipe 4, the bottom of the tank 1 is equipped with a liquid discharge pipe 5, and the tank 1 is connected to the liquid discharge tank 3 through the liquid discharge pipe 5, and the middle of the liquid discharge tank 3 and the liquid supply tank 2 is equipped with an electrolytic treatment tank 6, which is connected to each other through the pipe 7. At the same time, the electrolytic treatment tank 6 is used to treat the discharged electrolyte 9, which flows into the inlet tank after treatment, so that the waste liquid can be recycled, and the electrolyte density sensor 12 is used to intelligently control the opening and closing of the valve 13, which ensures the density of the electrolyte 9 and achieves an intelligent effect, and at the same time plays a role in reducing costs and increasing resource utilization. It can effectively improve the electrolytic capacity inside the tank, increase the copper precipitation rate and copper grade, while using the electrolytic treatment tank to treat the discharged electrolyte and flow into the inlet tank after treatment, so that the waste liquid can be recycled, and using the electrolyte density sensor to intelligently control the opening and closing of the valve to ensure the density of the electrolyte and achieve the intelligent In order to avoid vaporization of electrolyte, a sealed shell is used to ensure that the air is not polluted and to protect the environment. The titanium plate is used as the anode, which is not easy to be consumed, and the purity of the electrolytic copper is very high, basically reaching over 99.95% purity.

(3) Goals Achieved

- ❖ The purity of copper obtained by this method can reach 99.95% to 99.98%, meeting the requirements of national standards.
- ❖ The total copper removal rate of the discharged wastewater is >98%, without any pollution to the environment.
- ❖ The microetching solution after electrolysis can also continue to be recycled by adding an appropriate amount of sulfuric acid, achieving zero emission.

This method is fast, low energy consumption, and the whole process is completed by fully automatic mechanical control, with little human intervention, saving human resources costs; achieving the recycling of resources; and achieving environmental protection.

3. Difficulties of the technology.

Using this technology is mainly in the control of current during operation, if the current is too high, it will cause the coating of anode plate to fall off to reduce its service life, and the copper electrolyzed is not dense and smooth; with the growth of energizing time, the cation (copper ion) of sulfuric acid solution is extremely reduced, the energizing performance is getting worse and the current is getting weaker, so the control of current size is crucial in this project.

4. Conclusion

The method is used to treat the waste liquid produced by the production of circuit boards, and the appropriate amount of sulfuric acid is added to the etching solution after electrolysis can also continue to be recycled to achieve zero emissions, and the purity of copper obtained using this technology can reach 99.95% to 99.98, which meets national standards, and the total copper removal rate of the discharged wastewater is greater than 98%, with no pollution to the environment. Of course, there are still shortcomings in this method, which is also the direction of future research needed.

Acknowledgements

This paper is supported by Xi'an Science and technology plan project (2020KJRC0150); Key R & D plan project of Shaanxi Province (2019GY-038); Shaanxi Province Natural Science Basic Research Program (2021JM-539); Scientific and technological innovation team of computer vision and image processing technology.

References

1. Chen Ru. The impact of the development of printed circuit board industry on China's economy [J]. Journal of Economic Research,2017(28):38-39.
2. Chen Ru. The impact of the demand for electronic products on PCB [J]. Journal of Economic Research,2017(33):29+38.
3. Wang Hui. Separation and recovery of copper from copper-containing etchants - separation of copper sulfate and sodium sulfate and sulfuric acid [C]// Proceedings of the 4th National Symposium on Application of Membrane Separation Technology in Metallurgical Industry. ,2014:230-231.
4. Liu Houchuan,Qi Jianjian,Lu Zhaohui,Tang Zhengtao,Yu Shaoming. Research progress of printed circuit board etching and copper-containing etching waste liquid treatment technology[J]. Contemporary Chemical Research,2019(15):109-110.
5. Xu Qiang,Li Chen,Du Jun. Technical solutions and engineering applications of wastewater treatment for printed circuit board production[J]. Resource Conservation and Environmental Protection,2019(03):102-103+108.
6. Peng Yiming. Research and discussion on the treatment and recycling of circuit board browning waste liquid[J]. Resource Conservation and Environmental Protection,2020(01):94.

https://doi.org/10.1051/e3sconf/202233801052

Analysis of well and layer selection method for fracturing displacement in thin-and-poor layers in the transition zone of A Oilfield

Yanhong Pan*

Dynamic room of Geological Research Institute of the fifth oil production plant of Daqing Oilfield China

Abstract: This paper mainly provides the well and layer selection method of fracturing displacement. It mainly solves the problem of insufficient formation energy and lack of forming effective communication between oil and water wells, resulting in poor water injection capacity in thin-and-poor layers, poor oil well production capacity, formation deficit and poor seepage capacity. The research includes the following two parts. (1) Target wells were optimized by selecting those with relatively perfect injection production relationship, poor oil-water well connectivity and long-term formation deficit. The water injection wells should be those with porosity, low air permeability and some development potential. They are required to meet the construction requirements of large capability of fracturing fluid injection into water wells. (2) Target layers were optimized based on the selection of the injection-production relationship of the target well, reservoir development thickness, interlayer thickness, liquid production, liquid production intensity, formation pressure, production situation and other parameters. Then, the sedimentary unit with poor production and high potential is selected as the target layer. This method improves the effect of stimulation and development in thin-and-poor layers.

Key words: Transition zone; fracturing oil displacement; well and layer selection.

1. Background

At present, the conventional selection for well and layer fracturing mainly focuses on the well layers with pollution whose reservoir seepage requires improvement. It improves oil production by changing the seepage conditions of the formation within a small domain, removing reservoir pollution and improving reservoir seepage capacity. However, the fracturing oil displacement technology mainly selects thin-and-poor layers, energy deficit layers and poor seepage layers. Large-scale oil displacement fluid was injected into the water injection well to supplement the formation energy. The seepage capacity was improved between the oil production well and the water injection well within a large domain. Then, the water injection well and the oil production well with a spacing of 200m or more can be effectively connected. Therefore, the conventional fracturing well and layer selection method is not suitable for fracturing oil displacement technology.

2. Technical methods

2.1 Optimization of target wells

We select the wells of relatively complete injection-production relationship, poor oil-water well connectivity and long-term formation deficit. The water injection wells of the selected well group shall be those with low porosity, low air permeability, an average porosity range of 17-25% and air permeability of 20-30md, poor or no water absorption for a long time, and the injection production well spacing range of 150-300m. In addition, they should be with large spacing between injection production wells, poor production of the well group, enrichment of remaining oil and certain potential for tapping. The operational requirements of pressure fracturing for water injection wells should be met considering the ground condition, cementing quality and casing damage.

* Corresponding author: 123988345@qq.Com

2.2 Optimization the target layer of the target well

Parameters were optimized on the selected wells including injection production relationship, reservoir development thickness, interlayer thickness, liquid production, liquid production intensity, formation pressure, production situation, geological reserves of single sand layer, water cut level, recovery degree. The target layers are those sedimentary units with poor production and high potential. The calculation of formation deficit was completed by the balanced injection-production ratio method. The five-point water injection method is taken as an example, as shown in Figure 1.

$$Q_1 = Q_a h_2 / (h_1 + h_2 + h_3 + h_4)$$

$$Q_2 = Q_b h_5 / (h_5 + h_6 + h_7 + h_8)$$

$$Q_3 = Q_c h_9 / (h_9 + h_{10} + h_{11} + h_{12})$$

$$Q_4 = Q_d h_{13} / (h_{13} + h_{14} + h_{15} + h_{16})$$

Where H1, H2, H3,... and H16 are the connecting thickness between oil and water well; a, b, c and d are the four oil wells; Q_a , Q_b , Q_c and Q_d are the cumulative liquid production of corresponding oil wells; Q_1 , Q_2 , Q_3 and Q_4 are the amount of liquid provided by well a to corresponding oil wells. The cumulative injection liquid is calculated as follows.

$$Q = Q_1 + Q_2 + Q_3 + Q_4$$

The cumulative injection volume of well a is P . If $Q > P$, the formation is in deficit.

Specifically, the well group is comprised of an oil well which is connected to four water wells. The number ratio of oil and water wells is 1:1. The water well A provides water to surrounding oil wells a, b, c and d. The oil well a is supplied with water from the well A and its liquid production becomes $Q_1 = Q_a h_2 / (h_1 + h_2 + h_3 + h_4)$ where the proportion of liquid production equals the connection thickness between wells a and A divided by the thickness between the well a and its surrounding connected water wells. Similarly, the water supply of oil well b from well A becomes $Q_2 = Q_b h_5 / (h_5 + h_6 + h_7 + h_8)$, where the proportion of liquid production equals the connection thickness between wells b and A divided by the thickness between the well b and its surrounding connected water wells. For the oil well c, its water supply from well A becomes $Q_3 = Q_c h_9 / (h_9 + h_{10} + h_{11} + h_{12})$, where the proportion of liquid production equals the connection thickness between wells c and A divided by the thickness between the well c and its surrounding connected water wells. For the oil well d, its water supply from well A becomes $Q_4 = Q_d h_{13} / (h_{13} + h_{14} + h_{15} + h_{16})$, where the proportion of liquid production equals the connection thickness between wells d and A divided by the thickness between the well d and its surrounding connected water wells. For the water injection well A, the sum of the cumulative liquid production of its four surrounding oil wells is $Q = Q_1 + Q_2 + Q_3 + Q_4$. If the cumulative water injection from the water well A is less than the liquid production from its four surrounding oil wells due to water injection, it confirms that the formation is in deficit. This method of calculating the formation deficit is referred to be as the balanced injection-production ratio method.

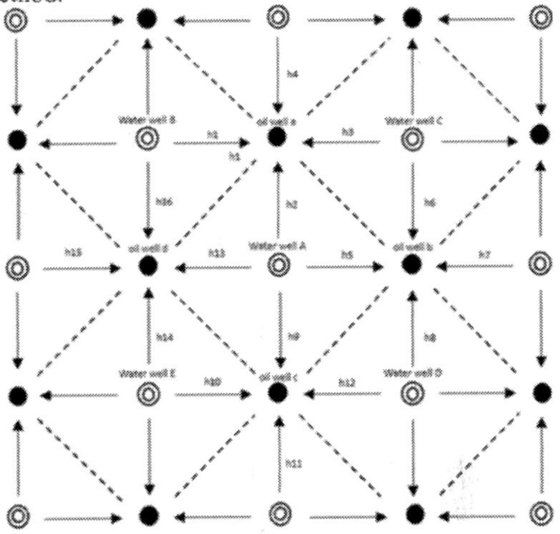

Fig. 1 Schematic of water injection by the five-point method

It guarantees the requirements for improving the overall development effect of the well group. Because the connectivity of thin-and-poor layers of selected wells are improved, the recovery degree of thin layers of connected wells are increased. For the water wells, the injection capacity is greatly improved following the field operations. This improves the water absorption in thin-and-poor layers and the degree of water drive control is improved.

3. Field Cases

Within the selected wells, parameters were considered for optimization which included injection production relationship, reservoir development thickness, interlayer thickness, liquid production, liquid production intensity, formation pressure, production situation, geological reserves of single sand layer, water cut level, recovery degree. The results are that 13 sedimentary units with poor production and high potential are selected as the target layers, such as CII11, CII12, CII13, CII41, CII42, CII50, CII92, CII100, CII111, CII112, CII114, CII115 and CII120.

The geological reserves of single sand-layer of well A-10-XIE 117 are calculated as follows. The well c-10- XIE 117 was injected in July 2012, where 29 sedimentary units were shot. The sandstone of CII formation was shot with 17.5m length and the effective thickness is 3.9m and geological reserves reaches 13298 tons. The geological reserves of single sand-layer are calculated according to the geological reserves, sand body characteristics, single sand-layer thickness, reservoir physical properties and other parameters. Table 1 shows the geological reserve of each interval of the well.

Finally, according to the parameters such as interlayer thickness, production situation and reservoir physical properties, the target layers are divided to specific intervals according to the principle of similar production situation and reservoir physical properties. It is divided into 4 fracturing intervals. The thickness of fractured sandstone is 11.8m and the effective thickness is 3.3m. Table 2 shows the division of each interval of the well.

Table 1 The geological reserves of each interval of the well A-10-XIE 117

Layer #	Thickness (m)			Formation pressure (MPa)	Geological reserves (t)	Recovery degree (%)
	Interlayer thickness	Sandstone thickness	Effective thickness			
CII1$_1$	1.6	0.6		8.46	178	22.4
CII1$_2$	0.6	0.6		8.34	178	21.4
CII1$_3$	4.8	0.5	0.3	8.33	409	50.5
CII2$_0$	2.2	0.8		8.12	238	22.7
CII3$_1$	0.6	0.4		8.34	162	25
CII3$_2$	0.8	0.6	0.6	8.39	315	8.1
CII3$_3$	4.4	0.6		8.9	242	6.7
CII4$_1$	1.5	1.1		8.65	1096	9
CII4$_2$	3.2	0.6		8.5	178	10.3
CII5$_0$	4.2	2.3	1.4	8.57	3251	20.6
CII7$_1$	0.4	0.4		8.53	197	10.3
CII7$_2$	1.1	0.5		8.79	149	8.7
CII8$_1$	1.4	1.1		8.77	327	6.3
CII8$_2$	0.6	0.8		8.98	238	12.8
CII9$_1$	2	0.5		9.02	175	10
CII9$_2$	4.8	0.8	0.4	8.61	1606	24
CII10$_0$	1.5	0.5		8.94	149	2.7
CII11$_1$	3.3	1.1		8.98	1105	22.8
CII11$_2$	1.7	1.1	1.2	9.48	1606	4.2
CII11$_4$	0.7	1.5		9.93	1172	24
CII11$_5$	1.3	0.5		9.64	149	5.6
CII12$_0$	60.1	0.6		9.91	178	4.8
合计		17.5	3.9	8.83	13298	15.1

Table 2 The division of each interval of the well A-10-XIE 117

Sub-layer #	Perforated interval (m)		Thickness (m)			Fracturing stuck section
	from	to	interlayer	Shoot	Effective	
CII1$_1$	1059.1	1058.5	1.6	0.6		一
CII1$_2$	1061.3	1060.7	0.6	0.6		
CII1$_3$	1062.4	1061.9	4.8	0.5	0.3	
CII2$_0$	1068	1067.2	2.2	0.8		
CII3$_1$	1070.6	1070.2	0.6	0.4		
CII3$_2$	1071.8	1071.2	0.8	0.6	0.6	
CII3$_3$	1073.2	1072.6	4.4	0.6		
CII4$_1$	1078.7	1077.6	1.5	1.1		二
CII4$_2$	1080.8	1080.2	3.2	0.6		
CII5$_0$	1086.3	1084	4.2	2.3	1.4	
CII7$_1$	1090.9	1090.5	0.4	0.4		
CII7$_2$	1091.8	1091.3	1.1	0.5		
CII8$_1$	1094	1092.9	1.4	1.1		
CII8$_2$	1096.2	1095.4	0.6	0.8		
CII9$_1$	1097.3	1096.8	2	0.5		
CII9$_2$	1100.1	1099.3	4.8	0.8	0.4	三
CII10$_0$	1105.4	1104.9	1.5	0.5		
CII11$_1$	1108	1106.9	3.3	1.1		
CII11$_2$	1112.4	1111.3	1.7	1.1	1.2	四
CII11$_4$	1115.6	1114.1	0.7	1.5		
CII11$_5$	1116.8	1116.3	1.3	0.5		
CII12$_0$	1118.7	1118.1	60.1	0.6		

The technical operations were completed for the well A-10-XIE 117 on November 17, 2017. A total of 10320 631m3 of oil displacement fluid was injected. After that, the pipe string could not be pulled out and required overhaul. This well was re-opened after the overhaul on March 15, 2018. The injection capacity was greatly improved. Up to now, the cumulative water increase is 43881m3.

Four effective oil wells are connected to the well A-10-XIE 117.The injection allocation was increased from 50m3 to 65m3 on May 3, 2018. On May 7, 2018, the water injection was temporarily increased to 80m3.

After the implement of the selection of well and layer, large-scale oil displacement fluids were injected. The connection relationship was improved for the thin-and-poor layers between water-injection and production wells. The current connection distance is 3.5 times that of the original one. The water injection volume of the injection well is 79m3 compared to zero. The injection pressure is reduced from 13Mpa to 10MPa, and the average liquid production intensity of the oil well is increased from 1t / D.M to 6t / D.M. The utilization degree of thin-and-poor layers was increased from 31% to 55%. Up to October 31, 2019, the functional period reached 922 days, with a cumulative increase of 1041t.

4. Conclusions

This method can effectively select the well layers with long-term formation deficit and poor connection between production and water-injection wells. The connecting distance between the production and water-injection wells is more than 3 times of the original connecting distance, which greatly improves the seepage capacity of the fluid. This improves the production capacity, and the purpose of increasing production and oil was met. It also provides a necessary guarantee for improving the overall development of the well group. The connectivity of thin-and-poor layers of selected wells is improved, which increases the recovery degree of small layers of connected wells. For the water injection well, the injection capacity is greatly improved. The water absorption of thin-and-poor layers is improved, and the degree of water drive control is also improved.

References

1. Lin Fazhi. Application of new fracturing oil displacement technology in three types of reservoirs [J]. Chemical engineering and equipment, 2019 (1): 139-140
2. Xu Jianjun, Huang Lida, Yan Limei, Yi Na. Insulator Self-Explosion Defect Detection Based on Hierarchical Multi-Task Deep Learning[J]. Transactions of China Electrotechnical Society, 2021,36(07):1407-1415.
3. Na Yi,Jianjun Xu,Limei Yan,Lin Huang. Task Optimization and Scheduling of Distributed Cyber-physical System Based on Improved Ant Colony Algorithm. Future Generation Computer Systems, 109(Aug. 2020),134-148.
4. Jing Han, Xi Wang, Jianjun Xu, Na Yi. Seyed Saman Ashraf Talesh. Thermodynamic analysis and optimization of an innovative geothermal-based organic Rankine cycle using zeotropic mixtures for power and hydrogen production. International Journal of Hydrogen Energy, 45(2020) 8282-8299.

5. Yang Zhao, Jianjun Xu, Jingchun Wu. A New Method for Bad Data Identification of Oilfield Power System Based on Enhanced Gravitational Search-Fuzzy C-Means Algorithm. IEEE Transactions on Industrial Informatics. VOL. 15, NO. 11, NOVEMBER 2019 5963-5970
6. Xu jianjun, Deng Fanliang, Zhang Xiaolei, et.al., Application of Distributed power Grid-Connection based on improved GA-GPC algoritthm. Journal of Northeast Petroleum University Vol.44, No.4,2020:105-112

AUTHOR INDEX

Ao, Jindi 86
Bai, Jingbiao 17
Bi, Yongbin 43, 47
Cao, Jian 38
Cao, Tingting 190
Cao, Tongfeng 43, 47
Chai, Zhe 219
Che, Yongqiang 206
Chen, Mingshi 80
Chen, Xing 219, 224
Cui, Shiti 1
Cui, Yangang 13
Dai, Yilun 152, 181
Ding, Weixin 31
Fan, Fan 75
Fan, Hao 52
Fan, Lianlian 62
Fan, Zhiqiang 58
Fang, Guangxu 115
Fang, Zhengwei 122
Feng, Baicheng 22
Feng, Jiabin 224
Fu, Tieqiang 80
Fu, Yanhua 126
Gao, Mingqiu 80
Gao, Shiqian 140, 156
Gao, Yajie 38
Geng, Yudi 101
Gong, Xiaoke 58
Gong, Yufeng 62
Guo, Bingqing 7
Guo, Wanjiang 1
Guo, Xingwu 219, 224
Hang, Zhou 130
He, Haiyan 43, 47
Hu, Jing 52
Hu, Xiao 92, 97
Hu, Zhixin 97
Hua, Dongwen 186
Huang, Bibin 52
Jian, Wang 130
Jiang, Bo 215
Jiang, Limin 7
Jiang, Tingting 58
Jin, Man 219, 224
Jin, Peng 26
Jin, Yan 22
Jing, Min 58
Kan, Zhongfeng 215
Li, Aifen 1
Li, Bo 122
Li, Chen 62, 66
Li, Donglin 215
Li, Hao 7
Li, Jian 173
Li, Jingsi 144, 165
Li, Li 66
Li, Nana 52
Li, Qionghui 52
Li, Xi 92
Li, Xiang 92, 97
Li, Xiaofei 1
Li, Xucheng 38
Li, Yan 169
Li, Yanan 181
Li, Yi 31
Li, Yuyuan 92, 97
Li, Zaishun 62
Li, Zhenxin 215
Lia, Jiefu 215
Liang, Haijun 70
Liao, Xiawei 26
Liu, Dong 43, 47
Liu, Peng 66
Liu, Shiqi 1
Liu, Wei 75
Lu, Jian 62
Lu, Yao 219
Lv, Haizhen 206
Ma, Rui 115
Ma, Xiaoming 26
Mu, Zhezhe 160
Pan, Jin 115
Pan, Yanhong 232
Peng, Hongbo 109
Peng, Hu 66
Ran, Jiantao 13
Ru, Chen 211, 228
Shen, Jianglong 152, 181
Shen, Zhihao 66
Shuo, Zhai 38
Song, Hanhua 62
Sun, Wei 26
Sun, Xiaomei 186
Sun, Yutong 181
Teng, Hongda 105

Tian, Wei 62
Wang, Dong 92, 97
Wang, Dongna 119
Wang, Fengbin 80
Wang, Huan 115
Wang, Jian 144, 148, 165, 186, 190, 194
Wang, Jipeng 115
Wang, Kaifei 13
Wang, Na 169
Wang, Peng 169
Wang, Qunyi 43, 47
Wang, Shiqian 224
Wang, Siyao 109
Wang, Xin 219
Wang, Xixi 31
Wang, Yong 92
Wang, Yongshi 122
Wang, Yuqing 86
Wang, Zhaozhen 86
Wei, Xiaolong 70
Wen, Kaifeng 58
Wen, Xiaoyong 66
Wu, Jing 52
Wu, Xueying 134, 177
Xia, Liheng 134, 177
Xie, Weidong 97
Xin, Peng 215
Xu, Ningning 122
Xu, Yan 148
Xue, Lijun 13
Yang, Bo 26
Yang, Chenxi 144, 165, 194
Ye, Qingying 198, 202
Yin, Shuo 219, 224
Zeng, Rui 92, 97
Zhang, Haidong 7
Zhang, Haiou 190
Zhang, Hexing 22
Zhang, Huanjun 31
Zhang, Mingzhi 80
Zhang, Qing 7
Zhang, Shoupeng 122
Zhang, Sirui 7
Zhang, Tao 58
Zhang, Xuena 43, 47
Zhang, Yanfei 206
Zhang, Yang 43, 47
Zhang, Yuqiong 86
Zhang, Zhenhuo 70
Zhao, Bo 140
Zhao, Chuanting 13
Zhao, Huiyan 38
Zhao, Qiang 86
Zhao, Yutong 140, 156
Zheng, Xuerui 215
Zhou, Hang 148
Zhou, Jinghua 92
Zhou, Jun 101
Zhu, Mingming 75